An Introduction to Pension Schemes

by E. M. LEE M.A., F.I.A., F.P.M.I.

Published by the Institute of Actuaries
and the Faculty of Actuaries

Printed in England by The Chameleon Press Limited,
5-25 Burr Road, Wandsworth, London SW18 4SG

CONTENTS

(A more detailed list of contents appears at the beginning of each chapter)

PREFACE

This book is a development of an earlier book entitled 'An Introduction to Pension Funds', intended for the use of students studying for the examinations of the Institute of Actuaries or the Faculty of Actuaries. Although continuing to provide no more than an introduction to the subject of occupational pensions in the United Kingdom, the present book is, regrettably, much longer than its predecessor. This is due mainly to the fact that I have included a discussion in reasonable depth of contracting-out, while retaining the numerical approach to a hypothetical scheme which featured in the earlier book. The resulting volume of figures is daunting, but I hope that students who do not encounter pension schemes in the course of their daily work will find the example of 'Scheme X' helpful, and will bear in mind that the figures are important only as an aid to the understanding of principles and practice.

The subject of pensions is continually developing, so that no book can be completely up to date. The present text was settled in all its essentials in April 1984, at which time production of a temporary version for the use of students was put in hand. I have reviewed the text for the present edition in December 1985, against the background of the White Paper entitled 'Reform of Social Security' containing proposals which if implemented will transform the subject of pensions. In the circumstances I have included no reference to the White paper proposals and have made only such changes to the 1984 text as are needed to outline developments up to September 1985, mainly in connection with the Health and Social Security Act 1984 and the Social Security Act 1985.

I have had the benefit of discussions with many professional colleagues in preparing the material for the book. I record my thanks in particular to Dr. L.W.G. Tutt for much support and encouragement, to Mr. V.J. Chambers, Mr. A.J. Low, Mr. T.M. Ross and Mr. J.D. Sparks for many detailed and constructive comments and to Mr. G.H. Day for carrying out the computer work. I am also greatly indebted to Miss P. Baker for dealing with endless revisions of the draft with unfailing competence and good humour. Any errors and imperfections that remain are entirely my responsibility.

E.M.Lee.

INTRODUCTION FOR STUDENTS

The subject of occupational pensions is extensive and it can be approached by a number of ways. The sequence in this book is as follows.

	Chapter
Introduction	1
Legislative framework	2 to 4
Scheme design	5 to 7
Funding plans	8
Formulae	9 and 10
Basis	11 and 12
Various matters that have to be dealt with when a scheme is being set up	13 to 20
The actuarial investigation of a scheme	21 to 28
Miscellaneous further matters	29 to 32

The chapters are intended to be studied in sequence. Some readers may prefer to approach the subject by way of the chapters on scheme design and formulae rather than in the order shown, although if this course is followed there will be a few points that will not be clear until the chapters on legislation have been read.

The additional layer of complexity arising from contracting-out is dealt with mainly in Chapters 4, 15 and 31.

As stated in the preface, the volume of numerical work is substantial, but the figures are not important in themselves. The reader should draw on them only to the extent that they cast light on principles and practice.

The book has been produced by a method which will enable alterations to the text to be made reasonably easily. This is desirable because the subject changes quickly, but it also enables corrections and improvements to be made, and the author would be grateful for any comments or suggestions in this connection.

Further reading

With the growth in public interest in pensions and related matters, books in print on the subject are numerous and continually changing and it has not been thought practicable to provide a list of these. This note on further reading deals mainly with matters covered by the first seven chapters of this book. Later chapters deal with more technical actuarial issues, and further reading is mentioned in the text of these chapters where appropriate.

There are two main sources of information about benefit and contribution arrangements and related points. The first is the sequence of surveys of occupational pension schemes prepared by the Government Actuary. The most recent of these at the time of writing is the Sixth Survey entitled 'Occupational Pension Schemes 1979' published in 1981 by H.M.S.O. The second source of information is the Annual Survey of Occupational Pension Schemes drawn up by the National Association of Pension Funds from information provided by member funds in response to a questionnaire.

A comprehensive reference work is the Handbook on Pensions and Employee Benefits (Kluwer-Harrap Handbooks/NAPF). Volumes 1 and 2 deal with the provision and administration of benefits and there is a companion volume setting out statutory instruments and official documentation.

A full description of the statutory framework of occupational pension schemes in the United Kingdom is given in the book 'Private Occupational Pension Schemes' by R. Ellison (Oyez Publishing Limited). This book is devoted entirely to English law as it affects pension schemes.

The thesis 'Development and Analysis of Pension Schemes in the United Kingdom with Particular Reference to Financing and Investment' by Dr. L.W.G. Tutt, dated September 1981, which is available in the Institute and Faculty Libraries, deals in great detail with its subject. The more general reader may find valuable the comprehensive list of references and publications annexed to the document, although inevitably the list is now somewhat out of date.

Three monthly periodicals covering the pension scene in the United Kingdom are as follows, the title being followed by the publication's own description of itself and a brief comment.

Pensions World

An independent journal by the proprietors CARL Communications Ltd. By arrangement it carries the Information Bulletin of The National Association of Pension Funds and is distributed to all their members as the official journal of the Association.

Many articles will be found quite accessible even by a reader without specialist knowledge of pension schemes.

Pensions

The monthly journal of employee benefits and retirement planning.

This periodical will probably be found most rewarding by those who have a basic acquaintance with United Kingdom pension schemes, since many of the articles assume a fair degree of background knowledge.

Pensions Today

The monthly advisory service for specialists in the pensions industry.

This is a publication of normally eight pages providing fairly specialist information in a compressed form, and is therefore most suitable for the specialist reader.

Taxation

For a detailed knowledge of S.F.O. practice it is necessary to study the Practice Notes and memoranda referred to in paragraph 2.10. Indeed, even this may not be sufficient; practitioners sometimes learn of new developments from the newspapers or the technical press and then have to approach the S.F.O. for further clarification.

A series of articles by Miss D.M. Bates explaining and commenting on aspects of S.F.O. principles and practice appears in 'Pensions World' under the heading 'Tax Notes'. These articles are likely to be found useful if further explanation of a particular feature is sought.

Preservation

As with taxation, the only way to acquire and maintain a detailed knowledge is by study of the relevant memoranda. In this case they are issued by the O.P.B., or by the S.F.O. and O.P.B. jointly.

CMND 8271, the O.P.B. Report referred to in paragraph 3.8, provides a comprehensive and readable statement of the preservation position at May 1981, the ways in which this position was considered unsatisfactory and possible courses of action.

The Social Security Pensions Act 1975 and contracting-out

As with the other aspects of legislation, the only way to acquire and maintain a detailed knowledge of contracting-out is by study of the relevant O.P.B. memoranda, and other documents including those issued by the Department of Health and Social Security ('D.H.S.S.').

Many organisations prepared booklets giving a simple description of the arrangements at the time when employers and employees were preparing for the original decision as to contracting-out or participation. Although the money amounts and some of the details in these booklets are now out of date, they remain useful as a straightforward introduction to the subject. One such booklet that is still available is 'Notes on Pensions No. 3 : The Social Security Pensions Act 1975', issued by the N.A.P.F.

Two D.H.S.S. booklets that may be found useful are as follows.

NP23 (July 1980) Employer's Guide: Occupational pension schemes and contracting-out.

NP29 (Oct. 1978) Social Security Pensions Act 1975. Guide to procedures on termination of contracted-out employment and related matter.

Pensions Management Institute

Although the aims of the Pensions Management Institute are directed towards the competent running of pension schemes rather than their actuarial theory, the course of reading for the P.M.I. examinations covers many points touched on in this book and might well be found useful reading by many students.

At the time of writing the P.M.I. course covers the following subjects.

1. Law
2. Taxation
3. Social Security
4. Scheme Structure
5. Scheme Financing
6. Investment
7. Scheme Constitution
8. Scheme Management
9. General

INTRODUCTORY CHAPTER

INTRODUCTION

The background

1.1 An occupational pension scheme is an arrangement by means of which an employer or group of employers provide pension and other benefits to an employee or a group of employees. An employer in the United Kingdom is not required by law to have a pension scheme and it is unlikely, for instance, that a small shop-keeper employing two assistants would have such a scheme. Most substantial employers, however, do run one or more schemes, and there are many tens of thousands of schemes in the United Kingdom. Although a large number of these may be arrangements for an individual set up by an exchange of letters and with no advance funding, most sizeable schemes are in the form of trust funds with contributions being invested to meet future liabilities and this is the type of scheme with which we shall be concerned. The words 'scheme' and 'fund' are usually regarded as interchangeable in this context. The accumulated assets of the United Kingdom occupational pension scheme movement as a whole are vast, and these schemes therefore form an important part of the country's financial structure. The major body representing the interests of occupational pension schemes in the United Kingdom is the National Association of Pension Funds.

Public and private sector

1.2 The United Kingdom has a mixed economy in which the public sector (i.e. the operations of central government, local government, the nationalised industries and various public boards and organisations) and the private sector are both substantial. A few occupational pension schemes in the public sector operate on the 'pay-as-you-go' principle used in the State pension scheme, under which outgo is met as it arises and no fund is accumulated, and they thus form an exception to the general practice of funding. Public and private sector employers compete for labour in the same market, so that two sectors influence each other in pension matters as in general employment conditions. Furthermore the Inland Revenue authorities, who as explained in the next chapter exercise a close control over pension schemes, use the general scale of benefits in public sector schemes as the broad yardstick of what is reasonable in private sector schemes. Good current practice in the design and funding of pension schemes does not therefore differ greatly between the two sectors, and we shall not usually need to distinguish between the two in this book. A notable exception to this general principle in the United Kingdom at the time of writing of this book is that very many public sector schemes, but virtually no private sector schemes, guarantee in their rules that pensions in course of payment will be increased regularly to maintain fully their real value in the face of increases in the cost of living.

Private sector schemes

1.3   It is interesting to note briefly the differing history of pension arrangements in the two sectors. The history of private sector pension arrangements in the United Kingdom is not well documented. Formal schemes with written rules have grown up mainly during the present century: previously pensions were usually granted, if at all, in an informal ad-hoc way. Charles Lamb in his essay 'The Superannuated Man' describes a scene (though not perhaps an outcome) that must have been common in the late eighteenth and the nineteenth centuries.

'On the evening of the 12th of April, just as I was about quitting my desk to go home (it might have been about eight o'clock), I received an awful summons to attend the presence of the whole assembled firm in the formidable back parlour. I thought now my time is surely come; I have done for myself; I am going to be told that they have no longer occasion for me. L – I could see, smiled at the terror I was in, which was a little relief to me, when to my utter astonishment, B -, the oldest partner, began a formal harangue to me on the length of my services, my very meritorious conduct during the whole of the time (the deuce, thought I, how did he find out that? I protest I never had the confidence to think as much). He went on to descant on the expediency of retiring at a certain time of life (how my heart panted!), and asking me a few questions as to the amount of my own property, of which I have a little, ended with a proposal, to which his three partners nodded a grave assent, that I should accept from the house, which I had served so well, a pension for life to the amount of two thirds of my accustomed salary – a magnificent offer!'

By the early years of the twentieth century formal pension schemes had been set up by a number of employers; many railway companies were amongst the pioneers in this field. During this century, and particularly since 1945, the growth of schemes has been very rapid.

Public sector schemes

1.4 Public sector schemes involve the spending of public money, which needs statutory authority. They have not therefore evolved from informal beginnings, as did private sector schemes, but have always been set up with full published rules under the authority of Acts of Parliament or statutory instruments. The history of these schemes is thus well documented.

Membership statistics

1.5 The earliest reliable statistics on occupational scheme membership in the United Kingdom relate to the year 1936, when an enquiry whose results were published in the Ministry of Labour Gazette for May 1938 indicated that about one and a half million workers were covered by private sector superannuation schemes. An increasing volume of statistics and general information has become available as occupational pension schemes have grown in importance. In particular, the Government Actuary makes regular surveys of occupational pension schemes, as mentioned in the list of further reading. Tables 2.3 and 3.1 from his Sixth Survey are reproduced below. Both show numbers in millions. The 1936 figures for private sector schemes in the first table are the Ministry of Labour Gazette figures and the corresponding public sector figures totalling 1.0 million are estimates made by the Government Actuary.

Employees in pension schemes 1936-79

| Year | Private sector | | Public sector | | Total |
	Men	Women	Men	Women	
1936	1.3	0.3	0.8	0.2	2.6
1953	2.5	0.6	2.4	0.7	6.2
1956	3.5	0.8	2.9	0.8	8.0
1963	6.4	0.8	3.0	0.9	11.1
1967	6.8	1.3	3.1	1.0	12.2
1971	5.5	1.3	3.2	1.1	11.1
1975	4.9	1.1	3.7	1.7	11.4
1979	4.7	1.5	3.8	1.8	11.8

Number of pensions in payment 1936-79

| Year | Private sector | | Public sector | | Total |
	Former Employees	Widows & dependants	Former employees	Widows & dependants	
1936	0.1	–	0.1	–	0.2
1953	0.2	–	0.6	0.1	0.9
1956	0.3	–	0.7	0.1	1.1
1963	0.6	0.1	0.9	0.2	1.8
1967	0.8	0.2	1.1	0.2	2.3
1971	1.1	0.2	1.3	0.3	2.9
1975	1.1	0.2	1.7	0.4	3.4
1979	1.2	0.2	1.8	0.5	3.7

Financial statistics

1.6 In recent years a substantial volume of financial information on United Kingdom pension schemes has become available. Summaries of certain information for each quarter year appear in a monthly booklet entitled 'Financial Statistics' issued by the Central Statistical Office, and more detailed information covering insurance companies and pension schemes appears in the booklet 'Quarterly Statistics MQ5' issued in the 'Business Monitor' series by the Business Statistics Office.

Trust funds and trustees

1.6A We mentioned in paragraph 1.1 that most United Kingdom pension schemes are 'trust funds'. Trust funds were well established in English law long before the appearance of pension schemes. The general concept is that a group of persons, the 'trustees', hold assets to be used not for their own benefit but for that of another group of persons, the beneficiaries. This concept proved well suited to a funded pension scheme, where the intention is to accumulate assets, independent of the employer's resources and outside his control, for the benefit of retired employees and others.

1.6B This book is not the place for a lengthy discussion of the legal position. Some points which may help the reader with no practical experience to form a clearer picture of the situation are as follows.

(i) The legal document governing the operation of a pension scheme is the Trust Deed and Rules. The Deed usually covers such matters as the appointment of Trustees, the way they are to organise their affairs, their powers of investment, the procedure for altering the Deed or Rules and what is to happen if the scheme is terminated. The Rules set out in detail the contributions and benefit provisions.

(ii) The trustee body will normally include senior officials of the employer amongst its number and is also increasingly likely to include persons drawn from the general membership or from any trades unions involved. It may include persons who have no connection with the employer or the workforce but have been invited to join the trustees because of special skills or knowledge, although this is not yet very common.

(iii) In their work as trustees, the individuals in (ii) are not to represent the separate interests from which they are drawn but must see that the scheme is operated in the interests of the members. In practice this will involve taking note of reasonable views put forward on behalf of the employer.

(iv) Trustees are required to act prudently and in good faith.

(v) Trustee bodies usually meet fairly regularly to discuss such matters as investment policy and performance and the destination of capital sum death benefit payments (see paragraph 2.27).

(vi)   Trustees are usually laymen in pension matters and need to employ experts of various sorts, such as investment advisers, solicitors and actuaries, to help them in their work.

(vii)   The trustee body may consist of individual trustees or it may be in the form of a trustee company. In this latter case the persons who would otherwise be individual trustees are instead directors of the trustee company, but their function and work is essentially the same as that of individual trustees.

The scope of this book

1.7   We shall be concerned in this book with the design and financing of the range of benefits which it is possible to provide through an occupational pension scheme in the United Kingdom. The main benefits are as follows:

On death during employment:	A capital sum (which may include a return of the member's contributions)
	A widow's or widower's pension
	A dependant's pension
	Children's allowances
On the member's leaving the scheme because of a change of employment:	A return of the member's contributions
	A deferred pension preserved in the scheme
	A 'transfer payment' to the scheme of the new employer
	In the case of contracted out schemes (see Chapter 4) a payment to buy the member back into the State scheme
On the member's retirement at the normal pension age or upon earlier retirement (which may be possible in a variety of circumstances):	An immediate pension
	A capital sum

On the death of a pensioner: A widow's or widower's pension

A dependant's pension

Children's allowances

Payments under any guarantee of the member's pension.

1.8 As to the financing of schemes, the trustees promise various benefits to the members and their dependants, the scales of the benefits and the circumstances in which they are payable being set out in the trust deed and rules of the scheme. The trustees back the promises that they make to the members by investing the contributions paid to the scheme by the employer and (unless the scheme is 'non-contributory') the members. The scheme is legally a trust and its assets are separate from those of the employer. The three main methods of investment used by trustees are as follows:

(i) Direct purchase of stock exchange investments, property units, properties etc. (a 'directly invested scheme').

(ii) Purchase of equity units, fixed interest units, property units etc. in a 'managed fund', which is similar to a unit trust, usually set up by a company connected with an established insurance company, and available only to the trustees of tax-approved occupational pension schemes.

(iii) Payment of premiums under a policy or policies issued by an insurance company (an 'insured scheme').

1.9 We deal in this book with the actuarial aspects of occupational pension schemes other than those matters, such as the calculation of life office premium rates and the financial structure of life office annuity funds, which are covered in other parts of the courses of reading for the examinations of the Institute of Actuaries and the Faculty of Actuaries. The ground covered by the book is therefore as follows.

(1) Matters common to all United Kingdom pension schemes such as relevant legislation and the design of the benefit and contribution arrangements.

(2) The actuarial principles and techniques used by the actuary in the formulation of the advice to be tendered to the trustees of schemes and to other interested parties.

(3) Actuarial aspects of insured schemes other than those dealt with elsewhere in the reading. In the United Kingdom advice on pension schemes is provided by consulting actuaries, pension consultant companies, life offices and other organisations who employ actuaries. For brevity the transmission of advice from the actuary to the ultimate recipient is referred to in this book as the tendering of advice by the actuary to his client.

The plan of this book

1.10 The main part of this book deals with matters in the order in which they arise when a scheme is set up, but with the complications associated with contracting-out being segregated as far as possible. The order is as follows.

(i) Legislation.

(ii) Design of benefit and contribution arrangements.

(iii) Actuarial formulae, methods and bases.

(iv) The setting up and running of a scheme.

(v) The actuarial investigation of a scheme.

(vi) Various miscellaneous matters.

1.11 The detailed plan of the book is as follows.

Chapters 2, 3 and 4 deal respectively with the three main aspects of pension scheme legislation, namely taxation, preservation and the Social Security Pensions Act 1975, and introduce the two main supervisory bodies, namely the Superannuation Funds Office of the Inland Revenue (the 'S.F.O.') and the Occupational Pensions Board (the 'O.P.B.').

Chapters 5 and 6 deal with the design of benefit scales.

Chapter 7 deals with miscellaneous matters of pension scheme design which are of actuarial interest.

Chapter 8 introduces the subject of funding and contains examples of various different funding levels.

Chapter 9 deals with the basic formulae.

Chapter 10 describes a method of calculation which has been found suitable for computer use and does not involve the commutation columns developed in chapter 9.

Chapters 11 and 12 deal respectively with the economic and statistical assumptions for the actuarial calculations in connection with pension schemes.

Chapter 13 introduces a hypothetical occupational pension scheme in the United Kingdom, Scheme X, which is used as a large-scale worked example throughout the rest of the book.

Chapter 14 introduces the detailed methods for the calculation of contribution rates, ignoring the complexities arising from contracting-out.

Chapter 15 deals with contracting-out as it affects contribution rates.

Chapter 16 brings together the work of Chapters 14 and 15 in order to arrive at contribution rates allowing for contracting-out.

Chapter 17 outlines various procedural matters in connection with the setting up of a scheme.

Chapters 18 and 19 deal with various detailed provisions, Chapter 19 being devoted to the complex subject of the treatment of early leavers.

Chapter 20 deals with some points about investments which are of particular relevance to pension scheme work.

Chapters 21 to 28 deal with the various aspects of the actuarial investigation of a pension scheme.

Chapter 29 is concerned with the projection of the expected year by year amounts of contribution and benefit flow.

Chapter 30 deals with the pension implications of takeovers and mergers.

Chapter 31 provides a review of contracting-out.

Chapter 32 is involved with those aspects of insured schemes about which an independent actuary is likely to be asked to advise a client.

CHAPTER 2

TAXATION

TAXATION

Historical outline

2.1 The Inland Revenue's general position is that occupational pension arrangements involve various taxation privileges, and the scale and scope of such arrangements should therefore be controlled. This control is exercised by the Superannuation Funds Office of the Inland Revenue and in pension scheme work the terms 'Inland Revenue', 'Revenue', 'Superannuation Funds Office' and 'S.F.O.' are often used as if they were interchangeable. In this chapter we provide a brief description of the main points of the legislation and Revenue practice. We assume only a small general knowledge of pension schemes, but some readers may find it useful to make a first reading of Chapters 5 and 6 for background information before studying this chapter.

2.2 The Inland Revenue became involved in the supervision of occupational pension schemes following the rise in rates of income tax during the first World War. The Finance Act 1921 laid down the framework of a system of supervision which contained certain conditions that a scheme had to satisfy in order to be considered for approval, but under which the Inland Revenue were not obliged to approve any scheme. They were given power to impose such further conditions of approval as they thought fit, and a mass of largely unwritten Inland Revenue practice and precedent developed. This was reinforced and amended as occasion required by further statutes, and in particular by the Finance Act 1947. The discretionary element gave flexibility of control but also led to complexity. By 1970 the position had become extremely complicated, at least five different types of tax approval of pension schemes being possible. The various statutes were consolidated, without any change in their effect, in the Income and Corporation Taxes Act 1970, and the arrangements were subsequently known as the 'old code' of Revenue approval. The old code ceased to

have effect on 6th April 1980 and can be ignored for present
purposes, although in practice residual influences of that code
remain in some schemes.

The Finance Act 1970

2.3 The Finance Act 1970 as amended by subsequent legislation,
principally the Finance Act 1971, laid down the framework of the
new and simplified system of Revenue supervision of occupational
pension schemes which is currently in force and which was initially
known as the 'new code' of approval. This system, like its
predecessor, provides for the Revenue to impose such conditions
of approval as they think fit. There is only one set of tests and
conditions for approval and, for practical purposes, only one type
of approved scheme, namely the 'exempt approved scheme'. In
this book we shall usually refer simply to 'approval' or 'an
approved scheme' for taxation purposes, it being understood that
the reference is to an exempt approved scheme.

The basic position on taxation

2.4 Contributions to an approved scheme by employees and
employers are in general allowed against tax, and the investment
accumulation of the schemes is free of tax. Pensions in payment
are taxed as earned income and capital sum (also known as 'lump
sum') retirement benefits are free of tax in the hands of the
recipient. The tax position of capital sum benefits on death in
service is mentioned in paragraph 2.27.

The basic legislation

2.5 The arrangements operate under sections 19 to 26 of the
Finance Act 1970 and Schedule 5 to that Act, and sections 21 and
22 of the Finance Act 1971 and Schedule 3 to that Act. The text of
sections 19 and 20 and the first eight subsections of section 21 of
the 1970 Act as amended by the 1971 Act is reproduced verbatim
in the remainder of this paragraph, not because it should be
studied in detail but because it shows the essential structure of
control. The 'Board' referred to is the Board of Inland Revenue,
and references to a 'Chapter' are part of the formal language of the
Act. Comments are given in paragraph 2.6 et seq., and readers
may find it useful to note the general explanation provided in

paragraphs 2.6 to 2.9 before embarking on the convolutions of the text below.

Text of section 19

19(1) The Board shall not approve any retirement benefits scheme for the purposes of this Chapter unless the scheme satisfies all of the conditions set out in subsection (2) below.

(2) The said conditions are:-

(a) that the scheme is bona fide established for the sole purpose of providing relevant benefits in respect of service as an employee (as defined in this Chapter), being benefits payable to, or to the widow, children or dependants or personal representatives of, the employee,

(b) that the scheme is recognised by the employer and employees to whom it relates, and that every employee who is, or has a right to be, a member of the scheme has been given written particulars of all essential features of the scheme which concern him,

(c) that there is a person resident in the United Kingdom who will be responsible for the discharge of all duties imposed on the administrator of the scheme under this Chapter,

(d) That the employer is a contributor to the scheme,

(e) that the scheme is established in connection with some trade or undertaking carried on in the United Kingdom by a person resident in the United Kingdom,

(f) (Repealed by Finance Act 1973)

(g) that in no circumstances, whether during the subsistence of the scheme or later, can any amount be paid by way of repayment of an employee's contributions under the scheme.

(2A) Subject to subsection (1) above, the Board shall approve a retirement benefits scheme for the purposes of this Chapter if the scheme satisfies all of the conditions in the subsection, that is

(a) that any benefit for an employee is a pension on retirement at a specified age not earlier than 60, (or, if the employee is a woman, 55) and not later than 70, which does not exceed one-sixtieth of the employee's final remuneration for each year of service up to a maximum of 40,

(b) that any benefit for any widow of an employee is a pension payable on his death after retirement such that the amount payable to the widow by way of pension does not exceed two-thirds of any pension or pensions payable to the employee,

(c) that no other benefits are payable under the scheme,

(d) that no pension is capable in whole or in part of surrender, commutation or assignment, except so far as the scheme allows an employee on retirement to obtain, by commutation of his pension, a lump sum or sums not exceeding in all three-eightieths of his final remuneration for each year of service up to a maximum of 40.

The conditions set out in subsection (2) above and in this subsection are referred to in this Chapter as 'the prescribed conditions'.

(3) If in the opinion of the Board the facts concerning any scheme or its administration cease to warrant the continuance of their approval of the scheme, they may at any time by notice in writing to the administrator withdraw their approval on such grounds, and from such date, as may be specified in the notice.

(4) Where an alteration has been made in a retirement benefits scheme, no approval given as regards the scheme before the alteration shall apply after the date of the alteration unless the alteration has been approved by the Board.

(5) For the purpose of determining whether a retirement benefits scheme, so far as it relates to a particular class or description of employees, satisfies or continues to satisfy the prescribed conditions that scheme shall be considered in conjunction with any other retirement benefits scheme or schemes relating to employees of that class or description, and, if those conditions are satisfied in the case of both or all of those schemes taken together, they shall be taken to be satisfied in the case of each of them but otherwise those conditions shall be taken to be satisfied in the case of none of them.

(6) No approval shall be given as respects any period before 6th April 1970.

Text of section 20

20(1)   The Board may, if they think fit, having regard to the facts of a particular case, and subject to such conditions, if any, as they think proper to attach to the approval, approve a retirement benefits scheme for the purposes of this Chapter notwithstanding that it does not satisfy one or more of the prescribed conditions.

(2) The Board may in particular approve by virtue of this section a scheme

(a) which exceeds the limits imposed by the prescribed conditions as respects benefits for less than forty years' service, or

(b) which provides pensions for the widows of employees on death in service, or for the children or dependants of employees, or

(c) which provides on death in service a lump sum of up to four times the employee's final remuneration (exclusive of any refunds of contributions), or

(d) which allows benefits to be payable on retirement within ten years of the specified age, or on earlier incapacity, or

(e) which provides for the return in certain contingencies of employee's contributions, or

(f) which relates to a trade or undertaking carried on only partly in the United Kingdom and by a person not resident in the United Kingdom, or

(g) which provides in certain contingencies for securing benefits by means of an annuity contract with an insurance company of the employee's choice, being a contract which has for its main object the provision for the employee of a life annuity in old age and is so framed that the liabilities undertaken by the insurance company under the contract correspond with liabilities against which the contract is intended to secure the scheme.

(3) In applying this section to an existing scheme the Board shall exercise their discretion, in such cases as appear to them appropriate, so as

(a) to preserve benefits earned or rights arising out of service before approval under this Chapter or before the date on which section 23 of this Act comes into force, whichever is the earlier, and

(b) to preserve any rights to death in service benefits conferred by rules of the scheme in force on 26th February 1970.

Text of part of section 21

21(1) This section has effect as respects

(a) any approved scheme which is shown to the satisfaction of the Board to be established under irrevocable trusts, or

(b) any other approved scheme as respects which the Board, having regard to any special circumstances, direct that this section shall apply, and any scheme which is for the time being within paragraph (a) or (b) above is in this Chapter referred to as an 'exempt approved scheme'.

(2) Exemption from income tax shall, on a claim being made in that behalf, be allowed in respect of income derived from investments or deposits if, or to such extent as the Board are satisfied that, it is income from investments or deposits held for the purposes of the scheme.

(2A) Exemption from income tax shall, on a claim being made in that behalf, be allowed in respect of underwriting commissions if, or to such extent as the Board are satisfied that, the underwriting commissions are applied for the purposes of the scheme, and would, but for this subsection, be chargeable to tax under Case VI of Schedule D.

(3) Any sum paid by an employer by way of contribution under the scheme shall for the purposes of Case I or II of Schedule D and of the provisions of Chapter I or Part XII of the Taxes Act relating to expenses of management, be allowed to be deducted as an expense, or expense of management, incurred in the chargeable period in which the sum is paid; Provided that

(a) the amount of an employer's contributions which may be so deducted shall not exceed the amount contributed by him under the scheme in respect of employees in a trade or undertaking in respect of the profits of which the employer is assessable to tax (that is to say United Kingdom income tax or corporation tax),

(b) a sum not paid by way of an ordinary annual contribution shall for the purposes of this subsection be treated, as the Board may direct, either as an expense incurred in the chargeable period in which the sum is paid, or as an expense to be spread over such period of years as the Board think proper.

(4) Any ordinary annual contribution paid under the scheme by an employee shall, in assessing tax under Schedule E, be allowed to be deducted as an expense incurred in the year of assessment in which the contribution is paid.

(5) Relief shall not be given under section 19 and 20 of the Taxes Act (life assurance premiums and other payments) in respect of any payment in respect of which an allowance can be made under subsection (4) above.

(6) (Repealed by Finance Act 1971)

(7) For the purposes of capital gains tax a gain shall not be a chargeable gain where it accrues to a person on his disposal of investments if, or to such extent as the Board are satisfied that, those investments were held by him or on his behalf for the purposes of the scheme.

Comment on Sections 19 and 20

2.6 It will be seen that sub-sections 19(1), 19(2) and 19(2A) combine to form a curious structure. Under s.19(2A) approval is mandatory if the conditions of s.19(2A) are satisfied, provided the conditions of s.19(2) are also satisfied. The conditions of s.19(2A) are, however, so highly restrictive as to be virtually out of the question; they do not, for instance, permit any benefits to be provided to early leavers or on death in service or the retirement of a man before age 60. This road to approval is therefore not used in practice.

2.7 Sub-section 20(1) is crucial. It provides for the Revenue to approve a scheme, subject to such conditions as they think proper, even though the scheme does not satisfy one or more of the 'prescribed conditions', i.e. the conditions laid down in s.19(2) and s.19(2A). This continues the general pattern of discretionary control noted in paragraph 2.2 and it is the basis of the procedure for approval used in practice. Sub-section 20(2) indicates some of the ways in which the Revenue may relax the statutory requirements for approval by exercising their discretionary power, and sub-section 20(3) provided for transitional concessions as schemes changed from the old code to the current arrangements. In practice the Revenue do not normally relax the conditions of s.19(2)(a) to (d).

Comment on section 21

2.8 Sub-section 21(1) defines an 'exempt approved scheme'. The section goes on to provide that the proceeds of the investments of such schemes shall be free of income and capital gains tax, that the contributions of the employer shall be allowed as an expense (although tax relief in respect of special contributions may be spread over a period of years) and that the ordinary annual contributions of the employee shall be allowed against his personal tax.

Comment on sections 22 to 26

2.9   We do not show the text of these sections, but this paragraph gives an outline of their general effect. Section 22 deals with exemptions and reliefs under certain statutory schemes. Sections 23 and 24 together provide a powerful sanction to ensure compliance with the Revenue's requirements. Section 23 provides that the employer's contributions (or notional contributions, if no contributions are in fact paid) to a scheme are to be taxed in the employee's hands as if they were additional pay, but section 24 exempts from the effect of section 23 contributions under a scheme which is an approved scheme (or a statutory scheme or belonging to a category of certain foreign government schemes). Sections 25 and 26 are formal and need not concern us here.

Taxation approval in practice

2.10   The effect of exempt approval is very simple; contributions are tax allowed and the investment accumulation is tax free. The complications of the subject arise mainly in connection with the scales of maximum permitted benefits laid down by the Revenue. These scales and various other relevant matters are set out in detail in the Inland Revenue Practice Notes IR12 (the current edition at the time of writing of this book being dated 1979) as amended or clarified in memoranda and other documents which are issued from time to time by the S.F.O. or by the S.F.O. and O.P.B. jointly. Document IR12 has 94 pages and cannot be summarised here, but some of the main features are described below. Because of the practical complications of the subject the following paragraphs should not be taken as full and exact specifications of the points covered.

2.10A   The reader should note that the revenue rules do not in themselves confer any rights on the members of a scheme. For instance, it will be seen later that Revenue rules permit part of a pension to be converted into a capital sum on retirement, but for members of a scheme to be able to do this it must be specifically provided for in the trust deed and rules of the scheme. The Revenue rules thus define the framework within which the trust deed and rules of the scheme (which define the arrangements between the trustees and the members) must operate.

2.11 It will be realised that the Inland Revenue rules form a 'ceiling', above and separate from the main operating rules of each particular scheme. Whenever the amount of a benefit is calculated under the main rules of a scheme a separate calculation of the maximum amount permitted under Revenue rules must in principle be made, and the former amount must be reduced if it exceeds the latter.

2.12 In practice it is comparatively unusual for the main rules of a scheme to produce a level of benefit so close to Revenue limits that this dual calculation needs to be made in every case. A much more important point is that it is very common for the trust deed and rules of a scheme to give the trustees power to augment the benefits at their discretion in individual cases, and in exercising such a discretion the trustees obviously need to be able to establish the maximum amount permitted by the Revenue, since this determines how far they can go. A similar point arises in respect of any benefits provided by the additional voluntary contributions of members, as mentioned in paragraph 2.36.

Final Remuneration

2.13 Whether or not there is a power of augmentation, Revenue limits have to be observed. The trust deed and rules of each scheme have therefore to include provisions incorporating the Revenue maxima. Sometimes this is achieved by the inclusion, in the rules of the scheme, of a self-contained rule in a standard form issued by the S.F.O., setting out the main Revenue limits. In other schemes the appropriate Revenue provisions are scattered through the rules. In either case an important point of definition arises. This stems from the fact that many of the Revenue rules about maximum benefits are expressed in terms of 'Final Remuneration', and if the trustees of each scheme were free to define what they meant by this term for the purpose of Revenue control, there would be no such thing as a standard set of Revenue maxima applying to all schemes. The Revenue therefore have to lay down the definition of this term.

2.14 Practice notes 6.12 and 6.14 of IR12 contain the main definitions of Final Remuneration as far as the present discussion is concerned. They read as follows.

6.12   Scheme rules may provide for 'final remuneration' to be calculated on any basis which falls within the following:

(a)   Remuneration for any one of the 5 years preceding the normal retirement date. (For this purpose 'remuneration' means basic pay, e.g. wage or salary, for the year in question, plus the average over a suitable period (usually 3 or more years) ending on the last day of the basic pay year of any fluctuating emoluments such as commission or bonuses. Directors' fees may rank either as basic pay or as fluctuating emoluments according to the basis on which they are voted).

(b)   The average of the total emoluments for any period of 3 or more consecutive years ending not earlier than 10 years before the normal retirement date.

6.14   Whenever 'final remuneration' is that of a year other than the 12 months ending with normal retirement date, or is an average of 3 or more years' remuneration, each years's remuneration may be increased in proportion to the increase in the cost of living* for the period from the end of the year up to normal retirement date. 'Final remuneration' so increased is known as 'dynamised final remuneration'.

2.15   The provisions of practice note 6.14 were of particular importance to senior executives who retired during the periods of pay restraint which were experienced in the United Kingdom during the 1970s. Salary at retirement was sometimes a good deal less than a figure arrived at by increasing a previous year's salary in the ratio of the change in the cost of living in the meantime. Provided that the rules of the pension scheme permitted augmentation, practice note 6.14 could be used to ensure that the employee's standard of living in retirement was not depressed by the accident of his having retired at a time when salary levels were being held down. At the time of writing the point has diminished in importance because the rate of inflation has lessened and there is no statutory control of pay levels.

---

*   Increases in the cost of living may be measured by the index of retail prices published by the Department of Employment or by any other suitable index agreed for the particular scheme by the Superannuation Funds Office.

2.16   The following points may be noted.

(i)   If retirement is taking place before normal retirement date the definitions of Final Remuneration are the same except that the date of leaving service is substituted for normal retirement date.

(ii)   A particular point on the application of practice note 6.14 in respect of capital sum retirement benefits is mentioned at the end of paragraph 2.20.

(iii)   The Revenue definition of Final Remuneration for the purpose of specifying the maximum lump sum benefits on death in service is somewhat different from that for pensions as outlined above.

Normal retirement date

2.17   Broadly speaking the Revenue rules centre on the maximum benefits that may be provided upon retirement at normal retirement date, the maximum benefits that may be paid in other circumstances being derived from these and being smaller if retirement takes place early and greater if retirement is delayed. The settling of 'normal retirement date' in a particular scheme is thus crucial to the whole pattern of maximum benefits for that scheme, and it is necessary to define a specific date for men and for women in the rules of a scheme as the 'normal retirement date' for the purpose of Revenue control, and to have the arrangements approved by the Revenue, even if in practice members retire on grounds of age over a range of ages. The Revenue rules refer both to 'normal retirement date' and 'normal retirement age' according to context and we shall do the same. The Revenue will normally approve a particular normal retirement age if it is the age at which a majority of the employees concerned do in fact normally retire and if it is within the range 60-70 for men and 55-70 for women. In certain special occupations much lower normal retirement ages are permitted.

Member's pension at normal retirement date

2.18   In the context of maximum permitted benefits the word 'pension' includes the pension equivalent of any retirement benefit being provided in lump sum form. When an employee retires at normal retirement date, his employer may provide him with a pension of up to 1/60th of Final Remuneration for each year of

service (with a maximum of 40) with that employer irrespective of
any retirement benefits to which the employee may be entitled
from pension schemes of another employer by reason of earlier
service with that other employer (these entitlements from previous
employments being known as 'Retained Benefits').

2.19 If the employer desires to give a pension in excess of this
scale, the maximum amount of pension which may be provided
depends on the employee's years of service with that employer at
retirement and on Final Remuneration according to the
'accelerated accrual' of the following table.

Number of years of service at normal retirement date	Maximum pension expressed as sixtieths of Final Remuneration
1 to 5	1 for each year
6	8
7	16
8	24
9	32
10 or more	40

If advantage is taken of this table, Retained Benefits as defined
above have to be taken into consideration. The position is that the
pension from the current employment, when aggregated with the
pension equivalent of such Retained Benefits as the Revenue may
require to be taken into account, must not exceed two-thirds of
Final Remuneration. Subject to this point there is thus permitted
on retirement at normal retirement date 'a two-thirds pension
after 10 years' service'.

Lump sum retirement benefits

2.20 Part of the maximum retirement pension permitted under
the rules outlined above may be taken in the form of a capital sum
of equivalent value, which is tax free in the hands of the recipient.
This is often referred to as 'commutation' of pension. Under
S.F.O. rules any commutation option provided under the rules of
the scheme must be exerciseable when the pension starts to be
paid; a pensioner may not, for instance, give up part of his pension
for a lump sum if the pension has been in payment for some time.

When an employee retires at normal retirement date he may be provided with a lump sum of up to 3/80ths of Final Remuneration for each year of service with the employer irrespective of any Retained Benefits. If it is desired to give a capital sum in excess of this scale, the maximum amount of the sum which may be provided depends on the employee's years of service with the employer at normal retirement date, and on his Final Remuneration, according to the 'accelerated accrual' of the following table.

Number of years of service at normal retirement date	Maximum lump sum expressed as eightieths of Final Remuneration
1 to 8	3 for each year
9	30
10	36
11	42
12	48
13	54
14	63
15	72
16	81
17	90
18	99
19	108
20 or more	120

Advantage may be taken of the dynamisation provisions of practice note 6.14 (see paragraph 2.14) in the calculation of the maximum permissible capital sum in a particular case only to the extent that such dynamisation has in fact been used in arriving at the pension benefits in that case.

2.21 If advantage is taken of this table Retained Benefits have to be taken into consideration. The position is that the lump sum from the current employment, when aggregated with the value at retirement of such lump sum retirement benefits received or receivable in respect of service with a former employer as the Revenue may require to be taken into account, must not exceed 1½ times Final Remuneration. Subject to this point there is thus permitted on retirement at normal retirement date a lump sum retirement benefit equal to 1½ times Final Remuneration after 20 years' service, within the overall limits referred to in paragraph 2.19.

Terms of conversion

2.22 The terms upon which pension is converted into lump sum are subject to Revenue approval. This is to counter a possible abuse in that if the maximum permitted pension were first calculated and a part of it then converted into lump sum on too generous terms, the value of the two benefits together would exceed that of the original pension. The pension that is given up is the member's personal pension; the terms are not meant to be in cancellation of any dependants' contingent pensions. The Revenue recognise that a pension which carries the right to (but not merely the possibility of) regular post-retirement increases (see paragraph 2.33 et seq) is more valuable than one that does not, and they will permit an appropriately higher rate of capital sum for each 1 p.a. of initial pension given up. Some of the terms at present approvable by the Revenue are as follows.

Pension not carrying the right to post-retirement increases

(i)   If the rate of commutation is not to vary with age at retirement and sex, 9 for each 1 p.a. of pension given up.

(ii)   If the rate is to vary according to sex but not with age at retirement, 9 for men and 11 for women.

(iii) If the rates are to vary with age and sex, rates of which the following are specimens.

Age at retirement	Male	Female
	£	£
55	–	12.2
60	10.2	11.0
65	9.0	9.8
70	7.8	–

Pension carrying the right to post-retirement increases

Factors on an appropriate mortality basis and based on a rate of interest calculated as follows.

	Rate of interest per cent.
Post-retirement increases limited to 2 per cent. p.a. or less	6
For each 1 per cent. by which the maximum post-retirement increase rate exceeds 2 per cent.	A reduction of 1 from the figure of 6 above, but not less than 3.

Thus however favourable the pension increase provision, the commutation terms may not be more favourable than a 3 per cent. annuity. For a male at age 65 with a pension guaranteed for five years this implies on PA(90)M a maximum possible rate of conversion of about 11.5 for each 1 p.a. given up.

Commutation of total pension

2.23 As far as taxation approval is concerned, a pension may be commuted in full, even though the resulting lump sum is greater than that permitted under the above rules, in two particular cases. The first is if the amount of the pension would be trivial (the definition of 'trivial' being laid down from time to time by the Revenue). The second is in exceptional circumstances of extreme ill-health of the pensioner. It should be noted that we are referring here only to Revenue rules; other legislation such as the contracting-out conditions oulined in Chapter 4 below may operate to prevent full commutation.

Other termination capital sum payments

2.24 Certain other capital sum payments may be made on the termination of an employment, e.g. those known as 'golden handshake' payments. These are provided for under separate legislation. They are paid by the employer from his own resources and they do not affect the provisions governing the maximum capital sum benefits that may be provided from the pension scheme as discussed here.

Early retirement due to incapacity

2.25   If a member of a pension scheme has to retire early because
of incapacity, the maximum permitted scales of immediate pension
and capital sum are those which would have applied had the
member remained in service with unchanged Final Remuneration
until normal retirement date and then retired. Thus if a person
joined a pension scheme at age 35 and would normally have
retired at age 65 but is forced by ill-health to retire at age 45, the
maximum permitted immediate pension and lump sum are
calculated on the basis of 30 years' service even though only ten
have been completed. The implications of this will depend not
only on whether the main rules of the scheme provide for the
payment of a pension greater than that based on actual service but
also on whether the Revenue provisions which have been included
in the scheme in respect of maximum benefits on retirement at
normal pension age do or do not include the 'accelerated accrual'
provisions of paras 2.19 and 2.20.

Early retirement on grounds other than incapacity

2.26   The rules of a scheme may define various circumstances in
which a member may leave before normal retirement date in
normal health (so that an incapacity pension is not involved) but
may nevertheless have a pension with payment starting
immediately. The general topic of early retirement is dealt with in
Chapter 5, but as far as taxation approval is concerned the main
points are that only if a leaving member is aged 50 or over may he
be provided with an immediate pension (instead of the other
benefits to early leavers mentioned in paragraph 2.32 below) and
that the maximum permitted amount of the immediate pension is
in principle the maximum amount which would have been
approvable at normal retirement date had the member remained a
member until that date with unchanged pay, reduced in the ratio
which actual service at the date of leaving bears to total potential
service up to normal retirement date.

Late retirement

2.26A   The Revenue rules permit benefits greater than those
outlined above to be provided if the member delays his retirement
beyond normal retirement date. The detailed provisions are
complex.

Death during employment

2.27 An approved scheme may provide both a capital sum and pensions to dependants upon death during employment. The maximum lump sum benefit allowed is £5,000 or, if greater, four times Final Remuneration (which may for this purpose be defined as the annual rate of salary at the date of death) plus an amount equal to the member's contributions to the scheme accumulated with interest. It is only in highly unusual circumstances that the figure of £5,000 has any relevance in practice. Capital sums paid from a scheme on the death of a member are liable to capital transfer tax in the following circumstances.

(i) If they form part of his freely disposable property passing under his will or intestacy and his executors or administrators had a legally enforceable claim to the benefit.

(ii) If the member immediately before his death had the right to nominate the benefits to anyone he pleased.

To avoid capital transfer tax liability, the rules of a scheme usually convey upon the trustees a discretion as to the person to whom a capital sum death benefit is to be paid. If the trustees have such a discretion they will probably ask each member to lodge with them a statement indicating how he would wish them to exercise this discretion, but they are not bound to follow his wishes.

2.28 The maximum pension that may be paid to a widow, widower or dependant upon the member's death during employment is equal to two-thirds of the maximum pension that could have been approved for the member if he had remained in service until his normal retirement date at the rate of remuneration current at the date of his death. Subject to this provision, the maximum total amount of pension that may be shared between two or more such beneficiaries is equal to the whole amount of the member's maximum approvable pension. It will be noted that these limitations are expressed in terms of the maximum pension to the member which would have been approvable, and not to the pension which the scheme would actually have provided.

Death after retirement

2.29 The pension payable to a retired employee may continue for a period of up to 10 years after his retirement even if he dies within that period. If the guarantee period does not exceed 5 years from retirement, an immediate lump sum may be paid on the pensioner's death equal to any excess of the total amount of pension which would have been payable during the guarantee period over the amount of pension actually paid.

2.30 Pensions arising on death after retirement are limited in amount on much the same lines as those on death during employment. A pension may be provided as of right to a widow, widower or dependant of a pensioner of an amount not exceeding two-thirds of the maximum approvable pension that could have been paid to the deceased pensioner, and multiple pensions may be provided up to a total amount equal to the maximum approvable pension payable to the pensioner were he still alive.

Withdrawal from service

2.31 The law relating to the benefits payable upon the withdrawal of a member from a scheme as an 'early leaver' (i.e. not with an immediate pension) provides a striking example of different areas of legislation operating in virtual independence of each other. The rules of tax approval impose one set of conditions, those of the preservation legislation (see Chapter 3 below) a second and, if the scheme concerned is contracted out, those of the contracting out legislation (see Chapter 4 below) a third. At times during the 1970s the whole situation was one of almost impenetrable complexity; the position at the time of writing is somewhat less complicated though by no means straightforward.

2.32 As far as taxation approval in isolation is concerned, an approved scheme may provide one of the following benefits if a member leaves the scheme because he is leaving the employment and he is not retiring with an immediate pension.

(a)   A refund of the member's own contributions. The Revenue rules state that such a refund may include interest on the contributions 'at a reasonable rate' and most schemes provide such interest at a modest rate. If a refund is made, the trustees of the scheme have to pay a tax charge equal to 10 per cent. of the amount payable and it is often provided in the rules of a scheme for the trustees to deduct this amount from the refund, so that the tax charge is passed on to the withdrawing member. The effect of other legislation is greatly to limit the extent to which refunds may be taken.

(b) The preservation in the scheme of the member's accrued pension rights. This benefit is usually called a 'deferred', 'preserved' or 'frozen' pension. The maximum permitted amount of the preserved pension is in principle the maximum approvable amount at normal retirement date had the member remained a member until that date with unchanged pay, reduced in the ratio which actual service at the date of leaving bears to total potential service up to normal retirement date.

(c) The payment of a cash sum, usually called a 'transfer value', to the scheme of the new employer. No tax charge arises on this transaction.

(d) The payment of the cash sum in (c) to an insurance company in purchase of an annuity policy for the ex-member. Here again no tax charge arises on the transaction.

Increases in pensions in course of payment

2.33 Taking first under this heading the case where trustees have a power of discretionary augmentation and are considering what increases to grant on pensions in course of payment, the Revenue rules provide that the maximum amount of the pension of a retired employee at any time is the amount of the maximum approvable pension of the person concerned at retirement, increased in the ratio of the increase in the cost of living since the date of retirement with an adjustment to take account of any part of the retirement benefit taken in the form of a capital sum. If, for example, an employee retired on a pension of £2,000 per annum (with no capital sum) which has since been increased to £2,800 per annum, and if the maximum pension at retirement which would have been allowed under Revenue rules is £3,000 per annum and the cost of living has increased by 50 per cent. since retirement, then the pension of £2,800 per annum could be increased to £4,500 per annum. The question of what cost can be afforded, and hence what increases can in fact be granted, is of course a quite separate one.

2.34 The previous paragraph was concerned with discretionary increases. Pension increases may be promised in advance under the rules of a scheme, as an alternative to or in addition to discretionary augmentation. Under Revenue rules the following are acceptable.

(i) A promise to raise pensions in the ratio of the increase in the cost of living after retirement. At the time of writing this undertaking is common in public sector schemes but almost unknown in private sector schemes, a matter discussed further in Chapter 5.

(ii) Pension increases of up to 3 per cent. per annum whether or not the cost of living rises by this much.

(iii) Pension increases at an annual percentage rate higher than 3 per cent. but with the resulting amounts subject to the maximum indicated in paragraph 2.33.

Contracting-out and participation

2.35 In Chapter 4 we shall be dealing with the State earnings-related pension scheme in the United Kingdom. Without anticipating that discussion, a point of immediate relevance is that some employees who are members of an occupational pension scheme also participate in the State earnings-related scheme while other employees who are members of an occupational scheme do not participate in the State scheme (because they are 'contracted out' by virtue of their membership of the occupational scheme). It might have been expected that the Revenue rules laying down maximum benefits in an occupational scheme would be different according to whether or not the members participated in the State scheme. This is not, in fact, the case. The Revenue rules that we have discussed in this chapter apply to occupational pension schemes irrespective of whether or not the members also participate in the State scheme. The maximum pension benefits from State and occupational scheme together are therefore greater for an employee who participates in the State earnings-related Scheme than for one who does not, other things being equal.

Members' contributions

2.36 The Revenue rules are framed mainly in terms of maximum benefits. There is no Revenue restriction on the maximum contribution which an employer may pay (although tax relief on special contributions may be spread over a period). There is, however, Revenue control on the amount of a member's contribution. This is restricted to 15 per cent. of his earnings in the year concerned. This is much in excess of the scales of members' contributions normally encountered, and the main practical effect is to impose a limit on the additional amount which members may pay under any facility in the scheme for members' additional voluntary contributions or 'AVCs'. The benefits provided in respect of AVCs have to be taken into account when the benefits of the scheme are tested against Revenue limits.

Employer's contributions: two special points

Hancock annuities

2.37 We end this chapter by mentioning two particular aspects of employers' contributions. The first concerns the purchase of a 'Hancock annuity', so called because this type of transaction was considered in the law case Hancock v. General Reversionary and Investment Co. Ltd. What is involved is the outright purchase by payment of a single premium of an immediate or deferred annuity for an employee at the time of or after his retirement, or for a widow, widower or dependant of a deceased employee, or in order to create a pension scheme for the employee shortly before retirement. Assuming that the arrangement constitutes an exempt approved scheme, the purchase price is treated as an employer's contribution allowed against his tax; it is not an ordinary contribution and tax relief may therefore be spread.

Funding of pension increases

2.38 The other special point concerns a payment to a pension scheme by an employer which is made solely to finance pension increases to existing pensioners. Even though such a payment is not part of a flow of normal contributions, and may indeed be a very large single amount, it is nevertheless normally allowed, in the computation of the employer's tax liability, in the year in which it is paid; there is no requirement as to spreading of tax relief. In times of high inflation the capital cost of providing a special increase (over and above any increase funded for in the pension scheme) on a substantial pension roll may be a very large sum, and there have been cases where the payment of such a sum to the scheme, with tax allowance of the whole amount in the year concerned, has been a significant feature in the finances of the employer.

CHAPTER 3

PRESERVATION

PRESERVATION

Introduction

3.1 The benefit scales of occupational pension schemes reflect wider social attitudes, and the treatment of early leavers is a good example of this. The novelist Anthony Trollope, who was born in 1815, joined the Post Office as a clerk in 1834. He left in 1867 in order to devote all his time to his work as a novelist, and was therefore an early leaver at the age of 52 with 33 years of service. In his autobiography he describes the pension position upon his leaving as follows.

'The rule of the service in regard to pensions is very just. A man shall serve till he is sixty before he is entitled to a pension, – unless his health fail him. At that age he is entitled to one-sixtieth of his salary for every year he has served up to forty years. If his health do fail him so that he is unfit for further work before the age named, then he may go with a pension amounting to one-sixtieth for every year he has served. I could not say that my health had failed me, and therefore I went without any pension.'

Although the first sentence of this extract may be misleading to a modern reader, in that the word 'just' may mean 'precise' in this context, rather than 'fair', the main point is that even the leading pension schemes at that time did not provide adequate benefits for voluntary early leavers.

The Social Security Act 1973

3.2 Little progress was made in early leavers' benefits during the next hundred years as the pension scheme movement grew. Members leaving a scheme to which they had contributed preferred an immediate return of their contributions to the promise of a pension payable in the distant future; employers felt little obligation to the early leaver. It became clear that legislation would be required if progress was to be made, and such legislation was included in the Social Security Act 1973. Most of the provisions of this Act disappeared with a change of Government, but those introducing preservation of retirement benefits, subject to age and service qualifications, when a member leaves an occupational scheme before retiring were accepted by the new Government, as were the provisions bringing into being the Occupational Pensions Board (the 'O.P.B.').

The Occupational Pensions Board

3.3 This is a convenient point at which to introduce the Occupational Pensions Board. The O.P.B. is a most important part of the pension scene in the United Kingdom, since it is the body through which statutory supervision of occupational pension schemes (except for taxation matters) is exercised. Membership of the Board is drawn from both sides of industry and commerce and from the professional and specialist bodies concerned with occupational pensions. In its early years the main part of the Board's work was concerned with the implementation of the preservation law with which this chapter is concerned. Its responsibilities were enormously increased when it was charged with the supervision of the contracting-out arrangements described in the next chapter. In addition the O.P.B. is the body from which the Government seeks reports on occupational pension matters, and the growing number of these reports provides a substantial volume of data and authoritative comment on many aspects of pensions.

1973 Act preservation in principle

3.4 In this chapter we first outline preservation as introduced by the 1973 Act and we then touch on the further provisions introduced under the Social Security Act 1985. The broad principle of the 1973 Act preservation legislation is that a member of a pension scheme who leaves the scheme before attaining the scheme's normal pension age and satisfies the qualifying conditions for preservation must have the retirement benefits which he has accrued at the date of leaving preserved for him in the scheme, becoming payable upon his attainment of the earliest age at which he would normally have become entitled to claim a pension had he not left. In deciding what this age is in a particular case, any facility which the scheme rules may provide for a member to retire early with an actuarially reduced immediate pension (see paragraph 5.42) are ignored, as is any provision for early retirement in special circumstances such as ill-health or any provision for early retirement which is conditional upon the consent of the employer. The age that has to be established is the earliest age at which the member, had he remained, could have claimed as of right an immediate pension calculated on the normal pension scale of the scheme. It may be noted that example (i) of paragraph 5.35 would result in the preserved pension of a male early leaver being payable before attainment of age 65 but example (ii) would not.

3.4A The original qualifying conditions were:

(i)   attainment of age 26, and
(ii)   completion of five years of qualifying service

but condition (i) has been deleted under the Social Security Act 1985.

For present purposes 'qualifying service' may be taken as meaning the total of:

(i)   the period of membership in the scheme concerned and any other schemes of the same employer, and
(ii)   the periods of membership in any previous schemes if the present scheme has taken over the liability for benefit rights arising under those previous schemes upon the receipt of a transfer value.

3.4B The preservation requirements relate to retirement benefits, both in lump sum and pension form, and also to benefits on death after retirement, but do not extend to benefits payable on death before attainment of normal pension age. There is a provision that when a pension which has been preserved comes into payment the recipient is not to be treated less favourably, with respect to such matters as commutation rights or increases subsequently granted on pensions in course of payment, than a person who remained in the scheme and retired in the ordinary way.

3.5 A further principle is that the value of the benefit to the early leaver must 'exceed or compare reasonably with the amount contributed by the member towards the scheme'. It is the duty of the administrator of the scheme to decide to his reasonable satisfaction whether this requirement is satisfied. The requirement does not apply if preserved benefits are increased during the period between the end of pensionable service and the time that the pension becomes payable at a rate not less than 3 per cent. per annum compound or by reference to the cost of living. In such cases it is assumed that the deal will represent 'value for money' to the member. It appears at the time of writing that this principle will shortly be removed from the legislative requirements, on the grounds that the 1985 Act provisions supersede it.

1973 Act preservation in practice

3.6 The principle of preservation is simple in concept but has proved complicated in practical application. The legislative framework is laid down in Section 63 of the 1973 Act, Schedule 16 to the Act and a number of statutory instruments notably Nos. 1469 and 1784 of 1973 and No. 1324 of 1974. At the time of writing the practical application is governed by Memorandum No. 78 of the O.P.B.; this runs to 274 numbered paragraphs and a number of appendices, an indication of the practical complexities involved. The O.P.B. issue further guidance as required. In the simple case of a 'final pay' type scheme (see Chapter 5) with a pension fraction of 1/60th applying to all years of membership, the preserved pension must not be less than 1/60th of the appropriate pensionable salary at the time of leaving for each year of pensionable service completed. The complications of the matter arise mainly under schemes where the rate of accrual of benefits is, for one reason or another, not constant throughout the whole of the member's service or potential service, and in the precise definition of qualifying service.

Refunds of contributions

3.7 In view of the fact that members leaving occupational schemes generally prefer to take a return of their own contributions rather than have benefits preserved for them, the 1973 Act did not ban such returns of contributions and substitute preservation immediately. The position on the continuing right to a refund is broadly as follows as far as the preservation law is concerned; the further requirements and conditions which operate in contracting out schemes are referred to in the next chapter.

(i) A leaving member who does not satisfy the qualifying conditions mentioned in paragraph 3.4A is not covered by the preservation legislation. Most persons leaving occupational schemes after short periods of membership in the future will no doubt continue to take a refund, although there is nothing to prevent the rules of the scheme concerned providing for preservation or for the payment of a 'transfer value' to the person's next pension scheme.

(ii) A person leaving an occupational scheme who satisfies the qualifying conditions may not take a refund and thereby extinguish his pension rights. These rights must be kept for him by preservation of the rights in the scheme, by purchase of a deferred annuity policy or by payment of a transfer value. This is subject to the concession that if the leaving member was a member of the scheme on 6th April 1975 he may take a refund of contributions paid in respect of qualifying service up to 6th April 1975. In this case the preserved pension is based on pensionable service after that date. In addition there must also normally be preserved any benefits in respect of any period of non-contributory pensionable service before 6th April 1975 (because a contribution refund is deemed to cancel the pension rights in respect only of the period for which the contributions were paid).

Revaluation

3.8 During the 1970s, periods of high inflation were a feature of the United Kingdom economy and there was growing criticism of the 1973 Act preservation law in that it required preservation of nothing more than a fixed amount of benefit calculated at the date of leaving; there was no protection against erosion of the value of the preserved benefits by inflation during the period between the date of leaving and the date that payment starts. In their Report on Improved Protection for the Occupational Pension Rights and Expectations of Early Leavers (CMND 8271 presented to Parliament June 1981) the O.P.B. recommended that preserved benefits should be increased to a limited extent during the period of deferment.

3.9 Legislation requiring certain such increases to be provided was brought in under section 2(c) of the Social Security Act 1985.

The detailed provisions appear in Part I of a new Schedule 1A to the Social Security Pensions Act 1975, the text of which is to be found in Part II of Schedule 1 to the 1985 Act. The 1975 Act is dealt with in some detail in the next chapter of this book. The new provisions (referred to in the 1985 Act as 'revaluation') are broadly as follows for 'final salary' schemes, i.e. schemes where the pension depends on the level of pensionable pay near to retirement and the length of pensionable service as described in paragraph 5.7 of this book. There are other provisions in the 1985 Act for other types of pension scale, but we shall not discuss these here.

(i) If the pensionable service of a member of a pension scheme ceases one year or more before his attainment of the scheme's normal pension age and he becomes entitled to a preserved pension, there is calculated that part of his preserved pension which is deemed to arise in respect of pensionable service after 1st January 1985.

(ii) The part of the preserved pension defined in (i) must be increased, in respect of the period before it comes into payment, by the lesser of
   (a) 5 per cent. p.a. compound over the whole of that period, and
   (b) the increase in a price index over the whole of that period.

Item (i) above is an oversimplification if a scheme is being used for contracting-out. This subject is dealt with in the next chapter, and we return to revaluation in paragraph 4.49.

3.10 Thus if at some future date a member leaves a scheme at age 45 with preserved rights of £2,000 p.a. of which £600 p.a. is deemed to have accrued after 1st January 1985, if normal pension age is 65 and if prices double during the 20 year period of deferment, the minimum amount of pension payable at age 65 is to be calculated as follows.

	Amount payable at age 65
	£ p.a.
Original amount of preserved pension	2,000
Part of preserved pension affected £600 p.a	
This part of pension to be multiplied by the lesser of	
(i) 5 per cent. compound for 20 years 2.65	
(ii) Prices 2.00	
£600 × 2.00 .... £1,200	
Increase in pension required by 1985 Act	600
Total amount of pension payable	£2,600

It will be noted that no improvement is required in respect of rights accrued before 1st January 1985, or in respect of the preserved pension rights of persons who became early leavers before the coming into the force of the new legislation. No additional costs are therefore imposed on pension schemes in respect of pensionable service already completed.

Transfer payments

3.11 The 1973 Act conveys upon a leaving member of a pension scheme who satisfies the qualifying conditions the right to a preserved pension. It is also provided that, if the leaving member and the trustees of the scheme are agreeable, the preservation liability may be discharged by payment of a transfer value to another pension scheme, but the 1973 legislation does not give the leaving member an absolute right to the payment of such a transfer value nor to any particular principle or method of calculation of the amount.

3.12 A leaving member's right to a transfer payment as an alternative to a preserved pension has, however, been brought in by section 2(d) of the Social Security Act 1985 and Part II of the new schedule 1A to the 1975 Act introduced by the 1985 Act as mentioned in paragraph 3.9 above. The main points are as follows.

(i) If the pensionable service of a member of a pension scheme ends more than one year before his attainment of the scheme's normal pension age and he becomes entitled to preserved benefits, the 1985 Act gives him the right to what is called in the Act the 'cash equivalent' of the preserved benefits.

(ii)   The cash equivalent must be used as a transfer to another scheme or in purchase of an annuity policy from a life office chosen by the member, or for such other purposes as may be prescribed. The trustees of another scheme are not, however, bound under the legislation to accept the transfer value; it is up to them to decide whether they will do so.

(iii)   Following termination of pensionable service with a preserved benefit the option to give up the preserved benefit in return for a cash equivalent must remain open until one year before attainment of normal pension age.

(iv)   The trustees of the scheme must give effect to the member's wishes within 12 months of receiving his application.

(v)   The legislation has been framed in the light of normal current practice under which a transfer value is usually calculated as the cash equivalent of the preserved benefits that would otherwise be provided. Regulations and professional Guidance Note GN11 (shown at the end of Chapter 19) have just been issued at the time of writing. These documents do not prescribe tables but leave the values to be determined by qualified actuaries.

(vi)   The legislation provides for minimum transfer payments; there is no objection in principle to larger payments being made.

(vii)   The matter is mentioned again in connection with contracting-out in paragraph 4.35A below.

The interaction of legislation

3.13   The reader should note that in schemes which are used for contracting-out, as described in the next chapter, important additional points arise in connection with early leavers' benefits. These are outlined in the next chapter and particularly in paragraph 4.49 et seq; the present chapter has been concerned with the preservation law in isolation.

Preservation and funding

3.14   The rules of pension schemes have to include provisions bringing into effect the preservation requirements. This, of course, does not in itself ensure that the necessary resources will be provided in the funds of the scheme. It is the duty of the trustees to seek to ensure that they will be in a position to pay the benefits, but as will be shown in the discussion of funding plans it is often necessary for a liability to be met by contributions payable over a period; the fund in hand is consequently built up only gradually. In the preservation requirements it is provided that if a scheme is wound up members who meet the preservation conditions are entitled to preserved benefits as if they were individual leavers, but it is accepted that they may not in fact receive their full entitlement because of an insufficiency of resources.

Mechanics of legislation

3.15 We mention for completeness a point in connection with the way the legislation operates. The 1973 Act required pension schemes rules to be changed to satisfy the requirements of the Act, and the necessary scrutiny of scheme rule amendments imposed a heavy workload on the staff of the OPB. Under this procedure the pension scheme administrator, having ensured that his scheme met statutory requirements, needed to refer only to his own trust deed and rules in order to run the scheme. We shall refer in the next chapter to the anti-franking provisions of the Health and Social Security Act 1984; these provisions, and some of the 1985 Act provisions discussed earlier in this chapter, override scheme rules, i.e. they apply whether or not the rules of a pension scheme have been amended in the light of these requirements. There will no doubt in future be an increasing number of areas in which the pension scheme administrator will have to have regard to pension legislation as well as to the trust deed and rules of his own scheme.

CHAPTER 4

THE SOCIAL SECURITY PENSIONS ACT
1975

THE SOCIAL SECURITY PENSIONS ACT 1975

4.1 We now turn to a third aspect of legislation. The Social Security Pensions Act 1975 introduced, with effect from 6th April 1978, a new section of the State pension scheme which provides earnings-related benefits on a specified slice of full taxable pay. Under the legislation employers are presented with a choice as to whether their employees should participate in this earnings-related scheme or should be exempted from it ('contracted-out') by virtue of their membership of an occupational pension scheme which has passed prescribed tests as to the scope and adequacy of the benefits and the degree to which those benefits are backed by assets. Contracting-out has created an additional layer of complexity in the design and financing of occupational pension schemes. In this book the detailed discussion of contracting-out requirements as they affect occupational schemes has been confined as far as possible to this chapter and Chapter 15. We provide a discussion of the financial issues involved in the partnership between State scheme and occupational schemes represented by contracting-out, and the financial experience during the first five years of contracting-out, in Chapter 31, after the actuarial technicalities involved have been introduced to the reader.

4.2 Contracting-out proved in the event to be very popular; the Government Actuary's 1979 Survey of Occupational Pension Schemes in the United Kingdom showed about 11.6 million active members of pension schemes of whom 10.3 million or about nine-tenths were contracted-out. In this chapter we give a broad outline of the arrangements and we set out the main points that employees and employers took into account in the initial consideration of whether to contract out or not. We then make brief reference to the 'Equal Access' provisions of the 1975 Act. This chapter ends with a note of the effect on schemes used for contracting-out of the abolition of 'franking' (see paragraph 4.36).

The State pension scheme

4.3 It is necessary to start with a brief description of the State scheme, since one of the principles with which we shall be involved is that if an occupational scheme is to be used for contracting-out it must provide benefits broadly corresponding to those of the State earnings-related scheme. The basic State retirement pension is a 'flat-rate' pension (so called because, although the amount is regularly increased (normally once a year) in the light of the level of inflation, it does not in principle differ from one employee to another). Virtually all employed persons become entitled to this pension on retirement at 'State pensionable age', which is age 65 for men and 60 for women. The flat-rate pension payable in respect of a married couple is greater than that for a single person. The question of whether the regular increase in these flat-rate pensions should be based on the increase in prices or in average earnings is a matter of continuing political controversy, but this question is not central to the present discussion.

4.4 The amount of the flat-rate pension for a single person serves the purpose of defining the lower and upper limits of earnings within which the State earnings-related pension scheme operates. The lower earnings limit in a particular tax year (i.e. the period from 6th April to next 5th April) is equal (subject to administrative adjustments) to the amount of the State flat-rate pension for a single person in force at the beginning of that year, and the upper earnings limit is equal to approximately seven times that amount.

4.5 In concept, the State earnings-related pension scheme provides, in respect of each tax year after 5th April 1978, a pension of 1/80th of that part of an employee's full taxable pay in that year which falls between the lower and upper earnings limits, revalued up to age 65 for men and 60 for women according to changes in national average earnings and indexed to the cost of living after it becomes payable. Each year of membership of the State earnings-related scheme after 5th April 1978 conveys entitlement to the 1/80th pension, except that if an employee has more than 20 years of such membership when he reaches State pensionable age only the best 20 such years are taken into the calculation of the pension, so that the maximum earnings-related pension is 25 per cent. of the appropriate revalued average annual earnings.

4.6 Although the previous paragraph conveys the spirit of the legislation it is not an accurate description of how the State earnings-related pension calculation is made in practice. The method is laid down in section 6 of the 1975 Act and for completeness a more precise description is given below. The reader who is concerned only to understand the contracting-out arrangements should note that not all the complexities described below are in fact carried over into those arrangements.

(i)   The first stage in the building up of the State earnings-related pension is that from the amount of the State scheme contributions that an employee pays in a particular tax year after 5th April 1978 there is calculated an 'earnings factor'. This is in principle an amount equal to the employee's total earnings up to the upper earnings limit in that year, but in practice it may not be exactly equal to those earnings because of the fact that it is derived from the contribution figure and not recorded directly. It should be noted that at this stage we are dealing with total earnings up to the upper earnings limit and not with the part of such earnings in excess of the lower earnings limit.

(ii) The earnings factor for each year as stored in the State pension scheme's records is increased each subsequent year in line with increases in the general levels of earnings in Great Britain, this procedure being laid down in section 21 of the Act.

(iii) When a person reaches the State pension age of 65 for men and 60 for women there will thus be stored in the State pension scheme records the figure of revalued earnings factors for each past tax year since the person concerned attained age 16, starting with that in which he first entered employment or the tax year 1978/79 if later and ending with the last complete tax year before the tax year in which the 65th or 60th birthday falls. This last complete tax year is called the 'final relevant year'. At this stage there is therefore a sequence of amounts, each of which may be broadly described as the amount of earnings up to the upper earnings limit in a previous tax year, revalued to final relevant year levels. The figure arising in respect of earnings in the final relevant year will not of course have been subject to any revaluation.

(iv) There is then deducted from each such amount of revalued earnings factor the amount of the lower earnings limit for the final relevant year. The resulting amounts are called the 'surplus' amounts for the past tax years concerned.

(v) If there are more than 20 separate figures of surpluses as described in (iv) above, the best 20 are taken.

(vi) The annual amount of the earnings-related pension is 1¼ per cent., i.e. 1/80th, of the total amount of these 20 or fewer surpluses.

It will be seen that it is in the treatment of the lower earnings limit that the method is more complex than was indicated in paragraph 4.5.

Widows' and widowers' pensions

4.7 The provisions relating to widows' pensions under the State pension scheme are complicated, but the main point to be noted here is that the widow's retirement pension comprises the whole of the flat-rate and earnings-related components of retirement pension which the husband was receiving on his own account when he died. The earnings-related pension is that accrued to the end of the tax year preceding the date of death if he died during employment. There is also paid to a widow, subject to overall limits, any earnings-related component she herself has earned. Widow's pensions in payment are increased in the same way as personal pensions in payment. There are limited provisions for a widower's pension if the wife was an employed person. All these benefits are subject to various qualification requirements.

Contracting-out

4.8 Contracting-out is a means by which a part of the State earnings-related pension referred to above becomes the responsibility of an occupational pension scheme instead of the State scheme, contributions to the latter being reduced in token of this fact. Since an occupational scheme used for contracting-out is in a sense taking over the obligations of the State scheme, the Government needs to be satisfied that the scheme is adequate for the purpose. The main tests that a scheme has to pass in order to be used for contracting-out are as follows.

(i)   A 'quantity' test. The broad principle is that the pension from the occupational scheme must not be less than the State pension forgone by contracting-out. This test involves specific money amounts calculated on the data for the individual concerned.

(ii) A 'quality' test. The scope and scale of the benefits of the occupational scheme must reach certain levels; these levels are not linked to the State scheme but are to do with such matters as the pension fraction and the definition of pensionable salary. The benefits to be provided by the occupational scheme are called in the Act 'requisite benefits'. This test involves the scheme documentation, not individual benefit calculations.

(iii) A solvency test. The resources backing the scheme must be adequate.

These matters are now considered in more detail.

Personal pension: the quantity test

4.9 For an employee to be contracted-out by virtue of membership of an occupational scheme, the employee's pension from the occupational scheme after he attains State pensionable age (65 for men, 60 for women) must satisfy a test of quantity. The broad principle is that the pension payable after attainment of State pensionable age must not be less than the pension to which the earner would have been entitled by way of earnings-related pension in the State scheme had he not been contracted-out for the period for which he was in fact contracted-out. This required amount of pension is called the 'guaranteed minimum pension' or 'G.M.P.'. It is calculated at State pensionable age and does not change thereafter. We stress that this G.M.P. amount must be paid as a pension. As will be seen later, there are circumstances where this requirement limits the amount of pension that may be given up in exchange for a capital sum.

4.10 As mentioned in paragraph 4.5 the pension fraction in respect of a particular year in the earnings-related State scheme is 1/80th, but if an employee has more than 20 years to serve from 6th April 1978 to the date he attains State pensionable age it will not be known until that latter date whether a particular year will fall amongst the best 20 and therefore be included in the pension calculation. The State earnings-related pension can thus be thought of as the sum of, at most, 20 separate 'eightieths', with years outside the best 20 not counting at all. For the purpose of defining the G.M.P., however, this entitlement has to be regarded as accruing over the whole period concerned, because it would be impracticable to have a system of contracting-out in which the minimum amount of pension to be provided in the occupational scheme depended on whether a particular year would or would not eventually turn out to be one of the best 20 for State scheme purposes.

4.11 For employees within 20 years of State pensionable age at the time that the new State scheme was introduced the rate of accrual of the G.M.P. is 1/80th, i.e. 1¼ per cent. For employees who had more than 20 years to elapse to State pensionable age in April 1975 the rate of accrual of the G.M.P. per year of employment is taken as

$$\frac{1}{N} \text{ of } \frac{20}{80} \text{ ths}$$

or as a percentage

$$\frac{25}{N} \text{ per cent.}$$

where N is the number of complete years in the employee's working life after 5th April 1978 up to the date that he reaches State pensionable age. This formula is written into s35(3) of the 1975 Act, the relevant wording being as follows.

'The appropriate percentage' means –

(a) if the earner is not more than 20 years under pensionable age when this section comes into force, 1¼ per cent.;

(b) in any other case $\frac{25}{N}$ per cent. where N is the number of years in the earner's working life (assuming that he will attain pensionable age) which fall after the coming into force of this section.

4.12 The words quoted above do not in themselves form complete working rules for the calculation of the G.M.P. rate of accrual for a particular individual. It is necessary to know that 'working life' for this purpose is defined elsewhere in legislation as the period beginning with the 6th April preceding the 16th birthday and ending with the 5th April preceding the date of attainment of State pensionable age. Thus if we consider a man born on 30th June 1955 the calculation proceeds as follows.

(i)	16th birthday	30.6.1971
(ii)	Later of (i) and 6.4.1978 =	6.4.1978
(iii)	65th birthday	30.6.2020
(iv)	5th April preceding date in (iii)	5.4.2020
(v)	Period from (ii) to (iv) =	42 years
(vi)	G.M.P. percentage 25/42 =	0.60 per cent.

4.13 It will be seen that the date of commencement of 'working life' is not affected by the date that the person in fact first entered employment. It will also be seen that the number 'N' is 49 (i.e. 65 less 16) for all males whose 16th birthday falls on or after 6th April 1978; in the distant future N will be 49 for all males and 44 for all females then alive. The average rate of accrual of G.M.P.s for the total contracted-out population will thus fall with time.

4.14 If an employee remains a member of one occupational pension scheme and retires at State pensionable age, the G.M.P. is calculated by applying the 'appropriate percentage' (i.e. 1¼ per cent. or 25/N per cent. as the case may be) to the total of the amounts of pay between the lower and upper earnings limits received during each year of contracted-out membership of the scheme, revalued up to State pensionable age by the revaluation factors used in the State earnings-related scheme. Any reader who would be helped by an example of the arithmetic involved should refer to paragraphs 15.3 to 15.9 and Table 18. Early leavers are considered later in this chapter.

The role of the G.M.P.

4.15 As noted above, the '20 best years' provision in the State scheme is not carried over as part of the G.M.P. requirement. The obligation is simply to revalue the G.M.P. accrued in any particular year in line with subsequent changes in general earnings levels. This does not mean, however, that an employee who is contracted-out receives less benefit in respect of the earnings-related part of the State scheme than one who participates. The position is that when an employee retires (assuming this takes place at State pensionable age) the State earnings-related pension is calculated as if he had never been contracted-out, and there is then deducted the amount of any G.M.P.s provided from occupational schemes, the State scheme paying the balance. This ensures that the earnings-related pension from State scheme and the G.M.P. from the occupational scheme taken together provide an amount not less than the State earnings-related pension that the employee would have earned had he not been contracted-out. The way in which the G.M.P. forms a link between State scheme and occupational scheme in the partnership brought about by contracting-out is sometimes found difficult to understand, and it may be of help to the reader if we illustrate the position by means of an example.

4.16   Suppose that an employee who retires at State pensionable age at some future date has had many different jobs during his career, sometimes belonging to a contracted-out pension scheme and sometimes participating in the State scheme. The State earnings-related pension is first calculated as if he had participated fully in the State scheme since April 1978, i.e. he had never been contracted-out. Suppose that this pension amounts to £2,000 per annum.

4.17   The records kept by the Department of Health and Social Security will show the G.M.P.s that the employee has accumulated as a contracted-out member of a succession of occupational schemes. Suppose that all the various amounts of G.M.P. revalued to age 65 (assuming the employee is a man) amount to £700 per annum. The amount of earnings-related pension payable by the State in the first year is £2,000 less £700, i.e. £1,300. The pension from State scheme and G.M.P.s together is £2,000, the same as if the employee had always participated fully in the State scheme. We are not concerned here with the non-G.M.P. part of the person's various occupational pensions.

4.18   The link between State and occupational pensions represented by the G.M.P. takes on a rather different aspect when a pension is in course of payment after the pensioner's attainment of State pensionable age. When there is a revaluation of State pensions in course of payment, the uplift factor is first applied to the total State pension which would have been payable had there been no contracting-out, and there is then deducted from this uplifted figure the same G.M.P. as before. Thus the State effectively provides increases on the G.M.P. after State pensionable age, even though the G.M.P. itself is being paid by the occupational scheme.

4.19   To illustrate this principle in the example above, suppose that State earnings-related pensions are increased by 10 per cent. one year after the member's retirement. The State earnings-related pension payable in the second year would be £2,200 less £700, i.e. £1,500 per annum. It will be seen that by this procedure cost-of-living increases on the G.M.P.s of £700 per annum payable from various company schemes are provided by the State scheme. This point is dealt with at rather more length in paragraph 5.34 in the context of a general discussion of pension benefits.

Covering the G.M.P.

4.20   We end this discussion of the quantity test by noting that, in testing whether the amount of an occupational pension is greater than the G.M.P. when a person who has been a member of the same occupational scheme for the whole of his contracted-out employment retires on attaining State pensionable age, the occupational pension that may be taken into account is not restricted to that part deemed to have arisen during contracted-out service. Suppose for example that a man retires at age 65 in 1990 having been a member of an occupational scheme since 1960. The occupational pension arises from the whole of this period and will be comparatively large (assuming that pensionable pay in the scheme is a substantial part of full pay), while the G.M.P. arises only from contracted-out service since 5th April 1978. The quantity test merely requires the total occupational pension to exceed the G.M.P.; it does not require the part of the former deemed to accrue during contracted-out membership to exceed the latter. The position when a person leaves an occupational scheme before attaining State pensionable age is more complicated, and is dealt with later in this chapter.

Personal pension: the quality test

4.21   The G.M.P. requirement is the means of bringing in the concept that for contracting-out the occupational scheme must provide, as a minimum, broadly the amount of pension forgone in the State scheme. This is a test of the quantity of the benefit. There is, however, a second test, set out in Section 34 of the Act, which is concerned with the general 'quality' of the occupational pension. Section 34(2) states that for contracting-out an occupational scheme must provide an annual rate of accrual of pension of at least one-eightieth of either average salary in the whole period of contracted-out membership or final salary. If the former pension base is chosen, each year's salary must be uplifted, for the purpose of the quality test, on the same lines as in the calculation of the G.M.P. We describe this requirement as one of the general quality of the benefits rather than their quantity, because the Act gives a great deal of freedom as to how 'salary' is to be calculated for this purpose. For instance, fluctuating earnings such as overtime may in general be excluded from salary for scheme purposes. Furthermore, an amount not exceeding 1½ times the lower earnings limit may be excluded from the earnings that are to constitute salary for the purposes of the occupational scheme.

4.22 The O.P.B. have issued a great deal of guidance on the provisions of the Act, and in particular on the quality test, because its broad nature requires much detailed interpretation. In general an 'eightieths' scheme based on the average of the last three years' salary, with salary excluding 1½ times the lower earnings limit, satisfies the test. There are numerous variations; a 'sixtieths' scheme, for instance, may be based on the average of the last five instead of the last three years, and even a 'one-hundredths' scheme is acceptable providing that it is based on pay defined in a satisfactory way, and in particular involving no exclusion of a first slice of pay.

Widow's pension: the quantity test

4.23 For an occupational scheme to serve for contracting-out it must provide, in addition to the scales of personal pension mentioned above, benefits to the widow of a member who dies in service or after retirement. There is no obligation to provide widowers' pensions in the case of women members. The amount of the widow's pension must be at least equal to one-half of the G.M.P. of the husband, or to one-half of the accrued G.M.P. of the husband if he dies before attaining age 65. It will be noted from paragraph 4.7 that in the State scheme the widow inherits the whole of her husband's pension, but this feature is not carried through as a requirement for contracting-out. The State retains responsibility to the widow of a contracted-out member for a pension equal to the excess of the member's full earnings-related pension over one-half of his G.M.P.

Widow's pension: the quality test

4.24 The second contracting-out requirement in respect of the widow's pension is similar to the quality test of the member's pension, but at the half rate, i.e. on a scale of 5/8ths per cent. instead of 1¼ per cent.

Widow's pension: flexibility

4.25 The Act provides for the O.P.B. to approve for contracting-out purposes provisions for widows which do not comply with the quality test requirements in respect of any excess of pension over the G.M.P., but only where the marriage takes place after the termination of the member's service in the contracted-out employment concerned and not more than six months before his death. These conditions are obviously very restrictive. The main significance is that, save for the above exceptions, widows' pensions have to be provided on the quality test scale, and not merely on the G.M.P. scale, even in cases of post-retirement marriages or, in the case of leavers with preserved benefits, post-leaving marriages. Before contracting-out it was unusual for occupational pension schemes to provide pensions to widows following such marriages.

4.26 The G.M.P. element of a widow's pension must be paid to the widow, but the occupational scheme rules may, with the approval of the O.P.B., contain a discretion for any pension in excess of the G.M.P. to be paid wholly or partly to a dependant or dependants of the member instead of to the widow.

4.27 Two further points are as follows.

(i) On the death of a husband before age 65, a lump sum may be paid instead of that part of a widow's pension which is in excess of the widow's G.M.P., provided that it must be equal to at least 11 times the annual amount of the excess.

(ii) Scheme rules may provide for widow's pension to be reduced if the person to whom it is payable was more than 10 years younger than the deceased member. The O.P.B. will accept a rule which provides for a reduction of 2½ per cent. for each year of age disparity in excess of 10, provided that the pension is not reduced below the amount of the G.M.P.

The contribution reduction

4.28 We turn from the benefits that have to be provided for contracting-out to the reduction in the contributions which a contracted-out employee and his employer pay to the State scheme. In setting the level of the reduction the Government's intention was that, taking into account all contracted-out employees, the reduction should broadly represent the cost of providing through occupational schemes the pension forgone under the State scheme. This cost is to be regularly re-assessed by the Government Actuary (the formal power to review every five years being with the Secretary of State for Social Services). For the first five years of contracting-out, from 6th April 1978 to 5th April 1983, contributions to the State scheme in respect of contracted-out employees were reduced by 2½ per cent. for the earner, and 4½ per cent. for the employer, of earnings between the lower and upper earnings limits. The rates of contribution abatement will fall over the years, other things being equal, as the number of employees who because of their age in 1978 have a rate of accrual of G.M.P. above the minimum of 25/49 per cent. for men and 22/44 per cent. for women falls to zero over a long future period. For the second five years of contracting-out the contribution abatement is 2.15 per cent. for the earner and 4.10 per cent. for the employer.

Cessation of contracting-out

4.29 In the first part of this chapter we have outlined the requirements as to occupational scheme benefits, and the abatement in State scheme contributions, for persons who are contracted-out members of an occupational scheme and retire from it at State pensionable age. An employee may, however, cease to be a contracted-out member of an occupational scheme before attaining State pensionable age for a variety of reasons, of which the following are of particular importance for present purposes.

(i)   He leaves the employment, and therefore ceases to be contracted-out as a member of the scheme, during his first five years of membership of the scheme, i.e. broadly in circumstances where he does not become entitled to a preserved pension under the preservation law.

(ii) He leaves the employment, and therefore ceases to be contracted-out as a member of the scheme, after his first five years of membership of the scheme, i.e. broadly in circumstances where he becomes entitled to a preserved pension under the preservation law. As will be seen from the next chapter, there are various circumstances in which a member leaving early may receive an immediate rather than a preserved pension and we will include such cases under this heading (ii).

(iii) He continues as a normal member of the scheme but the whole scheme ceases to be contracted-out.

In all these cases the member, at the time that he ceases to be contracted-out, will have accrued certain G.M.P. rights which define the minimum pension that must be payable to him as from State pensionable age. We now outline the various arrangements that may be made in respect of that G.M.P.

Early leavers during the first five years of membership

4.30 There is usually a substantial turnover of members of schemes during their first five years of membership, because of change of employment, and the arrangements when a member leaves a scheme in these circumstances are therefore of great importance. The scheme may, of course, provide the G.M.P. by preserving the necessary pension for the ex-member (because, although the law does not require preservation, neither does it forbid it), but the Act provides an alternative method. When a member leaves a contracted-out occupational scheme before he has been a member for five years in contracted-out employment, and where the preservation provisions of the Social Security Act 1973 do not operate, the liability in respect of the G.M.P. may be cancelled by payment back into the State pension scheme of a sum equal to the total amount by which the contributions of the earner and the employer to the State scheme have been abated by virtue of the earner's having been contracted-out. This sum is called the 'contributions equivalent premium' or C.E.P. This payment is to be made by the employer, and the Act gives power for him to recover, from any contribution refund due to the employee, that part of the premium representing the abatement of the employee's contributions, which is known as the 'certified amount'.

4.31 The Act provides that an employer shall not, in electing to pay or not to pay C.E.P., discriminate between different earners on any grounds other than their respective lengths of relevant service. This provision is directed against the possibility that, in its absence, an employer would choose to pay a contributions equivalent premium only for those combinations of age and sex at which such payment was cheaper than providing the benefit by way of a preserved pension in the occupational scheme or by purchase of a deferred annuity from an insurance company.

Early leavers after the first five years of membership

4.32 Where a member of a scheme leaves after membership longer than five years the facility of 'buying back' into the State scheme by payment of a C.E.P. is not available; the G.M.P. has to be provided from State pensionable age as part of a preserved or immediate pension from the occupational scheme, or passed on by means of a transfer payment. The original Bill that became the 1975 Act provided that the part of the preserved pension of an early leaver that represented the amount of the G.M.P. must be raised for each complete tax year between the date of leaving and the date of attainment of State pensionable age according to the movement in general levels of earnings, with no alternative procedure. The appropriate rate of increase is defined each year by an order issued by the Secretary of State under s21 of the Act. These orders are generally known as 'section 21 orders'. The liability for this 'full indexing' was placed on the occupational pension scheme without any escape provision. This point gave rise to strong representations to the Government. The difficulty put forward was that in course of time an occupational scheme might accumulate a great number of preserved pensions and the liability to increase their G.M.P. content in line with increases in general levels of earnings, however large such increases might be in periods of high inflation, could jeopardise the whole finances of the employer, on whom the ultimate liability would in practice fall.

Limited rate revaluation

4.33 Important options were introduced in response to the representations made. First, an occupational scheme may limit its obligation, in respect of the escalation of the G.M.P. of an early leaver during the period of deferment, to the lesser of

(i)   the normal indexing according to earnings levels, and
(ii) escalation of 5 per cent. per annum compound for each complete tax year from the date of leaving to the date of attainment of State pensionable age.

The use of this provision must almost inevitably lead to a greater part of the total pension being paid from the State scheme than if the G.M.P. were fully indexed, and consequently an amount, called the 'limited revaluation premium', has to be paid to the State scheme in each individual case if this option is chosen. This amount is not calculated on the same lines as the contributions equivalent premium, i.e. by having regard to the total contribution abatement enjoyed in the past. It is calculated by a foward-looking instead of a backward-looking method, namely by the application, to the amount of the G.M.P. at the time of leaving, of actuarial factors. The liability remaining with the scheme is limited to a 5 per cent. per annum increase and this arrangement has the advantage that, except for the possibility of scale (i) above being less than scale (ii), the amount of the preserved pension becomes known in advance, so that uncertainty is removed. It follows from this that the liability may be dealt with commercially (e.g. by purchase of a deferred annuity from a life office) as an alternative to retention in the scheme if this is desired.

Fixed rate revaluation

4.34 A second option is that the employer may elect for the G.M.P.s of early leavers to be increased at the fixed rate of 8½ per cent. per annum compound in place of earnings-related indexing. No premium is payable to the State scheme because on the actuarial basis used by the Government Actuary in framing the terms for contracting-out this rate of increase is equal to the assumed rate of full indexing of G.M.P.s. This option even more than that in the previous paragraph gives rise to a benefit that is of known amount and can be dealt with commercially. In a given scheme, different options may not be used from one individual to another. The policy, once settled, must apply to all leavers in the category of paragraph 4.32. The whole policy may, of course, be changed if desired, in which case the previous policy continues to apply to persons who left before the date of the change.

4.35 The Secretary of State for Social Services has power to review these arrangements. He did so as part of the first five yearly review of the contracting-out arrangements, which is discussed in Chapter 31, and decided to make no change.

Transfer payments

4.35A With the growth in the passage of transfer payments, and in particular the introduction under the Social Security Act 1985 of a member's right to ask for such a payment, it became necessary to provide for another type of State scheme premium. This is known as a transfer premium, and it is used to buy G.M.P. rights back into the State scheme when a person moves, with payment of a transfer value, from a scheme in which he was contracted-out to a scheme which is not used for contracting-out. The transfer premium is calculated using the same methods and tables as the accrued rights premium mentioned in paragraph 4.39.

The Health and Social Security Act 1984 and 'anti-franking'

4.36 In paragraphs 4.32 to 4.35A we have outlined the G.M.P. arrangements in respect of an early leaver who qualifies for preservation of pension under the 1973 Act. In Chapter 3 we described the provisions of the 1973 Act itself. Although the provisions of the 1973 Act and the 1975 Act originally operated independently in this connection, this led to difficulties, and the Health and Social Security Act 1984 introduced provisions (known as 'anti-franking' provisions) which changed the combined effect of the two earlier acts. As this chapter is mainly concerned with the details of the 1975 Act we do not pursue the subject at this point; it is, however, an extremely important one, and we return to it in paragraph 4.49.

Cessation of contracting-out of a scheme

4.37 The previous paragraphs deal with individual leavers. It might be, however, that a whole pension scheme ceased to be contracted-out. This might happen, for instance, because the employer ceased to carry on business, or decided as a matter of policy that contracting-out should cease, or was taken over by an employer whose policy was not to contract-out. In such a case it is necessary for arrangements to be made at the time of such cessation in respect of the G.M.P.s of the persons who are pensioners, early leavers with preserved pensions and active members of the scheme. The O.P.B. has power to approve arrangements for the preservation or transfer of the G.M.P.s, both as accrued rights and in course of payment, or for the scheme to continue to hold G.M.P. liabilities, but there are likely to be many occasions when a payment back into the State scheme would be convenient. The Bill originally provided for the premium payable to the State scheme in these circumstances to be calculated by applying prescribed tables of costs to the amounts which individual G.M.P.s had reached at the time under the effect of earnings-linking. The G.M.P. amounts, and hence the liabilities in respect of them, were not limited in any way in the Bill. Representations were made to the Government that there was a risk of overwhelming liabilities arising, particularly in respect of the preserved pensions of ex-employees who might be very numerous. The dangers seen were twofold; the G.M.P. amounts, and hence the liabilities, might be great because of inflation, and the market values of the assets of the scheme might be low at the time that they had to be realised to provide the State scheme premiums.

4.38 The Government responded to representations about these points. Firstly, it is provided in the Act that if a scheme ceases to be contracted-out then, unless the person liable to pay the State scheme premium otherwise elects, the G.M.P.s involved shall be calculated as if general levels of earnings had increased by 12 per cent. per annum in each of the five complete tax years before that in which the scheme ceased to be contracted-out, instead of by the actual percentage rates during that time. This provision goes a considerable way to reducing the risk that a scheme will be burdened by very large G.M.P.s before action is taken to cancel contracting-out, although the rate of 12 per cent. may itself represent a very substantial degree of liability. Secondly it is provided that the factors which are to be applied to the amount of the G.M.P. in order to calculate the amount of the State scheme premium shall vary with the yields on gilt edged stocks and equity shares and hence, to some extent, with market values of assets.

Thus it is intended that, other things being equal, the premiums should be low if market values of investments are low.

4.39 The premium payable in these circumstances in respect of an active member or an ex-member with a preserved pension is called an 'accrued rights premium', and that in respect of a pension already in course of payment, a 'pensioner's rights premium'. The adjusting factor to allow for market conditions is known as the Market Level Indicator or M.L.I. The Secretary of State for Social Services reviewed the terms of these arrangements as part of his five-yearly review of contracting-out, and decided to adjust the M.L.I. scales. The matter is mentioned further in Chapter 31.

Financial surveillance of contracted-out schemes

4.40 We have outlined above some of the main contracting-out provisions as to benefits, contributions and State scheme premiums. If an occupational scheme is to take over liabilities which would otherwise be met by the State the Government need in addition to be satisfied as to the finanical backing of the promises made by the scheme in respect of G.M.P.s. This is a question not only of the overall financial strength of the scheme but also of the position of G.M.P.s in the queue of potential beneficiaries if the scheme is wound up.

Assurance of benefits

4.41 As to the winding-up provisions, the Act states that for contracting-out an occupational scheme must have a rule giving certain specified liabilities of the scheme priority on a winding-up over other liabilities. The liabilities that must have priority are set out in section 40(3) of the Act, as follows.

(a) G.M.P.s in payment and accrued G.M.P. rights.
(b) Equivalent pension benefits under a superseded graduated scheme.
(c) Pensions in course of payment.
(d) State scheme premiums.

The trust deed and rules of an occupational scheme have to be amended to this effect in order that it may be considered for contracting-out. The Act provides that these priorities have to be established by a rule of the scheme which is to operate 'in respect of benefits attributable to any period of service after the rule has taken effect'. In practice the wording of the actuarial certificate mentioned below is of more importance than the detailed wording of the Act.

Sufficiency of resources

4.42 Before contracting-out will be permitted the O.P.B. therefore have to be satisfied that the occupational scheme is likely to have sufficient resources to pay G.M.P.s as they arise and to pay State scheme premiums. They also have to be satisfied that the assets would be sufficient to cover the prior charges mentioned above on an immediate winding-up. The O.P.B. rely on the certificate of an actuary, in a prescribed form, as to sufficiency of resources.

4.43 The text of the Standard Solvency Certificate (Certificate A) is set out at the end of this chapter. Guidance on the certificate and associated matters is given in O.P.B. Memoranda and guidance to the actuary signing a certificate is also contained in the Year Books of the Institute and Faculty of Actuaries. It will be seen from the text of the certificate that the actuary is required to state his opinion as to the likely adequacy of the resources of the scheme concerned 'in the normal course of events' over the five year period following the date of signing of the certificate. Some of the points that have to be weighed when a certificate is to be signed are indicated later in this book, when it will be seen that much responsibility is placed on the actuary.

No selection

4.44 An employer in deciding whether or not to contract-out a group of employees may not discriminate between different employees on any grounds other than the nature of their employment. Thus, for example, discrimination on grounds of age, sex or pay levels is not possible. The following two qualifications to this general principle should be noted.

(i)   It continues to be quite common for employees to have to serve for a defined period of employment, or attain a specified age, or both, before being admitted to a pension scheme. In this case the employees must normally participate in the State scheme during this period. There is provision in the legislation for such employees to be contracted-out during this period provided that the G.M.P. accrues during the period and the 'quality test' benefits are granted for this period when the employee eventually joins the scheme. It is not thought that this facility is widely used.

(ii) There may be excluded, from an application to contract-out, those members of a pension scheme who will be unable to complete a specified period of membership (not exceeding five years) before they reach the normal pension age of the scheme.

The choice

4.45 We end this discussion of contracting-out with an outline of the non-technical issues involved in the decision whether or not to contract-out. The decision is made by the employer, but consultation with recognised trade unions concerned, and the giving of formal notice to his employees of an employer's intention to contract-out, are required under the provisions of the Act. In preparation for the initial decision to take effect in April 1978 many employers thought it wise, on a matter of such importance, to enter into consultations with pension scheme members and other employees to a greater extent than is strictly required under the Act. As noted at the beginning of this chapter the trend of such consultations was such that contracting-out was on a very large scale as from April 1978. The factors that emerged in practice as being the most important in setting this trend were as follows.

(i) The better occupational schemes were able to satisfy the contracting-out tests at little extra cost. In these circumstances, contracting-out leads to a saving (initially 7 per cent. of full earnings between the lower and upper earnings limit) in State scheme contributions, with little extra contribution required to the occupational scheme. In theory a similar saving could be achieved by participation in the State scheme with the occupational scheme benefits reduced by an amount equal to the additional State benefits, but the complexity of the latter has tended to make this option impracticable.

(ii) Contracting-out represented continuity, since the occupational scheme with which members were familiar continued largely unchanged, and they were not asked to enter a new and unfamiliar State scheme.

(iii)   Members of an occupational scheme are often keenly aware that in a funded scheme money is being set aside and accumulated on their behalf; they may in certain circumstances take a refund of contributions upon withdrawal, and they may be able to elect to receive part of their retirement benefits in a lump sum. In the pay-as-you-go State scheme, on the other hand, the contributions are immediately used in payment of pensions to the retired population.

(iv)   Employees do not enjoy relief of personal income tax on contributions to the State scheme but they do enjoy this relief on contributions to an occupational scheme. Other things being equal, it is therefore more attractive to an employee to pay contributions to an occupational scheme than to the State scheme.

(v)   The State earnings-related benefits are of good quality in that they are well protected against inflation, but the variable effective rate of accrual (arising from the 20 year limit) means that the package is an awkward one to fit into a rational overall pension policy based on participation.

(vi)   Contracting-out has risks, in that it involves relying on the investment backing of a funded occupational scheme, but the legislation provides a number of means for an employer to buy the contracted-out benefits back into the State scheme if he contracts out but subsequently changes his mind.

4.46   The main factors tending towards participation in the new State earnings-related scheme were as follows.

(i)   The State scheme promises earnings-related benefits in return for a stated contribution, namely the difference between participating and contracted-out State scheme contributions referred to above. Although this difference is subject to re-calculation by the Government Actuary from time to time, it is in principle attractive for earnings-related benefits to be provided for a stated contribution.

(ii)   Participation is administratively simpler than contracting-out, even if a small-scale occupational scheme is used to top up the State earnings-related benefits.

(iii) There are investment and other controls over occupational schemes used for contracting-out. If employees participate in the State earnings-related scheme, any occupational scheme used for topping up the State earnings-related benefits is relatively free from control.

(iv) Since legislation may always be changed, there are risks to an occupational scheme in entering into a long-term partnership with the State. As the State scheme is on a pay-as-you-go basis, it is possible to change the State arrangements without great difficulty as far as financial organisation is concerned. The occupational scheme, on the other hand, represents long-term saving, and needs to be assured of a relatively stable long-term framework if proper funding arrangements are to be made.

4.47 The reader will appreciate that most of the above points have little to do with actuarial technicalities. They are simply some of the points that sway decisions in practice. A question which does involve actuarial calculations, namely whether the package of benefits representing the G.M.P.s of members and widows for the particular age, sex and pay distribution of a specific workforce or pension scheme membership is likely to cost more or less than the state contribution abatement, is one that can be, and in many cases has been, examined in great detail, and it is touched on in Chapter 31. In the 1978 discussions the result of such calculations was not usually the decisive factor in the situation, but took its place amongst all the other points to be considered.

Equal access

4.48 The 1975 Act provides for the 'equal access' of men and women to all occupational pension schemes, whether contracted-out or not. The main principle is '.......that membership of the scheme is open to both men and women on terms which are the same as to age and length of service needed for becoming a member and as to whether membership is voluntary or obligatory'. The Occupational Pensions Board issued a memorandum giving guidance on the implementation of the principle of equal access. It should be noted that the principle is concerned with access to schemes and not with contributions or benefit scales. In practice such scales are very often the same for men and women, but different normal pension ages for the two sexes persist in occupational schemes as in the State scheme.

Early leavers: the interaction of legislation

4.49 We return to the aspect of early leavers' preserved pensions mentioned in paragraph 4.36, namely the interaction of the preservation law and the G.M.P. requirements, and we will also cover in the context of contracting-out the revaluation provisions mentioned in paragraph 3.9. We shall use an example to illustrate the development of the legislation, bringing in successively the effect of

(i)   The Social Security Act 1973,
(ii)   The Social Security Pensions Act 1975,
(iii)   The Health and Social Security Act 1984, and
(iv)   The Social Security Act 1985.

4.50 The example is based on the following data for a man who has been contracted-out while a member of a pension scheme and is now an early leaver.

Date pensionable service started	1.1.1971
Date pensionable service terminated	31.12.1990
Preserved pension on leaving service, i.e. the pension calculated on the normal scale of the scheme	£3,000 p.a.
Amount of G.M.P. on termination of pensionable service	£800 p.a.
Age at which preserved pension is payable	65
Revaluation percentage at age 65	130%
Revalued G.M.P. at age 65	£3,200 p.a.

The meaning of most of the above items will probably be clear but the 'revaluation percentage' perhaps requires explanation. It was explained in paragraph 3.9 that revaluation of the part of the pension affected by the 1985 Act provisions is to be as set out in item (ii) of that paragraph. The detailed arrangement is that for each calendar year in future there will be prescribed, shortly before the start of that year, the percentage increase required under these provisions for persons whose preserved pension comes into payment during that calendar year. The percentage will depend on the year that the preserved pension was set up as well as the year that it comes into payment, so that a set of percentages will have to be prescribed each year. The figure of 130 per cent. in the example is the assumed percentage appropriate, at the date at which the pension becomes payable, to a preserved pension which was set up on 31.12.1990.

1973 Act and 1975 Act

4.51 The reader will recall from paragraph 3.4 that if only the preservation requirements under the 1973 Act were involved the pension payable on attainment of age 65 would be simply that calculated on the normal scale of the pension scheme concerned at the date of leaving, i.e. £3,000 p.a. As explained in paragraph 4.32, when contracting-out was introduced one new requirement for an early leaver was that the pension payable from State pension age should not be less than the amount of the revalued G.M.P. at that age. In the example this amount is £3,200 p.a. The combined effect of the 1973 Act and the 1975 Act would be to require the greater of £3,000 p.a. and £3,200 p.a., i.e. £3,200 p.a., to be paid as from age 65.

Anti-franking under the 1984 Act

4.52 As explained in paragraph 4.36, the 1984 Act introduced the requirement that the growth of the G.M.P. during the period of preservation should be an entitlement additional to the full amount of the scale preserved pension at the date of leavng. Allowing for this legislation, the amount of the pension at age 65 is therefore calculated as follows.

	£ p.a.
Amount of scale pension at date of leaving	3,000
Growth of the G.M.P. entitlement during the period of preservation: £3,200 p.a. – £800 p.a.	2,400
Total pension payable at age 65	£5,400 p.a.

The effect of the anti-franking provisions is therefore that G.M.P. growth becomes an extra entitlement instead of being largely met from the excess of the scale pension over the G.M.P. at the date of leaving, with a consequent increase in the amount of the pension actually payable.

Revaluation under the 1985 Act

4.53 We set out the principle of 1985 Act revaluation in simple terms in paragraph 3.9. It is now necessary to note that, in the context of a scheme used for contracting-out, the additional amount of pension arising under the revaluation provisions has to be calculated in accordance with the formula

$$\frac{A\,B}{C}(D - E)$$

which appears in Part II of schedule 1 to the 1985 Act. The various terms are defined as follows.

A   The revaluation percentage appropriate in the particular case.

B   The period of pensionable service after 1.1.85, i.e. six years in the example.

C   The total period of pensionable service, i.e. 20 years in the example.

D   The amount of the scale pension at the date of termination of pensionable service.

E   The amount of the G.M.P. at the date of termination of pensionable service.

The amount of additional pension arising under this formula is therefore

130% of $\frac{6}{20}$ (£3,000 – £800) = £858 p.a.

The total pension payable under the combined effect of all four Acts is therefore calculated as follows.

	£ p.a.
Original amount of scale pension on termination of pensionable service	3,000
Growth in G.M.P. during the period of preservation	2,400
Revaluation of non-G.M.P. during the period of preservation	858
Total pension payable	£6,258 p.a.

It will be noted that the provisions of the 1985 Act cover only the part of the non-G.M.P. pension deemed to arise in respect of pensionable service after 1st January 1985, so that the effect of the Act will build up only slowly in the future.

CHAPTER FOUR

OCCUPATIONAL PENSIONS BOARD

CERTIFICATE A: *Actuarial certificate for the purposes of the Social Security Pensions Act 1975 and the Social Security Pensions (Northern Ireland) Order 1975*

1   I hereby certify that, in my opinion, in the event of the ....
....*(name of scheme)* being wound up at any time in the next 5 years, the resources of the scheme are likely in the normal course of events (including events which might normally precede a winding-up) to be sufficient to meet in full any liabilities of the scheme in respect of:

(i)   guaranteed minimum pensions and accrued rights to such pensions in respect of those members of the scheme for whom no certificate by the Secretary of State under section 22(9) of the Social Security (Miscellaneous Provisions) Act 1977 is in force at the date of winding-up;

(ii)   equivalent pension benefits within the meaning of sub-sections (5), (6) and (7) of section 33 of the Act;

(iii)   pension and other benefits in respect of which entitlement to payment has already arisen other than those included in (i) and (ii) above;

(iv)   any other liabilities which are given priority equal to or greater than that accorded to (i), (ii) and (iii) above; and

(v)   expenses of administration so far as these expenses would be payable out of the resources of the scheme if it were to be wound up.

2   Taking into account the nature of the scheme's financial arrangements and the provisions of the trust documents, it is my opinion that the liabilities covered by 1(i) will be capable of being wholly met, for each individual with GMP rights in the scheme, by one of the following methods:

(i)   annuities *(a)* secured under present or future contracts of insurance with one or more insurance companies *(a)* so that the annuities in total meet the conditions of paragraph 17 of Memorandum No 76 and, if appropriate, by the payment of a limited revaluation premium;

or   (ii)   the payment of an accrued rights premium or a pensioner's rights premium.

3   (i)   For the purposes of this certificate I have adopted the assumptions specified by the OPB in Memorandum No 76 in regard to any state scheme premiums assumed to be payable on winding up.

(ii)   I have also assumed that the following amounts will be paid to the scheme:
[by members *(b)* —   [contributions at the rates provided in the rules]
[contributions at the rate of ....
....]] *(c)*

by the employer *(d)* —   [contributions at the rates provided in the rules]
[contributions at the rate of ....
....] *(e)*

(iii)   The amounts at (ii) above are based on a funding rate which, in my opinion, is satisfactory *(f)*:
[for the scheme as a whole]
[for the liabilities listed at 1(i)—(v) above]

4   At the time of giving this certificate I have received the form of undertaking relating to the events set out in Memorandum No 76, including such modifications as were specified by me in writing to the principal employer. *(g)*

[5   I have confirmed with the scheme administrator that the self-investment position is as follows:—
[There is no self-investment]
[Self-investment in aggregate does not exceed 10% of the scheme's total resources]
[A copy of the self-investment statement is enclosed:—
[(i)   I do not need to take the self-investment into account for the purpose of this certificate]
[(ii)   This certificate is subject to the qualification regarding self-investment set out in Certificate B]]] *(b)*

Signature	Date ....
Name	Qualification ....
Address	Name of employer (if applicable)
....	....
....	....

NB: Notes (a) to (b) appear overleaf

NOTES:

(a)   *The following expressions used in the certificate should read as having the meanings:*

     (i)   *"annuities" includes "annuity" where there is only one annuity contract in respect of any individual member.*

     (ii)   *"insurance companies" has the meaning given in paragraph 17(e) of Memorandum No 76.*

(b)   *Delete both items if the scheme is non-contributory, otherwise delete one only.*

(c)   *If this item is appropriate, add a statement about the basis for employees' contributions.*

(d)   *Delete as appropriate.*

(e)   *If this item is appropriate, add a statement about the basis for employer's contributions.*

(f)   *Delete as appropriate (see paragraph 10 of Memorandum No 76).*

(g)   *If an undertaking has not been received, see paragraph 94 of Memorandum No 76.*

(h)   *This item applies only to self-administered schemes. In the case of insured schemes, the whole item should be deleted. In the case of self-administered schemes, the statements which do not apply should be deleted (see paragraphs 61–65 of Memorandum No 76).*

CHAPTER 5

PENSION BENEFITS

CHAPTER 5

PENSION BENEFITS

A primary aim

5.1 In formulating pension policy, an employer usually considers first the position of an employee who retires at the normal pension age of the employment concerned after having served the employer for the whole of his working lifetime. In practice few employees now give such long service to one company, but the employer will expect an employee who serves for comparatively few years to look to his other employments for part of his pension benefits, particularly as the effects of preservation begin to build up. When the level of pension to be provided in respect of a full working lifetime has been settled, the level of pension for an employee retiring with shorter service usually follows from the normal working of the pension formula adopted. In this chapter we shall be concerned with the design of pension scales and with some of the matters that have to be considered when a member of a pension scheme leaves with immediate payment of a pension. Other types of benefit are dealt with in Chapter 6.

5.2 Subject to cost considerations, an employer will wish to ensure that a long-serving employee enjoys a standard of living after his retirement which is reasonable compared with that in the years preceding his retirement. The standard of living of an individual after retirement at normal pension age usually depends mainly on the total amount of his State pension and occupational pension together. His standard of living just before retirement depends mainly on his pay. The employer's policy therefore involves a decision about the relationship between pension, from State and occupational scheme together, immediately after retirement and pay in the years preceding retirement. Whether the standard of living immediately following retirement will be maintained in subsequent years depends on the extent to which occupational pensions are regularly increased while in payment to meet rises in the cost of living, but this is best treated as a separate matter.

The 'average pay' pension scale

5.3 In the earlier years of occupational pension schemes, pension scales were often designed not on the basis of the reasoning outlined above but rather on the basis that the pension entitlement in respect of a particular year of employment should be related to the amount of pay in that year; it might, for example, be defined as one-sixtieth of that amount of pay. The total pension was simply the total of such entitlements. Since the total pension earned over a period of N years under such an arrangement can be expressed as

$$\frac{N}{60} \text{ ths of } \frac{\text{total pay}}{N} \text{ , i.e.}$$

$$\frac{N}{60} \text{ths of (career average pay)}$$

such a scale is sometimes referred to as an 'average pay' scale, as opposed to the 'final pay' scales referred to later.

5.4 An average pay pension scale does not lead to an amount of pension which is a predictable proportion of pay near to retirement, because in modern conditions the rate at which general levels of earnings will rise because of rising standards of living or the falling value of money (the rate of 'earnings escalation' or simply 'escalation') cannot be predicted with confidence. Neither, therefore, can the relationship between pay shortly before retirement and average pay during the career. This type of pension scale is not therefore a satisfactory vehicle for carrying out the aim mentioned in paragraph 5.2, and such scales have virtually disappeared among good pension schemes.

The 'dynamised average pay' pension scale

5.5 The State earnings-related pension scheme, however, is essentially of this type, but with the additional feature that each year's pension entitlement is dynamised so that it does not lose its value up to State pensionable age. As mentioned in paragraph 4.21, an occupational pension scheme of this 'dynamised average pay' type may be used for contracting-out. Furthermore, this type of scale has had its advocates in recent years as far as manual workers are concerned, on the grounds that such workers may have passed their peak earnings in real terms, as opposed to money terms, as they near retirement (due, for instance, to a falling-off in overtime pay), so that a final pay pension scale is not ideal for them. The validity of this point clearly depends on conditions and practices in the employment concerned; to the extent that it is valid it represents a modification of the principle mentioned in paragraph 5.2. There is no evidence at present of any resurgence of average pay occupational pension schemes in this dynamised form.

The 'final pay' pension scale

5.6 The 'average pay' pension scale lost favour when inflation became a familiar feature of the economic scene. Even before this, however, the shortcomings of this scale had become apparent for salaried employees with an expectation of promotion. In particular the scale did not provide satisfactory benefits for a man who made rapid progress in his career and so reached salary levels near to retirement much higher than those earlier in his career. From the earliest days of the occupational pension scheme movement, therefore, many schemes incorporated the 'final pay' pension scale which is now almost universal.

5.7 Typically such schemes provide a pension equal to some fraction, such as 1/60th or 1/80th, of annual pensionable pay near to retirement, multiplied by the number of years of pensionable service in the scheme. The pensionable pay upon which the pension is based is commonly defined as that in the year before retirement, or the annual average of such pay in the three years or five years before retirement. For this purpose the 'years' concerned may be complete tax years, or complete scheme years, or periods of 12 months linked to the individual date of retirement, or one of many other definitions suited to the needs of the particular scheme. All such scales are usually referred to as 'final pay' pension scales, and we shall normally use the term 'final pay' as encompassing all these variations. We do not need at this stage to settle whether pensionable pay does or does not include such elements as bonuses and overtime payments.

Allowance for the State pension in occupational schemes

5.8 The pension scales discussed above developed during a period when State pensions were on a modest scale and were not provided automatically to all employed persons. The National Insurance Act 1946 introduced a comprehensive scheme of 'flat-rate' State pensions, and as the scale and cost of this scheme increased over the years it became increasingly necessary to take account of the State pension in the design of occupational pension schemes.

5.9 The employer's basic policy decision therefore became a decision about the relationship between annual pay in the years preceding retirement and the annual amount of pension from State and occupational scheme together. Many employers in fact ignored the existence of the State scheme in settling the scales of occupational pension, but this is likely to lead to excessive total benefits from the State and occupational scheme together, and hence excessive cost. It is now fairly widely accepted that State scheme benefits need to be borne in mind. Over the years during which the main State pension was a 'flat-rate' amount, occupational pension scales allowed for the State pension in one of two main ways, namely the use of a low pension fraction or the introduction of a specific offset for State pension. Both approaches remain broadly valid for contracted-out employees, since the State flat-rate pension is the main State pension to be received by such an employee assuming that he is contracted-out for most of his working lifetime. The two approaches are discussed in paragraphs 5.10 to 5.19. In paragraphs 5.21 to 5.25 we discuss the type of occupational scheme suitable when employees participate in the State earnings-related scheme, and in paragraphs 5.29 to 5.31 we return to contracted-out schemes with a discussion of some of the points arising under the 'quality test'.

State pension and marital status

5.10 We first discuss a preliminary point. Whatever method, if any, is chosen in an occupational scheme to allow for the State flat-rate pension, it is necessary to decide whether the amount of that pension taken into account should be the same for married and single members of the occupational scheme. The question arises because the State flat-rate pension is greater for a married couple than for a single person. Usually it is decided that the adjustment for State pension shall not depend on marital status, but shall be based on the single person's State flat-rate pension in all cases. There are three main reasons for this. The first is that if the deduction did depend on marital status, so that the amount of the occupational pension depended on this status, it would then be desirable on grounds of equity to have different occupational scheme contribution rates for single and married members. Different contribution rates would involve complications of adjustment for members who were first married, or ceased to be married, at some intermediate stage of their careers, and the occupational scheme would become complicated. The second reason is that earnings do not depend on marital status, and occupational pensions may be regarded as an extension of earnings; indeed the view is often expressed that pensions are deferred pay, although this is a gross oversimplification of a complex situation. The third argument is that Parliament intended that the pension for a married couple should be higher than that for a single person and that this intention should not be frustrated by the offsetting, in the calculation of scheme pension, of the married couple's State pension when this is payable. We shall assume in this discussion that it is the amount of the State flat-rate pension for a single person that is to be allowed for and we shall use the letter F to represent this amount.

The use of a low pension fraction

5.11 The first method of allowing in an occupational scheme for the State flat-rate pension involves the use of a fraction such as 1/80th which is somewhat lower than the fraction which would have been used had the State scheme not existed. We may illustrate this by supposing that an employer wishes his employees to have a pension from State and occupational scheme together on a scale of approximately '1/60ths', so that an employee who has served for 40 years will have a pension equal to two-thirds of pay near to retirement. We will consider whether an '1/80ths' occupational pension together with the State flat-rate pension would serve the purpose. Expressing final pay levels as a multiple of F at or near the date of retirement we have the following.

Final pay	Desired pension $= \frac{40}{60}$ (1)	Occupational pension $= \frac{40}{80}$ (1)	(3) + State pension $= (3) + F$
(1)	(2)	(3)	(4)
2 F	1.3 F	F	2 F
4 F	2.7 F	2 F	3 F
6 F	4.0 F	3 F	4 F
8 F	5.3 F	4 F	5 F
10 F	6.7 F	5 F	6 F
12 F	8.0 F	6 F	7 F

The employer might well decide that the pension in column (4) matched his aim as shown in column (2) fairly well over a wide range of pay levels, and he might find it an added attraction that rather more than the intended pension was provided at the lower pay levels where the need is greatest.

Integrated pension scales

5.12 Despite the attractive simplicity of this broad-brush approach, many employers wish to allow more precisely for the State pension in the design of the occupational pension scale. Clearly the idea that the desired 'target' pension is equal to the State pension plus the occupational scheme pension can be equally well expressed as

Scheme pension = target pension – State pension.

This led to the design of occupational pension scales containing an explicit offset for State pensions, and these have become known as 'integrated' pension scales.

5.13 One type of integrated pension scale involves a head-on approach to the matter by specifying that the pension in respect of each year of membership is to be

1/60th (say) of final pay

less

1/40th of (the amount of F at or near the date of retirement)

Writing P for pay, an employee retiring after 40 years of membership would receive an occupational pension of

$$\frac{40}{60} \text{ (P)} - \frac{40}{40} \text{ (F)}$$

$$= \frac{2}{3} \text{ P} - \text{F}$$

If he receives a State pension of F this gives a two-thirds pension in total.

5.14 Another approach involves the use of 'pensionable pay', derived from pay by the deduction of an amount related to the amount of the State flat-rate pension from time to time. Thus a scheme with a pension fraction of 1/60th might be based on pensionable pay equal to pay less 1½ times the amount of the State flat-rate pension from time to time. A member with 40 years' service at retirement would receive a pension of

$$\frac{40}{60} \text{ (P} - 1\tfrac{1}{2} \text{ F)}$$

$$= \frac{2}{3} \text{ P} - \text{F}$$

both P and F in this last expression representing values near to retirement. This gives the same result as the scale mentioned in the previous paragraph. Scales involving 'pensionable pay' have been widely used in recent years. One reason for this is that the idea of pensionable pay is a straightfoward one to present to the members. A second reason stems from the fact that in a scheme of the type mentioned in paragraph 5.13 there is the problem of settling contribution rates for the members which will look reasonable to them. A contribution equal to a percentage of full pay would not seem reasonable for a benefit involving a 'State scheme deduction', and a contribution formula incorporating some explicit deduction corresponding to the benefit deduction might seem very complicated to the members. If, however, 'pensionable pay' is introduced, it is natural to express the contributions as a percentage of this amount from time to time, as well as basing the retirement pension on the amount of pensionable pay shortly before retirement. Another factor encouraging adoption of the 'pensionable pay' approach is that it is explicitly allowed for in the quality test for contracting-out purposes.

Integrated schemes: the overriding guarantee

5.15 The proportion of occupational schemes which are integrated in some way with the State scheme has grown over the years, largely because of the pressure of cost. Nevertheless, an integrated pension scale is often not popular with the members. One reason is an instinctive dislike of the mixing together of occupational pension and State pension. A more specific reason is that, as the scale of State pensions increases, the offset in respect of the State pension appears to be cutting into occupational pension rights that have already accrued. A member of a 'sixtieths' scheme as in paragraph 5.13 with N years of past pensionable service and pay P would note, when the State flat-rate pension increased from F_1 to F_2, that his accrued pension rights had fallen from

$$\frac{N}{60} P - \frac{N}{40} F_1$$

to

$$\frac{N}{60} P - \frac{N}{40} F_2$$

5.16 Two main methods of meeting this point have been used in occupational pension schemes. The first and less satisfactory method, which is not now much used, is to include in the rules of the scheme an overriding guarantee of the minimum level of scheme pension expressed in some way in value terms. A typical provision is that the actuarial value of the pension when it starts to be paid will not be less than the amount of the member's accumulated contributions, or some multiple greater than unity of this amount if part of the employer's contribution is to be brought into the guarantee. This is not very satisfactory because in a modern pension scheme the various scales of benefit are not linked to the amount of the contributions paid by a particular member; his contributions are rather the subscription he pays to join the 'club' and become entitled to all its benefits. A final salary pension scale obviously follows this principle. A 'value for contributions' element for each individual, based on interest rates, actuarial values and so on, cuts across this general concept, quite apart from the fact that the notion of an 'actuarial value' will not be generally understood by the members.

5.17 A second and more satisfactory type of guarantee may be used if the scheme is designed on the 'pensionable pay' basis mentioned in paragraph 5.14. The danger from the member's point of view is that the deduction in respect of the State pension may grow at such a rate that the amount of pensionable pay will fall from one year to the next. The guarantee that is provided is that if the normal calculation of pensionable pay would, because of an increase in State pensions, produce a smaller amount than pensionable pay in the previous year, then that previous year's figure shall again be used in the current year and in subsequent years, until the normal operation of the formula produces a larger figure. Thus the members are assured that pensionable pay can never fall as a result of an increase in State pensions; this is a guarantee that most members will readily understand.

Specimen pension scales

5.18 Over the years a wide variety of pension scales has developed, as employers and their employees have settled on the scale that suited them best and could be afforded. In the following examples of scales met with in practice the pension indicated is the annual amount in respect of one year of pensionable service. As indicated earlier, the amounts of pay, pensionable pay and State flat-rate pension used for the calculation of the pension are usually the annual amounts in the final year before retirement or the average annual amount over the three or five year period preceding retirement.

Scale A

1/60 (P).

Comments

The straightforward 'sixtieths' scale incorporating no offset for State pensions. A member with 40 years' service and pay of say 4.5 F receives a pension of two-thirds of 4.5 F, i.e. 3 F, from the scheme, and F from the State, a total of 4 F. He is probably better off in retirement than at work, after allowing for the fact that in retirement he does not have to pay State scheme and occupational scheme contributions and is relieved of various other expenses. Furthermore, if he is a married man the State pension to the couple will be greater than F. The benefits from State and occupational scheme together are large and therefore expensive, and this scale is somewhat less widespread than it was. Nevertheless, it should be noted that in modern conditions the proportion of employees who complete 40 years of service with one employer is very small. This scale has its supporters on the grounds that it provides a reasonable benefit for the somewhat shorter average period of service encountered in practice.

Scale B

1/70 (P) or 1/80 (P).

Comments

Scales such as these achieve simplicity while being less expensive than 1/60ths. Comments on the 1/80th scale were made in paragraph 5.11.

Scale C

1/60 (P) – 1/40 (F).

Comments

The problems mentioned in paragraphs 5.14 and 5.15 should be noted.

Scale D

1/60 (P) – 1/40 (F) but not less than 1/80 (P).

Comments

The 1/80ths guarantee is to help the lower paid members, on pay of say 3 F. The first part of the scale gives:

$$40/60 \ (3F) - 40/40 \ (F), \text{ i.e. } F$$

from the occupational scheme after 40 years, but the guarantee ensures that the occupational pension is not less than

$$40/80 \ (3F), \text{ i.e. } 1.5 \ F.$$

Scale E

1/60 (P – 1½F)

Comments

Note the advantages mentioned in paragraphs 5.14 and 5.17.

Scale F

1/60 (P – F).

Comments

A scale somewhat higher and therefore more costly than when the deduction is 1½ F. The reasoning behind this scale is that it is rather severe on lower paid employees to offset the whole of the State flat-rate pension. In fact the advantage over the preceding scale is of course enjoyed by all members, not merely the lower paid. This scale appears to have been gaining ground in recent years. The State earnings related scheme is based on pay involving this deduction.

Scale G

1/60 (P) – 1/40 (F – K), i.e. 1/60 (P – 1½ (F – K))

Comments

'K' in this scale is a fixed money amount. Such a scale is sometimes used when allowance for the State scheme is being introduced in an occupational scheme, not previously integrated, at a time when the amount of the State flat-rate pension for a single person is K. Only subsequent increases in State pension over that amount are offset in the scheme. The formula is shown above in two forms to make it clear that this arrangement can be defined in terms of 1/60th of 'pensionable earnings'.

Contribution formulae

5.19 Although this chapter is primarily about pension benefits it is convenient to note the question of what contribution formulae are most appropiate to meet the cost of these various pension scales. As mentioned in paragraph 5.14, the position is that if the pension scale is expressible as a fraction of the 'final' value of some definition of pensionable pay it is usually convenient for contributions to be based on pensionable pay using the same definition. Where the position as to pension is more complicated the contribution scale may also be complex. In general simplicity is highly desirable, since the employees should be encouraged to understand their pension arrangements.

The effect of the 1975 Act

5.20   As from April 1978 occupational pension schemes are divided into those used for contracting-out under the 1975 Act and those not so used. If a scheme is to be used for contracting-out, the pension scale has to pass the tests outlined in Chapter 4. Many schemes involving pension scales of the types outlined above are used for contracting-out, with the pension scales being modified to whatever extent is necessary to meet the contracting-out requirements. In this book we shall generally be concerned with occupational schemes used for contracting-out, but we now discuss briefly some of the types of occupational pension scheme which are used when the members are not contracted out, i.e. when they participate in the State earnings-related scheme.

Occupational schemes and participation: 'topping-up' schemes

5.21   Suppose that it is desired to provide a pension, from occupational scheme and State earnings-related scheme together, on the scale of

$$1/60 \ (P - 1\tfrac{1}{2} \ F)$$

One approach is for employees to be contracted out by virtue of their membership of an occupational scheme using this scale, but suppose it is decided that the members should participate in the State earnings-related scheme. What pension scale should be provided in the occupational scheme in order to produce broadly the desired total pension? We will suppose that the problem is being considered as at 6th April 1978 and that immediately before that date the employees were in an occupational scheme incorporating the above pension scale. The following table gives figures for various male employees, all with pay equal to 5F but with differing ages at 6th April 1978. Column (3) represents the pension, for the potential years of membership after April 1978, under the scheme in force before April 1978, namely

$$n/60 \ (5 \ F - 1.5 \ F) = n/60 \ (3.5 \ F)$$

Column (4) represents the State earnings-related pension, namely $n/80$ths, with a maximum of $20/80$ths, of pay between the lower and upper earnings limits of F and 7 F. Column (3) would be based on final pay and column (4) on revalued career pay but for present purposes we will ignore differences between the two definitions of pay. Column (5) represents the pension fraction (expressed as a percentage) which would be required in the occupational scheme.

Age at April 1978	Years to age $65 = n$	Total target pension $\dfrac{n}{60}$ (3.5 F)	State earnings-related pension $\dfrac{n \text{ (Max 20)}}{80}$ (4 F)	Required occupational pension $\dfrac{(3) - (4)}{n}$
(1)	(2)	(3)	(4)	(5)
25	40	2.33F	1.00F	.033F
30	35	2.04F	1.00F	.030F
40	25	1.46F	1.00F	.018F
50	15	0.87F	0.75F	.008F
60	5	0.29F	0.25F	.008F

5.22 It will be seen from column (5) of the table that the occupational scheme would have to provide a different pension fraction according to age at April 1978; there would be further differences according to pay levels and sex. A further complication is that the pre-April 1978 scheme might well have been based on some definition of pay other than full taxable earnings, whereas the State earnings-related scheme is based on full taxable earnings between the lower and upper earnings limits. The difficulty of presenting and administering an occupational pension scheme with many different pension fractions and other complications, together with the difficulty of arriving at a member's contribution rate which would appear fair, led most employers to reject as impracticable the idea of participating and integrating closely with the State earnings-related scheme.

5.23 The Trades Union Congress (the central body of trades unions in the United Kingdom), in a booklet entitled 'Trades Unions and Contracting-Out' issued to assist trades union negotiators in the approach to April 1978, did not advocate either participation or contracting-out in principle, taking the line that the decision depended on individual circumstances. The booklet did, however, suggest that an occupational pension scale of 1 per cent. of full pay for each year of membership might be suitable for topping up the State earnings-related pension if the policy was participation. The following table indicates the effect of a 1 per cent. scale (shown in column (4)) for the examples in the table above. The total pension in column (5) is compared with the 'integrated sixtieths' pension in column (6), and it will be seen that the former substantially exceeds the latter for the examples used.

Age at April 1978 $65 = n$	Years to age	State earnings-related pension $\dfrac{n \,(\text{Max } 20)}{80}$ (4F)	1 per cent occupational pension $\dfrac{n(5F)}{100}$	Total pension $(3) + (4)$	$\dfrac{n}{60}$ (3.5F)
(1)	(2)	(3)	(4)	(5)	(6)
25	40	1.00F	2.00F	3.00F	2.33F
30	35	1.00F	1.75F	2.75F	2.04F
40	25	1.00F	1.25F	2.25F	1.46F
50	15	0.75F	0.75F	1.50F	0.87F
60	5	0.25F	0.25F	0.50F	0.29F

Unit schemes

5.24 Some employers who decided on participation in 1978 arranged for their employees to be able to choose to some extent the level of additional occupational pension with which they would be provided. In such an arrangement the occupational scheme is typically based on a unit system, with members being able to choose the number of units for which they will contribute. For instance, the members may be offered a scheme similar to the 1 per cent. scheme mentioned above except that they may subscribe for 1, 2, 3 or 4 units of pension, where each unit is a pension scale of 1/400th of final pay for each year of service.

Occupational schemes and participation: 'filling-out' schemes

5.25 Another approach in the context of participation in the State earnings-related scheme is to accept the State flat-rate and earnings-related pensions as providing the necessary level of pension upon age or ill health retirement. The occupational scheme is then designed to provide benefits which the State scheme does not provide, for instance a pay-related capital sum on death during employment and a capital sum retirement benefit. This concludes our discussion of the types of occupational scheme appropriate when employees participate in the State earnings-related scheme.

Pay for pension purposes

5.26 In designing a pension scale it has always been necessary to decide on the definition of pay to be used, whether or not pay as so defined is then subject to a deduction in respect of the State flat-rate pension in order to arrive at pensionable pay. The contracting-out requirements have an important bearing on this matter, but we first discuss the issues involved in more general terms.

5.27 Earnings often include substantial amounts in addition to a basic rate of pay, for instance the overtime earnings of manual workers and the commissions of salesmen. Such payments often come to be relied upon by the recipient as part of regular earnings, and thus help to determine his standard of living. There is therefore a prima facie case for these payments to be pensionable, since the pension is then linked to a realistic measure of the income before retirement.

5.28 It has, however, been comparatively unusual in the past for overtime pay to be pensionable, because of the following factors.

(i) The employer often did not wish such pay to acquire the formal recognition and semblance of permanence that pensionable status might confer.

(ii) The employee was often reluctant to see pension scheme contributions deducted from overtime pay.

(iii) Employees who did not have the opportunity to earn overtime pay were likely to resent their colleagues receiving not only such pay but also extra pension in respect of it.

(iv) Overtime payments may tend to fall as a person's energies wane in the final years of his career, and unless special arrangements are made, fair value may not be received for the contributions paid on such earnings.

Other fluctuating payments such as commission have often been made pensionable in the past if they form a part of the recognised pay arrangements. Commission payments are often large and widely fluctuating, and special administrative arrangements have to be made to define the amounts of such extra payments on which contributions are to be charged and benefits calculated.

Contracted-out schemes

The quality test

5.29 We mentioned the quality test for contracting-out in Chapter 4; the main points are that a scheme must provide a pension of at least 1/80th of final pay (or revalued career pay, but this alternative is ignored for present purposes) where 'pay' may exclude earnings of certain kinds (e.g. overtime pay and bonuses) and may exclude an amount of earnings not exceeding 1½ times the lower earnings limit. The exclusion of a *kind* of earnings may be thought of as cutting out a band at the top of an individual's pay, while the exclusion of an *amount* of earnings may be taken as cutting out a first slice of his pay. The method of ascertaining final pay for the purpose of the quality test (which involves both the definition of 'pay' and the way in which 'final' pay is defined), and the method of calculation of the pension by reference to that pay, are subject to approval by the O.P.B.

5.30 In considering whether the definitions of pay, pensionable pay and final pensionable pay used for his pension scheme satisfy the contracting-out requirements, an employer might find himself involved with a question on the following lines.

'In my pension scheme pensionable earnings in a given scheme year are equal to the amount of the member's annual rate of pay at the beginning of the scheme year, less 1½ times the annual amount of the single person's State flat-rate pension at that date. For this purpose 'pay' includes the commission of salesmen but excludes bonuses, overtime payments etc. 'Final pensionable pay' is equal to the average annual pensionable pay in the best five consecutive scheme years out of the last ten such years preceding retirement. The pension fraction is 1/60ths. Will this meet the requirements?'

5.31 These issues can obviously become very complicated. The O.P.B. issued detailed guidance on this matter; in broad terms the position is as follows. The reader should not study this paragraph in detail, because it does not in fact provide a fully comprehensive and accurate description of the position. The intention is to provide an indication of the issues that have to be dealt with.

(i) Final pay may be defined as pay in the last year, pay in the best year of the last three, average annual pay in the last three years or average annual pay in the best consecutive three years in any period beginning not more than 13 years before normal pension age.

(ii) Pay may instead be averaged over a period of five consecutive years if the pension scale is 1/60th or better, but if it is desired to use a five-year averaging period with an accrual rate less than 1/60th the earnings in each of the five years must be revalued before the average is calculated.

(iii) The O.P.B. will not normally query the exclusion of *kinds* of earnings if the accrual rate is at least 1/60th.

(iv) The O.P.B. will accept exclusions of *kinds* of earnings even if the accrual rate is only 1/80th provided that any *amounts* of earnings excluded do not exceed the lower earnings limit.

The quantity test

5.32 The above discussion is concerned with the quality test for contracting-out. The quantity test (i.e. the requirement that the pension provided should not be less than the G.M.P.) also has an important bearing on the question of the definition of pay to be used for pension purposes. Using the notation of previous examples, suppose that an employee's basic pay is 4F and that he is a member of a pension scheme providing a pension of

$$1/60 \text{ (basic pay} - 1\frac{1}{2} \text{ F)}$$

Suppose further that overtime regularly lifts his pay to 7F (a relationship to basic pay which, though fairly extreme, is by no means unknown for 'wages grades' as opposed to salaried employees) and that his G.M.P. fraction is 1/80th. Ignoring the difference between final pay and revalued career pay, the rate of pension accrual under the main pension scale is

$$1/60 \text{th } (4F - 1\frac{1}{2}F) = .042F$$

but the G.M.P. requirement is that the pension at age 65 should not be less than

$$1/80 \text{th } (7F - F) = .075F$$

Obviously the finances of such a scheme could be dominated by the levels of full rather than basic pay. Contributions would probably be based on pensionable pay equal to (basic pay $- 1\frac{1}{2}F$), but it would be necessary to consider whether it might be better for the contribution and pension scales to be based on a definition of pensionable pay involving full pay instead of basic pay. This concludes our discussion of the definition of pay for pension purposes.

Other consequences of the G.M.P. requirement

5.33 We turn to a brief discussion of some further aspects and consequences of the G.M.P. requirement for contracting-out, mainly in the context of early retirement.

5.34 It is convenient first to illustrate again the matter of increases on G.M.P.s in course of payment, mentioned in paragraphs 4.18 and 4.19. We will suppose that a male member of an occupational scheme retires at age 65 with a pension of £2,000 per annum from the scheme, and that the scheme administrator is notified at that time by the Department of Health and Social Security that the member's G.M.P. in respect of the period for which he had been a contracted out member of the scheme is £500 per annum. The obligation of the scheme under the quantity test is to pay the member from his retirement at age 65 a pension of not less than £500 per annum, and, as this requirement is met, the scheme administrator need take no special action. We will make the following further assumptions.

(i) If the employee had been at all times a fully participating member of the State earnings-related scheme the pension from that scheme would have been £1,200 per annum.

(ii) In the two years following retirement State pensions are increased by 10 per cent. and 15 per cent. respectively.

(iii) The occupational scheme pension of £2,000 is not increased (this unrealistic assumption is made for simplicity).

The amounts payable from the State earnings-related scheme and the occupational scheme will then be as follows, the State flat-rate pension being ignored for simplicity.

	Year 1	Year 2	Year 3
Percentage increase in State pensions		10	15
	£	£	£
Amount of full State earnings-related pension	1,200	1,320	1,518
G.M.P	500	500	500
Amount of State earnings – related pension actually payable by State scheme	700	820	1,018
Amount of occupational scheme pension payable	2,000	2,000	2,000
Total pension (ignoring State flat-rate pension)	£2,700	£2,820	£3,018

The increases in the figures in the bottom row of the table are the same as the increases in the top row, so that the man enjoys the same increases as if he had participated fully in the State scheme. This is the method by which the State provides increases on the G.M.P. even though the G.M.P. itself is payable as part of the occupational scheme pension. The consequences of this arrangement for the occupational scheme, as far as pension increases are concerned, are dealt with further in paragraphs 5.60 to 5.63.

Retirement before State pension age

5.35 The discussion so far has been in terms of the pension to be provided at retirement on grounds of age, and it has implicitly been assumed that the normal pension age of the occupational scheme is the same as State pensionable age, namely the 65th birthday for men and 60th birthday for women. There are, however, a number of circumstances in which an employee might retire from an occupational pension scheme before the attainment of State pensionable age. Some examples are as follows.

(i) The normal pension age of the scheme is less than State pensionable age, an example being a normal pension age for men of age 60.

(ii)   The normal pension age of the scheme is equal to State pensionable age, but the rules of the scheme provide for a member to elect to retire early with an appropriately reduced immediate pension.

(iii)   The rules of the scheme provide for a member to be granted an immediate pension before normal pension age if he is made redundant by the employer.

(iv)   The rules of the scheme provide for a member who has to retire because of ill-health to be provided with an immediate pension.

The position of the G.M.P. on early retirement

5.36 We consider first a matter which is common to all these cases, namely the G.M.P. element in the early pension payable from a contracted-out scheme. The essential points are as follows.

(i)   As far as the G.M.P. accrual is concerned, the legislation makes no distinction between a person who leaves an occupational scheme early with a preserved pension and a person who leaves early with an immediate pension. In both these cases the G.M.P. rights cease to accrue, and accrued amounts of G.M.P. rights cease to be automatically indexed to national earnings, when the member ceases to be a contributing member of the scheme. The G.M.P. rights as calculated at the date of this cessation are subsequently increased for the years up to attainment of age 65 for males and 60 for females according to the particular formula chosen for the scheme in respect of increases in the G.M.P.s of early leavers, i.e. at the rate laid down in section 21 orders or the alternatives described in paragraphs 4.33 and 4.34.

(ii)   The G.M.P. entitlement as so increased becomes payable at age 65 for men and 60 for women and there is no obligation on the occupational scheme to provide increases thereafter on the G.M.P.

5.37 The issues may be illustrated by the following example, in which it is assumed that a male member of an occupational scheme retires early at age 60 with a pension of £2,000 per annum. The practice in the scheme before contracting-out was introduced was to give increases of 3 per cent. per annum on pensions in course of payment, and for simplicity it will be assumed that such increases continue to be given on the whole of the pension in the context of contracting-out. After the retired member attains age 65 it is of course necessary to increase the amount of pension up to the G.M.P. figure if the amount is less than that figure. Suppose that the G.M.P. entitlement at the date of early retirement was £1,750 per annum and the option chosen as to G.M.P. increases for early leavers is to grant increases of 8½ per cent. per annum. Various figures are given in the following table.

Year of age	Pension payable under normal rules of scheme including 3% p.a. increases	Amount of G.M.P.	Minimum amount of pension which must be paid under the G.M.P. requirements	Pension payable from scheme
	£ p.a.	£ p.a.	£ p.a.	£ p.a.
60 – 61	2,000	1,750	–	2,000
61 – 62	2,060	1,899	–	2,060
62 – 63	2,122	2,060	–	2,122
63 – 64	2,185	2,235	–	2,185
64 – 65	2,251	2,425	–	2,251
65 – 66	2,319	2,425	2,425	2,425
66 – 67	2,388	2,425	2,425	2,425
67 – 68	2,460	2,425	2,425	2,460
68 – 69	2,534	2,425	2,425	2,534
69 – 70	2,610	2,425	2,425	2,610

In this example the G.M.P. rights received only four increases of 8½ per cent. in the period before attainment of age 65, even though there are five years from age 60 to age 65. This is a rough allowance for the precise way in which G.M.P. increases are calculated, a matter which is dealt with in detail in Chapter 15.

5.38 Although the point is not relevant for the purpose of the present argument, the reader may note the element of duplication of pension increases in this arrangement. The trustees are granting 3 per cent. increases on the full scale pension even though the State scheme provides full indexing on the G.M.P. This is not typical; the example was chosen to illustrate as simply as possible the effect of the G.M.P. requirement and is not to be taken as an example of normal procedure on pension increases.

5.39 The main point which will be noted from the above table is that when the trustees of a contracted-out scheme start to pay an immediate pension before the person concerned has attained State pensionable age, they must bear in mind the future liability to pay from State pensionable age at least the amount of the G.M.P., as increased between the date of early retirement and the date of attainment of State pensionable age. The finances of the scheme and in certain cases the options available to the individual member, must be framed accordingly. We now return to a more general discussion of the different cases mentioned in paragraph 5.35.

Normal pension age less than State retirement age

5.40 In the majority of occupational pension schemes the normal retirement age is 65 for males and 60 for females. This is a matter of tradition, reinforced by the fact that these are the pension ages in the State scheme. Nevertheless, many schemes in both the public and the private sectors have a normal pension age for males which is less than 65. An age earlier than 60 for females is much less common, and we restrict this discussion to male members. Sometimes the age is a definite age such as 60, with most members retiring at that age; in other cases retirement on the normal scale pension is permitted at any time between a defined age and age 65, often subject to completion of a specified period of service, with members retiring in practice over the whole possible range of the ages concerned. The reader should be aware that the anti-franking provisions of the 1984 Act mentioned in paragraph 4.36 have to be taken into account not only in the context of preserved pensions of early leavers, but also in cases of retirement with an immediate pension when the scheme's normal pension age differs from State pension age. We shall not examine these complexities in this book.

5.41 An important factor that has to be taken into account in such schemes is the fact that the State pension does not become payable to a retired male employee until he attains age 65. If the pension scale of the occupational scheme includes an offset in respect of the State flat-rate pension on the lines discussed earlier in this chapter, there will thus be a period of rather low income after retirement until the State pension comes into payment. Some integrated schemes therefore include a special temporary supplement to the pension, to carry the retired member over this period. Another device which is sometimes used is to permit the retiring member to convert his occupational pension into a 'stepped' pension of equal actuarial value, so that an amount larger than the normal entitlement is payable up to attainment of age 65 and a smaller amount thereafter.

Voluntary early retirement with a reduced pension

5.42 We turn to the second type of arrangement mentioned in paragraph 5.35 above, namely an early retirement provision under which the member may elect to retire, before the age at which he would be entitled to take a full scale pension, on terms which, broadly speaking, do not on the average place any extra liability on the scheme. The calculation of the terms involved will be considered later, but it will probably be obvious at this stage that it would not be possible to provide the full accrued scale amount (i.e. based on pensionable service completed, and final pensionable pay, at the date of early retirement) as an immediate pension on early retirement. This is because the assets of the scheme underlying the pension rights of the member concerned will not accumulate at interest for so long as had been expected, and the pension will be payable for a longer period than expected, and these two items of financial strain more than offset the fact that the pension will probably be based on a lower figure of final pensionable pay than if retirement had taken place at the normal age. The immediate pension is usually calculated by first working out the accrued pension on the normal scale and then reducing this amount by a percentage depending on the number of years by which retirement is early. The quality test for contracting-out has a bearing on this matter, in that the rate of such reduction must either be not more than 6 per cent. for each year by which retirement is early or must be on a basis certified as reasonable by an actuary.

5.43 The points that have to be considered in settling the rate of reduction in a particular case are quite complicated and they are discussed in detail in paragraphs 19.34 et seq. For the purpose of the present discussion we will assume that, before the advent of contracting-out, it was found in a particular occupational scheme that the amount of immediate pension which could be provided to a member retiring early without placing a financial strain on the scheme was equal to the amount of the pension calculated on the normal scale reduced by 4 per cent. simple for each year by which the age at retirement was less than normal pension age. We will use an example somewhat similar to that of paragraph 5.37 in which the normal pension age for males is 65 and a male member with accrued pension rights of £2,000 p.a. desires to retire early at age 60 with an immediate pension. We will assume as before that the scheme gives increases on pensions in course of payment at the rate of 3 per cent. p.a., that the G.M.P. entitlement at the date of early retirement is £1,750 p.a. and that the option chosen as to G.M.P. increases for early leavers is to provide increases of 8½ per cent. p.a. up to State pensionable age.

5.44 Before the advent of contracting-out the amount of the immediate pension would have been £2,000 p.a. reduced by 20 per cent. in token of the fact that retirement was five years early, giving an initial amount of immediate pension of £1,600 p.a. This amount would increase in payment at 3 per cent. p.a. so that on the retired member's attainment of age 65 the amount of pension in payment would have risen to £1,855 p.a. Under contracting-out, however, the G.M.P. requirement comes into effect when the pensioner attains this age. The amount of the G.M.P. at age 65 is taken as £2,425 p.a. for the reasons explained in paragraph 5.37.

5.45 The G.M.P. requirement clearly faces the trustees with a difficulty, namely that if they continue to follow their normal practice of offering members the facility to retire early on terms of broad actuarial equivalence, this will place a financial strain on the scheme because the amount of pension at age 65 resulting from the arrangements will be less than the G.M.P. requirement and will therefore have to be increased at age 65 to meet that requirement. It will be obvious to the reader that the difficulty arises from the fact that the G.M.P. requirement is laid down in terms of the amount of pension at age 65 and the legislation does not permit the liability to be met by a pension of lesser amount payable earlier.

5.46 It might be thought that this difficulty is simply one of cost and that if the cost could be met the trustees should continue their established practice. While this has some validity it should be noted that the intention in permitting early retirement with an immediate pension on terms which do not impose a strain on the scheme is in the broadest terms to maintain equity between a member who continues in the scheme and a member who retires early. Equity would not, however, be maintained if the member who retired early placed substantial additional cost on the scheme. Such additional cost may well be a feature of early retirement in a scheme where members may retire on the normal scale pension without an actuarial reduction over a range of ages, as mentioned in paragraph 5.40. In that case, however, the provision is part of the main benefit design and there is not such a strong implication of equity between one member and another.

5.47 The build up of G.M.P. entitlements dates only from 6th April 1978 and at the time of writing of this book the amounts of G.M.P. are comparatively small, so that the influence of the G.M.P. requirement is not as important as in the above example. Nevertheless, trustees are having to begin to consider whether the facility to take a reduced immediate pension on early retirement needs to be restricted. The alternative of a preserved pension is considered in the next chapter, against the background of the legislation covering early leavers' rights mentioned in previous chapters; improvements in early leavers' rights may well have an effect on the issues discussed above.

Redundancy pensions

5.48 Turning to the third situation mentioned in paragraph 5.35, namely redundancy, pension benefits are often an important factor upon cessation of employment on account of redundancy. A preserved pension, or an immediate pension of an amount reduced for early payment as discussed above, is typically provided, although it should be noted that the Revenue will permit only a preserved pension and not an immediate pension to be provided to an early leaver below age 50. The Revenue rules covering early leavers with an immediate or preserved pension do not include any special provisions for redundancy cases; only ill- health cases are treated specially. An employer may wish to provide a preserved or immediate pension greater than the strict entitlement in specific individual cases of redundancy, and this can be done from the scheme provided that the trust deed and rules permit discretionary augmentation, that the amounts of benefit do not exceed the overriding Revenue limits and that the cost can be met. In some schemes the trust deed and rules provide, as of right, specially favourable preserved or immediate benefits in all cases of redundancy; for instance, the immediate pension on redundancy after a specified age may be equal to the accrued scale pension without reduction for early retirement. It is often provided that the employer must meet any additional cost to the scheme involved in such arrangements by specific extra contributions, since redundancy is often a direct consequence of the employer's policy.

5.49 It is important in this connection that the rules of the scheme should be drafted so as to prevent the possibility of disagreement between the member and the trustees as to whether his retirement is due to redundancy or not. This can be achieved by providing in the rules of the scheme for the appropriate benefits to be paid only in cases where the employer certifies the case to be one of redundancy.

5.50 The general law on redundancy provides for cash payments to be made by the employer to certain employees on redundancy, but the liability upon the employer to make such payments may be reduced or extinguished if an immediate pension is payable from an occupational pension scheme. This has stimulated a tendency for employers to consider redundancy benefits and pension arrangements as related matters. The position as to the G.M.P. entitlement is the same as in the previous examples.

Ill-health retirement pensions

5.51 As has been seen, occupational pension scales are usually such that an employee who retires on grounds of age after less than a full working lifetime's membership receives a pension of an amount reflecting the shorter period of membership. We now turn to the case where an immediate pension is to be provided after a period of service which is less than a full working lifetime, and may be comparatively short, because of premature retirement by reason of ill- health.

5.52 It has always been common for the better occupational schemes to provide an immediate pension on ill-health retirement of an amount calculated on the normal pension scale of the scheme, on the basis of pensionable service and pensionable pay at the date of retirement, without actuarial reduction for early payment. This does not, however, give an adequate pension on ill-health retirement early in an employee's career (when the need is often very great), because the accrued pension is then small. It has therefore become increasingly common to provide a substantial minimum level of ill-health pension, sometimes subject to a period of qualification for benefit such as five years' pensionable service.

5.53 A substantial minimum pension on ill-health retirement is often provided by basing the ill-health pension on the same scale as the age retirement pension but taking into account a number of years of pensionable service greater than the actual number of years completed at the date of ill-health retirement. The ill-health pension after 'n' years of membership of a scheme might, for example, be calculated as if 'N' years of membership had been completed, where N is the greater of

(i)   n and
(ii) 20 years or the total number of years of membership which would have been completed at normal pension age, whichever is the less.

Alternatively N might be equal to n plus one-half, or the whole, of potential future service from the date of retirement up to normal pension age. Scheme rules often include provisions for an ill-health pension to be reduced or suspended if the recipient recovers sufficiently for him to be able to earn a living, and if the ill-health pension scale is generous these provisions may well be stringent.

5.54 The benefits payable from the State scheme upon incapacity are complicated, and are payable for various periods. For this reason it is very unusual indeed for the principle of integration with the State scheme to be carried out fully in cases of ill-health retirement. As indicated above, the normal procedure is for the scale of age retirement scheme pension to be settled first, with the scheme pension on ill- health retirement following, often with the adjustments described in the previous paragraph, from that scale.

The G.M.P. requirement

5.55 It is not a requirement for contracting-out that a scheme should provide an immediate pension upon early retirement on grounds of ill-health. The obligation remains to provide a pension not less than the G.M.P. upon attainment of age 65 for males and 60 for females. As in the previous examples, the G.M.P. is calculated and 'dynamised' up to State pensionable age in the normal way for an early leaver.

Permanent Health Insurance

5.56   Another way of providing help to an employee who suffers
a breakdown of health does not involve the payment of immediate
benefit from the pension scheme, but it is mentioned here for
completeness since its use is widespread. This involves Permanent
Health Insurance or P.H.I. taken out by the employer by means of
a policy with an insurance company. A typical arrangement is that
an employee who has to cease work because of ill-health remains
on the books of the employer and receives under the policy what is
in effect a continuing salary, expressed as a proportion of his salary
at the date of the breakdown, during the period up to attainment
of normal retirement age. The policy often provides for the
amount of the payments to increase annually. As far as the
pension scheme is concerned the position is as follows.

(i)   The P.H.I. policy may provide not only the 'salary' payments
       but also the appropriate pension scheme contributions
       relating to that salary. In this case the person continues to
       accrue pension rights based on the notional salary and these
       come into payment when the P.H.I. payments cease at
       normal retirement age.

(ii)   If pension scheme contributions are not continued in this way
       the person is treated as an early leaver from the pension
       scheme, and receives one of the normal range of benefits.

Late retirement

5.57   The specification of a 'normal pension age' in a scheme does
not necessarily make it compulsory for a member to retire upon
reaching that age; the position depends mainly on his contract of
employment. It may suit both the employer and the member that
the latter should defer his retirement, and the rules of a scheme
usually set out the method by which the pension is to be calculated
in these circumstances. It is generally thought desirable to aim,
within the pension scheme, at broad equity between a member
who retires at normal pension age and one who retires thereafter.
The augmentation of pension because of deferred retirement is
therefore often calculated on the basis of the actuarial
equivalence, as at normal pension age, of

(i)   the benefits which could then have been taken and

(ii)   the benefits which are actually to be enjoyed, allowing for any contributions paid after the attainment of normal pension age.

5.58   This type of calculation produces a substantial rate of augmentation, particularly in conditions of high interest rates, but even so it may not produce a larger amount than would the application of the ordinary pension scale at the actual date of retirement on the basis of the then pensionable service and pensionable salary. The pension calculated in the latter way will depend on salary increases after attainment of normal pension age, which may be substantial, as well as the additional pensionable service completed. This method implies that member and employer will continue to pay contributions during the period of extended service. It is sometimes provided that, subject to Revenue limits, the amount of pension to be paid in these circumstances is to be the greater of the amounts calculated by these two methods.

5.59   For contracting-out, a member of a scheme must be entitled to receive his pension from a date not later than attainment of State pensionable age, but scheme rules may permit pension to be postponed if the member stays in employment after attainment of State pensionable age, and the legislation lays down the minimum rate of increase to be provided on the G.M.P. entitlement in these circumstances.

Pension increases

5.60   We turn to the quesion of increases in an occupational pension after it starts to be paid. We have already noted the method by which the State provides increases in the G.M.P. after attainment of State pensionable age, even though that G.M.P. is payable from an occupational scheme. It is not a condition of contracting-out that an occupational scheme should provide increases in a pension after it starts to be paid, but many schemes do so. The position is briefly as follows.

Public sector pension increases

5.61   The area of pension increases is one of the few areas in which the practice in public sector and associated schemes on the one hand, and in the generality of private sector schemes on the other, is markedly different. Section 59 of the Social Security Pensions Act 1975 provides for 'official pensions' in course of payment to be increased by the percentage increase in the cost of living each year. Sub-section 59(5) provides that such increases are to apply only to the excess of such a pension over the amount if any of the G.M.P. The term 'official pensions' includes the pensions of civil servants, teachers, local government employees and police and firemen. The list does not include retired employees of public boards and nationalised industries, but it is common in those cases for the rules of the occupational pension scheme concerned to provide for pensions in excess of G.M.P. to be increased in line with increases granted under the Act. Thus a very large proportion of public sector pension outgo is indexed to the cost of living.

Private sector pension increases

5.62   In the private sector it is not generally regarded as prudent for the rules of a pension scheme to promise pension increases in line with increases in the cost of living, because the employer and the members could not be sure of being able to provide the additional finance that would be necessary if the cost of increasing payments to persons no longer contributing to the profitability of the employer was unexpectedly heavy. The Government recognised this position in providing for the G.M.P. element in an occupational scheme to be increased by the State.

5.63   Many private sector schemes do, however, provide pension increases to the extent considered possible. As mentioned in paragraph 2.34, the Revenue will permit the modest rate of increase of 3 per cent. per annum to be promised in the rules of a scheme. Many private sector schemes do this, with provision for larger increases to be considered on an ad-hoc basis each year; a higher increase may, for instance, be granted in a particular year if the investments of the scheme have performed well or if the employer is able to provide a special contribution to the scheme. Following the pattern laid down for public sector schemes as mentioned in paragraph 5.61, private sector schemes often provide increases only on that part of the pension in excess of the G.M.P., on the grounds that the State provides increases on the latter.

CHAPTER 6

MISCELLANEOUS BENEFITS

CHAPTER 6

MISCELLANEOUS BENEFITS

6.1 Occupational pension schemes provide various benefits in addition to members' pensions. The more important of these are discussed in this chapter.

Capital sums on retirement

6.2 Most pension schemes provide for part of the retirement benefits to be taken in the form of a capital sum. In a small minority of schemes the scale of capital sum retirement benefits and the scale of pension benefits are separate. In most schemes, however, capital sum retirement benefits are provided for by giving the member the option to commute some of his pension benefits at retirement, i.e. to give up some of his pension in exchange for a capital sum. This is a popular provision, because the member is attracted by the prospect of a tax-free cash payment and the trustees have no objection since the terms are usually framed so that one benefit is substituted for another of broadly equivalent actuarial value.

6.3 There are often in practice restrictions on the extent to which an option to commute part of a pension can be exercised, in addition to the restrictions imposed by Revenue rules. In a contracted-out scheme, the element of pension which represents G.M.P. must be payable as from attainment of age 65 for men and 60 for women in the form of a pension; the pension equivalent of any part of the retirement benefit that was in fact taken as a lump sum may not be brought into account when the amount of the pension payable from State pensionable age is being compared with the amount of the G.M.P. This clearly restricts in principle the extent to which a pension can be given up in exchange for a capital sum, although the practical effect was small in the early years of contracting-out. A separate point is that some employers and trustees decide, as a matter of policy, that commutation should not be permitted in their scheme to the full extent provided by the Revenue rules. Some general arguments for and against the provision of capital sum retirement benefits are as follows.

Arguments for capital sum retirement benefits

(i)   A capital sum is a flexible benefit: if the recipient needs capital it is provided, and if he prefers income he can use the capital sum to buy what is known as a 'purchased life annuity' under the provisions of the Finance Act 1956. There is a tax advantage in the purchase of such an annuity, compared with the more straightforward course of taking the benefit in the form of a pension from the scheme. This advantage is that part of each payment of a purchased life annuity is regarded by the Inland Revenue as a return of the purchase money; it is thus treated for purposes of tax as a capital payment and is not taxable. The taxable portion is treated as income. A pension paid from an occupational scheme is taxed as income.

(ii) At retirement a member of a scheme may need a capital sum to pay off outstanding commitments such as a mortgage, or he may wish to move and buy a new house or a small business.

(iii) A capital sum, being tax free, is a very attractive benefit for a highly paid employee, who may suffer substantial tax on his income even after retirement. Such an employee may have had experience of dealing with large amounts of money in his private or business affairs and can be expected to use a capital sum wisely.

(iv) An employer can more easily attract young persons into his employment if he can offer a pension scheme including capital sum retirement benefits.

Arguments against capital sum retirement benefits

(i)   Most people are not accustomed to dealing with comparatively large capital sums; they have had income all their lives, and that is what they need in retirement. If a cash retirement benefit is used unwisely the recipient would have been better served by a larger pension.

(ii) A prudent person would arrange to clear his capital commitments while he was receiving his full income; some organisations granting mortgages will only do so provided that the loan will be repaid before normal retiring age. An employee should not be encouraged to rely on the pension scheme of his employer, whose employment he may leave, for long term capital commitments connected with his private affairs.

(iii) Adequate pensions are expensive, and resources should be concentrated on providing these, and if possible augmenting them if the cost of living rises after retirement, rather than on providing capital sums.

(iv) Many schemes or employers have in practice provided cost-of-living increases on pensions in course of payment in recent years when these were not promised under the rules, or have provided increases greater than those promised. If part of the pension is given up as a lump sum, the member usually gives up not only the basic level of pension but also the possibility of increases on the part surrendered. The terms of commutation may allow for any promised level of increases on the pension given up, but it may turn out that greater increases are in practice given on the part taken as pension, in which case a member tends to lose by commutation.

Terms of commutation

6.4 The reader is reminded of the point made in paragraph 2.22, namely that although the Revenue rules lay down the maximum scale of capital sum retirement benefits, this does not in itself establish Revenue control over the position because in the absence of a specific ruling as to the terms on which pension may be converted into capital sum a large sum might be provided in exchange for a very small reduction in pension. The total of lump sum (expressed as a pension equivalent on proper terms) and pension together might then exceed the overall Revenue limits referred to in paragraphs 2.18 and 2.19. For this reason the Revenue have to be satisfied that the terms of commutation are appropriate. The Revenue rules dealing with the differing capital values of pension rights according to the guaranteed rate of increase associated with them were outlined in paragraph 2.22.

6.5 The trustees of a scheme will in any event normally desire that the terms of commutation should be broadly fair as between a member who exercises the option and one who does not. It will probably be clear to the reader that, in theory, many actuarial complexities might arise in the settling of the terms of commutation, since in principle members who would be expected to gain from the facility might be expected to exercise the option to a greater extent than members who did not expect to gain. In practice, however, commutation is so widespread that this point rather loses its force, except perhaps in fixing the terms for those who retire on grounds of ill-health. The effect of point (iv) at the end of paragraph 6.3 must also be noted in considering whether commutation is likely in practice to be an 'option against the scheme'. In many schemes the aim is to keep the terms of commutation reasonably stable with time, these terms being regarded as part of the benefit scales of the scheme. If the rules of the scheme provide for, say £9 for each £1 p.a. given up irrespective of age and sex (see paragraph 2.22), and this differs greatly from the values implied by the basis used by the actuary in his valuation of the scheme, he might decide to allow explicitly in his valuation for the commutation of an estimated proportion of pension on the stated terms. In a scheme where the terms are adjusted from time to time to ensure that they are broadly in line with the actuarial basis, the actuary might ignore the commutation option in his valuation calculations. In some schemes, mostly insured, stability is not the aim; the terms of commutation are varied so as to keep broadly in line with market conditions from time to time.

Contracting-out: the quality test

6.6 As noted in paragraph 6.3, a capital sum retirement benefit (whether provided under a scale separate from the pension scale or by commutation of the pension) cannot be brought into the comparison of scheme pension with G.M.P. for the purpose of the quantity test for contracting-out. Under the quality test, on the other hand, capital sum retirement benefits may be brought into account, the position being as follows.

(i) If the retirement benefits consist of a pension and a lump sum assessed on two separate scales, the O.P.B. take account of the pension equivalent of the lump sum and assess the value of the total benefits in pension terms when considering whether or not the quality test is satisfied.

(ii)   If the rules provide for part of the pension to be given up in exchange for a lump sum, the O.P.B. take account of the pension scale before exercise of the commutation option in considering whether the scheme meets the quality test. The O.P.B. require the basis of commutation to be certified as reasonable by an actuary.

Commutation in exceptional circumstances

6.7 The Revenue rules permit the whole of a pension to be commuted if this pension together with benefits to the member from any other pension schemes of the employer is of trivial amount, or in exceptional circumstances of serious ill-health, and power to commute pensions in such circumstances is usually included in the rules of a scheme even if capital sums are not included in the general scheme of retirement benefits. As far as contracting-out is concerned, commutation of a pension on grounds of triviality is permitted even in respect of the G.M.P. entitlement included in a pension. When a pension is being commuted in exceptional circumstances of serious ill-health, however, this may be done only in respect of the excess of the pension over the G.M.P.; the G.M.P. itself must be paid as a pension after the attainment by the person concerned of State pensionable age.

Benefits on death in service

6.8 The range of benefits on the death of a member of an occupational scheme during employment (often referred to as 'death in service') includes the following.

(i)   A capital sum.
(ii)   A pension to a widow.
(iii) A pension to a widower.
(iv)   Pensions to other adult dependants.
(v)   Allowances to children.

These benefits are discussed below.

Capital sums

6.9 Although under Revenue rules a capital sum payable on death in service may be as large as four times salary in addition to a return of the member's total contributions with interest, in practice most schemes provide capital sums on a more modest level, generally of the order of two to three years' salary. Starting from the notion that the available resources should be directed to the area of greatest need, there is a case for providing a different level of capital sum benefit according to the marital status of the deceased or the particular position in respect of dependants. In practice it is comparatively unusual to make such distinctions and the scale of lump sum benefits generally applies across the whole membership.

6.10 A substantial capital sum death benefit during the early years of membership will help to make a pension scheme attractive to young employees, who are likely to be concerned more with the security of their families during these years than with the remote matter of pensions. Furthermore, group cover is of great value to employees who would not be insurable on normal terms as individuals, and there is general social advantage in providing cover for employees who might not choose to buy it for themselves. On the other hand, some employers take the view that the provision of life assurance cover above a modest minimum level is the concern of the individual.

6.11 It was noted in paragraph 2.27 that in order to avoid the possibility of capital transfer tax arising when a capital sum death benefit is paid from an occupational scheme, it is customary for trustees to be given a discretion as to the destination of the payment. In many schemes the member is able to make a nomination in this connection and the trustees normally take account of this nomination, while not being legally bound by it.

Widows' pensions

6.12 The various benefits provided for widows under the State pension scheme form a complicated pattern and it is therefore not the practice for widows' pensions payable from an occupational scheme to be directly integrated with those of the State scheme. A widow's pension on death in service is often expressed as a proportion of the pension that would have been paid to the member had he retired on ill-health grounds on the day of his death, and if the members' pension scale includes an allowance for State pensions so will the widows' pension scale in such circmstances, so that widows' pensions are often indirectly integrated with State scheme benefits.

6.13 The needs of the widow of a man who dies at a comparatively early age during employment, and particularly of a young widow with children, may well be greater than those of the widow of a man who dies late in service, and the design of the benefit scales is a matter of providing for pressing needs as generously as possible. As noted above, the amount of a widow's pension upon death in service is often expressed as a proportion of the pension which the member would have received had he retired on grounds of ill-health on the day of his death, as in the corresponding Revenue maximum rule. Typically the widow's pension is one-half of the member's notional ill-health pension. This affords a convenient scale, particularly if the ill-health pension scale incorporates a reasonable minimum level during the early years of membership. This arrangement also makes less likely anomalies between the widow's pension if a man dies during employment and that if he dies shortly after ill-health retirement. Some schemes incorporate an 'age disparity adjustment' under which a widow's pension is reduced below the normal scale if she was younger than her late husband to an unusually large extent.

6.14 Sometimes the pension to a widow is expressed as a proportion of the pay or pensionable pay of the member at the date of death, irrespective of the length of service of the member. Under this approach the provision of a pension to a widow is regarded as somewhat similar to the provision of a capital sum death benefit; the aim is to provide a certain level of cover rather than to link the benefit to the standing of the deceased member as measured by length of pensionable service.

Period of payment

6.15 It has to be decided whether the pension to a widow should continue, should cease automatically or should be reviewed if she remarries. The case against automatic continuation rests on the principle mentioned earlier, that resources are necessarily limited and should be directed to the areas of greatest need; a widow who remarries may not be in such need of a pension as she was before. In public sector schemes a widow's pension usually ceases not only on remarriage but also in some cases of 'cohabitation'. In private sector schemes the most common current practice is for the widow's pension to continue for life. Where such pensions are discontinued or reviewed on remarriage, it is sometimes the case that a reduction is made in only that part of the pension which arose by bringing into account notional future membership of the deceased member at the date of his death, assuming that the scheme incorporates such a provision; it is unusual to reduce that part which arose from the actual service of the deceased member.

Contracting-out

6.16 The contracting-out requirements in respect of the scales of widows' pensions were mentioned in paragraphs 4.23 to 4.27. The requirements as to period of payment are complicated. The broad principle is that the widow's pension from the occupational scheme must be payable for any period during which the widow is receiving a pension from the State scheme by virtue of her late husband's contributions. A widow's pension from an occupational scheme may cease when the State widow's pension would cease to be payable, for example on remarriage before age 60. At age 60 a State scheme widow's pension becomes a retirement pension and thereafter the G.M.P. element in an occupational scheme pension must continue to be paid even if the widow remarries, but the rules of such a scheme may provide for the part of the scheme widow's pension which is in excess of her G.M.P. to cease on her remarriage after age 60.

Widowers' pensions

6.17 The provision of a pension to a widower upon the death of a female member of an occupational pension scheme is not a requirement for contracting-out. It used to be very unusual indeed, but is now becoming more common. Its rarity in the past was due to the principle mentioned previously, that the available resources should be directed towards the area of greatest need; it was assumed that a widower would normally be, or have been, an employed person and not in urgent need of a pension in respect of his deceased wife's employment. Against this consideration is the general tendency towards a more equal treatment of the sexes in pension schemes, as in other fields, and the fact that the assumption mentioned above is not as generally true as it once was. It is quite common, when widowers' pensions are provided, for these to be subject to a test of dependency, so that only when a husband was genuinely dependent to some extent on the deceased female member is he granted a widower's pension.

Pensions to other adult dependants

6.18 Under Revenue rules there may be paid, upon the death in service of a member of an occupational scheme, a pension to a dependant other than a widow or widower. For this purpose the word 'dependant' means a person who was financially dependent on the deceased member; a relative who was not supported by the deceased member is not his dependant. It is quite common for the rules of an occupational scheme to give the trustees discretionary power to pay a pension to a dependant, and in some cases trustees have to give much consideration to complicated circumstances in deciding on whether such a pension should be paid, and if so to whom.

Allowances for children

6.19 Under Revenue rules the child of an employee may always be regarded as a dependant until he reaches the age of 18 or ceases to receive full-time educational or vocational training if later. Allowances to dependent children on death in service are a comparatively inexpensive benefit to provide, since the number of cases of death in service which give rise to children's allowances payable for a substantial number of years is small. On the other hand, the benefit is extremely valuable to the recipient. It is therefore quite common in occupational schemes to provide allowances to dependent children. The Revenue rules do not distinguish between adult dependants and child dependants as far as maximum benefits are concerned, so that the allowances to children on death in service in a particular pension scheme take their place within the overall Revenue maxima.

Benefits on death after retirement

6.20 The range of benefits on the death of a member of an occupational scheme after his retirement on pension is the same as that set out in paragraph 6.8 on death in service. The issues involved differ, however, in a number of respects from those of death in service, and some points are discussed below.

Capital sums

6.21 It was noted in paragraph 2.29 that the Revenue permit a lump sum to be paid on the death of a retired member if his pension is guaranteed to be paid for a period not exceeding 5 years after retirement and he dies during this period, the lump sum then being equal to the excess of the total amount of pension which would have been payable during the guarantee period over the amount of pension actually paid. This is the normal way in which a capital sum benefit on death after retirement is defined.

6.22 The Revenue rules do in fact provide for capital sum benefits on death after retirement on a much wider scale than this, in that they permit continued life insurance cover to an employee after he retires. This benefit is not, however, very often met with in practice. This is partly because most individuals have much less need of substantial life insurance cover after retirement. A further reason is that the single premium value at retirement of the continued cover has to be included, in any calculation involved with Revenue limits, as part of the capital sum retirement benefit (see paragraph 2.20) and hence in the total benefits.

6.23 A special case that is of interest relates to an employee who has retired early on grounds of ill-health. He may, subject to various conditions laid down in the Revenue rules, continue to be covered until normal retirement date for a capital sum death benefit at the rate that applied under the occupational scheme just before his retirement, without the cost having to be included in the value of the benefits at retirement for the purpose of Revenue limits.

Widows' pensions

6.24 The contracting-out requirements mentioned in paragraphs 4.23 to 4.27 had a considerable impact on the provisions of occupational pension schemes in respect of death in service benefits, because prior to contracting-out it was quite common to provide a capital sum on death in service but no widow's pension. Even before contracting-out started, however, a high proportion of schemes provided a widow's pension upon the death of a retired male employee. The amount of such widow's pension is usually expressed as a proportion of the pension which the member was receiving at the date of his death, except that if the member had given up part of his pension on retirement, either for a lump sum or to provide an increased dependant's pension (see paragraph 6.30 below), the widow's pension is normally calculated as a fraction of the pension which the retired member would have been receiving had he not made these surrenders.

6.25   The fraction relating the widow's pension to the member's pension is commonly one-half. A widow's pension on death after retirement is a comparatively expensive benefit to provide (since female mortality is in general lighter than male mortality), so that when in the past a scheme introduced this benefit for the first time the widow's pension was quite often expressed as a fraction of only that part of the member's pension which would arise in respect of pensionable service after the date of introduction of the benefit. Because of this, it is not unusual to find in scheme rules that a widow's pension payable on the death of a pensioner is calculated as one-half of only a part of the member's pension and not of the whole of his pension.

6.26   The issues which arise in connection with the cessation or otherwise on remarriage of a widow's pension on death after retirement, and the detailed requirements in connection with contracting-out, are essentially the same as those for widow's pensions on death in service.

Widowers' pensions

6.27   As in the case of death in service benefits, it was at one time very unusual indeed for a widower's pension to be provided on the death of a female pensioner, but it is now becoming somewhat more common, subject often to a test of dependency.

Pensions to other adult dependants

6.28   The comments in paragraph 6.18 apply equally to dependants' pensions on death after retirement.

Allowances for children

6.29   The comments on allowances for children in paragraph 6.19 apply equally to allowances which arise on the death of a pensioner. As would be expected, the number of cases of death after retirement which give rise to the payment of allowances to children is very small indeed.

Dependants' pensions by allocation

6.30 The discussion so far has been in terms of a pension provided as of right to the widow or other dependant of a deceased pensioner. Many schemes provide in addition for extra pension to a widow or a dependant on the death of a pensioner to be arranged, if required, by the voluntary surrender of part of the member's pension at the date of retirement. Such options are not greatly used in practice, probably because the member regards his own pension as too modest to be reduced or because the scheme provides a widow's pension which is thought sufficient. In theory the option should be arranged on terms which impose no liability on the scheme, both on grounds of cost and also in order to preserve broad equity between a member who so allocates part of his pension and one who does not. If the principle of no additional liability is adhered to strictly, however, complicated procedures are necessary to avoid selection against the scheme. In practice a more flexible and simple arrangement which may involve extra liability is usually acceptable. It is sometimes provided, indeed, that the terms of surrender of an ill-health pension are to be calculated as if the member was in normal health. This clearly imposes a financial strain on the scheme but it is usually of small amount and the provision is of great value in cases where the expectation of life is severely curtailed.

Benefits on withdrawal

6.31 As noted in paragraph 2.31, the complications which can arise from the fact that the three sets of legislation relating to tax, the preservation of pensions and contracting-out work in parallel and largely independently are particularly notable in the area of early leavers from an occupational pension scheme. Chapter 19 is devoted to a technical study of some aspects of early leavers' benefits, but the following paragraphs provide a more general outline of the points involved.

Refunds of members' contributions

6.32 One area of complication arises in connection with the extent to which a leaving member may take, as his leaving benefit, a capital sum equal to the amount of the contributions he has paid into the scheme with interest. Under Revenue rules a capital sum leaving benefit payable to the member (as distinct from a transfer payment to the trustees of another scheme) may not include any contributions made by the employer (as will be seen later, it is in any event normally impracticable in a final pay scheme to associate a specific amount of employer's contributions with an individual member). We are therefore involved only with the member's contributions in this discussion. As noted in paragraph 2.32, a liability for tax arises when a leaving member is paid a capital sum representing the whole or a part of his accumulated contributions, this tax charge being equal to 10 per cent. of the amount payable. This tax is a liability of the trustees of the scheme, but it is normally provided in the rules of the scheme for the trustees to deduct the amount from the refund so that the tax charge is passed on to the withdrawing member.

6.33 In Chapter 3 we discussed the preservation of pension rights for members leaving a scheme, and it will be recalled that the general principle is that a member who has 5 years of qualifying service and has attained age 26 must have a preserved pension rather than a refund, but that there is a continuing right to a refund of contributions paid up to 5th April 1975.

6.34 It was mentioned in paragraph 4.30 that an early leaver in his first 5 years of contracted-out membership of a scheme may in principle have his G.M.P. rights cancelled by payment back into the State pension scheme of a 'Contributions Equivalent Premium' payable by the employer, the Act giving the employer power to recover an appropriate part of the C.E.P. from any contribution refund due to the leaving member. The facility to pay a C.E.P. is not available if the leaving member qualifies for a preserved pension under the preservation law. The reader will note that there is separate reference above to the preservation law (which itself hinges on the completion of 5 years qualifying service) on the one hand and to the completion of 5 years contracted-out membership on the other hand. This is a minor example of the complications arising from two similar but not identical items of legislation working simultaneously. Detailed differences between the two include the fact that 'qualifying service' need not necessarily be the same as contracted-out membership and that the preservation law involves reference to age 26 (now removed by the Social Security Act 1985) whereas the contracting-out arrangements do not.

6.35 The following table shows, for various circumstances, whether the facility to pay a C.E.P. is available and whether the member may have a refund in respect of his contributions paid

(i)   between 6th April 1975 (when the preservation law came into force), and 5th April 1978 (when contracting-out started), and

(ii)   after 5th April 1978, assuming that we are dealing with a scheme used for contracting-out.

The right to a refund of contributions paid up to 5th April 1975 continues irrespective of the various different circumstances. The asterisked note to the table arises because in the circumstances concerned there is an option under the contracting-out rules for the preserved pension to be simply the G.M.P. and not the full pension under the normal scale of the scheme. The point is of little concern to the reader seeking only an introduction to the subject.

CIRCUMSTANCES			CONSEQUENCES	
Leaver qualifies for preservation?	Contracted-out for more than five years?	C.E.P. facility available?	Permitted to refund contributions paid in period shown?	
			6.4.1975 – 5.4.1978	After 5.4.1978
No	No	Yes	Yes	Yes
No	Yes	No	Yes	See note*
Yes	No	No	No	No
Yes	Yes	No	No	No

*Note: Yes if G.M.P. only to be provided for post 5.4.1978 membership.
      No if full benefits to be provided for post 5.4.1978 membership.

Preserved pensions

6.36 The extent to which the benefit to an early leaver from an occupational scheme takes the form of a preserved pension has been steadily increasing in recent years and will grow more rapidly as the preservation law and the contracting-out requirements take increasing effect. The requirement under the preservation law of the 1973 Act is to provide a preserved pension, usually calculated on pensionable service and final pensionable salary at the date of leaving and starting to be paid at the earliest age at which the leaving member would normally have been entitled to receive a pension had he remained in the scheme. Under the contracting-out arrangements the G.M.P. element in the preserved pension of an early leaver is dynamised under whatever method has been chosen (see paragraphs 4.33 and 4.34) until it comes into payment at State pensionable age. The Social Security Act 1985 requires a degree of revaluation of the non-G.M.P. element and the anti-franking provisions of the Health and Social Security Act 1984 require both these increases to be provided. The combined effect of these provisions was illustrated in paragraphs 4.50 et seq, as part of the discussion of legislation.

Preserved pension: death benefits

6.37 The position as to the benefits if an ex-member of a scheme with a preserved pension dies before the pension starts to be paid is briefly as follows.

Capital sum

Substantial life assurance cover expressed as a multiple of pay would have ceased when the person became an early leaver. The rules of the scheme will probably provide for a modest lump sum, often expressed as a return of the ex-member's accumulated contributions, but sometimes expressed as a multiple of the annual amount of preserved pension, to be paid on death in the circumstances mentioned. It is common in insured pension schemes for an ex-member with a preserved pension to be able to opt for continuation, at his own cost but without medical evidence, of the life cover which he enjoyed as a contributing member of the scheme, and it is believed that many such persons do so.

Widow's pension

The preservation requirements of the 1973 Act do not require any benefit to be paid.

As to contracting-out, the G.M.P. amount of the deceased ex-member will have grown to a certain figure at the date of his death, under whatever revaluation method has been adopted, and the widow's G.M.P. of one-half of this amount must be provided if the widow is entitled to State benefits. The amount of the widow's pension under the normal scale of the scheme must also be provided, i.e. the 'quality test' continues to apply. The anti-franking provisions of the 1984 Act have to be taken into account, but we shall not pursue this complex matter here.

6.38 As to an ex-member's death after his pension has started to be paid, the preservation law requires the provisions to be the same as if his pension had started following direct retirement from the scheme instead of on his attainment, as an early leaver, of pension age. Contracting-out and anti-franking lead to complications in practice.

Transfer values

6.39 It is frequently possible to arrange when a member of a scheme moves to a new scheme upon a change of employment that a payment should be made by the trustees of the first scheme to the trustees of the second scheme in cancellation of any other benefits to which the member was entitled as an early leaver from the first scheme. Such a payment is often referred to as a 'transfer value'. As explained in paragraph 3.12, a member's right to request such a payment has been introduced under the Social Security Act 1985.

Public sector transfer values

6.40 There is a widespread network of arrangements of this type in the public sector. This is based on standard tables of factors which are applied to the amounts of preserved benefit which would otherwise have been provided. Preserved pensions in the public sector are commonly of high quality in that their amount is dynamised in line with increases in prices both while the benefit rights are preserved and after they start to be paid. The transfer value factors reflect the high quality, and therefore high capital value, of the preserved benefits. There is laid down a detailed procedure for the application of these factors, and for the translation of the amount received by the transferring member's new scheme into a period of credited service in that scheme.

Private sector transfer values

6.41 The situation is different in the private sector, in that there are no standard tables of factors. If the trust deed and rules of an occupational scheme provide for the payment of transfer values, the trustees will need to discuss with their advisers the method by which transfer values should be calculated. The principle that the transfer value of a leaving member should be calculated as the capital equivalent of the preserved benefits which could otherwise have been provided is almost universally adopted, since this provides broad equity between the member who leaves with preserved benefits and the member who leaves with payment of a transfer value, and as noted in paragraph 3.12 this principle has been incorporated in the 1985 Act. The technicalities of the subject are considered in Chapter 19, but it will be clear to the reader that assumptions on such matters as interest rates and mortality rates have to be made in order to place a capital value on preserved benefits, and the trustees of a scheme therefore require actuarial advice in this connection.

Section 32 annuities

6.42 The above discussion of transfer values has been in the context of a payment from one set of pension scheme trustees to another when an employee moves to the new pension scheme. This is indeed the appropriate use of the word 'transfer'. A rather different transaction has in recent years been included under the general heading of 'transfers' and we therefore mention it here although it is not strictly a transfer.

6.43 Section 32 of the Finance Act 1981 provides that if the trustees of a pension scheme have the power to provide the benefits under the rules by purchase of an annuity policy, and if they decide to exercise this power to provide the preserved pension of an early leaver by the purchase of a deferred annuity policy in the early leaver's name, the scheme rules may give the leaver the right to decide from which insurance company the trustees should purchase the policy. A member's right to such an arrangement has been introduced by the 1985 Act. Many insurance companies offer such annuities, which are often sold on the basis of the expected future proceeds on various assumed future yields. It is not easy for the leaver to weigh the attractions of this against the increases that might be granted on the deferred pension which he could have preserved for him in the scheme.

CHAPTER 7

MISCELLANEOUS POINTS OF PENSION SCHEME DESIGN

MISCELLANEOUS POINTS OF PENSION SCHEME DESIGN

7.1 Many of the matters that have to be settled when a pension scheme is being set up are of little actuarial importance. Some points that are of actuarial interest are discussed in this chapter.

Membership

7.2 The question of whether a particular employee becomes a member of the pension scheme of his employer depends both on whether he is eligible for membership and on whether membership is voluntary or compulsory. As noted in paragraph 4.48 the law has a bearing on this matter in that the Social Security Pensions Act 1975 lays down the principle of equal access for men and women to membership of an occupational pension scheme. The principle is that membership of a scheme is to be open to both men and women on terms which are the same as to age and length of service needed for becoming a member and as to whether membership is voluntary or obligatory.

Eligibility for membership

7.3 The rules of a pension scheme will define the class or classes of employee eligible for membership. They will also define the length of any 'waiting period' of employment which the employee must serve before becoming eligible for membership, and also any upper and lower age limits for entry to membership. In some schemes persons are eligible for admission to the scheme as soon as they enter the employment, while in others a waiting period is imposed. At the time of writing both types of arrangement are common, with neither type predominating. A waiting period has the effect of reducing the administrative burden on the pension scheme which would be caused by the entry and almost immediate withdrawal of numerous transitory employees. Power is often taken to waive the waiting period in special cases, e.g. when a transfer value is being received from another scheme and a hiatus would be inconvenient. An employee who is not accruing pension rights because he is serving such a waiting period must participate in the State scheme for this period.

7.4   The following points in respect of the equal access legislation may be noted.

(i)   Different upper age limits for the admission of men and women are permitted in a scheme which has different normal pension ages for men and women. The age limit may be lower for the sex with the lower normal pension age, provided that the period between the upper age limit for entry and normal pension age is either the same for both sexes or less for the sex with the lower pension age. Thus in a scheme with a normal pension age of 65 for men and 60 for women and a maximum admission age of 60 for men the maximum admission age for women may be set anywhere from 55 to 60.

(ii)   A rule which gives a discretion to the scheme administrators such that one person may be treated more, or less, favourably than another in connection with entry to the scheme does not contravene the equal access requirements so long as the rule does not provide for the distinction to be exercised so as to discriminate between men and women.

Voluntary or compulsory membership

7.5   The issue of voluntary or compulsory membership hardly arises in a scheme to which the member is not required to contribute (usually referred to as a 'non-contributory' scheme) since an employee has nothing to lose by joining the scheme. When a contributory scheme is being set up for the first time by an employer, existing employees who are eligible to join are almost always allowed to choose whether to do so or not; it is not practical (and perhaps not legally possible) to compel them to join. The rules of the scheme (as referred to in the contract of employment) will determine whether entrants to the employment after the scheme has been set up will or will not be required to join as soon as they become eligible for membership.

7.6 The main argument for compulsion is that if membership is voluntary and an employee chooses not to join, the employer may nevertheless feel an obligation to provide a pension when such an employee retires after many years of service. If the employer does not provide a pension from his own resources he may be subject to criticism which may be damaging even though ill-informed; if the employer does provide a pension, employees who chose to join the scheme and have therefore helped to pay for their own pensions may be aggrieved. A further point to be noted is that if membership is voluntary younger members will tend not to join. This obviously has the effect of reducing the numbers and increasing the average age of members compared with the position arising from compulsory membership. As will be explained in Chapter 31, the membership distribution by age and sex is one factor in the financial appraisal of contracting-out, and the effect on average age of voluntary membership may be a marginal influence in this connection.

Qualification for benefit

7.7 The rules of a pension scheme may provide that, even when an employee has completed the period of employment if any necessary for eligibility, and has joined the scheme, he must complete a stated period of membership of the scheme before being covered for certain benefits on the full normal scale of the scheme. If, however, an employee is to be contracted-out by virtue of membership of a scheme it is in principle necessary for him to accrue retirement pension rights, and for a married male member to be covered for the prescribed accrual of widow's pension rights, immediately upon entry.

7.8 A waiting period may, however, be imposed in respect of entitlement to cover for such benefits as a capital sum on death in service and an ill-health pension without offending against the contracting-out requirements. The general argument for such a waiting period is that it helps to concentrate the resources of the scheme on longer serving members who have established themselves as stable employees. On the other hand, the members' wish to be covered for the full range of benefits as soon as possible, and the employer's wish to be seen to be a good employer, have tended over the years to reduce and in many cases to eliminate waiting periods. Such periods do not in any event always in practice serve their purpose, since if an employee dies or suffers serious ill-health before having completed a waiting period an employer will often feel obliged to provide a benefit even though this is not promised under the rules of the scheme.

Discretionary augmentation

7.9　Although the main benefit scales of a pension scheme will be precisely set down in the trust deed and rules, it is common for these documents also to confer upon the trustees a power to increase benefits in individual cases to such extent as they decide, often subject to the consent of the employer. This is usually referred to as a power of discretionary augmentation. The benefits including augmentation have, of course, to be within Revenue limits. The ability to make discretionary augmentation of benefits in individual cases is often very useful, but it is important that there should not be confusion or uncertainty as to whether the cost of a particular augmentation of benefit is to be met from the resources of the scheme or by special contributions of the employer. In general it is therefore necessary to ensure that if the trust deed and rules of a scheme contain a general power of augmentation they also contain appropriate provisions for the meeting of any resulting extra cost.

7.10　One possible use of a discretionary augmentation clause is in the case of a senior executive entering an employment, to whom the employer has promised specially favourable pension arrangements as part of the terms of employment. This is considered further in the more general discussion of senior executive benefits later in this chapter. Another example of the use of discretionary augmentation concerns pension increases. If the rules of a pension scheme simply provide for a stated rate of increase to be granted on pensions in course of payment each year, this may sometimes be found inflexible. The employer or the trustees may, for instance, desire on a particular occasion to give a larger increase (subject to cost) or to give small pensions a larger proportionate increase than large pensions, on the grounds of greater need, and this is made simpler if the trustees have the flexibility given by a general power of augmentation. We refer to 'the employer or the trustees' because the use of the trustees' discretion in such circumstances is often at the employer's request and would usually require his agreement.

Members' contribution scales

7.11 In designing a pension scheme it is necessary to consider whether or not the members shall be required to contribute. The normal contributions of both the members and the employer are allowed against tax, so that the question of the division of the total cost between them is not very much influenced by tax considerations and can be decided on general policy grounds; some points are now discussed.

Members' contributions and marital status

7.12 It might be thought that if substantial benefits are payable from a pension scheme to widows, the level of a male member's contributions should depend on his marital status. Although at one time differential contribution rates of this type were met with, they are now rare. One reason is that under such an arrangement the administration of the scheme is made more complicated. This is not only because of the obvious need to keep up-to-date records of marital status with consequent changes in the contribution rate of an individual from time to time. A further complication is that if a member who has paid higher contributions at some time during his membership dies or retires in circumstances in which a widow's pension cannot be payable it may be thought necessary to provide for some extra benefit to be granted in respect of the additional contributions. Contracting-out represents a further influence militating against differential contribution rates, because widows' pension rights must accrue during the membership of a contracted-out male employee even for periods during which he is unmarried.

The cost to the employer

7.13 At first sight it might appear obvious that the cost to an employer of a contributory scheme must be less than the cost of a non-contributory scheme, since in the former scheme part of the cost is met by the members. It can be argued, however, that pay and pension costs together will probably be little different be the scheme contributory or non-contributory, because to attract and retain labour the employer with a contributory scheme will have to pay higher wages and salaries than his competitor with a non-contributory scheme in order to offset the cost of the employees' contributions. It is difficult to assess the validity of the above argument in practice. It should be noted that higher wages and salaries lead to higher pensions, so that the question affects the overall scale of the scheme as well as the distribution of costs, and also lead to higher National Insurance contributions by both employee and employer. In the public sector the level, or absence, of pension scheme contributions is taken into account as part of the formal procedures in pay negotiations. In the private sector the argument may well have different weight for hourly paid employees on the one hand and salaried employees on the other.

General arguments in favour of a contributory scheme

7.14 Apart from the question of cost to the employer, arguments in favour of a contributory scheme are as follows.

(i) A contributory scheme is in the nature of a joint venture. Not only will employees take a more active interest in such a scheme but it may, as an area where employees and employer meet, play a part in fostering good relations between them.

(ii) It is desirable that an employee leaving a scheme without entitlement to a preserved pension under the 1973 Act should receive some benefit, and in a contributory scheme a payment equal to the amount of his own contributions, normally with interest, is a way of achieving this. This payment may appear attractive to the member because he has enjoyed tax relief on the contributions that he has paid whereas he receives back, subject to any deduction for C.E.P. (see paragraph 4.30), the gross amount less tax at the rate of only 10 per cent.

(iii) Another aspect of the C.E.P. arrangement is that, since the law provides for part of a C.E.P. to be recovered from any refund due to the member, a contributory scheme fits in with this aspect of the legislation.

General arguments in favour of a non-contributory scheme

7.15 Arguments often advanced in support of a non-contributory scheme are as follows.

(i) It is administratively simpler, since it is not necessary to collect contributions from the members and to keep accounts of each member's contributions with interest for withdrawal benefit purposes.

(ii) An employer will sometimes think it an advantage if the employees have no voice in the affairs of the scheme, and it may be easier to deny them representation on the management committee or amongst the trustees if they have not contributed to the scheme. The procedure for the amendment of rules may thereby be simplified. This argument is now rather outdated.

(iii) There are advantages in making a pension scheme compulsory, since if membership is optional the employer may nevertheless feel a moral obligation to make some provision after the retirement of a member who chose not to join the scheme. It is obviously easier in practice to make compulsory a non-contributory scheme than a contributory scheme.

(iv) If it is desired to cut down scheme pensions because of an increase in State pensions it may be easier to do so if the member has not contributed towards the cost of scheme pensions.

Contributory or non-contributory: the general position

7.16 It will be noted that some of the arguments outlined above reflect differing attitudes in a wider context. A contributory scheme has its supporters as an area where employer and employee can meet but others advocate a non-contributory scheme because, it is asserted, representatives of the employees need not be brought in. The decision as to whether a new scheme is to be contributory or not will be made in the light of the employer's overall employment policy and his general attitude to his employees. Contributory schemes outweigh non-contributory schemes in the United Kingdom at the present time; a current estimate is that in the private sector roundly three-quarters of members are in contributory schemes.

The general level of members' contributions

7.17 If a scheme is to be contributory it is necessary to decide on the level of the members' contributions. This is usually decided as a matter of policy, contributions being fixed at a level which it is thought reasonable to require the members to bear. It is usual for the members' contributions to be defined by some broad and simple scale. Members' contribution rates generally lie within the range of 3 per cent. to 8 per cent., with a large proportion at the level of about 5 per cent.

Members' contributions to an integrated scheme

7.18 The integration of occupational pensions with State pensions was discussed in Chapter 5. As noted in paragraph 5.14, if the pension scale involves the use of 'pensionable pay' the contributions of members (and probably of the employer) will also normally be defined in terms of pensionable earnings. If a pension scale includes an offset for State pensions but does not involve the concept of pensionable earnings it may nevertheless be convenient to introduce such earnings as a base by reference to which contributions may be defined. If we consider the scale in paragraph 5.13, for instance, it is clear that it would not be appropriate to base contributions to the scheme on full earnings. The arrangement would be potentially unstable, since contributions would be related to full earnings while the pension would not. For the same reason the arrangement would not appear to be fair as between one member and another. Furthermore, it is desirable for contributions to the occupational scheme to tend to fall if the scope and cost of the State scheme rises and this would not be the case if contributions were charged on full earnings.

7.19 In principle the concept of offsetting the State scheme arrangements could be applied directly to the members' contributions. Under such an arrangement the member pays a contribution calculated in some simple way, such as a percentage of earnings; the amount of contributions which the member is required to pay for State flat-rate retirement benefits (not the member's total contribution for social security benefits) is deducted from this total contribution and passed on to the State scheme and the balance is paid to the occupational pension scheme. The employer meets the balance of the cost of the benefits payable from the occupational scheme. Clearly this method is attractively simple in principle. It is, however, very rarely found in practice. The following points on the method are therefore of theoretical rather than practical importance, but they should be noted.

7.20 Since the State scheme is financed on a pay-as-you-go basis, members' contributions to it may well be increased from time to time without corresponding increases in expected State benefits, or with an increase in State benefits not related to the increase in State contributions. When this happens, the balance of the members' contributions payable to the occupational scheme falls, without a corresponding fall in the liabilities of that scheme. The finances of the scheme are therefore disturbed, and it is necessary either for the employer to pay more than he had expected or to increase the total percentage contribution payable by the member. Employers would probably find it difficult to take the latter course. The practical implication of such a scheme is therefore that the employees' contributions could become zero.

7.21 There are also in such schemes problems of presentation, and practical complications, of which the following are examples.

(i) The employer may feel that his scheme, if presented in this way, will appear expensive to members, who will not always realise clearly how large a part of their total contribution is passed on to the State scheme.

(ii) The part of the member's contribution payable to the occupational scheme attracts tax relief as far as his personal tax is concerned, but the part payable to the State does not; this must be allowed for in the administrative arrangements.

(iii) Pensionable earnings for occupational scheme purposes may well not correspond exactly to earnings for State scheme purposes, since the latter include overtime, bonus and other irregular earnings. This complicates the split of the contribution and increases the instability of the part that is paid to the occupational scheme.

(iv) Normally in such schemes there is deducted from the member's contribution only that part of the total contribution to the State scheme which is deemed to relate to State retirement benefits. The member continues to pay separately the State scheme contributions related to other benefits. This not only reduces the simplicity of the arrangement from the member's point of view but also raises the difficulty of deciding how much of the State scheme contribution (which is pay related) should be deemed to apply to the State basic pension (which is flat-rate). There is no official split of State scheme contributions in this respect.

7.22 We deal with the question of the employer's contributions in Chapter 8. The reason that this subject is not dealt with here is that, although it is almost universal for the rate of members' contributions to be settled as a matter of policy and laid down in the rules of the scheme, the question of the employer's contribution rates raises much wider issues and is approached in Chapter 8 as part of the general consideration of how pension costs are met.

Additional voluntary contributions

7.23 The rules of a pension scheme will lay down the normal scale of members' contributions if the scheme is contributory. It is, however, common for schemes to provide for members to make additional voluntary contributions or 'A.V.C.s' should they so desire. Under Revenue rules, a member may pay additional voluntary contributions up to a total amount, inclusive of compulsory contributions, of 15 per cent. of full earnings. Additional voluntary contributions count for tax relief as far as the members are concerned in the same way as compulsory contributions provided that they are made regularly and not discontinued except for good reason. A.V.C. schemes vary widely, but as a broad generalisation they may be divided into two types, firstly those in which the additional benefit is related to the proceeds from the investment of the member's additional contributions and secondly those in which the additional benefit is not so related. This distinction is amplified in the following paragraphs.

A.V.C.s as an investment medium only

7.24 The first type of A.V.C. arrangement, under which the benefit is related to the contributions paid in by the individual, is illustrated by the following three examples. In all these cases it is unusual for the employer to make any contribution. The intention is to provide an additional and tax efficient medium of investment by the member.

(i) Under one type of arrangement the member pays an additional contribution, which may be a fixed money amount or a percentage of pensionable pay. The amount is accumulated for that member in the books of the pension scheme by setting up an individual account credited with a rate of interest which is settled by the trustees from time to time. When a benefit becomes payable under the main rules of the pension scheme, the accumulated amount in the A.V.C account is used to augment the benefits in any way desired by the member. There are no separate assets held in respect of A.V.C.s.

(ii) A second arrangement is similar to the first except that the A.V.C.s are paid over to an insurance company and accumulated in an individual account in the name of the member. The rate of interest guaranteed on the account is usually modest, but bonuses from time to time raise the yield to competitive levels.

(iii) A third arrangement is also similar to the first except that the A.V.C.s are paid over to a building society which sets up an individual account for each member and credits this with a gross rate of interest

Although under (ii) and (iii) the A.V.C.s are invested separately from the main part of the pension scheme, they are legally part of the same trust and the Inland Revenue limits apply to the combined benefits.

7.25 In deciding which of these three methods to employ, the trustees of a pension scheme will consider the following factors amongst others.

(i) If the A.V.C.s are invested within the main scheme it is necessary for the trustees to settle the rate of interest to be granted on these contributions from time to time, at a level which is fair to both the members paying such contributions and the other members. It is not always easy to settle on a correct figure. In many cases the trustees base it on the rate of interest available on short term deposits in the market from time to time, but this rate may vary quite rapidly.

(ii) If investment is with a building society, members must be prepared for substantial variations in the rate of interest credited from time to time. The rate of interest which building societies are able to grant is linked to the rate that they are able to earn on mortgage loans and this rate is not only influenced by market conditions but may also be subject to political influences from time to time.

(iii) If investment is with an insurance company, the rate of interest which is being granted may not always be clear. The contract is usually in the form of a long term accumulation based on a modest guaranteed rate of interest with bonus additions and the bonus arrangements may not always appear wholly straightforward to the members.

7.26 It will be noted that the three types of arrangement outlined above, although providing a benefit linked to the member's contributions, do so by way of an interest accumulation rather than by relating the amounts to the capital values of equity shares and other market investments. The reason for this is that the market values of equity shares and other investments vary widely from time to time and trustees of pension schemes do not in general think it advisable to offer an A.V.C. contract under which the accumulated amount might, because of market conditions, be low at the time of retirement or death of a particular member. The majority of members of pension schemes are not sophisticated in financial matters and it is normally thought better to provide them with a steady interest return on the A.V.C. accumulation, rather than to expose them to the possibility of a heavy loss as well as a substantial gain.

A.V.C.s as an addition to the main benefits

7.27 The discussion so far has been in terms of A.V.C.s as an investment medium. We now turn to another type of A.V.C. contract, in which the benefit promised to the member in return for his A.V.C.s is in much the same form as the benefits promised under the main rules of the scheme. An example of this is the 'added years' arrangement. Typically, there is set down the additional contribution depending on age and sex which the member must pay during the remainder of his membership in order to purchase one additional year of pensionable service. The contribution will normally be expressed as a percentage of pensionable pay from time to time, in exactly the same way as the compulsory contributions. The member can choose how many additional years to purchase subject to Revenue limits on contributions and on benefits.

7.28 It will be noted that this type of A.V.C. contract is different in principle from those described previously. In those other contracts, the intention is simply to provide the member with a medium for voluntary investment of his own money, with no contribution by the employer. In the added years arrangement, however, the extra benefit that the member is buying by way of A.V.C.s is the. right to have pensionable service greater than his actual pensionable service counted when a benefit becomes payable. In a 'final pay' scheme the amount of such an additional benefit, and therefore its cost, cannot be known until the benefit becomes payable. It is therefore only by chance that the contributions paid by the member would exactly meet the cost of his extra benefit. This type of contract therefore raises difficulty as to its funding, because the individual member will in practice either pay too much or too little towards the cost of his additional benefits. The arrangement is suitable only in a scheme where this feature can be accommodated without unfairness to the members who do not pay A.V.C.s, and this usually means that the scheme must be one in which the employer meets the 'balance of cost'. This leads to the wider question of employer's contributions, which is discussed in Chapter 8.

Interest guarantees

7.29 A feature of pension scheme arrangements which used to be met with quite frequently but has now virtually disappeared is the provision of an 'interest guarantee' by the employer. The typical arrangement was that if in a particular period the rate of interest earned on the funds was less than a rate prescribed in the rules, the employer would pay into the fund an amount equal to the shortfall. It is instructive to consider why this feature is now seldom encountered.

7.30 In the first place, the arrangement is not a very rational one. If the guaranteed rate of interest is very low it is likely to have no practical effect. If it is higher than the long-term rates likely to be obtainable in the market, and the actuarial calculations in connection with the scheme had been made on this higher rate, the security of the members' benefits is dependent to an undesirable degree on the continuing prosperity of the employer, since this determines his ability to continue to make the payments involved.

7.31 An equally important reason for the decline of this feature arises from considerations of investment policy. The rate of interest earned on the funds measured simply by the flow of investment income each year may be low because the trustees buy equity shares or properties with a comparatively low yield instead of fixed interest securities. As explained in Chapter 20, these investments are purchased in the expectation of growth in income, and hence in capital value, and a low initial income is accepted; in these circumstances it would not be appropriate for the employer to be required to make interest guarantee payments. If it were desired to implement such a guarantee this would have to be in terms of the change in capital values as well as the level of income from year to year, and the matter would become extremely complicated.

Winding up of a scheme

7.32   Under trust law it is necessary for a trust deed to have a provision which limits its term, and in the past this was normally done by the inclusion of a formal clause which linked the duration of the trust to the lifetime of the last survivor of some defined class of publicly identifiable persons, e.g. members of the Royal Family. The whole matter of winding up was commonly thought of as one of no great practical importance.

7.33   With the increasing complexity of industrial and commercial life, however, pension schemes are to an increasing extent wound up or changed in some fundamental way, in whole or in part. Partial discontinuance is often encountered when a company of a group is sold to another group, because it is then very common for the part of the pension scheme of the first group which relates to the members of the scheme who are employees of that company to be passed over to the pension scheme of the second group. The precise terms of the appropriate provision in the trust deed and rules of the first scheme are then very important, because as noted in Chapter 8, the pension rights of the transferring employees in the second scheme may well be influenced by the amount of the assets passing over. The matter is discussed in more detail in Chapter 30.

7.34   The effect of pension scheme legislation in a winding up is broadly as follows.

(i)   As far as tax approval is concerned, the rules of a scheme may provide that, in the event of a surplus arising on the winding up, benefits may be augmented within Revenue limits, but the rules of the scheme must provide for the return of any eventual surplus (after any such augmentation) to the employer. The amount so returned will be liable to tax and the surplus may not be paid direct to a third party to be applied for some other purpose. The winding up rule must provide for the benefits to the members at the time of winding up to be in the form of a preserved pension or a transfer payment; the winding up rule may not provide for a refund of his own contributions to any member who is an employee still in service when the scheme is wound up.

(ii) The preservation requirements under the 1973 Act require preserved benefits to be provided for members in service when a scheme is wound up as though the relevant employments had terminated, subject to adequacy of resources.

(iii) The contracting-out requirements relate to the order of priorities on a winding up, and the likely sufficiency of resources in that event.

Actuarial valuations

7.35   The trust deed and rules of a scheme will include provision for actuarial valuations to be made from time to time; it is normal for such investigations to be made every three years. The events that flow from the results of an actuarial investigation will depend partly on whether the contributions of the employer are laid down on a 'balance of cost' basis or otherwise, as discussed in the next chapter.

Senior executive retirement benefits

7.36   This chapter is concerned with miscellaneous points of pension scheme design, and the question of senior executive retirement benefits falls conveniently under this heading, because there are virtually no special points of law or actuarial theory; the matter is simply one of designing the pension arrangements to meet whatever special requirements are decided on.

7.37   It is a very widespread practice to provide special retirement benefits for senior employees. This received special impetus in the United Kingdom during periods when increases in the direct pay of such persons were restricted, so that retirement benefits became one of a number of alternative ways of effectively providing extra remuneration. Although that particular aspect is of less importance at the time of writing, it remains the case that most organisations find special retirement benefit terms a useful means of attracting and retaining people with special skills and abilities. The following aspects of the subject are discussed below.

Eligibility for membership
Various aspects of benefits and contributions
Funding structure

Eligibility for membership

7.38 It is necessary to settle how the membership of a senior scheme is chosen. It is common for the employer to have virtually complete discretion in this matter; it would be possible to make entry automatic upon the attainment of certain specified grades of employment or specified salary levels but in practice more flexibility is found to be desirable. The matter is very much one of policy; one group of companies may have many hundreds of members in a senior executive scheme, while another group of similar size may provide senior executive retirement benefits to very much fewer persons than this.

Various aspects of benefits

7.39 In many senior schemes the aim is to provide a package of benefits approaching the maximum scales permitted under Inland Revenue rules. Because of this, coupled with the fact that a certain flexibility is often desired, it is sometimes decided that the rules of a senior executive scheme shall not be absolutely specific in setting down the scales of benefit. The effect of the trust deed and rules is to permit benefits within Revenue limits, and it is left to the employer to specify in individual cases what the benefits are to be. Thus for example a person entering a senior executive scheme might become entitled to a pension at normal pension age of 50 per cent., 60 per cent. or two thirds of final pay depending on an individual decision which is made in his case at the time that he is admitted to the senior scheme and may be changed from time to time. Such an arrangement has the advantage of maximum flexibility. On the other hand this would not be thought an advantage by all employers; some prefer the benefit scales in the senior scheme to be virtually the same for everyone.

Normal retirement age

7.40 Many senior schemes provide for a normal retirement age earlier than that for the generality of members. The settling of the retirement age for senior executives is clearly bound up with the employer's general policy for such employees. In some occupations the pace of technical development is such that some specialist personnel find it difficult to keep abreast of current knowledge, and in such circumstances it is obviously convenient for the employer to be able to retire such an employee early with adequate retirement benefits should he so desire. Similarly it is often thought desirable for senior managers to be able to retire early because of the stress of their work. The question of whether an earlier retirement age should apply to all members of a senior executive scheme or should to some extent be at the discretion of the employer is one that has to be settled in the light of the particular circumstances.

Pensionable pay

7.41 The arguments for some degree of offsetting of the State flat-rate pension in the occupational pension scheme are as valid for senior employees as they are for the generality of employees but it is nevertheless quite common for there to be no such offsetting in the pension arrangements of senior executives, largely as part of the stance of providing a fairly generous level of benefits.

Benefit scales

7.42 The scales of benefit to be provided in the various circumstances discussed in Chapters 5 and 6 all need special consideration in the design of a senior executive scheme. As to the rate of pension accrual, it is quite common for a pension of two-thirds of final pay to be provided on retirement at the normal pension age subject to 20 years of employment, with appropriately lower benefits for shorter periods of service. As noted in Chapter 2, Revenue rules permit the provision of a two-thirds pension at the normal pension age after only 10 years of service, but it is unusual even in senior schemes to go quite this far. Under arrangements such as these the total target pension has in principle to include benefits in respect of earlier employments of the person concerned which have been preserved in earlier pension schemes.

As to the level of death benefits, a widow's pension equal to two-thirds (instead of the usual one-half) of the member's pension is common, as is a capital sum of four times salary on death during employment.

Contributions

7.43 As to members' contributions, although some senior executive schemes are contributory it is much more common for them to be non-contributory. Because of the generally high level of benefits, the employer's contribution to senior executive schemes is often a substantial percentage of the earnings of the members. This is not only because the benefits are in themselves generous but also because often an employee is admitted to a senior executive scheme after serving the employer for a not inconsiderable time as a member of the ordinary pension scheme, so that the period remaining until retirement is less than a typical working lifetime and the extra cost of the benefits in respect of the whole period of employment has to be funded over this shorter period, leading to a comparatively high contribution rate.

7.44 Since the same scales of Inland Revenue maximum benefits apply whether or not members of a scheme are contracted-out, higher overall benefits (from State and occupational scheme together) can be provided if members of a scheme participate in the State scheme. For this reason senior executives are sometimes not contracted-out, even in cases where the main group of salaried staff employees are contracted-out.

Funding structure

7.45 Turning to the question of the funding of senior executive benefits, the following three main methods are all encountered in practice.

(i)   The executives belong to the main salaried staff scheme of the employer. The trust deed and rules of this scheme contain a discretion permitting the trustees to augment the benefits of individuals, and the employer lays down a policy as to the use of this augmentation provision for specified senior executives and meets whatever extra cost is involved.

(ii) The persons concerned are members of the main scheme. They are also members of a separate 'topping-up' scheme, open only to selected senior executives, and this scheme provides the balance of whatever total benefits are decided on for these employees.

(iii) Senior executives are not members of the main salaried staff scheme. Their benefits are provided wholly from an entirely separate scheme.

We discuss briefly below the advantages and disadvantages of these three arrangements.

7.46 The first arrangement is not very common. The reason is partly to do with confidentiality. There is, increasingly, member representation on the trustee body of schemes; the trustees drawn from the membership are bound to be aware under arrangement (i) of what is being done for selected individuals and this is often thought a substantial drawback. In some organisations it is considered that the pay levels and retirement benefit arrangements of the most senior group of employees are confidential, and this can hardly be achieved if the totality of their benefits is paid from the main scheme. There are differing views about how important this is. The accounts of companies show information about the salaries of highly paid individuals, and for this reason some employers are not greatly concerned at the prospect of virtually the same information (although now relating to identifiable individuals) being part of the pension scheme administration records. Another factor which cannot be ignored is that the ordinary members of the scheme may object to resources which they consider to be theirs being used to provide enhanced benefits to senior executives. An advantage of arrangement (i) is that it may be easier to reinsure the large death benefits involved if the persons concerned are members of a large scheme.

7.47 Arrangement (ii) is very common. As far as the main scheme is concerned, the senior executives are normal members. Any special arrangement is carried out through a separate scheme which can be kept on a confidential basis. The trustees of the topping-up scheme are, of course, selected accordingly. The difficulty about confidentiality of high pay levels of isolated individuals remains under arrangement (ii), because these individuals are full members of the main salaried staff scheme.

7.48 In cases where this is thought an important point it is sometimes arranged that the senior executives will be normal members of the main salaried staff scheme up to a stated salary level. This might for instance be a multiple of the lower earnings limit of the State scheme from time to time. The separate topping-up scheme then deals not only with a specially favourable pension fraction (or other special benefits) on the salary covered by the main scheme but also with the normal accrual of benefit on that part of the salary not covered by the main scheme.

7.49   Alternative (iii), namely the provision of all senior benefits from an entirely separate scheme, is sometimes encountered in practice; it is partly dependent on the number of persons concerned being sufficient for such a scheme to be viable. Where the main pension scheme is well funded this type of arrangement is sometimes regarded as having a disadvantage in that senior employees do not share in the security of benefits represented by the main scheme.

7.50   It has to be accepted that the contribution levels for a senior executive scheme that contains a comparatively small number of highly paid people tend to be unstable. This is unavoidable and the disadvantage has to be weighed with the other factors noted above.

CHAPTER 8

MEETING THE COST

MEETING THE COST

Introduction

8.1 If it is proposed to set up or alter a pension scheme those concerned will need to have an estimate of the cost. Costs are usually expressed in terms of the capital sums or regular contributions which if set aside in advance and accumulated are expected, on the actuarial assumptions used, to be sufficient to provide the benefits when they fall due. There is no single pattern of regular contributions which is regarded as the normal funding arrangement; indeed, the subject of funding plans has become quite extensive in recent years. This chapter contains the main discussion of funding plans in this book and because of this, and the use of numerical examples, it is rather lengthy. A detailed knowledge of the chapter is not necessary for the understanding of the subsequent text, and some readers will prefer to aim for only a general impression of funding plans at a first reading. In this chapter we first explain why advance provision is generally thought desirable in occupational pension schemes, even though the State pension scheme in the United Kingdom does not involve advance funding, and we set out some criteria by which funding plans may be judged. We then illustrate some of the points involved in different funding plans by way of a simplified example. We end the chapter with a discussion of various different ways of specifying the obligations of members and employers in respect of their contributions to a scheme.

8.2 The following points about the discussion in this chapter should be noted.

(i)   In some countries the rates of price increase and pay increase have over lengthy periods exceeded the rates of return available on investments. In such circumstances there is clearly a strong argument in principle against saving of any sort. We shall not consider such circumstances, but will assume that we are dealing with the United Kingdom or some other economy where advance saving is prima facie a reasonable proposition.

(ii)   In the discussion of principles we shall proceed as if the desirability or otherwise of funding is a completely open question. We ignore, for instance, the fact that a certain level of funding is required by law for schemes used for contracting-out.

(iii)   We will also for simplicity ignore in this chapter the contracting-out requirements in respect of the dynamisation of G.M.P.s of individual early leavers, or members leaving a scheme in a group.

We shall discuss four aspects of funding plans which we shall refer to as security, stability, durability and liquidity.

Security

8.3   At one extreme of pension provision is a method which does not involve advance funding, namely the payment of the benefits, as they fall due, from the current resources of the parent organisation. This method of pension provision is usually referred to as 'pay-as-you-go'. The State pension scheme in the United Kingdom is run on this basis; contributions and the supplement from taxation are set at a level that broadly matches outgo. Another example of a pay-as-you-go arrangement is a pension scheme provided by an employer for a particular employee which consists of an exchange of letters promising certain benefits, with no arrangements for funding; the benefits are to be provided from the employer's resources when the time comes. Such an arrangement constitutes a retirement benefits scheme as far as the Inland Revenue are concerned, and therefore requires Revenue approval in the normal way as outlined in Chapter 2, but this of course does not confer any security of pension rights; security in this case depends on the ability of the employer to pay the benefits from his own resources when the time comes.

8.4   Pay-as-you-go is acceptable for a State pension scheme because the State is, for practical purposes, assured of a continuing existence. The members of the workforce at a particular time are willing to pay for the pensions of the retired population because they have confidence that when they themselves retire the then workforce will provide their benefits. The position is quite different in the case of an occupational scheme, since an employer's business may cease to exist. Thus a fundamental disadvantage of a pay-as-you-go occupational scheme from the point of view of the employee is the lack of security which results from the absence of a fund of investments independent of the employer. Failure of the employer's business would mean the loss of both the job and the pension rights of the employee.

8.5 Quite apart from this possibility of disaster, the extent to which the pension rights of a group of employees are backed by an independent fund often proves important in practice. The issue commonly arises when a part of a business is being purchased by one company or group from another, a subject which is considered in more detail in Chapter 30. The pension rights of the transferring employees will be an important aspect of the negotiations, and the position and prospects of the individuals concerned as to the pension rights they have earned with the first employer are obviously improved if there is a substantial volume of assets to be transferred from the first pension scheme to the second in respect of those rights. The point is an important one in practice, because the amounts involved on the pensions side are often not small in the context of the whole transaction.

8.6 An independent fund of assets in respect of pension rights is not in principle the only means by which security of these rights can be achieved. It would be possible, for example, for pensions to be paid directly from the resources of each employer and for it to be provided by a system of mutual insurance within an industry or other wide grouping of employers that if a particular employer ceased to exist, the pension rights of his employees would be secured by means of support from the other employers participating in the arrangement. This method has obvious difficulties, not least of which is the implication that efficient companies would be paying contributions to a fund which was intended to protect the employees of less efficient companies. Versions of the method are nevertheless used in some countries of Western Europe. Such arrangements are outside the scope of this book, and it will be assumed for present purposes that the existence of a trust fund of investments independent of the employer is an important advantage of funded occupational pension schemes.

8.7 Although the desirability of security is a straightforward concept, its practical interpretation is not always clear cut. For example, the mere existence of a trust fund separate from the assets of the employer obviously does not in itself guarantee security of pension rights. The size of the fund in relation to its liabilities is crucial. In the discussion later in this chapter of various possible funding plans we therefore consider the extent to which the accumulated assets back the promised pension rights in each case.

8.8 Furthermore, it must not be assumed that complete security is an overriding principle. For instance, an employer may intend to provide increases on pensions in course of payment which will maintain their real value to a substantial extent, but may not feel able to undertake to pay the contribution rate which would be required if such future increases were to be guaranteed in the rules of his scheme. In this case it may well be decided to guarantee, and fund for, only a modest rate of pension increase, with additional increases being paid from the employer's revenue, or provided from the scheme with the cost being met by special payments of the employer, when possible. Security of the desired benefits is incomplete, but the members are nevertheless in a better position than if the scheme had not been started because the cost of funding the full desired benefits was judged unacceptable.

Stability

8.9 A further factor involved in pension funding will be clear from consideration of the cash flows involved. If an employer establishes a pension arrangement with pensionable service for the purpose of calculation of benefits counting from the starting date, it is evident that the outgo in the early years is likely to be very small, because the employees who retire in the early years will have been accruing pension benefits for only a short period. With the passage of time the outgo on pensions will rise, both because of the increasing numbers of pensioners and because the average benefit will grow as the number of years of pensionable service increases. Under the pay-as-you-go method an employer may find as time goes on that he has taken on a greater liability than he realised. A funded scheme, on the other hand, imposes the discipline of cost from the start, because the contribution rates are a measure of what has to be set aside regularly in respect of the long-term burden. Funding thus represents an equalisation of burdens over time as well as a discipline.

8.10 Another aspect of the same point is that under a pay-as-you-go scheme the pension outgo for a particular generation of the workforce is met from the labours of a later generation of the workforce. Thus, not only is the outgo not equalised over time but it forms a charge on the goods and services being sold by the employer at the date at which the outgo occurs and not at the date on which the obligations arose. This suggests that a principle in pension funding should be that the cost of the goods or services provided by the employer should be loaded with an appropriate charge for pension rights at the time that the pension rights are accruing.

8.11 The points noted in the previous two paragraphs are concerned with the incidence of the cost to the employer. He will wish to have, for the purpose of his business planning, an estimate of the long term relationship between pension costs and payroll and it is clear that stability of this relationship is in general desirable. The employer will look for a contribution plan which will not be unduly disturbed by random fluctuations in the membership of the scheme. In the examples later in this chapter this aspect of funding is examined under the heading 'Stability'.

Durability

8.12 In the above discussion of stability we have been concerned with the equalisation of pension costs in a continuing scheme, i.e. in what may be thought of as normal circumstances. Although pension schemes are usually designed on the assumption that they will have an indefinitely continuing life, commercial and economic conditions are such that pension schemes often have to be terminated, or merged into another scheme, or in some other way radically changed. A particularly severe test of the funding plan of a pension scheme arises if the flow of new entrants diminishes or ceases but the scheme remains in full force for the existing members. For convenience we shall regard this as a separate aspect of stability; it is discussed in the examples later in this chapter under the heading of 'Durability'.

8.13 In some discussions of funding theory in the past it was expected that the situation referred to in the previous paragraph would arise if an employer's business was in decline. It was assumed that new employees would not be attracted to the undertaking concerned but that existing employees would remain, so that the average age of the workforce would gradually increase. In the United Kingdom there have been in the recent past a number of examples of employers (and sometimes whole industries) in decline, but the effect on the workforce has not in general been that mentioned above. There has indeed been a falling off in the number of young new employees, but many older employees have left under redundancy schemes and in many cases the overall effect on the age distribution has not been great.

8.14 It is nevertheless useful to use a steadily increasing average age as a test of the durability of a funding plan. One reason for this follows from the fact that takeovers and mergers, which were mentioned briefly in paragraph 8.5 and are discussed in more detail in Chapter 30, involve the move of a defined group of employees from one employer to another and therefore from one pension scheme to another. In considering the finances of the pension arrangements in such a case the receiving employer may regard these employees as a closed group whose average age will gradually increase, so that the issues which we discuss under the heading of durability will arise.

Liquidity

8.15 In normal circumstances a pension fund grows for a long period, contributions and investment income being sufficient to meet outgo and provide a balance for investment. Within this broad trend there will be minor fluctuations from year to year because of differences in the numbers of members dying, withdrawing or retiring, the numbers of new entrants, the progression of earnings and so on. It should be asked of a particular method of funding whether, in the face of these random fluctuations, the method is likely in the normal course to provide a supply of cash sufficient to meet outgo year by year without the need to realise investments in a particular year. The question is thus one of liquidity.

8.16 Most methods of funding met with in practice are satisfactory from the point of view of liquidity. In schemes invested in the normal range of securities, properties and other assets the contribution and investment income together normally exceed benefit outgo (unless the scheme is running down because, for example, it has been closed to new entrants) so that there is no problem as to liquidity. In a scheme financed by means of the purchase of deferred annuities the issue does not arise, since the insurance company provides the pensions when the time comes by means of the annuity contracts purchased in the past. Considerations of liquidity may, however, arise in a scheme in which the investments are in the form of units where the income for the underlying investments is automatically reinvested in the units. In these circumstances the regular income of the trustees is limited to the contributions, and it may happen in practice in a mature scheme that the contribution income alone is not always sufficient to cover benefit outgo. In the simplified examples in this chapter, we shall not normally comment on liquidity; it will be assumed that the position is satisfactory.

Different funding plans

8.17 We now consider some simplified examples to illustrate various aspects of funding plans and we subsequently touch on the codification of the many different plans encountered in practice. In these examples we consider a pension scheme which provides a pension to men at age 65 equal to 1/60th of final year's pay for each year of membership. We consider a member who enters at age 30 with pay of £6,000 p.a. For simplicity it is assumed that pay remains unchanged during each year of age and is increased annually, and that contributions (payable entirely by the employer) are paid into the pension scheme at the end of the year. We ignore the possibility of any type of exit before attainment of age 65 and we therefore use compound interest functions only during the period of accumulation. We assume an investment yield of 9 per cent. p.a., a rate of increase of general levels of earnings of 8 per cent. p.a. and no promotional increases. On these assumptions pay in the year of age 64 to 65 will be £6,000 increased by 8 per cent. p.a. compound for 34 years, giving £82,141 and the

pension at age 65 will be 35/60ths of this amount, namely £47,916
p.a. We assume that, when allowance is made for the increases to
be provided on pensions in course of payment and for benefits on
death after retirement, the capital required at age 65 for each £1 of
initial amount of annual pension to the member is £11, so that the
total capital required at age 65 is £527,076. These huge figures do
not indicate that the member will be very highly paid at
retirement; they reflect instead the fall in the value of the pound
implied by pay increases at the rate of 8 per cent. The various
different funding plans now considered represent different ways of
accumulating the required amount at age 65.

Capital sum in advance

8.18   As an example of an extreme course of action we consider
the payment of a capital sum when the member enters the
employment, sufficient to fund the whole of the pension liability.
This capital sum is calculated as the amount required at age 65
discounted for 35 years at the assumed rate of interest of 9 per
cent. per annum, giving a required amount of £25,820.

8.19   The proposition is therefore that a capital sum equal to
more than four times annual pay should be paid into the pension
scheme in respect of this new entrant. It is obvious that it would be
out of the question to follow this funding plan in practice. The first
objection to the plan is that the employer might not be able to
afford it; the profits which will accrue to him from the work of the
employee during the first year are hardly likely to be so large as to
support the cost of pension rights for 35 years' service. On the
other hand, he would not have to make any contribution for the
persons already in his employment, since their pension rights
would have been funded on entry. This objection is therefore not
conclusive. A second objection is that the employer's recruitment
policy may well result in irregular numbers of new entrants to the
pension fund from one year to another, implying under this
method of funding greatly varying capital sum payments by the
employer into his pension scheme from year to year. It would not
be possible to plan the finances of the company rationally in these
circumstances. A third objection is that, even if the required sum
was calculated accurately on the basis of a set of actuarial
assumptions, these are unlikely to be borne out in practice. For
instance, the new employee might leave after very short service

with small benefits. A once-for-all payment does not permit the regular adjustments in the light of experience which can be made to more gradual funding plans. From the point of view of the member the plan would have the great attraction that the whole of his expected pension benefits for the remainder of his working life were fully secured at the date of entry. Comments on this funding plan are therefore as follows.

Security

8.20 Security is highly satisfactory for the member in that the whole of his prospective pension rights are secured from the start.

Stability

8.21 The call on the employer's resources is highly unstable. It may be noted that an employer whose business was purchased after he had set up pension rights for numerous new employees under this plan would certainly consider that the apparent profitability of his business, on which the terms of purchase would have been based, had been distorted by the funding method used.

Durability

8.22 This method represents the ultimate in durability, in that the whole of the pension provision is secured immediately so that subsequent unexpected events do not cause the employer, or the trustees of the pension scheme, any difficulties. We do not analyse this very artificial funding plan further.

Capital sum funding on retirement

8.23 We next consider, as the other extreme of plans involving a degree of funding, the payment of the capital cost of a benefit into the pension scheme at the instant that the benefit starts to be paid. For capital sum benefits this is, of course, a pay-as-you-go system. For a pension it involves the payment into the scheme at the time that the pension starts to be paid of an amount equal to the assessed capital cost of the pension. In the example it involves the payment into the scheme when the member attains age 65 of £527,076, which is equal to over six times pay at the time.

Security

8.24 Under this plan the member is provided with full security once he has retired, but there is no security separate from the employer's business during the years that the pension rights are accruing. Thus this method of funding is not very satisfactory from the point of view of security.

Stability

8.25 This funding plan has nothing to be said for it from the point of view of stability, since no payments were made by the employer during the years in which the pension rights were accruing and a large payment is made in the year of retirement; there is no broadly predictable and stable charge from one year to another.

Durability

8.26 If the flow of new entrants to a pension scheme diminishes or ceases this may be because the employer concerned is in decline, either because the whole industry concerned is in decline or because the particular employer is losing ground. In either case, circumstances are likely to be difficult for the employer. Under this funding plan, however, he would have to continue to find large sums of money when each member retired and this would obviously become more and more difficult as the workforce and the profitability of the employer declined with the passage of time. This method of funding is therefore unsatisfactory from the point of view of durability.

Regular contributions

8.27 We turn to more orthodox funding plans, of which we shall consider six examples. We will investigate the contribution required to be paid, and the amount of the fund required, at each age. It will be appreciated that in practice the contribution rate is settled as a percentage of total payroll; the analysis by age is necessary to reveal the basic structure of each plan. We shall ignore any part of the fund in respect of persons already on pension.

Plan A

8.28 Under the first plan that we consider, the aim is simply to provide a fund sufficient to cover at any time the pension rights that the member has accrued at that time based on his then level of pay, and thus to provide assets which would be sufficient, if the scheme were discontinued, to provide the member with the rights which he would have enjoyed as an individual early leaver if subject only to 1973 Act preservation. For this reason, this plan is sometimes described as 'Discontinuance Funding'. Various figures are as follows.

(1) Pension accrued at end of first year
(1/60th of £6,000) .... £100 p.a.
(2) Capital needed at age 65 to provide
pension in (1) £1,100
(3) First year's contribution = (2) discounted
for 34 years at 9% p.a. £59
(4) (3) as % of £6,000 .... 1.0%
(5) Pay in year of age 49 to 50 .... £25,894
(6) Accrued pension at age 50 = 20/60ths
of (5) .... £8,631 p.a.
(7) Capital needed at 65 for pension in (6) £94,941
(8) Fund at age 50 = (7) discounted for 15
years at 9% p.a. £26,065
(9) Fund in (8) as multiple of annual pay 1.01
(10) Pay at age 63 .... £76,056
(11) Accrued pension at age 64 = 34/60ths of
(10) £43,098
(12) Capital at age 65 for pension in (11) £474,078
(13) Capital needed at age 65 for total
pension £527,076
(14) Contribution at age 65 = (13) − (12) £52,998
(15) Pay at age 64 .... £82,141
(16) (14) as % of (15) 64.5%

8.29 The reasoning underlying these figures will probably be clear. Item (1) reflects the fact that the aim is simply to take account of pay in the year ended on the date that the calculation is being made, and not projected final pay. At the end of the first year, the member has accrued pension rights equal to 1/60th of his pay during that year. The contribution required is the present capital value of those rights, as shown in item (3). As to the fund at age 50 (this age being chosen arbitrarily), we need to calculate the present capital value of the pension that has accrued immediately before attainment of that age, namely 20/60ths of salary at age 49, giving the amount of pension shown in item (6) and the capital value shown in item (8). The fund includes the contribution paid at age 50 in respect of the 20th year. The contribution needed immediately before attainment of age 65 is calculated by deducting the fund accumulated at age 65 as a result of the investment of the first 34 contributions from the total sum required at age 65.

8.30 Let us now suppose that the scheme has 35 members, one at each exact age from 31 to 65; all entered at age 30 and have therefore accrued the appropriate number of years of pensionable service at the date that the calculation is being made. We will assume that interest rates and pay increases have always been as expected so that funds have been accumulated in line with the liabilities. We are assuming that there are no promotional increases in pay (see paragraph 8.17) and since we are dealing with all members at the same date, there are no differences in pay from one member to another due to inflation. Each member therefore has the same annual rate of pay, which we will take as unity without defining the units. The contributions now to be paid for the members aged 31 and 65 are 1 per cent. and 64.5 per cent. respectively of pay (from items (4) and (16) of the above table). The fund held for the member aged 31 immediately after payment of the contribution is 0.01 times pay (because the fund is simply the amount of the contribution just paid). The fund for the member aged 50 is 1.01 times pay in the previous year (from item (9) of the above table) and the fund for the member aged 65 is 6.42 times pay. This is obtained by dividing item (13) by item (15) in the table, or alternatively it can be calculated as simply

$$\frac{35}{60} \times 11, \text{ from the data of paragraph 8.17}$$

8.31 Similar calculations over the whole range of ages lead to the figures shown in the following table.

Age	Year's contribution as percentage of pay per cent.	Fund as multiple of pay
31	1.0	.01
32	1.1	.02
33	1.3	.03
34	1.5	.05
35	1.8	.07
36	2.1	.09
37	2.4	.11
38	2.7	.14
39	3.1	.18
40	3.5	.21
41	4.0	.25
42	4.6	.30
43	5.2	.36
44	5.9	.42
45	6.7	.49
46	7.5	.57
47	8.5	.66
48	9.6	.76
49	10.8	.88
50	12.1	1.01
51	13.6	1.15
52	15.3	1.32
53	17.1	1.50
54	19.2	1.71
55	21.5	1.94
56	24.1	2.19
57	26.9	2.48
58	30.1	2.81
59	33.6	3.17
60	37.5	3.57
61	41.8	4.03
62	46.7	4.53
63	52.0	5.09
64	57.9	5.72
65	64.5	6.42
Total	597.2	54.24
Total expressed in terms of total payroll (= 35 units)	17.1	1.55

8.32   It will be obvious to the reader that if, immediately after the date at which the above table was drawn up, the member age 65 retired and a new member entered at age 30, and interest earnings and pay increases were as expected, calculations one year later would again lead to a fund of 1.55 times pay and an overall contribution of 17.1 per cent. of pay. The data would be identical except that pay would be 8 per cent. higher. The amount of the contribution and the fund would of course be 8 per cent. higher, because pay had increased by this amount. Taking pay per head at the beginning of the year as unity, the position (expressed in multiples of the pay of one individual at the beginning of the year) would therefore be as follows.

Time	Fund	Contribution
0	54.24	5.97
1	58.58	6.45

It may be helpful to show how this position arises through the working of the fund; the process is as follows. It is assumed for simplicity that the cost of the benefit to the retiring member is paid out as a capital sum.

Fund at time 0	54.24	
Benefit paid at time 0	6.42	
Residual fund at time 0+	47.82	
Interest at 9% for year	4.30	
Fund at time 1 before contribution	52.12	
Contribution at time 1	6.45	
Fund at time 1 after contribution	58.57	c.f. 58.58

Security

8.33   As to security of benefits, the plan involves the accumulation of a fund (equal to 1.55 times payroll in the example) sufficient to cover the accrued pension rights based on pay at the time. This represents the level of finance required to fund the preserved pension to which an early leaver is entitled under the preservation law of the 1973 Act referred to in Chapter 3. As indicated below, however, it does not follow that this level of funding is satisfactory from the point of view of security.

8.34 It was indicated in paragraph 8.5 that a more significant aspect of security is the position if an appropriate part of the fund is transferred to another pension scheme when a part of the membership moves from one employer to another upon a takeover or merger. Suppose for simplicity that pay levels in the two employments, and the provisions of the two pension schemes, are identical, that we are dealing with the 35 members and the amount of fund shown in the example and that it is desired that the transferring members should be credited with past service pension rights in their new scheme which effectively continue without any loss in value the rights that they had accrued in their previous scheme. This is to be achieved by granting the employees a year of pensionable service in the new scheme for each such year in the original scheme. The past service credits to be granted in the new scheme will eventually give rise to benefits based on the final pay of the persons concerned. Under the funding plan now being considered, however, the amount of the fund to be passed over is equal to the capital value of the accrued pension rights based on pay at the date of transfer and not on projected final pay. The amount transferred would therefore be inadequate to cover the liabilities taken on by the new scheme.

8.35 It can be argued that if Plan A was the normal funding plan used by virtually all employers, the amount received by the second scheme would be the same as the amount held by the second scheme in respect of similar employees who had been members of the second scheme from the start, so that the position might be wholly acceptable. While this is true, it is common in practice to employ funding plans in which allowance is made for expected future pay increases, so that the amount transferred would be regarded as inadequate and the question of who would make up the difference would need to be settled as part of the agreement. If no further resources were made available the members would lose by the change, since the assets in hand are sufficient to fund the past service rights only on current pay levels; irrespective of whether the rights are preserved in the first scheme or transferred to the second, benefits related to final pay would accrue in the new scheme only from the date of transfer.

8.36 A different aspect of security is that it has become increasingly common in recent years for the annual accounts and report of trustees of a directly invested pension scheme to have attached to them a statement by the actuary to the effect (if such be the case) that the assets would be sufficient, on a winding up, to secure the pensions then in payment to the retired members and the accrued pension rights (on current pay levels) of the active members. This degree of security of accrued pension rights implies as a minimum the level of discontinuance funding under discussion. If, however, it is planned to achieve this level and no more, there is a clear risk that in some years it would not be possible to give the desired actuarial statement. For instance, suppose that a fund accumulated by this method exactly matched the discontinuance liabilities at the beginning of a particular year, the experience up to that time having been precisely as expected, and that in the year concerned the experience continued to follow the basis except that the pay increase was in excess of that expected. At the end of the year the fund would have increased by virtue of the investment return over the year and the contribution paid during the year, but the fund at the end of the year would not match the then liabilities (because they would have been raised by the excess pay increase). The fund would therefore be insolvent on a discontinuance assessment and the desired statement could not be given. In practice the various features of the financial experience of a pension scheme are constantly deviating from the basis, so that if a scheme was funded by the plan under consideration the position in practice might well be that sometimes the scheme was solvent and sometimes insolvent on a discontinuance basis. The trustees would certainly prefer a funding plan somewhat above discontinuance funding, since this would enable the scheme to absorb a degree of unfavourable experience while still remaining solvent on a discontinuance basis.

Stability

8.37   A question mentioned in paragraph 8.10 in the discussion of stability was whether the funding plan leads to a fair charge in respect of pension costs in the year concerned. This is not the case under Plan A if we consider different ages individually. At the youngest age, for instance, the contribution is sufficient to fund the year's pension rights based only on that year's pay, whereas the pension will in fact be based on the final year's pay. The contribution cannot be regarded as an adequate provision for the true pension cost. On the other hand, the contribution paid at age 65 covers not only the cost of the pension which accrues in the year of age 64 but also the extra cost involved in basing the 34/60ths pension earned in previous years on pay from age 64 to age 65 instead of pay from age 63 to age 64. This contribution is therefore substantially greater than a fair charge for the year concerned. Over the membership as a whole the question is whether a contribution of 17.1 per cent. is a reasonable measure of cost. We shall be better able to answer this question when the later examples in this chapter have been studied.

8.38 It should be mentioned that some practitioners would regard the discussion of the previous paragraph as begging the whole question of whether the pension cost of a pay increase should be provided for in the year that the pension accrues (by incorporating an allowance for expected future pay increases in the calculations of cost) or in the later year that the pay increase occurs (on the lines of Plan A). The reader will realise from all that has gone before that our stance in this book is generally to regard the cost of a particular year's accrual of pension rights as including the effect of expected future pay increases.

8.39 We turn to the question of whether Plan A is likely, in the normal course of events, to produce a predictable and stable charge from one year to another. On the face of it, the plan fails to satisfy this requirement, since the contribution paid at the youngest age is 1.0 per cent. of salary while that paid at the oldest age amounts to 64.5 per cent. of salary. This is not, however, conclusive, because in practice the workforce would normally consist of a spread of persons of various ages and length of membership, and the average percentage contribution assessed over the whole of the payroll might not vary very greatly from one year to another. If in our example a steady flow of new entrants maintained the overall distribution unchanged as members retired, the contribution rate would, of course, remain unchanged. The reader will be able to judge from the figures in paragraph 8.31 the extent to which random changes in the age distribution would lead to deviations of the overall contribution rate from the figure of 17.1 per cent. shown.

8.40 It is of course the case that if a new scheme was being set up with one member at each age as in the example but with no past service counting, the contribution rate to cover the accrual of benefits in the first year would be much less than 17.1 per cent. This will be obvious from the fact that the contributions at the older ages in the table of paragraph 8.31 have a large element to cover the cost of the year's pay increase operating on the past service rights, and there would be no past service rights in the situation envisaged in this paragraph. The contribution rate would gradually rise to 17.1 per cent. over a period of 35 years.

8.41 There is a clear difficulty in respect of Plan A in a contributory scheme, in that the members' contribution rate might be say 5 per cent. of pensionable pay but only 1 per cent. of pensionable pay is being put aside for the youngest member in the example. In practice each member would need to be entitled to benefits worth at least as much as his own contributions, so that the position would be more complicated than the example indicates.

Durability

8.42 As to the position under Plan A if the flow of new entrants ceased, or the members were regarded as a closed group in the circumstances of a takeover or merger as mentioned in paragraph 8.14, the figures in paragraph 8.31 show that the contribution required rises steeply as the age of the member increases. The average contribution required as the mean age of the workforce increased would thus steadily rise, and this plan is therefore not very satisfactory from the point of view of durability. The administrators of the receiving scheme in a takeover or merger would no doubt observe that if a year-for-year credit was to be granted while assets of only 1.55 times payroll were to be received, the contribution rate of these members regarded as a closed group would rise steeply with time.

Plan B

8.43 We now consider a plan similar to Plan A, in that the aim is to accumulate funds sufficient to provide at any time the preserved pension benefits to which the member would be entitled as an early leaver at that time. Under Plan B, however, we provide for increases of 5 per cent. p.a. on the preserved rights during the period of preservation, in view of the revaluation provisions of the Social Security Act 1985. Various figures are as follows.

(1)	Pension accrued at end of first year (1/60th of £6,000)	£100 p.a.
(2)	Amount in (1) increased at 5% p.a. compound for 34 years	£525 p.a.
(3)	Capital needed at age 65 to provide pension in (2)	£5,775
(4)	First year's contribution = (3) discounted for 34 years at 9% p.a.	£308
(5)	(4) as % of £6,000	5.1%
(6)	Pay in year of age 49 to 50	£25,894
(7)	Accrued pension at age 50 = 20/60ths of (6)	£8,631 p.a.
(8)	Amount in (7) increased at 5% p.a. compound for 15 years	£17,943 p.a.
(9)	Capital needed at 65 for pension in (8)	£197,373
(10)	Fund at age 50 = (9) discounted for 15 years at 9% p.a.	£54,187
(11)	Fund in (10) as multiple of annual pay	2.09
(12)	Pay in year of age 63 to 64	£76,056
(13)	Accrued pension at age 64 = 34/60ths of (12)	£43,098
(14)	Amount in (13) increased at 5% p.a. for one year	£45,253
(15)	Capital at age 65 for pension in (14)	£497,783
(16)	Capital needed at age 65 for total pension	£527,076
(17)	Contribution at age 65 = (16) − (15)	£29,293
(18)	Pay in year of age 64 to 65	£82,141
(19)	(17) as % of (18)	35.7%

The general reasoning is the same as that for Plan A as described in paragraph 8.29.

8.44 Similar calculations over the whole range of ages lead to the figures shown in the following table.

Age	Year's contribution as percentage of pay per cent.	Fund as multiple of pay
31	5.2	.05
32	5.4	.11
33	5.9	.17
34	6.2	.23
35	6.7	.30
36	7.1	.37
37	7.5	.45
38	8.0	.53
39	8.5	.62
40	9.0	.72
41	9.6	.82
42	10.2	.93
43	10.7	1.05
44	11.4	1.17
45	12.0	1.30
46	12.8	1.44
47	13.5	1.59
48	14.3	1.75
49	15.1	1.92
50	16.0	2.09
51	16.9	2.28
52	17.9	2.48
53	18.8	2.69
54	19.9	2.92
55	21.1	3.15
56	22.1	3.40
57	23.4	3.67
58	24.8	3.95
59	26.1	4.25
60	27.4	4.56
61	29.2	4.90
62	30.5	5.25
63	32.2	5.62
64	33.6	6.00
65	35.7	6.42
Total	574.7	79.15
Total expressed in terms of total payroll (= 35 units)	16.4	2.26

8.45 We will not comment in detail on this plan since it is conceptually similar to Plan A. Calculations similar to those of paragraph 8.32 can readily be made. The reader will observe the greater degree of security, stability and durability compared with Plan A, arising from the increase in funding level. As to security, the fund in hand in the example is equal to 2.26 times payroll, compared with 1.55 times payroll under Plan A. Stability is increased since the range of contribution rates from the youngest to the oldest age is much diminished compared with Plan A. It should be noted that the point made in paragraph 8.35 about an actuarial statement on discontinuance solvency for the annual report and accounts continues, in principle, to apply. In other words, in a scheme funded under Plan B, deviations of the experience from that expected might mean that in particular years it would not be possible to give an actuarial statement that the scheme was solvent on discontinuance allowing for 5 per cent. p.a. increases on all the preserved pensions arising. It might, of course, be the case that although such increases were funded for, they were not promised under the rules except to the extent required under the 1985 Act. In that case the actuarial statement on discontinuance solvency would need to cover only any increases so promised.

Plan C

8.46 We turn to a funding plan superficially similar to the first two but with the important difference that allowance is made from the start for the projected level of final pay. Various figures are as follows.

(1) Expected final year's pay .... £82,141 p.a.
(2) Pension accrued at end of first year = 1/60th of (1) .... £1,369 p.a.
(3) Capital needed at age 65 to provide pension in (2) £15,059
(4) First year's contribution = (3) discounted for 34 years at 9% p.a. £804
(5) (4) as % of £6,000 .... 13.4%
(6) Accrued pension at age 50 = 20/60ths of (1) £27,380
(7) Capital needed at 65 for pension in (6) £301,180
(8) Fund at age 50 = (7) discounted for 15 years at 9% p.a. £82,686
(9) Pay in year of age 49 to 50 .... £25,894
(10) Fund in (8) as multiple of pay in (9) 3.19
(11) Contribution needed at age 65 to cover final year's accrual of pension = (3) £15,059
(12) (11) as % of (1) 18.3%

8.47 Under this plan the accrual of pension rights in each of the 35 years concerned is deemed to be equal to 1/60th of the expected final year's pay, giving a constant yearly accrual of £1,369 p.a. The contribution for the first year is equal to the capital value at age 65 of one year's accrual discounted for 34 years, giving the figure of £804 shown in item (4). The final year's contribution is the capital value at age 65 of the 1/60th pension accrued in the final year, as shown in item (10). The fund at any time is the capital value at that time of the pension rights then accrued.

8.48 Similar calculations over the whole range of ages lead to the figures shown in the following table.

Age	Year's contribution as percentage of pay per cent.	Fund as multiple of pay
31	13.4	.13
32	13.5	.27
33	13.6	.41
34	13.8	.55
35	13.9	.70
36	14.0	.84
37	14.2	.99
38	14.3	1.14
39	14.4	1.30
40	14.6	1.46
41	14.7	1.62
42	14.8	1.78
43	15.0	1.95
44	15.1	2.11
45	15.2	2.29
46	15.4	2.46
47	15.5	2.64
48	15.7	2.82
49	15.8	3.01
50	16.0	3.19
51	16.1	3.38
52	16.3	3.58
53	16.4	3.78
54	16.6	3.98
55	16.7	4.18
56	16.9	4.39
57	17.0	4.60
58	17.2	4.81
59	17.3	5.03
60	17.5	5.25
61	17.7	5.48
62	17.8	5.71
63	18.0	5.94
64	18.2	6.18
65	18.3	6.42
Total	550.9	104.37
Total expressed in terms of total payroll (= 35 units)	15.7	2.98

Calculations similar to those of paragraph 8.32 can readily be made.

Security

8.49 The pension rights of the members are secured by the fund in hand (equal to 2.98 times payroll in the example) to the extent of the accrued entitlement based on expected final pay. This is a good measure of security, and the method is therefore satisfactory from this point of view. As to the position if another pension scheme is to take on the pension rights for past service in connection with a takeover or merger, the new employer and trustees should be satisfied on the major point of security involved, namely that the assets are sufficient to cover the past service rights allowing for the fact that pensions are to be based on final pay.

Stability

8.50 The percentage contribution for the youngest member is 13.4 per cent. and that for the oldest 18.3 per cent. The method may be said to lead to a fair charge in respect of the pension rights accrued in each year, and, unlike Plan A, the difference between the opening and closing percentage contributions is not very great, so that random variations in the age distribution of the members would not lead to significant variations in the contribution rate. The criterion of stability is well satisfied.

Durability

8.51 The contribution rate required rises with age, but not very markedly. If the flow of new entrants ceased, with a gradual increase in the average age of the membership, the contribution required would increase over the years but not to an unmanageable extent. The funding method is therefore fairly satisfactory from the point of durability.

8.52 The new employer involved in a takeover or merger might perhaps point out that the contribution rate payable while the transfer amount was being accumulated had started at 13.4 per cent. for each employee involved and had gradually risen to 15.7 per cent. (as shown in paragraph 8.48), and that he was being asked to take over the obligation to pay contributions at this level and to meet further increases up to the level of 18.3 per cent. in the final year. Nevertheless, he would probably regard this degree of funding as satisfactory.

Plan D

8.53 Plans A, B and C have a feature in common, namely that in principle the aim is to accumulate a fund which matches the past service liabilities, i.e. the present capital value of the benefit rights arising from pensionable service completed at the date as at which the calculation is being made. The differences between the three plans arise because of different ways of defining the precise benefit rights to be funded for. The contribution rate from time to time is calculated as the rate required to achieve this funding aim. The plans do not involve the calculation of the present value of the benefit rights expected to arise in respect of future service, or of the contributions expected to be paid during such service. We now consider a plan based on a different approach. Under this plan the contribution rate is fixed at the level percentage of pay which, if paid throughout the working life of a new entrant to the employment (assumed to take place at age 30) would provide the necessary resources at retirement at age 65.

8.54 We shall need to calculate the present value at age 30 of a contribution of 1 per cent. of pay, paid into the scheme at the end of each year throughout membership. The function at age 30 to be applied to the initial amount of 1 per cent. of pay in the year of age 30 to 31 is evidently of the form

$$\frac{1}{1.09} + \frac{(1.08)}{(1.09)^2} + \quad + \frac{(1.08)^{34}}{(1.09)^{35}}$$

$$= \frac{\ddot{a}\,\overline{35|}}{1.09} @ \text{ rate of interest i where } 1 + i = \frac{1.09}{1.08}$$

i = 0.926 per cent.

The value of this function is 27.572. We shall also need a corresponding function at age 50 in respect of annual contributions paid from the 51st to the 65th birthdays inclusive; this value is 12.912.

8.55 Various figures are as follows.

(1) Total capital required at age 65 .... £527,076
(2) (1) discounted to age 30 at 9% p.a. £25,820
(3) Present value at age 30 of contribution of
     1% of pay throughout membership
     .01 × £6,000 × 27.572 .... £1,654
(4) Percentage contribution required =
     (2) ÷ (3) 15.6%
(5) (1) discounted to age 50 at 9% p.a. £144,703
(6) Pay in year of age 49 to 50 .... £25,894
(7) (5) as multiple of pay in (6) 5.59
(8) Pay in year of age 50 to 51 .... £27,966
(9) Present value at age 50 of contribution of
     15.6% of pay from age 51 to age 65
     .156 × £27,966 × 12.912 .... £56,331
(10) (9) as multiple of pay in (6) 2.18
(11) Fund at age 50 = (5) − (9) £88,372
(12) (11) as multiple of pay in (6) 3.41

We have no occasion to calculate contribution rates at different ages, because we have settled that the contribution throughout is to be at the rate of 15.6 per cent. of pay calculated in item (4).

8.56 Various figures at age 50 are as follows, expressing all values as multiples of pay from age 49 to age 50.

Present value of total benefits expected to arise from past and future service ((7) above)	5.59
Present value of past service benefits allowing for expected future pay increases ((10) from paragraph 8.45)	3.19
By difference, present value of future service benefits allowing for expected future pay increases	2.40
Fund in hand ((12) above)	3.41
Value of future contributions ((10) above)	2.18

8.57 Similar calculations over the whole range of ages lead to the figures shown in the following table, all amounts being expressed as multiples of pay in the previous year.

Age	Past service liabilities	Future service liabilities	Value of future contributions	Net liabilities = fund
31	.13	4.56	4.53	.16
32	.27	4.46	4.42	.31
33	.41	4.37	4.30	.48
34	.55	4.27	4.19	.63
35	.70	4.17	4.07	.80
36	.84	4.07	3.95	.96
37	.99	3.97	3.83	1.13
38	1.14	3.86	3.71	1.29
39	1.30	3.75	3.59	1.46
40	1.46	3.64	3.47	1.63
41	1.62	3.53	3.34	1.81
42	1.78	3.41	3.22	1.97
43	1.95	3.29	3.09	2.15
44	2.11	3.17	2.96	2.32
45	2.29	3.05	2.84	2.50
46	2.46	2.92	2.71	2.67
47	2.64	2.80	2.58	2.86
48	2.82	2.66	2.44	3.04
49	3.01	2.53	2.31	3.23
50	3.19	2.40	2.18	3.41
51	3.38	2.26	2.04	3.60
52	3.58	2.11	1.90	3.79
53	3.78	1.97	1.76	3.99
54	3.98	1.82	1.62	4.18
55	4.18	1.67	1.48	4.37
56	4.39	1.52	1.34	4.57
57	4.60	1.36	1.20	4.76
58	4.81	1.20	1.05	4.96
59	5.03	1.04	.91	5.16
60	5.25	.88	.76	5.37
61	5.48	.71	.61	5.58
62	5.71	.53	.46	5.78
63	5.94	.36	.31	5.99
64	6.18	.18	.15	6.21
65	6.42	–	–	6.42
Total	104.37	88.49	83.32	109.54
Total expressed in terms of total payroll (= 35 units)	2.98	2.53	2.38	3.13

8.58 The position may be summarised as follows.

	Multiple of payroll
Past service liabilities	2.98
Future service liabilities	2.53
Total liabilities	5.51
Future contributions	2.38
Net liabilities (equal to fund in hand, since experience assumed to be as expected)	3.13

Although the approach differs from that of the earlier plans, calculations on the lines of paragraph 8.32 can again be made.

Security

8.59 The fund in hand (equal to 3.13 times payroll in the example) is somewhat higher than that under Plan C. This is due to the fact that under Plan D the fund not only covers the accrued pension rights based on expected final pay but also provides the resources necessary to permit the future contribution rate to remain at 15.6 per cent. and not to increase with time. The degree of security for the members is thus very high. If the members were transferred to the identical scheme of a new employer and the full amount of the fund were transferred with them, this would be sufficient not only to provide year for year benefits in the new scheme but also to ensure that the future contribution rate in the new scheme need be only that for an entrant at age 30 and not that appropriate to the actual ages at entry.

Stability

8.60 Provided that the average age at entry is in fact equal to that assumed, Plan D leads to a highly stable percentage contribution rate even if the age distribution of the contributing members varies substantially from time to time, and it is therefore very satisfactory from the point of view of stability.

Durability

8.61 This funding method is highly satisfactory from the point of view of durability, since as noted above the dwindling or discontinuance of the flow of new entrants would not necessitate an increase in the percentage contribution rate with the passage of time provided that the assumed average age at entry in the calculations was correctly chosen.

A comparison of funding plans

8.62 It may be helpful to compare various features of Plans A, B, C and D at this stage. The figures of funds and annual contributions, in the stable state (subject to constant escalation) envisaged in our example, are as follows.

Plan	Fund Multiple of total payroll	Contribution Percentage of total payroll
		per cent.
A	1.55	17.1
B	2.26	16.4
C	2.98	15.7
D	3.13	15.6

8.63 Perhaps the first point to discuss is the paradox that the larger the contribution, the smaller the fund. This would evidently not be the case if the contributions had always been at these rates under each plan. To solve this problem it is necessary to return to the past time when the first employee entered at age 30 and to follow the build up of the funds over the next 34 years as succeeding members joined each year. It will be seen from paragraph 8.31 that the amount of the annual contribution built up slowly under Plan A; under the other plans a substantial contribution level built up more quickly. The apparent paradox is therefore due to differences in the time at which contributions were received.

8.64 Another way of investigating this paradox is by the method of paragraph 8.32. In the stable state benefit outgo and 8 per cent. escalation of the past service liabilities are covered by interest on the fund and the amount of the contributions. Although the logic is not complete, this suggests that a larger fund (and hence greater interest) permits a lower contribution.

8.65 Another point that should be noted is that if the basis and data remain stable (except for constant escalation of pay in the data) then so will the fund and contribution rate in terms of payroll. Thus the payment of a lower percentage contribution rate does not mean that at some future date a higher contribution rate must inevitably be paid, or vice versa. Nor does a low level of funding carry the implication that the necessary resources will not be available when each member retires. Provided that the scheme and the flow of new entrants continue, the appropriate resources are provided for each member as he reaches age 65 under each plan, whether the contribution rate is 15.6 per cent. or 17.1 per cent. It is only if the scheme is discontinued, or a takeover or merger occurs, and the funds that have been accumulated at that time become a crucial factor in determining the 'winding up' benefits to each member, that the differences in security consequent upon the different funding levels become apparent. In practice this point is of more importance than it may appear here, because the differences in the contribution rates under different funding plans are usually greater than our example would suggest. It should be noted that in making the comments in this paragraph we are assuming stable data, including past service at each age. We noted in paragraph 8.40 that if a scheme with the age distribution of our example is being started with no past service credits, so that past service rights build up only gradually, the contribution rate under Plan A would start at a low level but would be expected to rise. This is also to some extent the case under Plans B and C.

8.66 It may be noted that in none of these plans is it wholly true to say that future escalation of pay is not allowed for. It is certainly the case that in Plan A the fund in hand is intended to cover only the past service liabilities with no allowance for future escalation. However, the contribution rate includes the element necessary to cover the effect of each year's escalation on past service liabilities, as that escalation occurs. As in the previous paragraph, the test of whether escalation is covered hinges on whether the necessary resources are provided when each member retires. Provided the scheme and the flow of new entrants continues, these resources are provided so that escalation is allowed for.

The treatment of a shortfall

8.67 We have assumed so far in our examples that past experience has been in line with the expectation and that appropriate funds have been accumulated. To illustrate further the significance of various funding plans we will consider another example. We will use the same membership data as before, but we will now assume that the fund in hand is equal to only once times payroll. This element is introduced because the example of an inadequate fund is in some ways more instructive than that of an adequate fund. We will now consider the action which might be taken under each of the four funding plans previously discussed. We will assume that there is a continuing flow of new entrants in the future so that the age distribution of the membership remains unchanged with time.

Plan A

8.68 The aim in this plan is to arrive at a fund which matches the past service liabilities calculated at current pay levels. These liabilities amount to 1.55 times payroll as shown in paragraph 8.31. The available resources amount to once times payroll, so that it will be necessary to decide on a scheme of special contributions which will be payable in addition to the normal contributions of 17.1 per cent. (see paragraph 8.31) and which has a present capital value of 0.55 times payroll, in order to build up a fund to the required level. We shall expect to arrive at the funding position of paragraph 8.31 when all the special contributions have been paid. There is a variety of ways of planning these extra contributions and we shall not go into detail at this stage. Clearly the degree of security will depend on the period over which the special contributions are paid; the best course from the members' point of view would be a capital payment equal to the full amount of the shortfall, but this would probably not be attractive, or even possible, from the employer's point of view. The matter is discussed in connection with the initial financing of the hypothetical Scheme X which is introduced later in the book.

Plans B and C

8.69 The position under these plans is similar to that under Plan A. The desired level of fund is equal to 2.26 times payroll and 2.98 times payroll respectively, and the special contributions will therefore be directed to the making good of the corresponding shortfall over a period.

Plan D

8.70 Although this plan hinges on the contribution level rather than the amount of the fund, the procedure is much the same as under the earlier plans. The contribution rate is that approriate to a new entrant to the employment, i.e. 15.6 per cent. of payroll. The calculations may therefore be represented as follows, drawing on the figures of paragraph 8.58.

Present value of total benefit expected to arise from past and future service	5.51
Value of future contributions equal to 15.6 per cent. of payroll	2.38
Net liabilities	3.13
Value of assets in hand	1.00
Initial shortfall of resources	2.13

There is therefore an initial shortfall equal to 2.13 times payroll and it will be necessary to decide on the series of special contributions by which this will be met. When it has been met the special contributions will cease and the contribution will be at the normal level of 15.6 per cent.

Plan E

8.71 We end our discussion of funding plans by mentioning two further plans which represent a more pragmatic approach than those discussed earlier. The first of these, Plan E, may be described as follows.

(i)   The normal contribution rate is defined as the rate which, if paid throughout the expected future membership of the members at a valuation date, would meet the cost of the future service liabilities.

(ii) As to past service, the fund in hand is compared with the past service liabilities and any difference dealt with by special contributions.

8.72 In terms of our example the position is as follows.

(i)   The future service liabilities are 2.53 (this figure was calculated for Plan D).

(ii) The value of a 15.6 per cent. future contribution (calculated in connection with Plan D) is 2.38 times payroll.

(iii) The fixed percentage contribution rate payable under Plan E throughout the future membership of the members to match the future service liabilities is therefore

$$15.6 \times \frac{2.53}{2.38} = 16.6 \text{ per cent. of payroll}$$

As far as past service is concerned, the fund is once times payroll and the past service liabilities 2.98 times payroll (see Plan D). The security of the members will depend materially on the speed with which this shortfall is cleared by means of special contributions.

8.73 Under Plan E the normal contribution rate (i.e. that required to cover the cost of the future service benefits) will depend, at each actuarial valuation of a pension scheme, on the particular position revealed by that scheme. There is a prospect that the rate will not change very greatly from one actuarial valuation to another, but the approach is not directed primarily towards long term stability. The reader who wishes to pursue this point will see that (assuming any past service shortfall has been corrected) Plan E is essentially a variant of Plan C, but with the contribution rate being set at 16.6 per cent. instead of the level of 15.7 per cent. shown in paragraph 8.48. The latter rate represented stability, and if the higher rate is paid it will gradually fall as new entrants contribute their rate of 15.6 per cent. to the composite rate of Plan E.

Plan F

8.74 The final plan which we consider is different from all the others in that there is a virtual absence of formal structure. The aim is not to arrive at a fund which matches past service liabilities defined in some particular way (Plans A, B and C), nor to arrive at a contribution rate which matches future service costs for a new entrant (Plan D) or for a group (Plan E). The aim is simply to arrive, in the particular circumstances of a specific case, at the contribution rate which, if paid throughout the future membership of the group concerned, is expected to achieve solvency. The calculations in the present example are as follows.

Present value of total liabilities expected to arise from past and future services	5.51
Value of fund	1.00
Uncovered liabilities	4.51

The present value of a contribution of 15.6 per cent. of payroll payable throughout the future membership to the persons concerned is 2.38 times payroll (from Plan D) and it follows by proportion that the percentage contribution required under Plan F is equal to

$$15.6 \times \frac{4.51}{2.38} = 29.6\%$$

8.75 Under this plan the contribution rate required for these members considered as a closed group (i.e. with no new entrants in future) therefore amounts to 29.6 per cent. of payroll. Assuming that there will in fact be a regular flow of new entrants (for whom a contribution rate of 29.6 per cent. will be paid even though only 15.6 per cent. (Plan D) is required) the required contribution rate will gradually fall. Each successive valuation is expected to lead to a lower contribution rate, ultimately stabilising at the new entrant level.

Codification of funding plans

8.76 It will be noted that some of the plans that we have considered are specified in terms of the level of the fund from time to time whereas under other plans attention is directed towards the contribution rate. Funding plans do indeed fall under these two broad headings and a further sub-division is between plans of type A, where no account is taken of future growth when the cost of pension rights is being calculated (often referred to as current unit plans) and plans in which future projections of growth of either the preserved pension of an early leaver (Plan B) or the final pay related rights of a member (Plans C to F) are allowed for (known as 'projected unit' plans). The three plans which hinge more on a contribution rate are also classified as follows.

Plan D New entrant contribution rate
        (The contribution rate is that appropriate for the future service of a new entrant)

Plan E Attained age contribution rate
        (The contribution rate is that appropriate for the future service of the members, based on the ages attained at the time of the calculation)

Plan F Aggregate contribution rate
        (The contribution rate is that required for solvency when all other liabilities and assets are aggregated)

8.77 Under all these headings except Plan F there is of course a wide variety of ways of arriving at special contributions to clear a shortfall, or a special relief of contributions representing a use of surplus. Codification is not therefore a wholly precise subject.

Further notes on funding plans

8.78 The first point is that we have projected pay increases, contribution flows and other relevant factors throughout the whole of the expected future period of scheme membership of the persons concerned. Some funding plans involve a control period, the projections being made over this future period. The details of such methods vary and we shall not pursue this aspect of funding plans in this book.

8.79 As to which of the plans considered is most widely used in practice, it is believed that Plan A would generally be regarded as inadequate; most plans now involve funding for some element of projection of pay. Plan B reflects 1985 Act legislation. Plans C, D, E and F are all employed on a considerable scale. Plan D was at one time regarded as the most orthodox approach but it has been criticised on the grounds that it involves the accumulation of larger funds than are likely to be needed, because a closed fund with the membership gradually ageing (which is the situation in which Plan D displays the advantage of a stable contribution rate) is hardly ever encountered in practice.

8.80 The diversity of funding plans encountered in practice has implications from the point of view of the employing company's accounts as well as from the point of view of the pension scheme. Two companies may be operating at much the same level of profitability before pension costs are taken into account, but if they are following radically different pension funding plans, the level of profitability after allowing for pension costs may be materially different. This matter is currently exercising the minds of those in the professions concerned, but further discussion is outside the scope of this book.

The funding plan and the actuarial basis

8.81 The contribution required to be paid to a pension scheme in a given year is clearly a function of both the cost of providing a unit of benefit and the plan under which the liabilities are being funded. Employers and employees often find both these aspects difficult to grasp. If different proposals to provide a given scheme of benefits are being compared (this may, for example, arise when different quotations for an insured scheme are being considered) it is therefore necessary for the actuary to ensure that his client understands the position and will not take the amount of the contributions to the various proposed schemes in the first year as a true measure of the relative long term cost.

8.82   Equally, the contributions paid in a given year to a number of different schemes do not provide a measure of the relative value of the benefits provided from each of the schemes, even if the cost of providing a unit of benefit is identical in all of them. It is often desired to compare the value of different schemes of benefits, and frequently the best way to do this is to ignore the pace at which the schemes are in fact being funded and to express the value of each scheme of benefits in terms of the level percentage contribution rate required to support the benefits at a typical new entrant age.

The funding of specific liabilities

8.83   The discussion so far has been mainly in terms of the contribution to cover the ordinary year by year accrual of benefit rights, but we have touched on the question of the scheme of contributions to meet a specific liability. This may arise, for instance, if a pension scheme is being set up for the first time and the persons concerned are being granted pension rights in respect of the years of service with the employer that they have already completed. Similarly, if the benefits under a pension scheme are being improved and it is decided that this is to apply not only to the benefit rights arising in future but also to the benefit rights for past service at the date concerned, a capital liability will clearly arise in respect of the increased cost of the past service rights.

8.84   In the past it was often common for such capital liabilities to be met by the payment of a contribution of a fixed amount of money payable for a specified period of years. This is not, however, a satisfactory arrangement if continuing inflation is assumed. One criticism of the plan is that if the payroll is increasing steadily because of inflation, a fixed money amount payable over a period of years will be a larger proportion of the payroll at the beginning of the period than it is at the end. Thus, the criterion of stability is not met. Partly for this reason, it has become more common for specific liabilities to be met by a contribution expressed as a percentage of payroll payable for a specified period of years. This has the advantage that the burden in real terms remains stable. It has a further advantage when, as is normally the case, the capital liability being dealt with relates to benefits calculated on final pay. In these circumstances, pay increases higher or lower than those allowed for in the calculations will increase or diminish the liabilities; if the contributions are based on pay from time to time the resources provided by the contributions will similarly be increased or diminished by pay increases greater or less than those allowed for in the projections.

Obligations as to funding

8.85 We turn to the final aspect of funding mentioned in paragraph 8.1, namely the obligations of members and employer. It will be obvious that the cost of a pension scheme cannot be accurately calculated in advance, since the experience will differ, sometimes markedly, from the assumptions on which the calculations of cost have been based. It is thus not possible to set up a final pay pension scheme with the rate of contribution of both the members and the employer rigidly specified and with no provision for adjustments to be made to the contributions or benefits when an actuarial valuation is made. Some of the arrangements that are met with in practice are outlined in the next three paragraphs.

Balance of cost

8.86 In some schemes the rate of contribution of the members is fixed and the employer undertakes to meet the balance of the cost. In these circumstances the main purpose of an actuarial valuation is to fix the contribution rate of the employer. The valuation involves placing a capital value on the total liabilities of the scheme, including the benefit rights expected to arise from the future service of active members, deducting from this figure the value of the assets and of the future contributions payable by the members and hence arriving at the contribution rate required from the employer to meet the balance of the cost. The main feature of the 'balance of cost' arrangement to which attention needs to be drawn is, of course, that the employer accepts a virtually unlimited (sometimes referred to as an 'open-ended') liability. The trust deed and rules of a scheme will almost certainly provide that the employer may terminate the scheme in extreme circumstances, so that the funding obligation of the employer is not absolute. Nevertheless, many employers are reluctant to have their obligations defined in this way, although there are on the other hand many schemes in which the provision operates.

Fixed contribution rates with valuation adjustments

8.87   The second type of arrangement discussed is that in which the rates of contribution of both the members and the employer are laid down in the trust deed and rules but it is provided that if an actuarial valuation shows a surplus or deficiency appropriate action will be taken by way of adjustment of the benefits or contributions. Although the detailed provisions of schemes using this method vary considerably, the general framework is that variations in benefits or contribution rates are left to be dealt with in the light of the particular situation revealed by the actuarial valuation. In practice it is often the case that if further contributions are shown to be required, the employer will do his best to deal with the situation by way of an increase in his own contributions rather than require the members to increase theirs, while if a surplus is revealed such surplus is often used to increase benefits (commonly, in recent years, to increase pensions in course of payment) rather than to reduce contributions. However, other courses of action are met with in practice, depending partly on the prosperity of the employer concerned.

Fixed proportions

8.88   The third type of arrangement we discuss is one in which the employer's contribution is specified in the rules as a fixed multiple of the total contributions of the members. Clearly, this arrangement differs from that outlined in the preceding paragraph in that an increase or decrease in contributions flowing from the result of an actuarial valuation is automatically divided between the members and the employer. It is often provided in schemes that, despite these provisions, the employer may shoulder all or a larger part of any additional costs should he so decide. It might be thought that the arrangement is notably fair as between members and employer, but it does have one particular disadvantage. This follows from the fact that if an actuarial valuation shows that further contributions are required, this will usually be because rates of pay increase have outstripped investment performance. The bulk of the additional liabilities will arise in respect of the older members with longer service, but the members who will contribute most by way of extra contributions are the younger members with a long future period of contributory membership. Thus, the arrangement is not equitable between generations of members, and for this reason it is uncommon for this provision to be applied in its full rigour.

The 'Contribution Holiday'

8.89 A particular aspect of costs which flows from the result of an actuarial valuation but is conveniently mentioned at this point is the so-called 'contribution holiday' which first came into prominence in 1984. Many pension schemes had enjoyed a period of exceptionally high investment returns with only modest growth in liabilities at that time, so that actuarial valuations were often revealing substantial surplus. In many cases the employer's desire was to use surplus to reduce costs rather than increase benefits, because benefit scales were thought to be already adequate, and employers were also mindful of the likelihood that increased benefits would eventually require increased contributions. Furthermore many employers were experiencing difficult trading conditions and were seeking all possible reductions in costs. This second factor led such employers to seek a substantial short-term reduction in costs rather than a smaller reduction in the long-term contribution rates.

8.90 In extreme cases an employer might in these circumstances desire to recover money already paid to a pension scheme, but the Inland Revenue did not approve of this course of action except as a last resort. A less extreme course is for the employer's contribution to be substantially reduced, or to cease altogether, for a limited period. The Inland Revenue permit such a 'contribution holiday' and this course of action has been widely followed. Generally only the employer's contributions are involved, particularly if the scheme is of the 'balance of cost' type referred to in paragraph 8.86. The question of a contribution holiday for the members is considered on its merits in individual cases.

8.91   The Inland Revenue position was set out in a letter from the Controller of the S.F.O. printed in 'Pensions World' of July 1984 and was also summarised in an answer to a parliamentary question by the Financial Secretary to the Treasury on 26th July 1985 which was recorded in 'Pensions World' of September 1985. An excerpt from this answer which provides a succinct summary of the S.F.O's position is as follows.

'Where a surplus is not too large, the Revenue is usually able to accept it until the next valuation is due, as a temporary fluctuation in the long-term fortunes of the scheme. If special measures are needed, a small temporary reduction in contributions - usually employers' contributions - is generally enough to reduce the surplus to an acceptable level by the time of the next valuation. If that is insufficient, a reduction in the long-term contribution rate may be all that is needed. But where the surplus is very large, in relation to the scheme's liabilities, immediate action may be required if the exempt approved status of the scheme is not be put at risk. This may take the form of improvements in scheme benefits (although the Revenue no longer insist on this in all cases) or a complete suspension of contributions by the employer, and if necessary, the employees.

If a complete contributions holiday for a period of, say, five years would still fail to achieve the desired result, the Revenue might require part or all of the surplus to be refunded to the employer. But such cases will be very rare: no-one should assume that a refund will automatically be permitted if a surplus would remain after a five year contributions holiday.'

Expenses
8.92   We end this chapter on costs with a reference to the expenses of management of pension schemes. In some schemes the employer meets all the expenses, so that when the trustees are seeking advice on contribution rates this element need not be considered. Even where the expenses of a scheme are met from the funds of the scheme, the question of the expense element in the contribution rate is by no means as complicated as is often the case in the calculation of life office premium rates. In pension schemes the matter is usually simply one of including a small element in the contribution rate calculated as being broadly adequate to meet those expenses of operation which fall on the trustees.

THE FRAMEWORK OF COMPUTATION: I

THE FRAMEWORK OF COMPUTATION: I

Introduction

9.1 Much of the advice that the actuary tenders to his client on such matters as statutory requirements and benefit design requires little computation. We now turn to those areas of advice which are based on calculations of various sorts. The nature and scope of the calculations to be made in a particular case need careful consideration; the calculations should be neither too detailed nor too broad.

9.2 The following points militate against a too detailed approach.

(i)   The calculations usually involve assumptions about future economic factors such as investment yields and rates of pay increase. These cannot be predicted with confidence, so that the actuarial basis chosen represents only one of a possible range of reasonable sets of assumptions. It has to be accepted that the experience will differ from the assumptions, and in a continuing pension scheme successive actuarial valuations provide the opportunity for the effects of such differences to be allowed for as the experience unfolds. It is clearly inappropriate in these circumstances for every aspect of the liabilities, however trivial, to be quantified to the last degree of accuracy.

(ii) Over-meticulous calculation is a waste of resources and may lead to unnecessarily high costs to the client.

(iii) Calculations often have to be made against pressure of time and should therefore be no more extensive than is required as the basis for advice.

(iv) It is important that the results should be presented to the client in such a way as to carry conviction; the finance director of a large company would probably not be impressed if results representing discounted values of large estimated cash flows over a long future period were presented to him in figures which purported to be accurate to single pounds.

9.3 Calculations must not on the other hand be too broad, because the advice given must be soundly based and this necessitates a certain degree of fullness in the calculations. For instance, there might be difficulty if the cost of a pension benefit payable at pension age or on earlier ill-health retirement had been arrived at by calculating the liabilities in respect of members' pensions on age retirement and adding a broadly assessed loading for the contingency of early retirement on ill-health, and the client then asked for an estimate of the cost of a complicated but minor change in the ill-health benefits. It is usually desirable to allow explicitly in the calculations for most of the main contingencies that may occur, provided that their incidence is reasonably predictable.

The form of the calculations

9.4 Over the years actuaries have developed tools and methods of computation which are appropriate to the requirements indicated above, in that they lead to cost estimates precise enough to form the basis of professional advice, while not involving an unmanageable volume of calculation. The basic functions of these traditional methods are dealt with in this chapter, while in the next chapter we outline a computer-based approach to the work.

9.5 One of the first major actuarial calculations that arises in connection with a proposed pension scheme is the assessment of the contribution rates required to support the scheme of benefits. This calculation normally involves most of the functions with which we shall be concerned, and we shall therefore introduce these functions by way of an outline of the contribution rate calculations. We will assume that we have adequate data about the employees who are likely to form the initial membership of the scheme.

9.6 Each future year of the scheme's operations will involve the receipt of contributions from the members (if they are to contribute) and the employer, and expenditure upon benefits of various types (ignoring any expenses charged to the scheme). Given the necessary data and assumptions it would be possible to calculate the expected amounts of income from a contribution rate set at a percentage of salary judged to be roughly appropriate, and benefit expenditure, in each future year in respect of the initial entrants. There could thus be constructed a series of expected annual revenue accounts over the very long period which would elapse before the last benefit payment from the scheme to or in respect of the initial entrants ceased. These revenue accounts would be complete (in respect of the initial entrants) on the basis of the chosen contribution rate, except that they would not allow for the investment of the contributions. To put the matter in another way, they would be accounts drawn up on the assumption that future income and outgo would simply be held in an account which did not earn interest. Clearly this procedure would not establish whether the contribution rate was adequate or not. The projections would merely show that in the early years contribution income exceeded benefit expenditure (assuming that the contribution rate had been pitched at an appropriate level) and in the later years the reverse applied. It is therefore necessary to carry the calculations a stage further.

9.7   The future operations of the scheme would in fact involve the investment of excess contribution income in the early years, and the sale or realisation of investments to meet excess outgo in the later years (in a scheme which has a continuing flow of new entrants this eventual disposal of investments takes place automatically by transfer to a new generation of members rather than by sale in the market, but this is irrelevant for present purposes). It would therefore be possible to summarise the long-term financial position of the scheme by accumulating contribution income and benefit outgo, at the rate expected to be earned, up to the time that the last person concerned ceased to have an interest in the scheme. This would establish whether income or expenditure would predominate in the long run, and hence whether or not the contribution rate was adequate.

9.8   In practice it is more convenient to discount the expected contribution receipts and benefit payments to present capital values, rather than to accumulate them to some remote future date. As a final step the two values are compared in order to arrive at the contribution rate necessary to achieve an equality of values. In order that the discounting process shall be valid it is necessary to carry it out at the same rate of interest as would have been assumed had the expected amounts been accumulated instead to a remote future date, i.e. at the average rate of interest at which the contributions are assumed to be invested in future. The rate of interest to be used in the calculations thus represents the long-term yield expected to be obtained on new investments made during the long future period involved.

9.9　To illustrate the argument by a simplified example, suppose that the projections show that the future income resulting from a contribution equal to 10 per cent. of pay is expected to consist of £100 at the end of the first year, £108 at the end of the second year and so on (the amounts increasing by 8 per cent. p.a. compound) for 15 years in all. The projections also show that the only liability is an undertaking to pay a benefit of £6,000 in 16 years' time. These figures throw no light on the question of whether the contribution rate is adequate or not.

9.10　Suppose that money invested in the future will earn on the average a rate of return of 9 per cent. p.a. The accumulation with interest to a time 16 years hence of the expected contribution income amounts to

$$£100 \left[(1.09)^{15} + (1.08)(1.09)^{14} + .. + (1.08)^{14} (1.09) \right]$$

$$= £100 (1.09)^{15} \ddot{\alpha}_{\overline{15|}}$$

@ interest rate $i = 0.926$ per cent. as in paragraph 8.54

$$= £ 5,126.$$

It follows by proportion that a contribution rate of 11.7 per cent. of pay is required to fund the payment of £6,000.

9.11　If we discount income and outgo to present values at 9 per cent. p.a., the present value of the income from a 10 per cent. contribution is

$$\frac{£100 \; \ddot{\alpha}_{\overline{15|}}}{1.09} \quad @ \; 0.926 \text{ per cent.} = £1,291$$

and the value of the liabilities is

$$£6,000 \; v^{16} \; @ \; 9 \text{ per cent.} = £1,511$$

As before, it follows by proportion that a contribution rate of 11.7 per cent. of pay is required.

9.12   Had the rate of interest used for discounting purposes been different from the rate of 9 per cent. expected to be earned in the long run, the present value calculations would not have led to a contribution rate of 11.7 per cent., even though the figures in paragraph 9.10 show that this is the required rate. This example illustrates the point made in paragraph 9.8, namely that the rate of interest used for discounting must be the rate expected to be earned.

Basic elements

9.13   Bearing in mind the description in earlier chapters of the benefit and contribution structure of the typical pension scheme, it will probably be clear from the above discussion that the basic elements of the required functions include the following.

(i)   Rates of probability of future events giving rise to benefit payments from the scheme. These rates will also be used to arrive at the number of survivors as contributing members from time to time out of an initial group, and hence at the pattern of contributions to the scheme.

(ii)   Rates of mortality of pensioners.

(iii)   Elements which will enable the amount of each future payment into and out of the scheme to be estimated.

(iv)   Compound interest functions.

9.14   We now consider in detail these basic elements and the construction of various functions from them. It will be obvious from the next paragraph that the basic elements themselves reflect the practical approach indicated in paragraph 9.2. Thus a single service table based on aggregate rates is normally applied to a large group of members of a scheme, although a strong case for rates which are select in respect of duration of employment could be made on theoretical grounds. Equally, a single salary scale is normally used for the pay projections of a large group of members although this may represent a sweeping simplification of a complex situation. As indicated in paragraph 9.4, these are the tools that over the years have been found adequate for the work in hand, which is directed towards the formulation of advice rather than to calculation for its own sake.

9.15   The actuarial formulae used in pension scheme work are constructed from the following main elements.

(i) Multiple decrement tables for employee members (called in this context 'service tables').

(ii) Scales for estimating members' future earnings.

(iii) Mortality tables for pensioners and ex-employees with preserved pensions.

(iv) Mortality tables for the wives and widows of active members, of ex-employees with preserved pensions and of pensioners, and corresponding tables for husbands, widowers and dependants if widowers' and dependants' pensions are provided.

(v) At each age, proportions married amongst active members and ex-employees with preserved pensions dying or retiring.

(vi) Age differences of husbands and wives and other family statistics.

(vii) Compound interest functions.

We deal in Chapters 11 and 12 with the issues that have to be considered when the numerical values of all these constituents of the basis are being settled in a particular case. We are concerned in this chapter with the development of formulae. Tables 2 to 13 at the end of this book illustrate the numerical work associated with some of the formulae and we shall refer to these tables where appropriate.

The service table

9.16 Active members of a pension scheme cease to be active members mainly by reason of withdrawal, death or retirement on pension. In the service table in the simple form in which it is usually used l_x represents the number of active members of a scheme at exact age x and w_x, d_x, i_x and r_x represent respectively the numbers out of l_x who withdraw, die in service, retire on grounds of ill-health and retire on other grounds at age x last birthday. These numbers are derived from dependent probability ratios wq_x, dq_x, iq_x and rq_x, where $w_x = l_x \times wq_x$ etc. The service table is built up by the repeated use of the relationship

$$l_{x+1} = l_x - w_x - d_x - i_x - r_x \qquad \qquad .... 9.16.1$$

An example of a service table (but not the underlying probability ratios) is shown in Table 2.

The withdrawal decrement: voluntary withdrawal

9.17 It would be possible for the service table to include a separate decrement for each type of benefit on each type of exit. For instance, there could be three separate decrement rates for members withdrawing voluntarily, according to whether the benefit was a payment equal to the amount of their own accumulated contributions, payment of a transfer value or entitlement to a preserved pension. Each group could be further divided in a contracted-out scheme according to the treatment of the G.M.P. element of the preserved pension. This, however, would be complicated. Furthermore, the benefit taken will depend heavily on duration of membership as well as on age, so that select withdrawal rates would have to be used in order that such detailed treatment should be meaningful. In practice calculations are often made on the assumption that all withdrawing members will take a preserved pension, and no sub-division of the withdrawal decrement is then necessary in the service table. In a contributory scheme the value at the date of exit of a preserved scale pension is often less than the amount of the member's accumulated contributions, and the value of the withdrawal benefits as calculated above may well be adjusted to allow for the liability involved in a 'value for money' guarantee (see paragraph 3.5).

The withdrawal decrement: enforced withdrawal

9.18 Enforced withdrawal usually happens because the member has been made redundant or because he is one of a group of employees associated with a part of the undertaking that is being disposed of. Cessation of membership in these circumstances is not allowed for explicitly as a decrement rate in the service table, for two reasons. The first is that its incidence is unpredictable. The second is that redundancy is hoped to be a short term measure, after which the withdrawal experience will return to a more normal level; it is not therefore appropriate to allow for it in long term projections.

Mortality and ill-health retirement

9.19 The decrement rates under this heading do not call for special comment at this stage.

The terminal age of the service table

9.20 The age at which a service table should end, the remaining members being assumed to retire immediately on attainment of that age, is often obvious in the light of an employer's policy on retirement or the observed experience of a scheme. If members of a scheme are entitled to a pension on retirement at age 65 or on earlier retirement on grounds of ill-health, and if virtually all members who reach age 65 retire immediately, then equation 9.16.1 will hold for values of x up to and including 64, and the l_{65} members who reach age 65 are assumed to retire immediately upon attaining that age.

9.21 Matters are not always so straightforward. The rules of a scheme might, for instance, provide for a pension on the normal scale of the scheme to be provided to a male member on his retirement

(a)   on grounds of ill-health at any age or
(b)   in normal health at any time after attainment of age 60.

If it were found that some male members in normal health exercised their option to retire between age 60 and age 65, that a considerable number stayed on until attainment of age 65, and that very few remained after that age, the actuary would probably decide that equation 9.16.1 should include an i_x element for values of x up to and including 64 and an r_x element for values of x from 60 to 64 inclusive, and that the service table should terminate at age 65. It will be seen that the service table in Table 2 is of this form.

Cessation of membership with a benefit equal to actuarial reserve

9.22 If a member whose cessation of membership is not anticipated in the service table leaves the scheme with a benefit equal to the actuarial reserve held in respect of him, the financial position of the remaining members of the scheme is undisturbed. It is partly on these grounds that exits with payments of a transfer value not greater than the actuarial reserve, or early optional retirements with an immediate pension not greater in value than the actuarial reserve, are not provided for explicitly in the service table. To the extent that the value of their benefits at exit falls short of the actuarial reserve held in respect of them as active members just before the date of exit, the scheme will profit and an item of surplus will emerge at the next actuarial valuation. We leave open the question of what is meant by the 'actuarial reserve'; the point is considered in more detail in Chapter 19.

9.23 Similar considerations apply if members remaining in service after attaining the normal retirement age cease to be covered by normal benefit scales of the scheme but become entitled instead to benefits actuarially equivalent to those they would have received had they retired at the normal age, together with the equivalent of any contributions paid in respect of the member after his attainment of that age. The finances of the scheme are not disturbed by deferment, so that even if many members delay their retirement in this way it would be appropriate for the service table to cease at the age at which the normal scale ceases to operate.

The salary scale

9.24 The contributions and benefits of most pension schemes are based on pensionable earnings, so that some method is required in the actuarial projections to estimate amounts of pensionable earnings from time to time in the future. It is, of course, impossible to predict the future pensionable earnings of an individual; what is required is a means of estimating the average annual pensionable earnings to be received from time to time by the survivors still in active membership of a group of active members all of the same age whose present annual pensionable earnings are known.

9.25 This immediately raises a point for decision in a scheme where pensionable earnings include an allowance for the State pension. To illustrate the point we use as an example Scale F of paragraph 5.18. In this scale pensions are based on the final average value of

$$(P - F)$$

where P represents annual earnings and F represents the annual amount of the State flat-rate pension for a single person from time to time. We will assume that contributions are also charged on pensionable earnings so defined. Some method is therefore required for the projection of expected future values of $(P - F)$. The question that has to be settled is whether the scale that is adopted for the projections should operate directly on $(P - F)$ or separately on P and F.

9.26 In practice it is usually necessary to operate separately on P and F, because the future progression of P for a group of members will involve both an element of personal promotion, as individuals progress throughout their career, and an element reflecting changes in overall levels of earnings from time to time in the future assuming that inflationary conditions continue. The future projection of F will not involve any element of personal promotion. In the following discussion we assume that the two constituents will be dealt with separately.

9.27 As to the projection of P, it is not necessary at this stage to define whether the earnings concerned are basic pay, full taxable pay or pay on some other definition. It is assumed that whatever type of earnings is involved, the salary scale will provide a basis for the projection of future earnings. The type of function almost invariably used in practice for this purpose is a relative scale, that is a scale representing the ratio of average annual earnings in each future year to present average annual earnings. It consists of a series of numbers s_x defined for all x from the youngest age of membership to one less than the terminal age, such that for a group of members of exact age x, s_{x+t}/s_x is the assumed ratio of the average earnings in the year of age $x + t$ to $x + t + 1$ to the average earnings in the year of age x to $x + 1$.

9.28 As noted above, this scale in practice usually covers both

(i)   those increases which would on average be expected because of the progress of individuals within their career if overall levels of earnings remained stable, and

(ii)   increases representing changes in the general levels of earnings on account of continuing inflation.

The scale is normally constructed by first forming a series of numbers representing increases of the first kind (as shown in Table 2) and then multiplying the value of s_x by $(1 + e)^x$ where e is the annual rate of general increase in pay levels to be used in the calculations (as shown in Table 3). The rate e is often called the annual rate of escalation of earnings and we shall use that term in this book.

9.29 The number of survivors in active membership of the original group of members aged x diminishes as time proceeds, but it is always assumed that the average salary career of members who cease to be members is the same up to the date of their cessation of membership as that of the survivors in membership, so that the same salary scale can be used for both groups.

9.30 If a homogeneous group of active members of a given age were followed through active employment and the average rate of annual salary of the survivors in active employment calculated at frequent intervals and plotted, the nature of the resulting graph would depend largely on whether salary increases were granted on the same date each year or were spread uniformly over the year. If rises were granted on a fixed date each year the graph would be step-shaped; if they were spread uniformly it would be a smooth curve. We shall normally assume in this book that increases are spread uniformly over the year.

9.31 In practice the information available about the earnings of each member of a scheme usually concerns either

(i)   the earnings in the year preceding a particular date,
(ii) the annual rate of earnings at the date, or
(iii) the earnings which it is expected will be received in the year following that date.

For a group of members aged x at the relevant date, the average earnings expected during the year of age $x + t$ to $x + t + 1$ are calculated by applying to the data in these three situations the ratio

$$\frac{s_{x+t}}{s_{x-1}} \, , \quad \frac{s_{x+t}}{s_{x-\frac{1}{2}}} \quad \text{or} \quad \frac{s_{x+t}}{s_x}$$

respectively.

Other basic elements

9.32 The reader will already be familiar with mortality tables and compound interest functions and these require no special comment at this stage. Additional basic elements are required in connection with benefits to adult dependants and dependent children. The derivation and use of proportions married and average age differences of members and dependants do not present any points of particular difficulty.

Construction of formulae
Pension formulae for a pension not related to earnings

9.33 Although it will be realised from previous chapters that a pension scale providing a fixed amount of annual pension, say £K, for each year of membership would not be suited to modern circumstances, the development of the actuarial formulae for such a scale provides a convenient introduction to the subject. We will suppose that parts of a year of membership count proportionately in the calculation of a pension, that the pension is payable on retirement at age 65 or on earlier ill-health retirement, and that we are valuing the pensions of a group of members all aged x nearest birthday (who we shall regard as being all aged exactly x). It is convenient to deal with the pension rights in respect of past service and expected future service separately.

Value of past service pension

9.34 Suppose that $\bar{a}_y'$ is the value on retirement at age y exact ($y <$ 65) of an ill-health pension of 1 per annum. The function $\bar{a}_y'$ will be based on a mortality table appropriate to ill-health pensioners, and will include allowance for any special provisions such as a guarantee that payments will be made in any event for a certain minimum period or to a certain minimum total amount. It will also include appropriate allowance for any regular increases in pensions after they start to be paid.

9.35 The value at age x of a pension of 1 per annum commencing in the event of a breakdown in health at age y last birthday (assumed to occur on the average at age $y + \frac{1}{2}$) is

$$v^{y+\frac{1}{2}-x} \; \frac{i_y}{l_x} \; \bar{a}_{y+\frac{1}{2}}'$$

which is usually written as C_y^{ia}/D_x where

$$C_y^{ia} = v^{y+\frac{1}{2}} i_y \bar{a}_{y+\frac{1}{2}}' \qquad\qquad \dots 9.35.1$$
$$\text{and } D_x = v^x l_x \qquad\qquad\qquad \dots 9.35.2$$

The calculation of C_y^{ia} is illustrated in columns (2) to (6) of Table 6.

9.36 The amount of annual pension arising in respect of the past service of an individual with exactly n years' membership is £nK. The past service of members at the date of the investigation will amount to years and fractions of a year if entry to the scheme takes place throughout the year. We shall assume that this is so, and that entries are distributed evenly over the year. The past service of each member in this case would usually be taken to the nearest whole number of years in the preliminary scheduling of the data, on the grounds that for a group of members the sum of past durations each expressed to the nearest year is not likely to differ seriously from the total of such durations each expressed in years and fractions of a year. The sum of the durations of all members in the group is represented by Σn.

Value of past service ill-health pension

9.37   The present value at age x of the past service pension upon a breakdown in health at any age after age x for an individual is thus

$$n.\ K.\ M_x^{ia}/D_x \qquad\qquad \dots\dots 9.37.1$$

$$\text{where}\quad M_x^{ia} = \sum_{t=0}^{64-x} C_{x+t}^{ia} \qquad\qquad \dots\dots 9.37.2$$

and the value for the group is therefore

$$(\Sigma n)\ K\ M_x^{ia}/D_x \qquad\qquad \dots\dots 9.37.3$$

Value of past service age retirement pension

9.38   Retirement on grounds of age occurs only on attainment of age 65 in this example, and the value at age x of the pension on age retirement in respect of n years of past membership is

$$n.\ K.\ v^{65-x}\frac{r_{65}}{\ell_x}\ \bar{a}'_{65} \qquad\qquad \dots\dots 9.38.1$$

$$= n.\ K.\ C_{65}^{ra}/D_x \qquad\qquad \dots\dots 9.38.2$$

where

$$C_{65}^{ra} = v^{65}\, r_{65}\, \bar{a}'_{65} \qquad\qquad \dots\dots 9.38.3$$

The annuity function $\bar{a}'_{65}$ is based on mortality appropriate to retirement in normal health and, as before, includes allowance for any benefits on death after retirement. It will be noticed that C_{65}^{ra} is of slightly different form from C_y^{ia}, being at the exact age instead of the half age because age retirement is assumed to occur immediately on attainment of age 65. The value of the past service age pension for all members in the group is

$$(\Sigma n)\ K\ C_{65}^{ra}/D_x \qquad\qquad \dots\dots 9.38.4$$

If retirements in normal health can take place at a spread of ages and not merely at the final age of the service table, values of C_{x+t}^{ra}

at those earlier ages will be involved, and they will be functions at the half-age as in formula 9.35.1. Columns (2) to (6) of Table 5 illustrate the calculation of the values of C^{ra}_{x+t} in such a case.

Total value of past service pension

9.39 In practice it is usually desirable to calculate the present capital values of the ill-health pension and the age pension separately. If in a particular case this is not needed then assuming no retirements in normal health before age 65 we may define

$$M^{ra}_x = (\sum_{t=0}^{64-x} C^{ia}_{x+t}) + C^{ra}_{65} \qquad \ldots\ldots 9.39.1$$

The total value of the ill-health and age pension in respect of past service is then

$$(\Sigma n)\, K\, M^{ra}_x / D_x \qquad \ldots\ldots 9.39.2$$

Value of future service pension

9.40 Consider for an individual aged x nearest birthday at the valuation date the pension benefits arising in respect of his membership of the scheme during the year beginning $(y - x)$ years after the valuation date $(x < y < 65)$. Since the member is regarded as being aged x exact, this year can be referred to conveniently as the year between the ages y and $y + 1$. The probability that the member will retire on ill health grounds during that year is

$$\frac{i_y}{l_x}.$$

It is assumed that ill-health retirement at age y last birthday takes place on the average half way through the year of age y to $y + 1$, so that the pension arising upon such ill-health retirement in respect of membership during that year is $K/2$. The probability that the member will retire on ill-health grounds during the year of age $y + 1$ to $y + 2$ is

$$\frac{i_{y+1}}{l_x}$$

and in this event the year of membership from age y to age $y + 1$ will give rise to a full year's pension K. Similar reasoning applies for ill-health retirement in each subsequent year and it follows that the value at age x of the ill-health pension arising in respect of the year from age y to age $y + 1$ is

$$K[\tfrac{1}{2}C_y^{ia} + C_{y+1}^{ia} + \ldots + C_{64}^{ia}]/D_x \qquad \ldots\ldots 9.40.1$$

The value at age x of the pension on retirement at age 65 arising in respect of the year of age y to $y + 1$ is

$$K C_{65}^{ra}/D_x \qquad \ldots\ldots 9.40.2$$

9.41   The total value at age x of the pension arising in respect of the year of age y to $y + 1$ is therefore

$$K[\tfrac{1}{2}C_y^{ia} + C_{y+1}^{ia} + \ldots + C_{64}^{ia} + C_{65}^{ra}]/D_x \qquad \ldots\ldots 9.41.1$$
$$= K[M_y^{ra} - \tfrac{1}{2}C_y^{ia}]/D_x \qquad \ldots\ldots 9.41.2$$

9.42   The total value at age x of the pension arising in respect of the whole of the expected future service of the member concerned is found by summing expression 9.41.2 for all values of y, from x to 64 (the summation ends at 64 and not 65 because the argument is in terms of the pension arising in respect of the year of membership from age y to $y + 1$, and the last of these years is clearly that beginning at age 64). If we write

$$\bar{M}_y^{ra} = M_y^{ra} - \tfrac{1}{2}C_y^{ia} \quad (y \leqslant 64) \qquad \ldots\ldots 9.42.1$$
$$\text{and } \bar{R}_x^{ra} = \sum_{t=0}^{64-x} \bar{M}_{x+t}^{ra} \qquad \ldots\ldots 9.42.2$$

the total value at age x of the pension arising in respect of the whole of the expected future service of the member concerned is

$$K \bar{R}_x^{ra}/D_x \qquad \ldots\ldots 9.42.3$$

The value for the group of members aged x is

$$\begin{bmatrix}\text{Total number} \\ \text{of members}\end{bmatrix} K \bar{R}_x^{ra}/D_x \qquad \ldots\ldots 9.42.4$$

If $\bar{R}_x^{ra}$ is expanded in terms of the basic 'C' functions it will be found that

$$\bar{R}_x^{ra} = \tfrac{1}{2}C_x^{ia} + 1\tfrac{1}{2}C_{x+1}^{ia} + \ldots + (64\tfrac{1}{2} - x) C_{64}^{ia} + (65-x) C_{65}^{ra}$$
$$\ldots\ldots 9.42.5$$

as would be expected.

Minimum ill-health pension

9.43   It was mentioned in paragraph 5.53 that the amount of an ill-health pension is often based on some minimum number of

years, even if that number of years of membership has not been
completed. If a minimum ill-health pension of £20K per annum
were introduced in the example under consideration for members
aged under 45 at entry, the array of 'C' functions needed in
connection with the pension liability for a member aged x with
$n(\ <20)$ years of past service $(x{-}n < 45)$ would be

$$20\,C_x^{ia} + 20\,C_{x+1}^{ia} + \ldots + 20\,C_{x+20-n-1}^{ia}$$
$$+ 20\tfrac{1}{2}\,C_{x+20-n}^{ia} + 21\tfrac{1}{2}\,C_{x+20-n+1}^{ia} + \ldots$$
$$+ (64\tfrac{1}{2}{-}x{+}n)C_{64}^{ia} + (65{-}x{+}n)\,C_{65}^{ra} \qquad \ldots\ldots 9.43.1$$

It is clear that this provides a pension based on 20 years' service
while the actual years of service are less than 20 (i.e. up to age
$x{-}n{+}20$ exact) and a pension based on the actual years of service
thereafter, as required. It will be found this array of 'C' functions
is represented by the expression in square brackets in the following
function, which represents the pension liability.

$$K[20\,M_x^{ra} + \bar{R}_{x+20-n}^{ra}]/D_x \qquad\qquad \ldots\ldots 9.43.2$$

Simplification of notation

9.44 If retirement on grounds of age, with a pension calculated
on the normal scale, is possible before age 65, the formulae will be
unchanged except that the 'C' function for the ages at which both
ill-health retirement and age retirement can take place will be
equal to

$$v^{y+\frac{1}{2}}\,[\,i_y\,\bar{a}'_{y+\frac{1}{2}}\,\begin{smallmatrix}\text{ill-health}\\\text{mortality}\end{smallmatrix} + r_y\,\bar{a}'_{y+\frac{1}{2}}\,\begin{smallmatrix}\text{normal}\\\text{mortality}\end{smallmatrix}\,] \qquad \ldots\ldots 9.44.1$$

The question arises of an appropriate symbol for this function,
since it covers both ill-health retirement and age retirement. We
mentioned in paragraph 9.39 that in practice it is usually necessary
to value the ill-health pension and the age pension separately but
in fact it is often unnecessary to use a different notation for these
two types of retirement in the algebraic development. For
simplicity in the rest of this book we shall not use a different
notation for ill-health and for age retirements; the functions
previously written as i_y and C_y^{ia} will in future be written as r_y and
C_y^{ra}. It will be taken for granted, but not shown explicitly, that
where necessary a C type function will be of the form of expression
9.44.1.

9.45 It should be noted that this simplification is not always possible. It sometimes happens that there are ages at which ill-health retirement and age retirement can both occur and the scales of pension in the two circumstances are different. It might be, for instance, that members could retire between age 60 and 65 in normal health with a pension based on years of service but if they retired on ill-health grounds at these ages the pension would be based on augmented years of service on the lines mentioned in paragraph 5.53. In this case the present values of the two types of pension would be assessed separately.

The formulae when only completed years count for pension purposes

9.46 So far it has been assumed that parts of a year count for pension purposes and give rise to a proportionate amount of pension. It is sometimes provided that only completed years of membership shall count for pension purposes although this is not very satisfactory because a member may derive no additional pension benefit from almost a full year of contribution payments. Nevertheless it is useful to consider the formulae in these circumstances, for a pension scale otherwise the same as that above. We consider as before a group of members aged x nearest birthday, but we shall now assume that the duration 'n' recorded for an individual is the curtate duration. Assuming that entries are evenly distributed over the year the average actual duration is equal to $n+\frac{1}{2}$.

Value of past service pension

9.47 The pension accrued at the valuation date in respect of the complete years of past service is $n.K.$, so that the value for the group is

$$(\Sigma n) K M_x^{ra} /D_x \qquad \qquad \ldots.. 9.47.1$$

as before. We have ignored all the extra parts of an uncompleted year of past service in defining the past service pension liability, and we must ensure that the future service pension liability is defined in such a way as to give the correct total liability.

Value of future service pension

Ill-health pension

9.48 As to the future service pension, we consider those who retire on grounds of ill-health during the year following the valuation date. Most of those who retire early in the year will not have enough service in that year to make any fractional part of a year of past service at the valuation date up to another complete year, so that they will derive no benefit from their service during the year of exit nor from the incomplete year of past service at the valuation date. On the other hand, most of those who retire late in the year following the valuation date will have completed enough service in that year to make the outstanding part of a year of past service at the valuation date up to another complete year ranking for pension purposes. On the usual averaging assumptions, therefore, one-half of the members retiring in the year following the valuation date will receive merely the past service pension allowed for in the valuation, and the other half will each receive a pension of £K per annum greater than this. The future service pension element to be allowed for in the valuation is thus one-half of a year's accrual for each member.

9.49 Considering now those who retire in the year beginning one year after the valuation date, each of these will receive £K per annum in respect of the year beginning on the valuation date together with £$\tfrac{1}{2}K$ per annum on the average for service during the year in which they retire (on reasoning similar to that of the previous section). The future service pension element to be allowed for is thus 1½ years' accrual. Dealing with subsequent years of membership on the same lines and introducing the same probability, discounting and annuity functions as before it is evident that the value of the future service pension on ill-health retirement is found by multiplying K by the total numbers of members in the age group and by the function

$$\tfrac{1}{2}C_x^{ra} + 1\tfrac{1}{2}C_{x+1}^{ra} + \ldots + (64\tfrac{1}{2} - x)C_{64}^{ra} \qquad \ldots\ldots 9.49.1$$

which is exactly the same as the ill-health retirement part of formula 9.42.5.

Age pension

9.50 Considering the pension on retirement at age 65, the past durations at the valuation date of members aged x nearest birthday at that date with curtate duration n will vary from exactly n years to just under $n + 1$ years. The members' exact ages at the valuation date vary from $x - \frac{1}{2}$ to $x + \frac{1}{2}$. The total durations upon attainment of age 65 will therefore vary from $n + 65 - (x + \frac{1}{2})$ to $n + 1 + 65 - (x - \frac{1}{2})$, i.e. from $n + (65 - x) - \frac{1}{2}$ to $n + (65 - x) + 1\frac{1}{2}$, with only completed years of service counting for pension purposes. It can be shown that, on the usual averaging assumptions, the pension to be received on retirement at age 65, in addition to that in respect of n years of past membership at the valuation date, is K multiplied by $(65 - x - 1)$ in one-eighth, $(65 - x)$ in three-quarters, and $(65 - x + 1)$ in the remaining one-eighth of the cases. It is therefore reasonable to value a future service age retirement pension of $(65 - x)K$ for all members, and the addition of a term for this for formula 9.49.1 reproduces exactly formula 9.42.5.

9.51 If, therefore, pension benefits are granted in respect of completed years only, and the past service recorded in the data for each member is the curtate past service, the same formulae can be used to evaluate the pension benefit as are used to value a pension based on years and parts of a year when the membership information shows nearest years of duration. This ends the discussion of the special case in which only completed years of service count for pension, and we now revert to the more usual case in which parts of a year count proportionately.

The adjustment required if years of service in excess of a prescribed number do not count for pension purpose

9.52 It is sometimes provided in the rules of a scheme that years of service in excess of some prescribed number (usually 40) are not to count for pension purposes. This is not a Revenue requirement, unless the pension scale is such that the pension in respect of 40 years' service is in fact equal to the maximum pension permitted under Revenue rules.

9.53 In the example of paragraph 9.33 et seq, expression 9.37.1 values a pension of nK for a member now aged x with n years of past service. If there is a '40 year maximum' provision it is necessary to restrict to $(40 - n)K$ the pension allowed for in the future service calculation. In expression 9.42.5 a future service pension of $(65-x)K$ is allowed for on retirement at age 65. If, therefore, $(65-x)$ is greater than $(40-n)$ for a particular member, an adjustment must be made to the future service pension value as so far calculated. What is required for the future service pension is a sequence of C functions multiplied by $\frac{1}{2}$, $1\frac{1}{2}$, $2\frac{1}{2}$, ... $38\frac{1}{2} - n$, $39\frac{1}{2} - n$, $40 - n$, ... $40 - n$. It will be found that the replacement of $\bar{R}_x^{ra}$ in expression 9.42.4 by $\bar{R}_x^{ra} - \bar{R}_{x+40-n}^{ra}$ achieves the desired effect. Members who have already completed more than 40 years' service need special treatment; the number 40 must be substituted for n in expression 9.37.1 and the future service pension liability made zero.

The basic importance of the functions C, M and R

9.54 Functions of the type C, M and R are fundamental to pension scheme work, because the accrual of benefit broadly according to years of service is universal. Much of the remainder of this chapter is concerned merely with the elaboration of these basic functions to meet particular situations. It should be firmly grasped that the function M, being simply a sum of 'C's, is used for the valuation of any benefit or part of a benefit whose amount will not be increased, as time proceeds, by virtue of an increasing number of years counting for the calculation of benefit. The function $\bar{R}$ on the other hand, being of the form shown in expression 9.42.5, is used for the valuation of a benefit or that part of a benefit which will be so increased. It will be taken for granted in the remainder of this chapter, which deals with the formulae for various different types and scales of benefit and contributions, that the point is thoroughly understood.

Certain assumptions made in the remainder of this chapter

9.55 We now turn to the discussion of more complicated formulae. We shall assume that a scheme is being valued at a particular date. The pension benefit is provided on retirement at age 65, or on earlier retirement on grounds of ill-health. Parts of a year count proportionately for benefit. We shall consider a group of N members of a scheme all aged x nearest birthday. The following information is assumed to be available at the valuation date for each member.

(TPS) = Total past earnings during membership of the scheme.
(AS)   = Earnings in the year preceding the valuation date.

n = Past pensionable service taken to the nearest whole number of years.

(TPC) = Total past contributions with compound interest at rate j.

A summation sign preceding any of the above symbols in the subsequent discussion means summation over all members aged x.

'Final average salary' pension scale
The salary scale function z

9.56 If the pension is based on the average annual earnings during the 'm' years preceding retirement it is necessary to introduce the function

$$z_y = \frac{1}{m}[s_{y-m} + s_{y-m+1} + \ldots + s_{y-1}] \qquad \ldots\ldots 9.56.1$$

Clearly

$$\frac{z_{x+t}}{s_{x-1}}$$

represents the ratio of the expected average annual earnings during the m years preceding attainment of age $x + t$ to the annual earnings in the year of age $x - 1$ to x. The function $\frac{1}{2}(z_x + z_{x+1})$ is found to be useful in practice, and is conventionally written as $z_{x+\frac{1}{2}}$.

The pension formulae

9.57 Assuming that the service table ends at age 65, and remembering that retirements at ages less than this are assumed to occur half-way through the year of age, the functions required for the valuation of the pension benefit are similar to those developed previously except for the introduction of the necessary z and s functions. They are as follows.

$$^zC_y^{ra} = v^{y+\frac{1}{2}} r_y z_{y+\frac{1}{2}} \bar{a}'_{y+\frac{1}{2}} \ (y \leqslant 64) \qquad \ldots\ldots 9.57.1$$

$$^zC_{65}^{ra} = v^{65} r_{65} z_{65} \bar{a}'_{65} \qquad \ldots\ldots 9.57.2$$

$$^zM_x^{ra} = \sum_{t=0}^{65-x} {}^zC_{x+t}^{ra} \qquad \ldots\ldots 9.57.3$$

$$^z\bar{M}_x^{ra} = {}^zM_x^{ra} - \frac{1}{2} {}^zC_x^{ra} \ (x \leqslant 64) \qquad \ldots\ldots 9.57.4$$

$$^z\bar{R}_x^{ra} = \sum_{t=0}^{64-x} {}^z\bar{M}_{x+t}^{ra} \qquad \ldots\ldots 9.57.5$$

The calculation of these functions is illustrated in Tables 5 and 6.

The denominator function

9.58 It is also necessary to introduce an 's' function into the denominator of the various valuation formulae, and (since the valuation information includes earnings in the year preceding the valuation date) we define

$$^sD_x = v^x s_{x-1} l_x \qquad \qquad \text{..... 9.58.1}$$

The pension values

9.59 For the group of members concerned, the value of the pension in respect of past pensionable service at the valuation date, supposing the pension fraction to be $1/K$, is

$$\frac{1}{K} [\Sigma ((AS) \times n)] \, ^zM_x^{ra} / ^sD_x \qquad \qquad \text{..... 9.59.1}$$

It will be appreciated that in the left hand part of this expression the product of annual earnings and duration is first found separately for each member and the result is then summed for all members. The value of the pension in respect of future service is

$$\frac{1}{K} [\Sigma (AS)] \, ^z\bar{R}_x^{ra} / ^sD_x \qquad \qquad \text{..... 9.59.2}$$

A special adjustment for members at the oldest ages

9.60 At the instant before the retirement of a member at the age of 65, the pension liability in respect of him, calculated by the formula set out above, would be

$$\frac{1}{K} [(AS) \times n] \, ^zM_{65}^{ra} / ^sD_{65} \qquad \qquad \text{..... 9.60.1}$$

$$= \frac{1}{K} [(AS) \times n] \frac{\frac{1}{m}(s_{65-m} + s_{65-m+1} + \ldots + s_{64})}{s_{64}} \bar{a}'_{65}$$

$$\text{..... 9.60.2}$$

The pension is therefore valued as if the member's earnings during the last m years had followed exactly the progression of the salary scale used in the actuarial formulae. The member's earnings during those years are, however, known, and the actual figures will be different from those implied by the above expression.

9.61 A similar point arises for all members aged between $(65 - m)$ and 65, where m is the averaging period. For such a member aged y, with annual salary of (AS) in the preceding year, the value of the prospective pension at age 65 will be calculated as if the average salary at age 65 would be

$$(AS) \quad \frac{\frac{1}{m}(s_{65-m} + s_{65-m+1} + \ldots + s_{64})}{s_{y-1}} \qquad \ldots\ldots 9.61.1$$

The value is therefore calculated as if the salaries in the years from age $65 - m$ to age y had followed the salary scale, whereas in fact they will not have done so. It is a matter of judgement whether to make a special adjustment to the calculated liabilities in this connection; if an adjustment is not made, any profit or loss at the instant of retirement emerges as part of the experience. If the averaging period is long, so that a comparatively large number of members may be concerned, or if the amount at issue is likely to be comparatively large, it may be necessary to make a special adjustment.

Final salary pension scale

9.62   If m is made equal to 1 in expression 9.56.1 the formulae become those appropriate to a pension based on earnings during the year before retirement. If the pension is based on the annual rate of earnings at the moment of retirement, the salary function included in $^{z}C_{y}$ will be s_{y} ($y \leqslant 64$) and $s_{64\frac{1}{2}}$ ($y = 65$), the latter being used to represent the annual rate of earnings at age 65. A figure for $s_{64\frac{1}{2}}$ is obtained in practice by extrapolation from the normal series of s_{y} which terminates at age 64. In fact, the Inland Revenue rules on maximum benefits rest on definitions of Final Renumeration expressed in terms of earnings over a period of a year rather than an annual rate at a particular time and Revenue objections may be raised if the ordinary pension scale of the scheme is expressed in terms of an annual rate.

'Escalated flat' functions

9.63   In constructing the formulae for an integrated scheme it is often necessary to deal with amounts of deductions which, although not directly related to salaries, will increase if inflation continues; a deduction related to the amount of the State flat-rate pension for a single person is a case in point. The problem is usually dealt with by the use of a modified form of salary scale. It will be recalled from paragraph 9.28 that if the series of numbers

s_x, s_{x+1}, s_{x+2} .... constitute a salary scale appropriate when overall levels of earnings do not change, the series of numbers $s_x(1+e)^x$, $s_{x+1}(1+e)^{x+1}$, ... form a salary scale incorporating a rate of earnings escalation of e per annum. Actuarial functions incorporating this type of scale but with s_{x+t} = unity for all t provide the means for dealing with deductions of the type under discussion, which are often referred to as 'escalated flat' amounts.

'Average pay' pension scale
Past service pension

9.64 The 'z' function is used when the pension scale involves the average earnings during the m years preceding retirement. For an average pay pension scale as described in paragraph 5.3 a different approach is necessary. If the pension scale is $1/K$ of total past earnings at the date of retirement, each payment of earnings can be regarded as having associated with it a pension of $1/K$ of its amount. The pension in respect of total past earnings at any given date is a known fixed amount equal to $1/K$ of those earnings. Returning to the data of paragraph 9.55, the liability in respect of the past service pension for the group of members aged x is

$$\frac{1}{K}[\Sigma\,(\mathrm{TPS})]\,M_x^{ra}\,/D_x \qquad\qquad \text{..... 9.64.1}$$

where M_x^{ra} is as defined in expression 9.39.1

Future service pension

9.65 Considering future service, the expected amount of the average earnings during the year of age $x+t$ to $x+t+1$ of a survivor of the group then in active service is

$$(\mathrm{AS})\,\frac{s_{x+t}}{s_{x-1}}\ .$$

The amount of pension associated with these earnings is

$$\frac{1}{K}(\mathrm{AS})\,\frac{s_{x+t}}{s_{x-1}}\ .$$

Using the reasoning of paragraph 9.40, the present liability in respect of this element of pension is

$$\frac{1}{K}(\mathrm{AS})\ \frac{s_{x+t}}{s_{x-1}}\ \frac{(\tfrac{1}{2}C_{x+t}^{ra}+\ C_{x+t+1}^{ra}+\ .....\ +\ C_{65}^{ra})}{v^x l_x} \qquad \text{..... 9.65.1}$$

$$=\ \frac{1}{K}(\mathrm{AS})\ \frac{s_{x+t}\,\bar{M}_{x+t}^{ra}}{{}^s D_x} \qquad\qquad \text{..... 9.65.2}$$

The total value of the pension in respect of earnings during all future years of membership is therefore

$$\frac{1}{K}(AS) \left[\sum_{t=0}^{64-x} (s_{x+t} \bar{M}_{x+t}^{ra}) \right] / {}^sD_x \qquad \ldots\ldots 9.65.3$$

If we define

$$^s\bar{R}_x^{ra} = \sum_{t=0}^{64-x} (s_{x+t} \bar{M}_{x+t}^{ra}) \qquad \ldots\ldots 9.65.4$$

expression 9.65.3 can be written as

$$\frac{1}{K}(AS) \, {}^s\bar{R}_x^{ra} / {}^sD_x \qquad \ldots\ldots 9.65.5$$

For all members in the group the total future service pension is therefore

$$\frac{1}{K}[\Sigma(AS)] \, {}^s\bar{R}_x^{ra} / {}^sD_x \qquad \ldots\ldots 9.65.6$$

The 'adjustment for maximum pension' in a career average scheme

9.66   Maximum duration rules for a pension scale of this type may take a number of different forms. A precise allowance for the operation of such a rule would often be a complicated matter. The effect of such rules is sometimes quite small, because all that is involved is the deletion from the pension calculation of earnings 40 or more years ago. These amounts are trivial because of the effect of earnings escalation in the meantime. The adjustment could therefore be made on approximate lines, and we shall not develop the theory of the matter here, particularly in view of the fact that such scales are now rare in the United Kingdom.

'Dynamised average pay' pension scale

9.67   There was envisaged in paragraph 5.5 a type of average pay pension scale in which the pension entitlement earned in a particular year is based on pay in that year but is dynamised in respect of each subsequent year until the date at which it comes into payment. It was noted in that paragraph that, although the State earnings-related pension is essentially of this type, there is no evidence of a resurgence of such a scale in occupational pension schemes. It is nevertheless instructive to consider what changes are necessary in the formulae of paragraphs 9.64 and 9.65 to allow for this arrangement.

9.68 In developing the formulae we need to make some assumptions about the procedure for dynamisation. We will assume the following.

(i)   The scheme is based on fiscal years, as is the State scheme.

(ii)   There is published each 5th April an earnings index. The index at 5th April in calendar year N is written I_N.

(iii) If earnings that were earned in the fiscal year ended on 5th April in calendar year N are taken into the calculation of a pension on retirement in the fiscal year ended on 5th April in calendar year M, they are taken in at an amount equal to their actual amount multiplied by

$$\frac{I_{M-1}}{I_N}$$

(iv)   We are making a valuation on a particular 5th April and in arriving at the amount of total past earnings (TPS) which forms part of the data for each individual, each past year's earnings have been dynamised by the method of (iii) above. All values of I up to and including that published at 5th April before the 5th April as at which the calculations are being made have been allowed for in arriving at the amount of (TPS).

Past Service

9.69 It follows from (iii) and (iv) above that if a pension is to be calculated in the fiscal year immediately following the valuation date, the past service element will involve (TPS) with no further dynamisation. For retirements in the next fiscal year revaluation for one year will be involved; we will employ a rate of revaluation e. We can build up a sequence of 'C' functions similar to those of expression 9.37.2 except that they will involve successive powers of $(1 + e)$. Retirement at age 65 is slightly more complicated, in that if we have a group of members aged x nearest birthday at the valuation date, one half of those retiring at age 65 will be expected to do so in the fiscal year ending $(64 - x)$ years after the valuation date and the remainder in the following fiscal year. The past service pension liability is therefore expresssed by the formula

$$\frac{1}{K}(\text{TPS})\,[r_x\,v^{\frac{1}{2}}\,\bar{a}'_{x+\frac{1}{2}} + (1+e)\,r_{x+1}\,v^{1\frac{1}{2}}\,\bar{a}'_{x+1\frac{1}{2}}$$
$$+ \ \dots \ + \ (1+e)^{64-x}\,r_{64}\,v^{64\frac{1}{2}-x}\,\bar{a}'_{64\frac{1}{2}}$$
$$+ (1+e)^{64\frac{1}{2}-x}\,r_{65}\,v^{65-x}\,\bar{a}'_{65}]/l_x \qquad \dots\dots 9.69.1$$

If we write

$$^{e}C_x^{ra} = (1+e)^x\,C_x^{ra} \quad x \leqslant 64 \qquad \dots\dots 9.69.2$$

$$^{e}C_{65}^{ra} = (1+e)^{64\frac{1}{2}}\,C_{65}^{ra} \qquad \dots\dots 9.69.3$$

$$^{e}M_x^{ra} = \sum_{t=0}^{65-x}\,{}^{e}C_{x+t}^{ra} \qquad \dots\dots 9.69.4$$

$$^{e}D_x = (1+e)^x\,D_x \qquad \dots\dots 9.69.5$$

The past service pension liability may be written

$$\frac{1}{K}[\Sigma\,(\text{TPS})]\,{}^{e}M_x^{ra}/{}^{e}D_x \qquad \dots\dots 9.69.6$$

Future service

9.70 Earnings in the fiscal year beginning t years after the valuation date are expected to be

$$(\text{AS})\,\frac{s_{x+t}}{s_{x-1}}$$

as in paragraph 9.65. The value at the valuation date of the pension rights arising from these earnings upon retirement in the fiscal year beginning $(t + n)$ years after the valuation date is as follows.

$$\tfrac{1}{2}.\frac{1}{K}(\text{AS})\,\frac{s_{x+t}}{s_{x-1}}\,\frac{r_{x+t}}{l_x}\,v^{t+\frac{1}{2}}\,\bar{a}'_{x+t+\frac{1}{2}} \qquad\qquad \text{if } n = 0$$

$$\frac{1}{K}(\text{AS})\,\frac{s_{x+t}}{s_{x-1}}\,\frac{r_{x+t+n}}{l_x}\,v^{t+n+\frac{1}{2}}\bar{a}'_{x+t+n+\frac{1}{2}}\,(1+e)^{n-1}$$
$$\text{if } 1 < n < 64-x-t$$

$$\frac{1}{K}(\text{AS})\,\frac{s_{x+t}}{s_{x-1}}\,\frac{r_{65}}{l_x}\,v^{65-x}\bar{a}'_{65}\,(1+e)^{63\frac{1}{2}-x-t}$$

on retirement at age 65.

The total expression may be summarised as

$$\frac{1}{K}(AS)\ \frac{s_{x+t}}{s_{x-1}}\ \frac{1}{v^x\,l_x\,(1+e)^{x+t+1}}[\tfrac{1}{2}r_{x+t}\,v^{x+t+\frac{1}{2}}\,\bar{a}'_{x+t+\frac{1}{2}}(1+e)^{x+t+\frac{1}{2}}$$

$$+\ \sum_{n=1}^{64-x-t}\ r_{x+t+n}\,v^{x+t+n+\frac{1}{2}}\,\bar{a}'_{x+t+n+\frac{1}{2}}\,(1+e)^{x+t+n}$$

$$+\ r_{65}\,v^{65}\,\bar{a}_{65}\,(1+e)^{64\frac{1}{2}}]\qquad\qquad \dots 9.70.1$$

9.71 The first expression in the brackets includes the factor $(1+e)^{x+t+\frac{1}{2}}$. The development of the commutation functions is much simplified if we use $(1+e)^{x+t}$ instead, and we shall accept the small error involved in this. Formula 9.70.1 then becomes

$$\frac{1}{K}(AS)\ \frac{1}{{}^sD_x}\ \frac{s_{x+t}}{(1+e)^{x+t+1}}\,{}^e\bar{M}^{ra}_{x+t}\qquad\qquad \dots 9.71.1$$

where ${}^e\bar{M}^{ra}_{x+t} = {}^e M^{ra}_{x+t} - \tfrac{1}{2}{}^e C^{ra}_{x+t}\qquad\qquad \dots 9.71.2$

using the notation of paragraph 9.69. Summing over all values of t gives a total future service value of

$$\frac{1}{K}(AS)\ {}^{es}\bar{R}^{ra}_x/{}^sD_x$$

where

$$ {}^{es}\bar{R}^{ra}_x = \sum_{t=0}^{64-x}\ \frac{s_{x+t}}{(1+e)^{x+t+1}}\,{}^e\bar{M}^{ra}_{x+t}\qquad\qquad \dots 9.71.3$$

Capital sums on retirement

9.72 As noted in Chapter 6, capital sum retirement benefits may be provided in a scheme either by way of a right to commute a part of the pension or by way of a scale of capital sum retirement benefits separate from the pension scale. In the former case the main valuation calculations will probably be carried out ignoring the commutation option. The actuary will adjust the resulting figures as necessary to allow for any extent to which the terms of commutation differ from the valuation basis. He will have to make an assumption about the extent to which the commutation option will be exercised.

9.73 If capital sum retirement benefits are provided on a scale separate from the pension scale it is necessary to develop separate actuarial functions for their valuation. These functions are similar to those for pension benefits except that the annuity is omitted. These functions are written C_x^r, M_x^r etc. instead of C_x^{ra}, M_x^{ra} etc.

Death benefits

9.74 We now develop the actuarial formulae in connection with the most common types of death benefit provided in pension schemes. We have already mentioned that the liability for capital sum benefits on death after retirement is allowed for in the annuity brought into the pension formulae. We now deal with capital sum benefits on death in service and with widows' and children's benefits on death in service or after retirement. As before we use in the discussion the data of paragraph 9.55.

Capital sum on death in service equal to the amount of a member's own accumulated contributions

The past service benefit

9.75 Suppose that the benefit on the death of a member during service is a capital sum equal to the amount of the contributions he has made to the scheme, accumulated with compound interest at rate j per annum. The probability of the death in service during the year of age y to $y + 1$ of a member now aged x exact ($y > x$) is d_y/l_x. Assuming that deaths occur on the average half-way through the year of age, the amount (TPC) will have accumulated at the date of death to

$$(TPC)(1+j)^{y+\frac{1}{2}-x}$$

The present value of this payment is

$$(TPC)\, v^{y+\frac{1}{2}-x} (1+j)^{y+\frac{1}{2}-x}\, d_y/l_x \qquad \ldots\ldots 9.75.1$$

$$= (TPC)^j C_y^d/{}^j D_x \qquad \ldots\ldots 9.75.2$$

where $\;{}^j C_y^d = (1+j)^{y+\frac{1}{2}} v^{y+\frac{1}{2}} d_y \qquad \ldots\ldots 9.75.3$

and $\quad {}^j D_x = (1+j)^x D_x \qquad \ldots\ldots 9.75.4$

The value of the death benefit during the whole of future employment arising from the accumulated contributions at the valuation date is therefore

$$(TPC)^j M_x^d/{}^j D_x \qquad \ldots\ldots 9.75.5$$

where $^{j}M_{x}^{d} = \sum\limits_{t=0}^{64-x} {}^{j}C_{x+t}^{d}$ 9.75.6

The function $^{j}M_{x}^{d}/{}^{j}D_{x}$ is often written as $^{j}\bar{A}_{x}^{d}$ although it is not, of course, a 'throughout life' function.

The future service benefit

9.76 Turning to the death benefit in respect of contributions payable in the future, the expected amount in the year of age y to $y + 1$ of a contribution of one per cent. of earnings is

$$.01 \, (AS) \, s_{y}/s_{x-1}$$

If the member dies during the year of age y to $y + 1$, only one half of a year's contribution will on the average have been paid during that year. It is conventional in valuing the benefit on death in service during that year to ignore any interest which may have accumulated on this contribution, whether or not the rules of the scheme provide for such interest. If the member dies during the year of age $y + 1$ to $y + 2$, one year's interest on average will have accrued on the contribution paid in the year of age y to $y + 1$. Extending this reasoning to later years, the value at age x of the death benefit arising from the contribution paid in the year of age y to $y + 1$ is

$$(.01)(AS) \frac{s_{y}}{s_{x-1}}$$

$$\frac{[\frac{1}{2}v^{y+\frac{1}{2}-x}d_{y} + v^{y+1\frac{1}{2}-x}(1+j)\,d_{y+1} + \ldots + v^{64\frac{1}{2}-x}\,(1+j)^{64-y}d_{64}]}{l_{x}}$$

..... 9.76.1

$$= (.01)(AS) \frac{s_{y}}{s_{x-1}} \, v_{(j)}^{y+\frac{1}{2}} \, \frac{1}{D_{x}} \, [\frac{1}{2}{}^{j}C_{y}^{d} + {}^{j}C_{y+1}^{d} + \ldots + {}^{j}c_{64}^{d}]$$

.....9.76.2

$$= (.01)(AS) \, s_{y} \, v_{(j)}^{y+\frac{1}{2}} \, {}^{j}\bar{M}_{y}^{d}/{}^{s}D_{x}$$ 9.76.3

where $^{j}\bar{M}_{y}^{d} = {}^{j}M_{y}^{d} - \frac{1}{2} \, {}^{j}C_{y}^{d}$ 9.76.4

The total death in service liability in respect of future contributions at the rate of K per cent. of earnings for the members concerned is therefore

$$\frac{K}{100} \, [\Sigma(AS)]^{sj}\bar{R}_{x}^{d}/{}^{s}D_{x}$$ 9.76.5

where $^{sj}\bar{R}^d_x = \sum\limits_{t=0}^{64-x} s_{x+t} \, v^{x+t+\frac{1}{2}}_{(j)} \, ^j\bar{M}^d_{x+t}$ 9.76.6

The function $^{sj}\bar{R}^d_x/^s D_x$ is often written as $^{sj}(\bar{I}A)^d_x$. If the rate of accumulation allowed on contributions happens to be the same as the valuation rate of interest, $^j M^d_x/^j D_x$ reduces to

$$\sum_{t=0}^{64-x} d_{x+t}/l_x,$$

which is simply the probability at age x of death occurring during subsequent service.

9.77 In developing these formulae it has been assumed, with the small exception stated, that interest accrues continuously. Usually the rules of a scheme specify how interest is to be calculated and a variety of methods are in use, but it is seldom worth while developing special formulae to allow for points of detail in the interest accumulation rule.

Capital sum on death in service related to earnings

9.78 Pension schemes commonly provide on death in service a capital sum equal to a multiple of annual earnings, instead of or in addition to the return of contributions dealt with above. The amount might for example be twice annual earnings; another possible scale is 1/40th of annual earnings multiplied by the number of years of membership.

9.79 Using the data of paragraph 9.55, the expected rate of salary at age $y + \frac{1}{2}$ for the member now aged x is $(AS)s_y/s_{x-1}$. The present value at age x of capital sum benefit equal to one year's earnings on death in service between age y and $y + 1$ is therefore

$$(AS) \frac{s_y}{s_{x-1}} \, v^{y+\frac{1}{2}-x} \frac{d_y}{l_x}$$ 9.79.1

$$= (AS) \, ^s C^d_y/^s D_x$$ 9.79.2

where $^s C^d_y = s_y \, v^{y+\frac{1}{2}} \, d_y$ 9.79.3

The total value of the death in service benefit for the group of members is thus

$$[\Sigma (AS)] \, ^s M^d_x/^s D_x$$ 9.79.4

where $\quad {}^sM_x^d = \sum_{t=0}^{64-x} {}^sC_{x+t}^d$ $\qquad\qquad$ 9.79.5

As this is not a benefit that accrues with length of membership the formula does not arise in the form of separate past and future service elements. The function ${}^sM_x^d/{}^sD_x$ is sometimes written as ${}^s\bar{A}_x^d$. It is not, of course, a 'throughout life' function as this symbol might suggest. The calculation of this function is illustrated in Table 12.

9.80 If the death in service benefit is, say, 1/40th of the rate of earnings current at death multiplied by the number of years of membership, it will be found, by reasoning very similar to that for pension formulae, that the value of the benefit in respect of n years of past service is

$$\frac{1}{40}\left[\Sigma\left\{(AS) \times n\right\}\right] {}^sM_x^d/{}^sD_x \qquad\qquad ..... 9.80.1$$

The value of the future service benefit is

$$\frac{1}{40}\left[\Sigma(AS)\right] {}^s\bar{R}_x^d/{}^sD_x \qquad\qquad ..... 9.80.2$$

where $\quad {}^s\bar{M}_x^d = {}^sM_x^d - \tfrac{1}{2}{}^sC_x^d$ $\qquad\qquad$ 9.80.3

and $\quad {}^s\bar{R}_x^d = \sum_{t=0}^{64-x} {}^s\bar{M}_{x+t}^d$ $\qquad\qquad$ 9.80.4

9.81 Although the formula of paragraph 9.79 may appear to be the obvious way of costing a capital sum payment of once times earnings on death in service, its use raises an interesting point related to the pace of funding. The formula places a present value on the capital sums payable on the deaths in service expected to arise in future from the group of members now aged x. It therefore brings into account the heavier mortality rates which will be experienced as these members grow older. It would be possible to convert this cost into a contribution rate by dividing by the contribution function developed later in this chapter. If, however, the trustees of the scheme obtained quotations from life offices for the insurance of the capital sum death in service benefit, the life offices would quote an amount related to the product of the current level of earnings and the mortality rates at the present ages of the members concerned. The cost of the year's cover as quoted might well be less than the first year amount of the contribution as calculated above. What advice should the actuary tender to the trustees?

9.82   As in many other issues related to the pace of funding, there is much to be said for the trustees' deciding the matter as a point of policy providing that the issues are understood. If it is decided that a current cost method is satisfactory the liability if accepted within the scheme would be calculated as the product of the amounts involved and the rate of mortality in the year concerned, for each member.

Widows' and children's benefits on death in service or after retirement

Widows' pensions: the 'collective' method

9.83   Widows' pensions are usually valued by formulae of the same general type as those already developed for members' pensions, but including such variations and extra functions as are required. We first deal with the most commonly used method which depends on the introduction of 'proportions married' or other proportions into the factors. This is known as the 'collective' method of valuation.

Death in service

9.84   The basic 'C' function for the valuation of widows' pensions payable on death in service is

$$C_y^{d(wa)} = v^{y+\frac{1}{2}} d_y h_{y+\frac{1}{2}}^d \bar{a}_{w+\frac{1}{2}}'' \qquad \qquad \dots\dots 9.84.1$$

In this formula d_y is based on a service table appropriate to all the male members concerned irrespective of marital status, $h_{y+\frac{1}{2}}^d$ is the proportion married amongst male members dying at age y last birthday and $\bar{a}_{w+\frac{1}{2}}''$ is the weighted average of the widow's annuity (ceasing on remarriage if appropriate) for widows of members dying at age y last birthday. These widows are assumed to be of average age w last birthday at the date of the member's death.

Death after retirement

9.85 Similarly, the basic 'C' functions for the valuation of widows' pensions payable on death after retirement are

$$C_y^{r(wa)} = v^{y+\frac{1}{2}} r_y h_{y+\frac{1}{2}}^r \, \bar{a}_{y+\frac{1}{2}\mid w+\frac{1}{2}}^{\prime\prime} \, (y \leqslant 64) \qquad \ldots\ldots 9.85.1$$

$$C_{65}^{r(wa)} = v^{65} r_{65} h_{65}^r \, \bar{a}_{65\mid w}^{\prime\prime} \qquad \ldots\ldots 9.85.2$$

In these formulae r_y and r_{65} are based on a service table appropriate to all the male members concerned irrespective of marital status and $h_{y+\frac{1}{2}}^r$ and h_{65}^r are the proportions married amongst male members retiring at age y last birthday and at 65 exact respectively. The reversionary annuities $\bar{a}_{y+\frac{1}{2}/w+\frac{1}{2}}^{\prime\prime}$ and $\bar{a}_{65\mid w}^{\prime\prime}$ are the weighted average values of the reversionary annuities (ceasing on remarriage if appropriate) to the wives of married members retiring at age y last birthday and at age 65 exact respectively.

9.86 The addition of further items such as salary scale functions to these formulae to define the quantum of benefit, and the development of M, $\bar{M}$ and $\bar{R}$ functions, proceed as before. The calculations are illustrated in Tables 8, 9 and 10. Calculations in respect of benefits to widowers of female members involve no new principles.

Capital sum benefits depending on marital status

9.87 The formulae for the valuation of capital sum benefits payable on death in service can be developed very simply into formulae for the valuation of capital sum benefits payable on the death in service of married members only, or on the death of unmarried members only. All that is required is the inclusion of the factor $h_{y+\frac{1}{2}}$ or $(1 - h_{y+\frac{1}{2}})$ respectively in the functions previously developed.

The use of proportions other than simple 'proportions married'

9.88 The features of a particular scheme may make it necessary to estimate rather more complicated proportions. For instance, it may be that all employees have to pay additional contributions for widows' benefits but there is a refund of the whole or a part of these contributions on the retirement of a member who at no time during his membership was married. In this case it would be necessary to estimate not the proportions of those retiring who were unmarried but the proportions of those retiring who had not been married at any time during membership. These proportions are then incorporated in the actuarial functions. This is a useful and simple method of dealing with complicated situations, the main difficulty being the assessment of suitable proportions. Such provisions have tended to become uncommon in the United Kingdom since the provision of widows' pension rights became a condition of contracting-out.

Widows' pensions: the 'reversionary' method

9.89   There is an alternative method of valuation of widows' benefits, known as the 'reversionary' method, which has certain theoretical advantages over the collective method. The reversionary method is seldom used in practice because it is more complicated in application than the collective method and its theoretical advantages are usually more apparent than real.

9.90   Under the reversionary method the probability that a member will be married at death is assessed separately for present married members, bachelors and widowers, and in respect of present and any subsequent marriages. The various rates which determine future proportions married are all brought separately into the formulae, and any observed or anticipated trends in these rates can be allowed for.

Present wives of married members: death in service

9.91   Under this method the basic function for the valuation of a pension payable during the widowhood of the present wife of an existing married member aged x and arising on the death of the member during employment before attainment of age 65 is

$$\frac{\sum\limits_{t=0}^{64-x} d_{x+t} \, D_{y+t+\frac{1}{2}} \, \bar{a}'_{y+t+\frac{1}{2}}}{l_x \, D_y} \qquad \dots\dots 9.91.1$$

where

l_x and d_{x+t} are derived from a service table appropriate to married male members

D_y and $D_{y+t+\frac{1}{2}}$ are based on a life table appropriate to wives of members

$\bar{a}'_{y+t+\frac{1}{2}}$ is based on the rates of mortality (and, if appropriate, remarriage) of widows of members.

Present wives of married members: death after retirement

9.92 The basic function for the valuation of a pension payable during the widowhood of the present wife of an existing member and arising on the death of the member after retirement at age 65 or earlier retirement on grounds of ill-health is

$$\frac{[\sum_{t=0}^{64-x} r_{x+t} \, D_{y+t+\frac{1}{2}} \, \bar{a}'_{x+t+\frac{1}{2}|y+t+\frac{1}{2}}] + r_{65} \, D_{y+65-x} \, \bar{a}'_{65|y+65-x}}{l_x \, D_y}$$

..... 9.92.1

the component functions being based on the appropriate service tables and life tables.

9.93 The liability in respect of the present wives of existing members usually forms the main part of the liability for prospective widows' benefits in a scheme, and as the formulae set out above are reasonably straightfoward in application they are occasionally used in practice. The formulae for less important parts of the liability, such as that in respect of future first wives of members at present unmarried, are complicated and the small liability involved hardly ever justifies their use.

Children's benefits

9.94 Children's and orphans' benefits usually form only a very small part of the liabilities of a scheme. They are often allowed for in a valuation by loading the value of widows' benefits by such percentages as seem appropriate for the particular benefits in the light of the actuary's general experience. It is unusual for a pensioner dying after retirement at normal pension age to leave dependent children. Only a small loading for children's benefits would therefore be added to the liability for widows' pensions on death after retirement. The loadings for children's benefits on death in service and on death after ill-health retirement would usually be larger.

Withdrawal benefits

9.95 The functions for valuing a benefit on withdrawal equal to the total amount of the member's contributions with interest are developed in the same way as the death in service benefit functions dealt with in paragraphs 9.75 and 9.76. The functions used are

$$^j C_y^w = v^{y+\frac{1}{2}} (1+j)^{y+\frac{1}{2}} w_y \qquad \dots\dots 9.95.1$$

$$^j M_x^w = \sum_{t=0} {}^j C_{x+t}^w \qquad \dots\dots 9.95.2$$

$$^j \bar{M}_x^w = {}^j M_x^w - \tfrac{1}{2}\, {}^j C_x^w \qquad \dots\dots 9.95.3$$

$$\text{and } \; {}^{sj} \bar{R}_x^w = \sum_{t=0} s_{x+t}\, v_{(j)}^{x+t+\frac{1}{2}}\, {}^j \bar{M}_{x+t}^w \qquad \dots\dots 9.95.4$$

The upper limit of summation is not shown because withdrawal rates commonly diminish to zero at an age well before the maximum age in the service table. The value of the benefit in respect of accumulated contributions (TPC) at the valuation date is

$$[\Sigma(\text{TPC})]\, {}^j M_x^w / {}^j D_x \qquad \dots\dots 9.95.5$$

The function $^j M_x^w / {}^j D_x$ is often written as $^j \bar{A}_x^w$ although it is not of course a 'throughout life' function. The value of the benefit in respect of future contributions of 1 per cent. of earnings is

$$(.01)\,[\Sigma(\text{AS})]\, {}^{sj} \bar{R}_x^w / {}^s D_x \qquad \dots\dots 9.95.6$$

$^{sj} \bar{R}_x^w / {}^s D_x$ is often written as $^{sj}(\bar{I}\bar{A})_x^w$

9.96 Because of the growing effect of the preservation legislation, it is necessary to develop the formulae for valuing a preserved pension on withdrawal. As explained in Chapter 3, the legislation requires a preserved pension to be provided subject to 5 years' qualifying service. In theory, therefore, the valuation of withdrawal benefits requires the use of select withdrawal rates. In practice these are little used and they are not developed in this book. The formulae normally used to value a deferred pension on withdrawal are somewhat similar to those used to value an immediate pension on ill-health retirement. By analogy with paragraph 9.57 the basic function may be written as

$$^z C_y^{w|a} = v^{y+\frac{1}{2}} w_y\, z_{y+\frac{1}{2}} \frac{D_{65}}{D_{y+\frac{1}{2}}} \bar{a}'_{65} \qquad \dots\dots 9.96.1$$

The 'D' functions are based on a life table, not a service table. The development of this function into more complicated formulae, including the regular increase of a preserved pension before it comes into payment, and the construction of functions to cover such benefits as that on death before the preserved pension becomes payable, involve no new principles. The calculations of a function involving increases at the rate of 5 per cent. p.a. during the period of preservation are illustrated in Table 7, the increases being incorporated in the value of the deferred annuities in column (7) of the table as explained in paragraph 14.11.

Contributions

Contributions related to salary

9.97 Using the data of paragraph 9.55, the earnings expected to be received during the year of age y to $y + 1$ by a member now aged x are

$$(AS) \frac{s_y}{s_{x-1}}$$

and the probability of survival as a member until the middle of that year is $l_{y+\frac{1}{2}}/l_x$. The value of a contribution equal to one per cent. of earnings is thus

$$(.01)(AS) \frac{\sum\limits_{t=0}^{64-x} v^{x+t+\frac{1}{2}} s_{x+t} l_{x+t+\frac{1}{2}}}{{}^s D_x} \quad \dots\dots 9.97.1$$

$$= (.01)(AS) \, {}^s \bar{N}_x / {}^s D_x \quad \dots\dots 9.97.2$$

where $\bar{D}_{x+t} = \frac{1}{2}(D_{x+t} + D_{x+t+1})$ \quad 9.97.3

and $\quad {}^s \bar{N}_x = \sum\limits_{t=0}^{64-x} s_{x+t} \, \bar{D}_{x+t}$ \quad 9.97.4

The contribution factor ${}^s \bar{N}_x / {}^s D_{x+t}$ is usually written as ${}^s \bar{a}_x$. It will be noted that $v^{x+t+\frac{1}{2}} l_{x+t+\frac{1}{2}}$ is taken as equal to $\frac{1}{2}[v^{x+t} l_{x+t} + v^{x+t+1} l_{x+t+1}]$ because the latter functions will have already been computed, and the error is small. The calculations are illustrated in Table 4.

Contributions on flat or 'escalated flat' amounts

9.98 If contributions are expressed as a percentage of $(P - F)$ the values of the contributions on full earnings and on the deduction will usually need to be calculated separately, for the reasons mentioned in connection with pensions. The formulae in paragraph 9.97 provide the means for the valuation of contributions on full earnings. Contributions on a flat amount are valued by formulae similar to those above but omitting the salary scale function. Contributions on an amount which is not related to salary but which may be expected to increase if there is inflation (an 'escalated flat' amount) are valued by formulae similar to those above but using a 'with escalation' salary scale with $s_x = 1$ for all x.

The 'collective' method applied to contribution formulae

9.99 The introduction of a proportion married or one minus this proportion in the contribution formulae enables the contributions of married members and of single members to be valued separately. The use of more complex proportions is possible, as in the case of the liabilities.

THE FRAMEWORK OF COMPUTATION: II

THE FRAMEWORK OF COMPUTATION: II

A computer method

10.1 This chapter provides a brief outline of one particular computerised valuation system. This system rests on the basic actuarial elements of paragraph 9.15 but it designed to replace the commutation columns and manual methods described in the previous chapter and to extend the range of calculations that can conveniently be made, compared with manual methods. The outline is based on part of the paper by R.G. Ashurst and G.H. Day entitled 'The Emerging Benefits of Computer Techniques or the Computer Techniques of Emerging Benefits' discussed by the Institute of Actuaries Students' Society on 3rd January 1978. We use the data of paragraph 9.55 but this is now regarded as relating to one individual member.

The liability for ill-health pensions

10.2 As an example of the approach we consider the liabilities in relation to an ill-health pension equal to 1/K of final average earnings for each year of membership. The annual amount of pension expected to become payable upon the retirement on grounds of ill-health between ages y and $y+1$ of a member now aged x is

$$\frac{(n + y + \frac{1}{2} - x)}{K} \text{ (AS) } \frac{z_{y+\frac{1}{2}}}{s_{x+1}} \qquad \qquad \dots \dots 10.2.1$$

There is no element of probability in this expression; the figure is simply the amount of the benefit rights accrued at the time. The method proceeds by the calculation of this figure for each combination of x and y. It is convenient to group the resulting figures in a triangular array, with present age x along one axis and future age y along the other, there being an entry for all y greater than or equal to x. It should be noted that the only actuarial assumption involved at this stage is the salary scale. The framework of the array is shown in the following diagram, which has a row for each present age of member (say from 16 to w, where w is the final age of the service table) and a column for each possible future age up to final retirement.

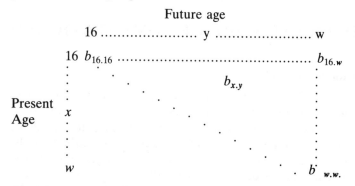

The amount of the accrued benefit for present age x exact and future age y last birthday as shown in expression 10.2.1 is represented by b_{xy}.

10.3 The next stage is to value the benefit rights set out in this array by the introduction of

(i)   the probability that an ill-health pension will become payable at age y last birthday,

(ii)   the capital value of unit benefit at the time that it starts to be paid, and

(iii)   the compound interest factor to discount the capital value to age x.

10.4 As to item (i) above, this is carried out by assigning a probability to each element of the benefit array, so that the original element b_{xy} which represents the amount of benefit is replaced by $b_{xy}p_{xy}$, where p_{xy} is the probability appropriate to the benefit. In the case of ill-health pensions which we are using to illustrate the method, p_{xy} is equal to i_y/l_x using the notation of paragraph 9.16.

10.5 The next step is to calculate annuities appropriate to the benefits in the year of age y to $y+1$, i.e. to the elements in the column for future age y. The form of the annuity 'ā' will vary according to the benefit to be valued, as shown by the following examples.

(i) For a member's ill-health retirement pension, $\bar{a}' = a'_{y+\frac{1}{2}}$ on the ill-health pensioner mortality table.

(ii) For lump sum benefits $\bar{a} = 1$.

(iii) For a widow's pension on death following age retirement, $\bar{a}' = \bar{a}_{y+\frac{1}{2}/z+\frac{1}{2}}$ (except when y = final retirement age, when $\bar{a}' = \bar{a}_{y/z}$) where z is the wife's age when the member is aged y. This annuity would of course be derived from the mortality tables of male age pensioners, wives and widows. It will be noted that it is the member's pension and not the widow's pension that is starting to be paid in member's year of age y to $y+1$ so that this method does not involve in all cases the calculation of the capital value of a benefit at the time that it starts to be paid. It is, nevertheless, convenient to value the widow's pension in this way.

10.6 The value of a benefit for members currently aged x is now computed as

$$V_x = \left[\sum_{y=x}^{w-1} (b_{xy}\, p_{xy}\, \bar{a}'_y\, v^{y-x+\frac{1}{2}}) \right] + b_{xw}\, p_{xw}\, \bar{a}'_w\, v^{w-x}$$

The computer will print out an array as shown below which enables the actuary to make spot checks on the calculations. The discounting factor is not printed out, as it is a straightforward compound interest 'v' function.

Future age and annuity

16 .... y .... w

$\bar{a}'_{16}$ .... $\bar{a}'_y$ .... $\bar{a}'_w$

16 $b_{16.16}\, p_{16.16}$ .... $b_{16.w}\, p_{16.w}\; V_{16}$

$b_{xy}\, p_{xy}$

Present Age $\quad x \qquad\qquad\qquad\qquad\qquad V_x$

$w \qquad\qquad\qquad\qquad b_{w.w}\, p_{w.w.}\; V_w$

$\qquad\qquad\qquad\qquad\qquad\qquad \Sigma V$

10.7 The method for the valuation of future contributions is essentially the same as that for the valuation of benefits. The probability involved is that of survival as a member to a particular future year and the annuity value associated with contributions is unity since the contribution is in concept a capital sum received by the scheme.

Advantages of the method

10.8 An important advantage of this approach is that it encourages clarity of thought, especially for non-technical office staff, by minimising the use of specialised formulae and symbols. The valuation formulae are constructed by simply considering the amount of benefit payable in any particular circumstance, probability and discounting being included subsequently. A good example of this is the imposition of a maximum number of years of pensionable service counting for benefit calculations. This is quite a complex adjustment in the valuation process, as was seen in paragraph 9.53. Here, however, it is merely necessary to insert a statement in the computer program limiting pensionable service to the appropriate maximum.

10.9 Since benefits are projected separately for each individual, limits may be imposed and comparisons made accurately for any set of valuation assumptions. Some examples of the benefits which may be dealt with fairly easily in this way are as follows.

A lump sum on death which is the greater of one year's salary and the member's accumulated contributions.

A limit (either flat or escalating) on the salary counting for pension purposes.

A withdrawal benefit which is a refund of contributions to members with less than five years service and a deferred pension for those with longer service.

A guaranteed minimum benefit, such as sometimes arises in connection with past service rights when a scheme is revised.

The comparison of scale pensions and G.M.P.s, especially in circumstances where the G.M.P. may be expected to be greater, for example, low-paid members of a scheme with a deduction of 1½ times the lower earnings limit.

10.10 It should be noted that a large volume of calculation is completed at the stage represented by the end of paragraph 10.4, before the rate of interest or rate of any post-retirement pension increase is introduced. These rates are not introduced until the stage at which annuities are calculated and the emerging benefits discounted. It is therefore possible to change these elements of the valuation basis and thus to produce alternative results with a minimum of additional calculation, since the earlier calculation steps do not have to be repeated. For example, if a valuation had been made with rates of interest, salary escalation and pension increase of 10, 8 and 5 per cent. respectively, further results could be produced using rates of 9, 8 and 3 per cent. respectively with little additional work. However, although the interest and pension increase elements of the basis may be changed, it is important to note that the rate of salary escalation cannot be changed without much more work, since the salary scale is fundamental in the calculation of the original benefit array.

Disadvantages of the method

10.11   One practical disadvantage of the method arises from the extent to which it is necessary to develop and test a unique computer program for each scheme. This disadvantage has been somewhat reduced as the system has been refined so that the relevant parts of a comprehensive program can more readily be brought to bear. Another factor which has helped in this connection is that the widespread modifications of schemes to meet the contracting-out requirements tended to some extent to reduce the great diversity of benefit and contribution arrangements previously found.

10.12   Another potential disadvantage of the technique is that of the temptation towards a spurious degree of accuracy, in dealing with such matters as limits and comparisons on an individual basis, which is presented by so powerful a tool. Those using the system have to bear in mind that the considerations of paragraph 9.2 continue to apply.

Further developments – select rates

10.13   The basic system described in the previous paragraphs calculates and values prospective benefits separately for each individual member. The individual nature of the calculation method offers the opportunity to take account of factors such as the duration of membership of the scheme. Despite the comment at the end of the previous paragraph, there are occasions when this is worth while. The introduction of selection in this way makes it possible to compare the effects of a variety of valuation assumptions; for example, the impact of differing sets of select withdrawal rates on contribution rates for new entrants may be examined. Although conceptually easy, selection adds to the practical complexities of implementing the system. We do not discuss the point further here.

Further developments – emerging costs

10.14   The method represents a convenient stage from which to develop a system for the calculation of emerging costs, i.e. the expected amounts of contribution income and benefit outgo in each future year in respect of the persons who have an interest in the scheme at the valuation date. Further extensive programs are required for this additional step. The new benefit outgo arising in each future year must be tracked through subsequent years; the projection of outgo on widows' pensions arising from the death after retirement of members, for instance, involves considerable work. In practice emerging cost figures are usually of most relevance in a scheme closed to new entrants, where with the passage of time it may become increasingly desirable to match the investments to the term of the liabilities.

The use of the computer: summary

10.15   It will be gathered from this chapter that the computer is in many ways ideally suited to the calculations that have to be made in the actuarial valuation of a pension scheme. Advantages that flow from its use are as follows.

(i)   Large volumes of data can be processed quickly and efficiently.

(ii)   The actuarial projections can be reworked on a different set of assumptions with comparative ease.

(iii)   A feature sometimes found in pension scheme rules is that the amount of a benefit is to be the greater of two amounts calculated in different ways. In some cases (particularly where pensionable pay is substantially less than full earnings) the G.M.P. requirement necessitates such an approach. Because the data processing power of the computer permits each individual member of a scheme to be treated separately for calculation purposes, a dual pension scale can be allowed for in actuarial valuation computer programs in a way that has no counterpart in manual calculations.

10.16   The computer brings with it these powerful advantages but it also increases the necessity for careful planning. An actuarial valuation employing a computer cannot usually be modified easily once it is in progress, so that it is necessary to settle fully in advance the calculations that are to be made and the form in which the output is desired. It would for instance obviously be possible to program the calculations underlying the actuarial valuation of a pension scheme so that the present capital value of the expected future benefit flow emerged simply as one total figure. This, however, would be by no means the most desirable presentation from the point of view of the actuary. In the first place it is part of his professional approach not only to scrutinise the figures that emerge and satisfy himself that they are correct but also to investigate their constituent elements to whatever degree is necessary for an adequate understanding of the workings of the scheme. In the second place, a valuation result may be such that the trustees of the scheme will wish to consider a change in a particular benefit, and may also perhaps wish to consider whether this change should be restricted to the benefit rights accruing in future or should also apply to benefit rights already earned at the valuation date. The actuary will need to have the figures in respect of this benefit shown separately in his valuation calculations in order to be able to give the appropriate advice. For reasons such as these it is necessary in practice for the results of valuation calculations to be set out so that intermediate processes and values are readily accessible.

CHAPTER 11

THE ACTUARIAL BASIS:
ECONOMIC ASSUMPTIONS

THE ACTUARIAL BASIS: ECONOMIC ASSUMPTIONS

Introduction

11.1 Before the actuarial valuation or other actuarial calculations in connection with a pension scheme can be made it is necessary to settle the actuarial basis, i.e. to assign numerical values to such of the elements listed in paragraph 9.15 as are involved. These elements are of two broad types, firstly those to do with economic conditions as a whole and secondly those more closely linked to the pension scheme or employer concerned and best approached on the basis of the statistics of the scheme itself or similar schemes. In this chapter we discuss some of the background information that is available and the issues that arise in assigning numerical values to the economic assumptions for pension schemes in the United Kingdom. We deal with the other type of assumptions in the next chapter.

The general position

11.2 An employer contemplating the introduction or improvement of a pension scheme will ask for estimates of cost and will then decide, probably after consultation with his employees, whether he and the employees can afford the new or improved scheme. If the cost is too high, even after allowing for the possibility of a low pace of funding in the early years, the proposal will have to be abandoned or a less ambitious scheme considered. The interested parties are therefore relying on the actuary to make as accurate an estimate as he can of the long term cost of the scheme. It follows that the actuarial basis should not contain large margins which would lead to an inflated assessment of cost, or be otherwise unduly conservative, because this might lead to the introduction by the employer of a scheme inferior to that which could have been afforded, or at worst to the abandonment of a scheme that could have been brought in.

Equally the actuary should not use a basis which would lead to an under-estimate of the cost, since the employer might then commit himself to a scheme which he could not in the long run afford. In particular cases it may be decided to make the calculations on a 'strong' or a 'weak' actuarial basis, but in this discussion we shall assume that the aim is to arrive at a set of assumptions towards the middle of the range of possible bases.

The economic assumptions

11.3   Assumptions will have to be made about some or all of the following economic elements. The reader may have expected the long term investment yield to feature as item (i) on the list instead of item (iii). We explain in subsequent paragraphs that this yield is mainly dependent on the dividend yield and dividend growth on ordinary shares, and these two elements therefore appear as items (i) and (ii) on the list.

(i)   The average future dividend yield 'd' on ordinary shares, i.e. the initial yearly rate of dividend flow resulting from unit investment in ordinary shares.

(ii)   The average annual rate of growth 'g' in the future in the yearly amount of dividends from a given holding of ordinary shares.

(iii)   The average long term yield 'i' which will be obtained on investments made in the future.

(iv)   The average annual rate 'e' at which general levels of pay will increase in the future.

(v)   The average annual rate 'p' at which prices will increase in the future.

(vi)   The average annual rate at which the amount of the State scheme lower earnings limit will increase in the future.

We will assume that we are concerned in (i) and (ii) with the F.T.-Actuaries' All-Share Index, differences between the return on the actual ordinary share holdings of a scheme and that on this index being left to emerge as items of profit or loss.

The nature of the investment yield

11.4   We first explain why assumptions (i) and (ii) above are necessary. In assigning a numerical value to the yield in item (iii) above it has to be borne in mind that most funded schemes in the

United Kingdom are invested to a substantial extent in ordinary shares and this is likely to continue to be the case. The immediate yield obtainable on ordinary shares (i.e. the current rate of dividend at purchase expressed as a percentage of the purchase price) is considerably lower than the yield obtainable on fixed-interest securities, because the ordinary share is bought in the expectation that the amount of the dividend income from year to year will grow in future. This assumption is based partly on the assumption of continuing inflation; some modest growth might be looked for if overall money values remained stable, but much of the anticipated growth in money terms reflects the assumption that inflation will continue and the hope that in these conditions dividends will fully maintain their value in real terms, or at worst will increase reasonably in money terms from year to year. It is also assumed that a rising flow of dividends will lead to increases in capital value. The total expected long-term yield on the investment represents the combined effect of dividend income and growth in capital value.

11.5   The yield which will be obtained on a future investment in ordinary shares will therefore depend on

(a)   the initial dividend yield 'd', i.e. the return on the purchase price represented by the initial annual amount of the dividend flow,

(b)   the average rate of growth 'g' in the amount of the dividend flow from year to year, and

(c)   the dividend yield at the time that the investment is sold.

In framing the long-term assumptions we will assume that the yields in (a) and (c) are the same. Any advantage obtained from buying ordinary shares when prices are comparatively low and selling them when prices are comparatively high will emerge as items of profit at successive actuarial valuations.

11.6   We shall now show how the total investment yield may be derived from the elements d and g. As a first approximation we may proceed as follows.

(i)   If unit investment is made in ordinary shares at the beginning of a year then, ignoring any dividend income produced during the year, the value of the investment at the end of the year will be $1 + g$. This follows from the fact that the price of an equity share is the price at which the future dividend stream is traded in the market, and the current rate of annual dividend stream is assumed to be $(1 + g)$ times greater at the end of the year than it was at the beginning.

(ii) If the dividend income is assumed to be received half way through the year the amount will include growth for one-half of a year and will therefore be equal to

$$d(1 + g)^{\frac{1}{2}}$$

If this amount is invested in the same shares for the remaining half year its capital value will have grown at the end of the year by a factor of $(1 + g)^{\frac{1}{2}}$, on the same reasoning as in (i) above, giving a capital value at the year-end of $d(1 + g)$.

If we ignore the income arising from the re-investment of the dividend we therefore arrive at a total yield i for the year defined by

$$1 + i = 1 + g + d(1 + g) = (1 + d)(1 + g)$$

so that

$$\delta_i = \delta_d + \delta_g$$

In other words, the force of total yield is equal to the sum of the force of initial yield and the force of dividend growth.

11.7 A fuller theoretical treatment proceeds as follows. If $M(t)$ is the value of a holding of ordinary shares at time t which is growing at annual rate i under the combined effect of dividend income and capital growth as indicated above, then using h instead of δ_t for a small increment of time,

$$M(t+h) - M(t)$$

has two elements, namely

(i) capital growth of

$$M(t).\delta_g.h$$

(from the normal definition of the force of interest, operating in this instance as the force of growth in capital value), and

(ii) dividend income of

$$M(t).d.h$$

(since the dividend yield at any time is d).

It follows that

$$\delta_i = \operatorname*{Lim}_{h\to0} \frac{1}{h}\frac{M(t+h) - M(t)}{M(t)} = \delta_g + d$$

Thus the force of total yield is equal to the sum of the force of dividend growth and the annual rate of dividend yield. It is not unusual in practice to use the approximate relationship that the yield expressed as an annual rate is equal to the sum of the dividend yield and the rate of growth expressed as annual rates, i.e.

$$i = d + g$$

11.8 It may be noted in passing that this analysis throws light on a point which is not always clearly understood. The investor in equities with their low immediate yield is sometimes thought of as accepting a disadvantage, which will be made good only at some later date, compared with the investor in fixed-interest securities. The analysis shows that this is not the case (provided that the immediate yield plus rate of dividend growth on the ordinary shares is comparable to the fixed-interest yield), since growth in capital values of the equity shares is expected to make up for the income shortfall, compared with fixed-interest securities, each year.

11.9 Pension schemes in the United Kingdom are invested in a wide range of assets in addition to ordinary shares, including fixed-interest securities, index-linked gilt-edged securities, properties and overseas investments. We discuss the various types of assets further in Chapter 20, but in the present chapter we shall concentrate, in the discussion of the numerical value of yields, on the expected return from United Kingdom ordinary shares. This simplification is considered reasonable not only because of the dominant position occupied by these investments in the total asset distribution of schemes but also because for many trustees the investment performance of these shares constitutes the benchmark against which the returns on other investments are judged.

Numerical values

11.10 We begin our consideration of the numerical values of the various assumptions by commenting on a proposition with which the reader may already be familiar, namely that the assumed difference between investment yields and rates of pay increase, and between investment yields and rates of price increase, is more important in an actuarial basis than the absolute values assigned to the various assumptions. The reasoning underlying this proposition will be clear if we consider the element

$$\frac{^{z}M_{x}^{ra}}{^{s}D_{x}}$$

of formula 9.59.1. This is a function of major importance in the whole actuarial structure of schemes. If we examine the basic constituents of this function it will be found that, disregarding the effect of the averaging period in the calculation of final pay, the various elements which relate to the period while the member is in service contain successive powers of the function

$$\frac{1 + e}{1 + i}$$

where e is the rate of pay escalation and i the rate of interest. As a first approximation this is equal to

$$\frac{1}{1 + (i - e)}$$

so that present values are broadly the same for varying e and i provided that $i - e$ remains unchanged. Even when the effect of an averaging period is allowed for, it remains the case that the excess of the assumed rate of interest over the assumed rate of pay escalation is a useful and significant measure of the strength of the actuarial basis, and that for many of the major benefits calculations could be made on the basis of a value of $(i - e)$ without assigning absolute values to either, as far as the period while the member is in service is concerned.

11.11   As to the position after retirement, in a scheme in which the rules provide that pensions in payment will be increased in line with prices the annuity elements in the formulae will contain successive powers of the function

$$\frac{1 + p}{1 + i} = \frac{1}{1 + (i - p)} \quad \text{approximately}$$

where p is the rate of price increase, so that in these circumstances the difference between i and p is of more importance than the absolute values assigned to them. In practice only a minority of schemes include such an undertaking in their rules. Nevertheless, many trustees would wish to provide pension increases if possible in times of inflation and many actuaries would (after discussion) settle the net rate of interest to be used for the annuity functions with a view to funding for a certain level of pension increases. Thus there is some validity in the concept that the difference between the two elements i and p is of more importance than their absolute values, although not to the extent that holds for the corresponding elements discussed in the previous paragraph (since e features in the calculations for most schemes, but p in only some).

11.12   There is, however, a further factor that is of fundamental importance in this discussion. This arises from the fact that in many schemes that are used for contracting-out no pension increases are provided on the G.M.P. element, since as explained in previous chapters this is effectively indexed from the State scheme. Thus it is necessary in the actuarial assessment of such schemes to place a value on a pension which remains of fixed amount while in payment, and for this purpose it is necessary to settle the absolute value of i. We cannot therefore avoid the need to place absolute values on the various elements of paragraph 11.3, despite the obvious problems involved.

11.13   Past experience suggests that, as indicated above, these problems may be approached by way of the expected differences between the various elements. For instance, the actuarial calculations for pension schemes set up in the United Kingdom during the early part of this century were typically based on a rate of interest in the region of 3 to 4 per cent. with no explicit allowance for escalation of pay levels or of pensions in payment. As economic conditions in the United Kingdom became less stable in the second half of the century the financial structure of such schemes showed a certain resilience; the adjustments to contribution rates necessitated by the unsettled economic conditions were not as sweeping as might have been feared. This was partly because, taking one year with another, investment performance in excess of the yield of 3 or 4 per cent. assumed helped to cover the cost of the additional liabilities arising from pay increases greater than those expected, and to provide resources from which discretionary pension increases could be granted. This is clearly the same concept of differences between rates as was expressed algebraically in paragraphs 11.10 and 11.11.

11.14 A further factor tending towards the approach by way of differences between the elements is that much economic discussion is framed in these terms. The rate of investment return, for instance, is often discussed in terms of the rate which will be obtained in excess of price increases. Rates of pay increase are also discussed in such terms.

11.15 The discussion of these issues in this chapter is necessarily brief and superficial. We touch on the following aspects, using the symbols of paragraph 11.3 and dealing throughout with the expected average long-term values of the elements concerned.

(i)   Dividend increases compared with price increases, i.e. the value of $g - p$.

(ii) The immediate dividend yield, i.e. the value of d.

(iii) Combining (i) and (ii), the total expected return on ordinary shares compared with price increases. We will take this as

$$(g + d) - p,$$

i.e. we will use the approximation

$$i = g + d$$

(iv) Consideration of the result in (iii) bearing in mind the yields on index-linked gilt-edged securities.

(v)   Rises in earnings compared with price increases, i.e. the value of $e - p$.

(vi) The assumption as to the average absolute value of the rate of price increase p in future, and hence the absolute value of the other elements.

11.16 The reader will see that this approach is open to criticism, in that whatever average rate of price increase we postulate in (vi) it is highly unlikely that this rate will have been experienced for any length of time in the past. The various values of (i) to (v) experienced in the past may not therefore be appropriate in the economic conditions implied by the assumption in (vi). Nevertheless, a set of assumptions has to be drawn up and it has to be accepted that these represent no more than the actuary's judgement of what constitutes a reasonable basis.

Data from the recent past

11.17   We will consider each of the elements in paragraph 11.15 and we begin by setting out in the following table some relevant data from the most recent 15 years period for which information is available at the time of writing; the choice of 15 years for the period is arbitrary. The information in the table is as follows.

Col.(2)	The General Index of Retail Prices All Items (UK) for December of the calendar year concerned.
Cols.(3), (4) and (5)	The F.T.-Actuaries All-Share Index relating to the last working day of the calendar year concerned. The notional dividend is the product of the price and the yield and is thus an index of the annual amount of the dividend flow produced by a holding in the index.
Col.(6)	The notional dividend flow divided by the price index to give a 'real' value.
Col.(7)	The Monthly Index of Average Earnings All Employees G.B. for December of the calendar year concerned. New Series Unadjusted with January 1976 = 100 from 1976 onwards. Old Series Unadjusted for years up to 1975, with the values multiplied by a constant so as to run into the New Series value of 100 at January 1976.
Col.(8)	The earnings index divided by the price index to give a 'real' value.

Table of economic data referred to in paragraph 11.17

Calendar year	Prices	F.T.-Actuaries All-Share Index price	yield	notional dividend (3)×(4)	Real value of (5) (5)÷(2)	Earnings	Real value of (7) 10(7)÷(2)
(1)	(2)	(3)	(4)	(5)	(6)	(7)	(8)
			per cent.				
1969	70.1	147.34	3.85	567	8.09	39.6	5.65
1970	75.6	136.26	4.39	598	7.91	45.1	5.97
1971	82.4	193.39	3.25	629	7.63	49.3	5.98
1972	88.7	218.18	3.15	687	7.75	56.9	6.41
1973	98.1	149.76	4.77	714	7.28	64.3	6.55
1974	116.9	66.89	11.71	783	6.70	83.2	7.12
1975	146.0	158.08	5.47	865	5.92	99.4	6.81
1976	168.0	151.96	6.42	976	5.81	111.3	6.63
1977	188.4	214.53	5.28	1,133	6.01	121.7	6.46
1978	204.2	220.22	5.79	1,275	6.24	138.0	6.76
1979	239.4	229.79	6.87	1,579	6.60	165.1	6.90
1980	275.6	292.22	6.10	1,783	6.47	197.3	7.16
1981	308.8	313.12	5.89	1,844	5.97	217.1	7.03
1982	325.5	382.22	5.26	2,010	6.18	233.8	7.18
1983	342.8	470.50	4.62	2,174	6.34	252.5	7.37

Dividend increases compared with price increases

11.18   It will be seen from column (6) of this table that over this period dividend income moved erratically in real terms but tended on the average to drift downwards by about 2 per cent. p.a. Daykin (see the list of further reading at the end of this chapter) shows much more extensive figures in Appendix 10 to his paper and notes in his paragraph 32 a steady lag of dividend growth behind price rises of 2 to 3 per cent. p.a. Wilkie (see list of further reading) notes in his paragraph 4.7 that real dividends appear to have long runs either of growth or decline (a comment made in relation to a period beginning in 1930). In fact, extraordinarily large dividend increases between the end of the period covered by the table and the time of writing have almost restored the real level of the notional dividend flow to its value at the beginning of the period. We will assume that a central range of values of $g - p$ of from 0 to -3 per cent. is a reasonable assumption.

The immediate dividend yield

11.19 Column (4) of the table shows widely varying figures. The average value is about 5.5 per cent., or about 5.0 per cent. if the exceptional figure for 1974 is omitted. Wilkie, quoting the report of the Maturity Guarantees Working Party (see list of further reading) notes that immediate yields have always tended to return to a mean level of around 5 per cent. We shall use this figure as our central assumption for the value of d, and will take the central range as being from 4 to 6 per cent.

The total expected return on ordinary shares

11.20 Combining the figures of the two preceding paragraphs gives a central range of expected long term yields on equities of 2 to 5 per cent. in excess of prices. It is thought that many actuaries would regard the expected long term rate of interest in excess of prices as lying within this range.

Index-linked British Government stock

11.21 An opportunity for the views of investors on the question of investment yields relative to prices to be tested in the market arose in March 1981, when the British Government issued for the first time an index-linked gilt-edged stock for which pension schemes and other institutions having U.K. pension liabilities were invited to tender. The stock was for a term of approximately $15\frac{1}{2}$ years with a coupon of 2 per cent., both interest payments and the proceeds on maturity being linked to movements in the Retail Price Index since the date of issue (subject to a specified time lag for administrative reasons). In the event that stock was issued exactly at par, implying that investors were ready to accept a yield of almost exactly 2 per cent. in excess of increases in the Retail Price Index.

11.22 A number of further index-linked gilt-edged securities have subsequently been issued. Market yields at the time of writing this book appear to be tending towards a value of 3 to $3\frac{1}{2}$ per cent. The general implication of these stocks is therefore that a yield of this order in excess of the rate of increase in the Retail Price Index is acceptable to investors in these stocks. It may be argued that an expectation of a somewhat larger yield in excess of prices is in the minds of investors as far as other investments

(including ordinary shares) are concerned, because such
investments do not carry the certainty of a margin over the Retail
Price Index as do the index-linked British Goverment securities,
and the investor is willing to pay a premium for the latter. In view
of this the range of expected long term yields mentioned in
paragraph 11.20 may perhaps be reduced to 3 to 5 per cent. in
excess of prices.

Increases in earnings

11.23 We turn to the next element mentioned in paragraph
11.15, namely the average rate of increase in general levels of
earnings compared with the average rate of increase in prices. We
are not of course concerned here with increases which individuals
may obtain by virtue of increasing seniority or promotion in their
careers, but with overall levels of earnings. Daykin provides a
detailed analysis of rises in national average earnings over a wide
range of periods in the United Kingdom starting in 1952. He shows
that the average real rate of increase of earnings over a range of
periods is not far from 2½ per cent. p.a. The figures in column (8)
of the table in paragraph 11.17 show that over the period covered
by that column the index of real earnings increased at an average
annual compound rate of about 1.9 per cent.

11.24 Economic commentators express a variety of views on this
question. It does not appear to be widely expected that pay levels
will fall in real terms over a long future period. On the other hand,
an expectation of real increases at the rate of 2½ per cent. p.a.
mentioned above would probably be thought optimistic in the
current climate of opinion. We will take the range of 0 to 2½ per
cent. as our estimate of the future real rate of increase in earnings.

11.25 It should be noted that the circumstances of the particular
pension scheme may be particularly important in this area. The
pay concerned may be full earnings or it may be some form of
'basic pay'; different views on future increase rates may be taken
in the different cases. Furthermore, expectations will vary from
one sector of the economy to another. Thus whatever figure is
chosen on overall grounds, it may need to be adjusted in the
circumstances of each particular scheme.

The absolute rate of price increase

11.26   We turn to the last element of paragraph 11.15, namely the absolute rate of price increase. No encouragement is to be drawn from Wilkie, who after lengthy analysis concludes that it is not easy to forecast inflation over any lengthy period. Views on this matter appear to vary substantially according to conditions from time to time. At the time of writing the value of p is in the area of 5 per cent. and there is some prospect that it will remain for some time at this figure, which is low compared with the figures that have been experienced in past years. It is believed that many organisations in their long term planning assume a rate of price increase in the range of 6 to 8 per cent. and we will assume without further consideration that a figure in this range is appropriate.

The assumptions as a whole

11.27   The above discussion leads to conclusions which may be summarised as follows.

Element	Assumed central range of future values
	per cent.
p	6 to 8
$e - p$	0 to 2½
d	4 to 6
$g - p$	0 to −3
$i - p$	3 to 5*

*It will be recalled that the range of 2 to 5 implied by the two preceding elements in the table was modified in the light of the yield on index-linked gilt-edged securities.

Even if these figures are accepted without question they lead to a very wide spectrum of possible actuarial bases. The reader should seek to form his own views on these matters. Many of the reports published by the Government Actuary from time to time on various matters involve assumptions on some or all of these elements, and the reader will find such reports a valuable source of information and comment. Later in this book we perform the calculations in respect of a hypothetical pension scheme, Scheme X, and for this purpose it is necessary to assign definite numerical values to the various constituents of the basis. The calculations have in fact been made on a rate of investment yield of 9 per cent. p.a. and a rate of general increase of pay levels of 8 per cent. p.a. Using the relationship

$$\delta_i = \delta_g + d$$

from paragraph 11.7 the yield of 9 per cent. was based on the assumptions of an immediate dividend yield of about 4.7 per cent. and dividend growth of 4 per cent. p.a. It was not necessary to make an explicit assumption about price increases in the calculations but in fact the assumed value of p underlying this basis was 6 per cent., it being assumed that earnings would rise in real terms (compared with prices) at the rate of about 2 per cent. p.a. and investment returns would provide a yield of about 3 per cent. p.a. net of prices.

The Lower Earnings Limit

11.28 We have not discussed item (vi) of paragraph 11.3, namely the average rate of increase in the Lower Earnings Limit. This is not only a matter of economic assumption but also an assessment of likely political decisions, because the Lower Earnings Limit is in principle equal to the amount of the State flat-rate pension for a single person, and at the time of writing there is statutory linkage of this amount to price increases but with a history of increases greater than price increases in some years. In a pension scheme where the amount of the Lower Earnings Limit is relevant it is necessary to make an assumption about the most likely linking principle in the long term future. It is believed that many actuaries assume the same rate of increase as is assumed for general levels of earnings, but this practice is not universal; other actuaries assume a rate of increase between those of prices and earnings.

The short-term 'patch'

11.29 The discussion of this chapter has been about long term assumptions. It is sometimes decided to allow for current conditions at the time that calculations are being made and to allow for a move to the long term assumptions over a period. This adjustment is seldom made meticulously, because of the complications involved. It can often be made very simply by a final adjustment to figures calculated on the long term assumptions.

CHAPTER 11

Further reading

The sources referred to in the text are as follows.

Long Term Rates of Interest in the Valuation of a Pension Fund
by C.D. Daykin   J.S.S. Vol. 21 Part 3

Updated J.S.S. Vol. 23

Indexing Long Term Financial Contracts
by A.D. Wilkie   J.I.A. Vol. 108 Part III

Report of the Maturity Guarantees Working Party
J.I.A. Vol.107 Part II

CHAPTER 12

THE ACTUARIAL BASIS: STATISTICAL ASSUMPTIONS

THE ACTUARIAL BASIS: STATISTICAL ASSUMPTIONS

Introduction

12.1 In this chapter we discuss, under the general heading of statistical assumptions, the elements in the actuarial basis of a pension scheme other than the economic factors discussed in the previous chapter. The elements now to be considered are as follows.

(i) The decrement rates from which the service table is constructed.
(ii) Mortality rates of members and spouses after retirement.
(iii) Other statistical elements.
(iv) The salary scale before allowing for inflation.

Some of these elements cannot be wholly divorced from economic influences; rates of withdrawal, for instance, are much affected by the level of economic activity and the level of unemployment. Nevertheless, the elements dealt with in this chapter are normally best approached on the basis of the statistics of the scheme concerned or similar schemes.

The complete theoretical model

12.2 The complete theoretical model of a pension scheme is extraordinarily complex. Consider, as an example, the group of members of a pension scheme who are male salaried staff employees of a given age. In practice these members would usually all be taken together for valuation purposes, one service table and salary scale being applied to the aggregated data, but the following reasons amongst others could be advanced for valuing various sub-groups on different bases.

(i) Rates of withdrawal from the scheme will almost certainly tend to diminish with duration of employment, so that long service members of the group would be expected to experience withdrawal rates lighter than those of members who entered more recently. If membership of the scheme is voluntary a further complication is introduced, because employees who had been in the service of the employer for some time but had only recently joined the scheme would probably experience low rates of withdrawal, whereas they would appear to be at a stage of high withdrawal rates if such rates were treated as select by reference to the period of membership of the scheme.

(ii) There will probably be some assessment of health at entry to employment. Members of short duration might therefore be expected to experience in the immediate future lower ill-health retirement and death in service rates than members of longer standing.

(iii) If a qualifying period of membership has to be completed before a pension is payable on ill- health retirement, some members in the group are at risk for an ill-health retirement pension immediately but recent entrants who have not completed the qualifying period are not so covered.

(iv) The group will probably contain well established employees earning substantial salaries and new entrants with lower salaries; it is not likely that the same ratio salary scale will be wholly appropriate for all.

12.3 The use of a single service table and salary scale for a group of employees thus represents a sweeping simplification of the full theoretical approach. It follows that the assigning of numerical values to the various elements is to be looked on as a practical matter rather than one in which extreme technical refinement is called for. Nevertheless, in settling the basis it is always necessary to have regard to the underlying implications of a situation and to consider the basis accordingly. The issues that sometimes arise may be illustrated if we suppose that the cost of a major improvement in the ill-health pension scales, and associated widows' pensions, is to be investigated. The change might itself affect the experience; members who are genuine ill-health cases but did not seek to retire when the benefits were inadequate may wish to do so if the benefits are improved. Future experience may therefore involve higher ill-health retirement rates, and possibly lower rates of mortality in service as a consequence. Thus in theory two different service tables might be required, one for the valuation of the existing benefits and another for that of the revised benefits. Although in practice full scale dual calculations are unusual, a possible change in the experience may often be allowed for on approximate lines.

The service table

12.4 We now consider the various rates of decrement upon which the service table is based. An employer setting up a pension scheme for the first time will probably not have kept records from which decrement rates could be derived. Even if such records were available they would be of doubtful value, because the introduction of a pension scheme would itself influence events, for reasons similar to those of the previous paragraph. For instance, fewer employees might leave, if to do so involved a loss of pension rights; more might retire on grounds of ill-health if they were assured of a pension in such circumstances; fewer might die in service if more were able to retire with a pension on grounds of ill-health. For the costing of a new scheme the actuary is therefore likely to draw more on his experience of the pension schemes of comparable undertakings than on the statistics available in the particular case.

Rates of retirement on grounds of age

Retirement at a fixed rate

12.5 A number of different cases of age retirement arise, and in illustrating these we consider only the position of men. Similar principles apply to women, usually in the context of a lower normal pension age. In the simplest case the rules of the scheme provide for a pension on age retirement on or after attainment of a specified age, say 65, and most members in normal health retire at this age, a few remaining in service until later ages. We need not specify for present purposes whether contributions continue to be payable after age 65 or not, nor whether on late retirement the ordinary pension scale holds or a special calculation is made; we shall assume that the numbers deferring retirement are so small that no material profit or loss to the scheme is caused. Active members at any time may therefore be treated as if they were all to retire at 65 exact, and the rates of retirement decrement at the later ages in active employment might be of the type shown in column (a) of the following table. Up to and including age 64 only ill-health retirement is anticipated, and at age 65 all remaining members are assumed to retire. The figures are purely illustrative and would not necessarily be suitable for use in practice.

Specimen rates of retirement $^r q_x$

age x	(a)	(b)	(c)
58	.010	.010	.010
59	.012	.012	.012
60	.014	.314	1.000
61	.016	.216	
62	.018	.118	
63	.020	.120	
64	.022	.122	
65	1.000	1.000	

Early retirement with a reduced pension

12.6 The next case is that in which the normal scale pension is provided on retirement at age 65 or earlier ill-health, but members in normal health may elect to retire during a period of a few years preceding attainment of this age (for instance, on or after attainment of age 60) with an immediate pension so calculated that the election places no, or only minimal, extra liability on the scheme. We discuss later in this book the methods of determining the appropriate amount of pension. Since the value of this benefit at the time of election is intended to be broadly equal to or less than the reserve immediately before election, and the numbers electing to take advantage of this option are not usually very large, the simplest course is to ignore this option in the actuarial basis and to use retirement rates similar to those in column (a) of the table. If a material number of members took advantage of this option the rates of age retirement derived from an experience would, of course, be quite substantial at ages 60 (assuming this to be the earliest age of voluntary retirement) to 64 last birthday, but it would be wrong to include these in the service table (unless in the valuation calculations the appropriate benefits, and not the scale pension, were allowed for on such retirement).

12.7 The method of ignoring a decrement rests on the principle that if the benefit payable on the occurrence of a particular event is equal to the reserve held, the event need not be allowed for in the basis, since the disappearance of the member from the group concerned leaves the financial position of the remaining members unchanged. It may be noted that if a widely used retirement option of this type is ignored in the service table the value of the death in service benefit might be overestimated, because fewer people would be exposed to risk at the later ages than anticipated. The actuary might decide to make an adjustment for this.

A range of normal retirement ages

12.8 We next consider the case in which a member in normal health may, in certain circumstances, retire with an immediate pension calculated on the normal pension formula of the scheme at any age between, say, 60 and 65. Sometimes this is subject to the condition that a prescribed period of service such as thirty years must be completed before early retirement is allowed. Select retirement rates according to entry age are then theoretically needed because only entrants at age $30 + x$ or below could retire at age $60 + x$. In practice, however, an aggregate service table would almost certainly be used. The retirement rates at ages between 60 and 64 inclusive would cover both ill- health and age retirement. In the valuation of a long established scheme the experience would help in determining the rates to be used; in the calculation of contribution rates for a new scheme the matter is one of judgement. Aggregate rates of the type required are illustrated in column (b) of the table in paragraph 12.5.

12.9 The financial position of a scheme providing for voluntary early retirement can be materially affected by comparatively small changes in the rates of optional age retirement assumed. If the average expected age at retirement is reduced, the present value of the contributions expected to be received in future is reduced whilst pensions are expected to be paid for a greater number of years than previously. The extra cost is only partly offset by the fact that the expected annual amount of the pensions, if they are related to salary and service, is reduced.

12.10 As an example of a further possible arrangement, suppose that the normal retirement age of a scheme is 60 but that if retirement is postponed beyond that age the normal pension formula of the scheme continues to apply (operating on salary, service, etc., at the date of retirement). Some members would probably retire at 60 and some between that age and 65, but many would probably not retire until age 65. Clearly, the scheme is then operating as if normal retirement age were 65 but members were entitled to retire on the ordinary scale pension at any age not less than 60. This is the type of scheme described in paragraph 12.8, and if the actuary thought that this age retirement experience was likely to persist he might decide to use rates resembling those of column (b) of the table in paragraph 12.5, even though the rules of the scheme defined normal retirement age as age 60. He might on the other hand consider that the use of column (b) would lead to underfunding, and that retirement at age 60 should be assumed for all members, leading to the rates of column (c). The matter is very much one of judgement.

A low normal retirement age with 'actuarial increases' on delayed retirement

12.11 Finally in this discussion of age retirement rates we consider a scheme in which the normal pension formula applies on retirement at age 60 and the rules provide that if retirement is deferred beyond that age the amount of the pension has to be certified by the actuary. The delayed pension in these circumstances is often calculated so that deferment results in little or no profit or loss to the scheme. The possibility of deferment can therefore be ignored in the contribution rate or valuation calculations, and the retirement rates would be of the type shown in column (c) of the table in paragraph 12.5. Members in service between ages 60 and 65 would probably be treated in a valuation as if they were expected to retire immediately, the pensions to which they would then be entitled being valued as immediate annuities.

Ill-health retirement rates

12.12 Ill-health retirement rates are much influenced by the circumstances of the particular scheme. The ill-health retirement rates and the mortality rates experienced will be influenced by the generosity or otherwise of the scale of benefits provided, as well as by the policy of the employer. Stringent conditions for ill-health retirement, or inadequate ill-health pensions, tend to produce low retirement rates with high rates of mortality in service and high rates of mortality of ill-health pensioners. Ill-health retirement rates also vary with age, sex, type of work and social class. In normal circumstances it is important not to underestimate the risk of ill-health retirement, since an excess of actual over expected retirements usually creates a strain on the scheme.

12.13 Points to be noted are as follows.

(i) There may be a qualifying period of membership before cover for an ill-health pension is provided, although such a provision is becoming unusual. If it is present, ill-health retirement rates may start in the service table at an age approximately equal to the youngest entry age plus the qualifying period. The very few members who leave the service for reasons of ill-health before completing the qualifying period receive withdrawal benefits and are regarded as withdrawals for the purposes of the decrement rates.

(ii) If the experience of a scheme shows high rates of ill-health retirement this may be an indication that the provision is being abused, particularly if potential future service features in some way in the calculation of the benefit. The proper initial response would be to investigate the administration of this part of the scheme, rather than to adjust the ill- health retirement rates.

Redundancy retirement

12.14 As mentioned in earlier chapters the need to provide immediate or deferred pensions on redundancy has, regrettably, become common in recent years. If such pensions are granted on a basis which effectively uses the actuarial reserve in the scheme, the contingency need not be allowed for in the decrement rates. If a more generous pension is granted, a cost will be imposed on the scheme. It is not, however, possible to anticipate this cost, in contribution rate or valuation calculations, with any precision, because the incidence of redundancy is unpredictable. Furthermore it has not up to the present been thought appropriate to allow for continuing redundancies in the long term actuarial projections, since redundancies are intended to be a short term feature of any employer's policy. Thus a rate of exit from membership on grounds of redundancy is not found as a constituent of the service table. Normally the employer meets any extra cost, since redundancies usually arise as a result of his policy; he pays extra contributions either as cases occur or when the cost is investigated as part of the valuation calculations.

Rates of mortality in service

12.15   Rates of mortality in service are often found to be very light, both because of initial selection and because of the removal of sub-standard lives from the service by ill-health retirement. The degree of incapacity necessary to enable the ill-health pension to be claimed and the scale of that pension will have repercussions on the rates of mortality in service. In some schemes the standard set for the granting of ill-health pensions to women is less severe than that for men, and women's mortality rates in service are then very light indeed. The rates of mortality will also depend on the nature of the employment. Unexpected features are sometimes found; a group of manual workers in a heavy industry, for example, may show lighter rates than a clerical group, because manual workers need to be physically fit and a tendency for the unfit to be removed by ill-health retirement may be more marked than in the case of clerical workers.

Margins in the mortality rates

12.16   Although the actuary's purpose is to provide a realistic estimate of costs, he will naturally tend slightly towards prudence in the choice of basis. The value of the benefits payable on death during service varies widely from one scheme to another, and it is necessary to investigate in a particular scheme the ranges of ages and classes of membership for which the value of the benefit payable on the death of a member is such that an unexpected death places a strain on the scheme. Without this knowledge it is impossible to tell whether prudence lies in using mortality rates slightly higher or slightly lower than those expected.

Rates of withdrawal

12.17   As noted earlier, withdrawal rates are strongly influenced by general economic conditions. Changes in these conditions may therefore result in great variations in the rates experienced in a particular scheme from time to time. Rates of withdrawal are also affected by the conditions of eligibility for membership. If a considerable period of employment has to be served before an employee may enter the pension scheme the membership of the scheme will tend to be more stable than would otherwise be the case.

12.18 The rates of withdrawal of female members are affected by the incidence of marriage, which is normally a function of age rather than of service, and the incidence of pregnancy. A composite rate covering withdrawals from all causes including these is usually employed. It must, however, be borne in mind that the shape of the underlying curve for the rate of withdrawal on marriage is quite different from that for the rate of ordinary withdrawal. Furthermore, there is some stability in the marriage rate while the rate of ordinary withdrawal varies with economic conditions as mentioned above. Female rates of withdrawal are therefore theoretically complex. In practice they tend to show much the same characteristics as male rates but often at a higher overall level.

12.19 In the United Kingdom rates of turnover of labour, and hence rates of withdrawal from pension schemes, were heavy in the 1960's and 1970's compared with earlier periods but have subsequently slackened. In deciding on rates of withdrawal at a time when labour turnover is high the actuary will have to decide whether to use rates reflecting the current experience or lower rates, and the main points to be taken into account are as follows.

(i)   If the benefit on withdrawal of a short service member is a payment equal to the amount of the member's own contributions with or without interest, the contributions which the employer has made in respect of the member remain in the scheme. Withdrawals in excess of those anticipated give rise to a profit. If the number of withdrawals falls short of the expectation an anticipated profit taken credit for in advance will not be realised. Withdrawals may not continue indefinitely at high levels, and it is therefore prudent to anticipate somewhat lower rates.

(ii) If members are contracted-out of the State earnings-related scheme, it is necessary for pensions at a certain level to be preserved on withdrawal. To the extent that the cost of this is met from a return of contributions which would otherwise be paid to the withdrawing member the scheme is not affected financially by the obligation to preserve. To the extent, however, that the employer may recoup any cost of preservation falling upon him from the contributions which he has himself paid to the scheme, the profit to the scheme is diminished. Nevertheless, the general reasoning in (i) above still holds good.

(iii) As the extent of preservation of accrued pension benefits on withdrawal, and the quality of the benefits, continues to increase, profits from excess withdrawals will be substantially reduced, or may disappear. This is a further reason for not anticipating large numbers of withdrawals. Indeed, it is not impossible at the present time for the withdrawal benefit at young ages at exit to be more costly than the value of the accrued benefit to a continuing member in a scheme with modest benefits funded on a weak actuarial basis. In such a case it would, paradoxically, be conservative to assume high rates of withdrawal.

(iv) It is occasionally decided to omit withdrawal rates from the basis altogether. Any profit from withdrawals is allowed to emerge as valuation surplus.

This ends the discussion of the service table.

Pensioners' mortality rates

Retirements at normal pension age

12.20 The mortality of pensioners who have retired on reaching the final age limit for active service is usually very light. Clerical and other non-manual employees often show rates in retirement approximating to those of life office annuitants. In general there are significant differences between the mortality rates after retirement of males and females and of salaried staff and wage earners, the mortality of manual workers being usually the heaviest. There are very few schemes in which the experience is large enough to justify the construction of a special life table for pensioners. In most cases a suitable standard table is adapted for use, rating the ages up or down as appropriate in the light of comparisons of actual and expected numbers of deaths. Although the investigation of the experience necessarily relates to persons currently on pension, it should be noted that different mortality rates are often used for current pensioners on the one hand and the future period of pension payment of current employees on the other (usually by means of different age ratings of a standard table), to allow for anticipated changes of mortality rates with time.

12.21 If the volume of statistics is adequate an investigation is fully justified, because the experience does indeed vary. In one recent large scale investigation of the mortality experienced by various groups of pensioners who had retired on grounds of age from a large undertaking it was found that a(55) mortality did not provide a close fit to the observed rates, being too light in the years following retirement and too heavy at advanced ages. It was found that PA(90) with a small age rating provided a much closer fit. In another such investigation relating to a different large concern, the opposite position was found.

Ill-health retirements

12.22 The mortality experience of members who retire owing to a breakdown in health is often very heavy immediately after retirement, but tends to improve as the most seriously impaired lives are removed by death. The degree and extent of the initial period of selection and the excess of the ultimate rates over the normal mortality of pensioners depend upon the standards set in the administration of the scheme and the general management policy of the employers. The mortality rates are therefore linked to the rates of ill-health retirement. The overall rates of mortality brought out at a given age by averaging the adopted rates of mortality in service and mortality after retirement should approximate to those which would be expected in a normal body of lives of the same class which had not been subjected to a process of segregation into active and retired classes.

12.23 Reversed selection may be particularly marked at the younger ages, for two reasons. Firstly, the employer is likely to be more lenient in permitting retirements with an ill-health pension at, say, age 55 than at age 35. Secondly, even if the scale of ill-health pension in the early years is generous, a member will usually suffer more financial difficulty on retirement at a younger than at an older age. The degree of disability among those retiring on ill-health grounds may therefore be expected in general to be higher in younger members than in older members.

12.24   It is therefore sometimes found that the rates of mortality immediately after ill-health retirement decrease as the age at retirement increases. The annuity values derived from such rates vary little over a wide range of ages at retirement, and a constant annuity value for all ages of ill-health retirement is therefore sometimes used if the actuary is satisfied that this is reasonable for the scheme concerned. This may cause difficulty in the investigation of the experience because it is not always clear exactly what the underlying mortality assumptions are. Alternatively a standard table with a substantial age rating may be used.

Optional retirements

12.25   It is necessary to consider the mortality after retirement of members who take advantage of an option to retire in the circumstances of paragraph 12.8. Their rates of mortality may be expected on general grounds to be between those of normal and ill-health retirement pensioners, because some, if not all, of these people will probably be in indifferent health. In practice normal retirement mortality would generally be assumed, unless there was fairly conclusive evidence that heavier rates would be justified.

Marital and family statistics

12.26   We will assume that if widows' pensions are included in the benefits of a scheme, calculations will be made by the collective method. Assumptions will have to be made about some or all of the following when the actuarial basis is being settled, if the benefit is payable only to the wife to whom the member was married at the date of retirement.

(i)   Proportions married amongst employees dying in service and amongst employees retiring.

(ii)   Age difference of husband and wife at the date of the husband's death in service and at the date of the husband's retirement.

(iii)   Rates of mortality of married male pensioners.

(iv)   Rates of mortality of the widows of men who die during employment and of the wives and widows of pensioners.

(v)   Rates of remarriage of widows.

Corresponding elements will arise if widowers' pensions are provided. The assumptions required are different if widows and widowers arising from post-retirement marriages are allowed for.

Proportions married

12.27   The collective method rests on the assumption that it is possible to determine a series of proportions married according to attained age which can be applied to the existing membership both at the present time and in the future. The proportions married at various ages in a general population at a particular time are the net result of rates of mortality amongst married and single men and their wives, of rates of marriage and remarriage and of differences between the ages at marriage of husbands and wives, all operating over many years. In a pension scheme the proportions married depend on all these factors and also depend on the service table decrement rates experienced by men of different marital status and by the proportions entering in each different status.

12.28   It is prima facie unlikely that all these factors, varying as they do with the passage of time and changing general conditions, will lead to proportions married in the future similar to the present proportions. It is nevertheless usually found that the proportions married in a particular scheme show considerable stability over a number of years if the conditions of membership have not changed. This fact, coupled with the practical convenience of the formulae, is held to justify the almost universal use of the collective method. It should, however, be noted that the method discards any information available about the trends over past years of the various rates involved.

12.29   In a particular scheme there may be different groups of members who may be expected to show different proportions married. For instance, widows' benefits may have been added to the scheme of benefits of an existing scheme and the additional benefits and contributions made optional for members at the date of change but compulsory for subsequent entrants. The proportions married at a given age would be expected to be higher amongst the survivors of the opters than amongst subsequent entrants. It is not an essential feature of the collective method that the same series of proportions married should be applied to the whole membership of a scheme. If thought desirable, two or more sets of proportions could be constructed and different actuarial factors used for different sections of the membership.

The use of proportions married amongst those living

12.30 Formula 9.84.1 incorporates the proportions married amongst male members dying at each age. In practice the experience of a scheme would seldom be sufficient for the derivation of such proportions. Usually the proportion married amongst members alive at each age would be used instead.

Proportion leaving dependant

12.31 The above discussion has been in terms of proportions married; it should be noted that if a scheme provides a benefit to a dependant, and not only a spouse, of a deceased member or pensioner, the proportion needed is not simply a proportion married but a proportion giving rise to a dependant's benefit.

Age difference of husband and wife on death in service

12.32 The weighted average value of an annuity to the widow of a member dying in service at age $(x + t + \frac{1}{2})$ is usually replaced in practice by the weighted annuity derived from the statistics of wives of members who are alive at age $(x + t)$ last birthday. This will theoretically lead to a slight overstatement of the liability, as can be seen by considering the probable trend of three tables showing the average difference between the ages of husbands and wives, in each case according to the age of husband,

(i)   at date of marriage,
(ii)   at a valuation date, of all husbands then alive, and
(iii) at date of death of husband.

The bachelor who marries young usually marries a wife whose age does not differ to any marked extent from his own, but the bachelor who marries at a later age has a much wider range of choice, and the marriage of an elderly bachelor to a comparatively young wife is not so unusual as the marriage of a young bachelor to an elderly wife. Thus the differences shown by table (i) may be expected to increase continuously and at the end to be fairly large. The difference shown by table (ii) at a particular age relates to husbands who have married at all previous ages and have survived with their wives. Those of them who married at young ages will have wives of about the same age as themselves, and those recently married will have younger wives, but the average difference in age will be less than that shown in table (i). Since marriage is to some extent a selective force, members who have recently married are less likely to die than members who have been married for some time, and deaths will therefore be largely composed of the latter. The difference shown by table (iii) at a particular age would therefore be less than that shown by table (ii) for the same age.

Age difference of husband and wife on retirement

12.33 The weighted average value of the annuity may be derived from the statistics of wives of members who retire in the scheme or in a larger but generally similar scheme.

Rates of mortality of wives and widows

12.34 No special points arise in this connection. It is prudent to assume somewhat lighter rates of mortality than those expected.

Remarriage rates of widows

12.35 Remarriage rates are essentially select in form, so that in theory it is not possible to combine mortality and remarriage rates of widows into one aggregate double decrement table from which could be calculated directly all values of an annuity payable to a widow until her death or remarriage. Given a volume of statistics sufficient to yield reliable remarriage rates select tables could be built up, but the volume of statistics is seldom sufficient in practice, and remarriage is usually taken into account by way of a reduction, estimated on broad lines, in the 'throughout life' annuity rate.

Salary scales

12.36 It will be recalled from previous chapters that the expected future increases in earnings of a group of employees are made up of the following constituents.

(i) Increases which would be expected if overall levels of pay remained stable. Such increases arise because of the progress in his career of each individual employee and represent the combined effect of

(a) the normal progress of individuals within a given grade or status, and

(b) promotions of individuals from one grade or status to another.

(ii) Superimposed on these, increases representing rises in the general levels of earnings.

We are concerned here with the first of these constituents.

The study of the employer's records

12.37 If a scheme is being set up, the information available about each employee will include earnings data, and the actuary will examine this, together with any recognised scales of pay currently in force for various grades of employees. Pensionable pay (before allowing for any deduction or special adjustment connected with integration with the State scheme) often differs from full pay because of the exclusion of such things as overtime and commission payments, but full pay is relevant in schemes used for contracting-out because this is the pay from which are derived 'relevant earnings' for G.M.P. purposes. The actuary will probably wish to study both the pattern of full pay and that of pay after exclusions.

12.38 This may cause difficulty if the amount of 'pay less exclusions' is not normally recorded. The information necessary to obtain this figure will almost always be contained in the detailed clerical records, but if its extraction would involve an excessive amount of work the actuary may accept the results of a sample investigation. The actuary will examine the progression of average earnings from age to age for each grade of employee, together with any recognised scales of pay in force, and he may also investigate the general pattern of promotion. He will then have a fairly clear idea of the pay structure at the date concerned and he will form a view as to whether this pattern of earnings indicates the expected progress of earnings in stable conditions.

12.39 Occasionally the employer's records may contain historical data in an accessible form. The actuary will then be able to study the pattern of earnings at the present date and some past date, and hence the progression of earnings between the two dates. If the pattern has changed during the period he will try to find out why, and will consider whether the reasons have significance for the future.

12.40 The next step is to consider the extent to which this information is useful in the construction of the salary scales for the calculations. The pay structure at any time represents the interaction of many factors. It reflects not only the needs of the moment but also past pay scales and past recruitment policies. In considering what assumptions to make about the future progression of earnings the actuary will consult the employer and will also use his own judgement. He may, for instance, believe that the workforce will become smaller but more highly paid, as machines take over more routine tasks or the company reacts to competition. Circumstances of employers vary so widely that it is hardly possible to generalise on this aspect of the actuary's task, but it is an important one.

12.41 Traditionally the typical scales of earnings of the main grades of employees have quite distinctive shapes, and as these persist to a considerable extent today they are briefly described below. It is emphasised that these notes describe the position ignoring any general escalation in levels of earnings.

Male salaried staff

12.42 The individual salaries of clerical and administrative male staff are fairly low at young ages at entry. They tend to increase fairly rapidly up to age 35 or 40, as experience is gained and positions of some responsibility reached. A slower rate of increase usually persists for a further 10 or 20 years. Only a comparatively few members attain large incomes in senior posts. The typical salary scale therefore increases fairly rapidly during the early years but tends to level off later on.

Female salaried staff

12.43 Similar considerations apply, but the proportion of more senior posts attained is usually smaller, so that the salary scale will usually show a smaller overall increase.

Male wage earners

12.44 It is often found for male wage earners that the full standard adult wage is reached at a young age, the scope for increases thereafter being limited. The earnings scale thus rises rapidly until about age 25 but then levels off, and this general pattern holds good whether or not overtime pay is included. Average weekly rates of total pay often tend to rise more rapidly than average hourly rates of basic pay for wages grades employees (the phenomenon of 'wage drift'). This is partly because negotiations on working conditions, leading to reductions in the number of hours in the standard working week, sometimes merely result in an increased proportion of an unchanged total number of hours counting for overtime pay rates. Such negotiations are often tacitly acknowledged to be negotiations about pay rather than working hours. The matter is relevant here because, as mentioned earlier, pensionable pay (before adjustment for integration) may exclude overtime pay. The actuary will bear in mind possible further reductions in the number of hours in the standard working week in considering the future progression of pensionable pay.

Female wage earners

12.45 The basic scales usually show much the same features as those of the corresponding male employees.

CHAPTER 13

STARTING A SCHEME:
OUTLINE AND DATA

STARTING A SCHEME: OUTLINE AND DATA

Introduction: Scheme X

13.1 We now introduce a hypothetical occupational pension scheme in the United Kingdom, Scheme X, which will be used to illustrate the processes of costing and valuation and other aspects of pension scheme work. It will be assumed that the members of the scheme are to be contracted-out of the State earnings-related scheme. This leads to various complications, and in order to keep matters as simple as possible the benefit scales of the scheme have been made straightforward and it will be assumed that all the employees are males with salaried staff status. We shall deal with the setting up of the scheme, the experience of the first three years and the first regular three-yearly actuarial valuation.

Outline of proposed Scheme X

13.2 We will suppose that the employer does not at present have a pension scheme, so that the employees are participating in the earnings-related part of the State scheme. The employer has suggested the following scheme and has asked for an estimate of the cost.

Outline Specification

Membership

Spec. 1

(i)   Persons entering the employment after the Commencement Date must join the scheme upon entry or later attainment of age 18, provided they are aged less than 60.

(ii)   Employees in the service at the Commencement Date may join the scheme subject to the same minimum entry age condition as future employees. The maximum entry age provision does not apply. They will not, however, be required to join.

Pensionable service

Spec. 2

Pensionable service, i.e. the period counting for the calculation of benefits, will be the period of membership of the scheme except that for employees joining on the Commencement Date pensionable service will include one-half of any period before the Commencement Date during which they would have been members of the scheme had it always been in force and they had joined when they first became eligible.

Retirement ages

Spec. 3

(i)   The normal retirement age is 65, but members may with the consent of the employer retire on or after their 60th birthday with an immediate pension calculated at the date of retirement on the normal pension scale outlined in Spec. 4 below.

(ii) Members may retire at any age between 55 and 65 without the consent of the employer, but in this case the immediate pension is to be equal to the normal scale pension calculated at the date of retirement, reduced actuarially to allow for early payment (except in the case of retirement under (iii) below).

(iii) A member who is forced to give up the employment because of ill-health may retire irrespective of age with an immediate pension equal to the normal scale pension calculated at the date of retirement.

Scale of members' pensions

Spec. 4

The pension is to be equal to 1/80th of the average annual salary during the three years preceding retirement multiplied by the number of years of pensionable service completed at the date of retirement (with parts of a year counting proportionately).

Capital sums on retirement

Spec. 5

There is to be provision for the commutation of pension for a capital sum within Inland Revenue limits.

Benefits on death during employment

Spec. 6

Upon the death of a member during employment the benefits payable are as follows.

(i) A capital sum equal to twice annual salary at the date of death or the amount of the member's own contributions accumulated with 4 per cent. compound interest, whichever is the greater.

(ii) A widow's pension equal to one-half of the pension to which the member would have been entitled had he retired on grounds of ill-health at the date of his death.

Benefits on death in receipt of pension

Spec. 7

Upon the death of a retired member the benefits payable are as follows.

(i) If death occurs during the period of five years immediately following retirement, a capital sum equal to the amount of the pension which would otherwise have been payable during the remaining balance of the five-year period. (This apparently simple provision is not in fact very satisfactory, as will be seen from paragraph 15.27.)

(ii) A widow's pension equal to one-half of the pension which would have been payable to the member at the date of his death had he not commuted any pension for lump sum on retirement (whether or not he in fact did so).

Early leavers

Spec. 8

(i) An early leaver for whom statutory preservation of pension does not apply is to be paid a lump sum equal to his own contributions to the scheme accumulated at 4 per cent. per annum compound, less the contribution to the C.E.P. as mentioned in paragraph 4.30.

(ii) An early leaver to whom statutory preservation does apply is to be provided with a preserved pension, payable from age 65. The initial amount is to be calculated on the normal pension scale at the date of leaving and increases before and after payment starts are to be as shown in Spec. 9.

Note Despite the provisions for retirement in normal health before age 65 contained in Spec. 3(i) and (ii) the pension preservation law does not entitle the ex-employee to claim payment of the preserved pension at an earlier age than 65. This is because, had the leaver remained a member, he could not have claimed payment of the normal scale pension without actuarial reduction as of right (i.e. without the consent of the employer) before attainment of age 65.

Pension increases

Spec. 9

(i) Pensions in payment are to be increased at 3 per cent. per annum except that the G.M.P. part is not to be increased after attainment of age 65.

(ii) The initial amount of the preserved pension of an early leaver is to be increased as follows during the period from the date of leaving to the date on which the preserved pension comes into payment upon the ex-member's attainment of age 65.

    (a) The G.M.P. element is to be increased at 8½ per cent. per annum.

    (b) The amount in excess of the G.M.P. is to be increased at 5 per cent. per annum.

Contribution rates

Spec. 10

(i) It is intended that the cost of the normal year-by-year accrual of benefit rights should be covered by contributions at a specified rate by the members and contributions by the employer which may vary between 1½ times and twice the total contributions of the members, as recommended by the actuary from time to time.

(ii) Since the pensionable service of the initial entrants is to include allowance for periods of service before the Commencement Date, there will be a once-for-all capital cost on the setting up of the scheme. The employer is to meet this cost by paying an additional contribution, the scale and duration of payment of which is to be settled as part of the general consideration of costs.

A simplification of the proposed benefits

13.3 Apart from any dual calculations of benefit which may be required because of contracting-out requirements, the only double calculation required under the proposed scheme of benefits relates to the capital sum on death during employment, which is to be the greater of two amounts calculated in entirely different ways. It is worth investigating whether this provision could be simplified. In the early years it is evident that a payment equal to twice salary would be much greater than the amount of the member's accumulated contributions. It is only after very long service that the amount of the accumulated contributions might conceivably be greater. In order to examine the position, we consider each £1,000 of salary of a member with many years of contributory membership at some future date. Let us suppose that the member has had no promotional increases, so that on the earnings assumptions mentioned in paragraph 13.4 salary will have grown at 8 per cent. per annum to the figure of £1,000. We will assume that the member has been paying a contribution rate of 5 per cent. Then the amount of the member's contributions accumulated at the rate of 4 per cent. compound interest to the date at which the calculation is being made is given by

$$50(v^{1/2} (1.04)^{1/2} + v^{1 1/2} (1.04)^{1 1/2} \ldots\ldots\ldots\ldots$$

where v is at 8 per cent., which simplifies to

$$50(1+j)^{1/2} a_{\overline{n}|}$$

where the compound interest functions are at about 3.85 per cent.

$$(\text{since } \frac{1.08}{1.04} - 1 = .0385)$$

and n is the period of membership. It is clear that even for long membership the amount would not be more than about once times salary. Any promotional element in the salary progression would further diminish the ratio of accumulated contributions to current salary. We will therefore assume that the lump sum benefit on death in service will always be equal to twice salary, and simplify the benefit specification accordingly.

The actuarial basis

13.4 As mentioned in Chapter 11, we will make the calculations on the basis of a rate of interest of 9 per cent. and an annual rate of increase in general levels of earnings of 8 per cent. The service table and promotional salary scale will be those appearing in the Tables for Actuarial Examinations issued by the Institute and Faculty of Actuaries. These are used because they are conveniently available; there is no implication that they would be suitable for use in practice.

Membership data

13.5 In order to calculate the contribution rates required to support the scheme it is necessary to collect information about the potential membership. This information is obviously required for the calculation of the once-for-all capital cost which would arise in respect of benefit rights for pre-scheme service on the setting up of the scheme if all employees entitled to join did so. It is also required in order to calculate the contribution rates to cover the cost of the year-by-year accrual of benefit rights once the scheme is in force, since the distribution of salaries by age has a bearing on this calculation.

13.6 We will assume that information has been collected about the current employees, and this is summarised in Table 1 at the end of this book. For simplicity the workforce is assumed to be divided into a number of groups, the employees within each group all having identical data. The salary figure is the amount received in the year ended on the date as at which the information is drawn up. We will assume for the moment that the age shown is the age nearest birthday, but we shall have to consider this further in the discussion of contracting-out in Chapter 15.

The calculation of costs

13.7 The settling of the contribution rates has a number of different aspects, as follows.

(i)   We shall need to calculate the contribution rate required to cover the cost of the year-by-year accrual of benefit rights during contributory membership of Scheme X. This contribution rate will depend not only on the actuarial basis employed but also on the funding plan chosen.

(ii) The calculations will need to allow for the various points arising from contracting-out.

(iii) When the contribution rate in (i) has been settled it will be necessary to decide on the proportion of the total which is to be met by the members. It will be necessary to reconcile the desired policy of the employer that his normal contributions should vary between 1½ times and twice the total contributions of the members with the need to fix the level of the members' contributions so that the costs and benefits of the scheme will look attractive to the members compared with those of the State earnings-related pension scheme.

(iv) It will be necessary to calculate the rate of additional contribution payable by the employer to cover the cost of the past service rights on the setting up of the scheme. It cannot be known at this stage whether all the members shown in Table 1 will elect to join the scheme but the calculations will be made on the assumption that all will do so.

(v)   Since the scheme is to be used for contracting-out, the Occupational Pensions Board will require the actuary to submit the solvency certificate A shown at the end of Chapter 4. The total contribution rate will need to be fixed at such a level that the actuary will be able to sign this certificate.

CHAPTER 14

SCHEME X: CONTRIBUTION RATES: FUNCTIONS AND VALUES

SCHEME X: CONTRIBUTION RATES: FUNCTIONS AND VALUES

Introduction

14.1 In the calculation of the contribution rates to cover the cost of the accrual of benefit rights during contributory membership of Scheme X it is necessary to allow for the contracting-out requirements and also for the fact that the part of a pension representing the G.M.P. will not be increased in payment. Precise allowance for these factors would best be made by the use of a computer; indeed, in practice most of the calculations for Scheme X might well be made by computer methods and most of the calculations for this book have been carried out by such means. For clarity, however, we shall show specimen calculations made by manual methods. As will be clear from the next chapter, this will inevitably entail some approximations in the areas of the contracting-out requirements and the G.M.P.

14.2 The settling of the rate of contribution payable by the employer to meet the past service liability on the setting up of the scheme is more straightforward, since contracting-out is not involved for the notional periods of membership to be credited.

14.3 The reader will find at various points in the discussion references to small differences between figures calculated by computer methods and those calculated manually. These discrepancies are due to the fact that the computer program used for the calculations is not based exactly on the formulae of Chapter 9. The discrepancies are of no consequence.

The plan of the work

14.4 The work is set out as follows.

Chapter 14

The manual construction of commutation columns and functions, and the calculation of various present capital values before the adjustments required to allow for the contracting-out requirements and the absence of pension increases on G.M.P.s after attainment of age 65.

Chapter 15

The adjustments required to allow for the contracting-out requirements and the absence of pension increases on G.M.P.s after attainment of age 65.

Chapter 16

The calculation of contribution rates under various different funding plans and the settling of the contribution rates for Scheme X.

14.5 We show in Table 2 the service table and salary scale before escalation which have been used for the calculations. As mentioned in paragraph 13.4, this basis has been used solely because it already appears in the Tables for Actuarial Examinations and there is no implication that it would be appropriate for practical use. Tables 3 to 12 show specimen calculations leading to the evaluation of various functions at exact age 55 (except for withdrawal benefit functions which are calculated at age 35). The annuity values have been calculated on a rate of interest of 9 per cent., allowing for a 3 per cent. increase in the pension each year. The annuity values are calculated using a rate of interest of 5.825 per cent., since

$$1.09 \div 1.03 = 1.05825$$

The use of this rate rather than 6 per cent. is a consequence of the use of computer programs which combine interest rates and increase rates in this way. The effect is to value the pension as if increases were continuous, and this is usually a reasonable approximation to the value which would be arrived at if the precise arrangements of a particular case were allowed for. In the following paragraphs we comment on points of interest in the calculations.

Salary and contribution functions

14.6 Table 3 shows the addition of escalation to the salary scale and the calculation of the function representing salary averaged over 3 years as required for benefit purposes, and Table 4 shows the building up of the contribution function. It is necessary to divide this function and the various benefit functions developed in later tables by ^sD_x in order to change them into the functions used to place a present capital value on future contribution income and benefit outgo. The earnings figures included in the valuation data represent earnings in the year preceding the valuation date, and it is therefore appropriate to define ^sD_x as $s_{x-1} D_x = s_{x-1} v^x l_x$. The calculation of the numerical values of ^sD_x is not shown in this book, but the process is entirely straightforward. The values of $^sD_{35}$ and $^sD_{55}$ are as follows.

$$^sD_{35} = 40.8 \times 1398 = 57,038$$
$$^sD_{55} = 311 \times 191.59 = 59,584$$

Member's pension on age retirement

14.7 In Table 5 we show the calculation of the commutation functions in respect of the member's pension on age retirement, which follow the formulae of paragraph 9.57. The only points calling for comment relate to the annuity values in column (5), as follows.

(i)   Retirements are assumed to be spread evenly over the year of age concerned except that all members reaching age 65 are then assumed to retire immediately. The annuities are accordingly those at the half age except for age 65 at which the exact age is used.

(ii) The annuities incorporate a 5-year guarantee as a close approximation to the capital sum death benefit mentioned in benefit specification 7(i).

(iii) The mortality rates assumed are those of the a(55) table.

Member's pension on ill-health retirement

14.8 Table 6 shows the calculation of the commutation functions in respect of the member's pension on ill-health retirement. The calculations follow the formulae of paragraph 9.57. The calculations differ from those in Table 5 in that there is no element at age 65. All retirements at this age are assumed to be in normal health. The procedure is similar to that of Table 5 but the annuities on this occasion have been based on the rates of the a(55) table rated up 5 years in token of the higher mortality rates to be expected after retirement on grounds of ill-health.

Member's preserved pension on withdrawal

14.9   Table 7 shows the calculation of the commutation functions in respect of a preserved pension for an early leaver. The calculations follow the method of paragraph 9.96. It will be recalled that benefit specification 8(i) provides for early leavers for whom statutory preservation of pension does not apply to be paid an amount equal to their own accumulated contributions to the scheme less their share of the C.E.P. Early leavers to whom statutory preservation does apply are to be provided with a preserved pension.

14.10   This benefit pattern requires in theory the use of select rates of withdrawal but as implied in Chapter 12 it is seldom that the extra work involved is justified. In costing the withdrawal benefit we will assume that all early leavers will receive a preserved pension with the appropriate G.M.P. element, the treatment of which is dealt with in the next chapter. We will then make an approximate adjustment to allow for those cases of leavers during the early years of membership for whom a return of contributions would be a more valuable benefit than the preserved pension with its G.M.P. content.

14.11   As to the details of Table 7, the main points calling for comment relate, as in previous tables, to the annuity value. The pension starts to be paid at age 65 and increases are provided between the date of leaving and attainment of that age at the rate of 5 per cent. per annum. The mortality of the a(55) table has been assumed both before and after the pension comes into payment. As an example, the calculation of the annuity value of 3.555 which is included at age 44 in the calculation is shown below.

$$(1.05)^{65-44\frac{1}{2}} \times \frac{D_{65}}{D_{44\frac{1}{2}}} \ (9\%) \ \times \ \bar{a}\ \overline{{}_{65\ \overline{5}|}} \ (5.825\%)$$

$$2.719 \ \times \ .1404 \ \times \ 9.309 \ = \ 3.555$$

Widows' pensions

14.12   It will be recalled from paragraph 4.25 that a condition of contracting-out is that, save in exceptional cases, a widow's pension must be provided at the 'quality test' level even if the marriage took place after the husband ceased to be a contracted-out employee member of the scheme concerned. This needs to be borne in mind in arriving at the proportions married to be used in the calculations of the various functions and values relating to widows' pensions in a scheme to be used for contracting-out. We shall use proportions married of 90 per cent. at all ages for the various calculations in this chapter, without any implication that this would be suitable in any particular case in practice.

Widows' pensions on death after age retirement

14.13 In Table 8 we show the calculation of the commutation functions in respect of the pension payable to the widow of a member who dies after having retired on grounds of age. The calculations follow the method of paragraph 9.85 et seq. The calculations are very similar to those of Table 5 but the annuity values included in the factors represent the value of the reversionary annuity to a widow at the time that the member retires instead of the annuity to the member incorporated in Table 5. Comments on the annuity values are as follows.

(i) The mortality of retired employees, their wives and widows is assumed to follow that of the a(55) table.

(ii) The wife is assumed to be 3 years younger than the member.

Widows' pension on death after ill-health retirement

14.14 In Table 9 we show the calculation of the commutation functions in respect of the widow's pension payable on the death of an employee after his retirement on grounds of ill-health. The calculations follow the method of paragraph 9.85 et seq. As in the corresponding tables for age retirements, the calculations are very similar to those of Table 6 but the annuity values included in the factors represent the value of the reversionary annuity to a widow at the time that the member retires instead of the annuity to the member incorporated in Table 6. Comments on points of detail are as follows.

(i) The mortality of retired employees is that of the a(55) table rated up 5 years while wives and widows are assumed to follow a(55) unadjusted.

(ii) The wife is assumed to be 3 years younger than the member.

Widows' pensions on death in service

14.15 Table 10 shows the calculation of the commutation functions in respect of the widow's pension payable on the death of an employee during service. Comments are as follows.

(i)   The mortality of widows is assumed to follow that of the a(55) table.

(ii)   The wife is assumed to be 3 years younger than the employee.

(iii) The values of C_x^d in column (2) are obtained from column (4) of Table 12.

Widows' pensions associated with early leavers

14.16 The outline of Scheme X contained in paragraph 13.2 does not specify the benefits payable in respect of an early leaver if he dies before the preserved pension comes into payment. The position upon his death after the pension starts to be paid is not explicitly mentioned but it is covered by benefit specification 7, which relates to benefits on the death of a pensioner whether the pension started to be paid on the attainment of age 65 by an early leaver with a preserved pension or on the retirement of a member from the scheme. Whatever death benefits are ultimately decided in respect of early leavers they will not give rise to a very material part of the contribution rate, and in the circumstances we shall make the calculations as if the death benefit is a half rate widow's pension whether the early leaver dies before or after attainment of age 65.

14.17 It will be recalled that the preserved pension of an early leaver is to increase at 5 per cent. p.a. before it comes into payment and at 3 per cent. p.a. thereafter, subject to the G.M.P. provisions dealt with in the next chapter. The function required to value the widow's pension in respect of an early leaver, before allowing for the G.M.P., therefore represents a widow's annuity starting on the death of the early leaver whether before or after his attainment of normal pension age, with allowance for the above pattern of increases on his pension; the widow's pension enjoys increases of 3 per cent. p.a. once it comes into payment. The annuity required is therefore not a straightforward reversionary annuity to the wife calculated at the date of leaving, but is of the following form.

$$\frac{1}{l_x \, l_y} \left[\sum_{t=0}^{64-x} d_{x+t} \, l_{y+t+\frac{1}{2}} \, v^{t+\frac{1}{2}} \, (1.05)^{t+\frac{1}{2}} \, \bar{a}_{y+t+\frac{1}{2}} \right. +$$

$$\left. l_{65} l_{y+65-x} \, v^{65-x} \, (1.05)^{65-x} \, \bar{a}_{65 \,|\, y+65-x} \right]$$

The calculation of this annuity for a leaver at exact age 44 is shown in Table 11(a). The value at age 44½ appears as the last entry in column (3) of the calculations for an early leaver at age 35 developed in Table 11(b), the widow's annuity being calculated on a(55) mortality without a rating. The calculations follow the method of paragraph 9.96 except that the function $\bar{a}_{x+\frac{1}{2}|y+\frac{1}{2}}$ is substituted for the function

$$\frac{D_{65}}{D_{x+\frac{1}{2}}} \, \bar{a} \, \overline{_{65 \, \overline{5}|}}$$

in formula 9.96.1. The values of $^z C_x^w$ in column (2) of Table 11(b) are calculated in column (6) of Table 7.

Capital sums on death in service

14.18 The commutation functions in respect of the capital sum payable on death in service are illustrated in Table 12. The calculations follow the formulae of paragraph 9.79. The benefit is defined in terms of the rate of salary at the date of death and this is reflected in the salary function taken into the calculations. The benefit does not accrue from year to year as does a pension entitlement, so that it is not necessary to develop an 'R' type function.

Summary of factors

14.19 Table 13 gives a summary of the factors which are required at the ages concerned in the initial calculations, and in the first actuarial valuation three years later, to value the various benefits and the contributions. These functions have been calculated by computer and differ slightly in some cases from values calculated by the manual methods illustrated in Tables 3 to 12, for the reason mentioned in paragraph 14.3. The column headings M/D and R/D are abbreviations for the full notation shown in the previous tables.

Calculation of values

14.20   Table 14 shows the calculation of various present capital values, using the employees in Group D of Table 1 as an example. Except for the final two sections of the Table, the first two items under each side heading show the values of the functions to be used and the next three items show present capital values of benefit rights as follows.

(i)   The first value shown is the value of the benefit rights expected to be earned in the first year following the date of the calculations (before allowing for contracting-out) taking into account expected future pay increases. These values will be needed in the subsequent discussion about funding rates, because one funding plan considered is that under which the contributions paid in a year are intended to cover the cost of the benefit rights arising in respect of that year, allowing for expected future pay increases.

(ii)   The second value shown is the present value of the benefits expected to arise in respect of the pensionable service credited in connection with pre-scheme employment. The use of salary times past pensionable service is in line with formula 9.59.1.

(iii)   The third value relates to the benefit rights expected to arise in respect of years of pensionable service to be completed in the future. The calculations are on the lines of formula 9.59.2.

14.21   A point which calls for comment relates to items (40) and (42) of Table 14 in respect of the cost of the lump sum benefit on death in service. As will be explained in more detail in Chapter 16, it may be appropriate in some funding plans to regard the cost of the lump sum benefits payable on death in service in a particular year as being met by an element of the contributions payable in that year. The 'cost' of the benefit, assessed on this basis, is equal to the expected claims in the year, and the first year cost is therefore calculated by multiplying the expected amount of the benefit by the probability of a claim. This is the reasoning underlying items (40) and (42) of the Table.

Summaries of values

14.22   In Tables 15, 16 and 17 values corresponding to those calculated in Table 14 are shown for the whole potential initial membership. The figures in these tables form the basis for the calculation of contribution rates, after the adjustments discussed in the next chapter. The figures at age 30 differ slightly in some cases from those of Table 14 because of the technical points of computer processes mentioned earlier. We shall use the values of Tables 15 to 17 in the subsequent discussion.

Benefits not costed

14.23 The values in Tables 15 to 17 include no allowance for voluntary early retirement with an actuarially reduced pension (benefit specification 3(ii)) or for commutation of pension for a capital sum on retirement (benefit specification 5). We will assume that the terms of these options are to be fixed so that on the average they will involve little if any extra cost on the scheme and need not be allowed for in the costing.

The initial membership

14.24 In practice the initial membership of a scheme would be highly unlikely to coincide exactly with the potential initial membership in respect of whom information was collected. Some employees would choose not to join, and there would be new entrants and leavers in the period before the scheme was set up. We will ignore these practical difficulties and assume that the employees summarised in Table 1 form the initial membership of Scheme X.

CHAPTER 15

SCHEME X: CONTRIBUTION RATES: CONTRACTING-OUT

SCHEME X: CONTRIBUTIONS RATES: CONTRACTING-OUT

Introduction

15.1 This chapter constitutes the main description in this book of the detailed calculations in connection with contracting-out. Before embarking on it the reader may find the following comments helpful.

(i) Table 17 is a summary of future service values before allowing for contracting-out, as described in the previous chapter. Table 24 is a corresponding summary after allowing for contracting-out. A brief comparison of these tables will indicate to the reader the total effect of the three aspects of contracting-out mentioned in the next paragraph.

(ii) The arithmetic of this chapter and the associated tables is tedious and lengthy, reflecting the various details of the G.M.P. arrangements.

(iii) It is not necessary to master this chapter before proceeding to subsequent chapters, and some readers will no doubt prefer to aim only for a general understanding at a first reading.

The approach to the work

15.2 The calculations of cost in the previous chapter included no allowance for the fact that the members of Scheme X are to be contracted-out of the State earnings-related pension scheme, and we now turn to this matter which is discussed under the following headings.

(i) Any additional cost arising from the requirements of the contracting-out 'quality test' as outlined in paragraphs 4.21 and 5.29 et seq. We shall in fact find that there is virtually no extra cost on this account, but the quality test will be mentioned for completeness at various points in the discussion.

(ii) Any additional cost arising from the contracting-out 'quantity test', i.e. the G.M.P. requirements as outlined in paragraph 4.9 et seq. We shall find that for a 'stayer', i.e. a member who remains in Scheme X until age 65, the final pay nature of the pension scale is expected to ensure that pensions will more than cover G.M.P.s. The G.M.P. requirement will, however, have an effect for early leavers.

(iii) The saving in cost arising from the fact that increases in pensions after a pensioner reaches State pensionable age are not to be provided on the G.M.P. content of each pension. We shall find that there is a significant saving, compared with the values from Chapter 14, on this account.

As noted in Chapter 14 the complexities of the G.M.P. are best dealt with by computer. The manual methods that we shall use in the interests of clarity will inevitably involve various approximations.

The amount of the G.M.P.

15.3 It will be necessary for us to deal separately with each of the main benefits when considering the impact of the G.M.P. on costs. However, the preliminary calculation of the amount of the G.M.P. is common to all the benefits, and we shall therefore first consider this in detail. We shall not repeat here the material of Chapter 4 in which the G.M.P. arrangements are described, but we shall illustrate the points involved by looking in detail at the position of an employee who is in Group D of Table 1 and is therefore aged 30 at the date of the initial investigation and received salary of £3,000 in the year ended on that date. Preliminary calculations are shown . in Table 18 and are explained in the following paragraphs.

15.4 In the discussion so far we have not needed to specify the date to which the information for the initial calculations for Scheme X relates, but it is now necessary to do so because the G.M.P. fraction depends on the employee's age at 5th April 1978 and sex. The State scheme and G.M.P. are based on fiscal years (i.e. years ending on 5th April) and for simplicity we will assume that the initial information for Scheme X as set out in Table 1 relates to the position as at 5th April 1979. We shall thus avoid the complications which arise if the occupational scheme year is not the same as the fiscal year; these complications are matters of practice rather than principle.

15.5 We shall need to apply the method of paragraph 4.12 to arrive at the G.M.P. fraction of each employee. In Table 1 the employees are grouped according to their age nearest birthday (see paragraph 13.6) at 5th April 1979. The employees in a particular group therefore reached the specified birthday in one of two periods, namely the 6 months ended on 5th April 1979 and the 6 months starting on 6th April 1979. These two groups of employees would have different numbers of complete tax years between 6th April 1978 and attainment of State pensionable age, and hence different G.M.P. fractions. In order to avoid this complication we will assume that all 345 employees in Table 1 have their birthday on 1st April. An employee in Group D thus attained age 30 on 1st April 1979 and will attain age 65 on 1st April 2014. The number of complete fiscal years between 6th April 1978 and 1st April 2014 is 35 and his G.M.P. fraction is therefore 1/140th. The assumption of 1st April as the birthday is made solely in order to simplify the G.M.P. calculations; in most of the discussion we shall treat the ages as exact ages on 5th April.

15.6 The calculation of a G.M.P. earned in a particular tax year involves the lower and upper earnings limit of the State scheme in that year. We will assume that the information as at 5th April 1979 is in fact an estimate of the expected position at that date, assembled in advance at a time when no information is available about the amounts of the lower and upper earnings limit of the State scheme for the fiscal year beginning 6th April 1979. For the fiscal year 6th April 1978 to 5th April 1979 (hereafter described as the year 1978/79 with a similar notation for other years) the State scheme lower earnings limit was £17.50 per week or £910 p.a. and the upper earnings limit £120 per week or £6,240 p.a.; we will take this as part of our data as at 5th April 1979.

15.7 On our assumptions, the employee's pay in the year 1979/80 is expected to be

$$\text{£3,000} \times s_{30} (25.7)/s_{29} (22.5) = \text{£3,427}$$

Earnings levels are assumed to escalate at 8 per cent. per annum and we have to decide whether to assume that the State scheme lower and upper earnings limits will also increase at this rate. The lower limit is linked to the amount of the State flat-rate pension for a single person and as noted in Chapter 11 this amount is not directly linked to prices or earnings. We will assume without further discussion that the State scheme lower and upper earnings limits will increase at 8 per cent. p.a. so that the figures which are expected for year 1979/80 at the time that the calculations are being made are as follows.

$$\text{lower earnings limit:} \quad £910 \times 1.08 = \quad £983$$
$$\text{upper earnings limit:} \quad £6,240 \times 1.08 = £6,739$$

The expected amount of the employee's G.M.P. earned in the year 1979/80 is therefore

$$1/140\text{th of } (£3,427 - £983) = £17.46$$

15.8 The calculation of the expected amount of the G.M.P. earned in each future year proceeds in the same way, except that for the year of age 57 to 58 and subsequent years the projected amount of annual salary exceeds the projected amount of the upper earnings limit (because of the promotional element in the salary scale) so that the amount of relevant earnings is then equal to the difference between the lower and upper limits. Since

$$(6240 \div 910) - 1 = 5.857$$

the projected amount of relevant earnings at ages 57 and above is equal to 5.857 times the lower earnings limit for the year concerned. Columns (3), (4) and (5) of Table 18 show these calculations for the opening and closing years of the period; it has not been thought necessary to show all values but the reader can readily calculate these if desired. Column (6) of the Table shows the amount of the G.M.P. earned in each year, i.e. 1/140th of the amount in column (5), rounded to whole pounds. The large figures expected in the distant future are a measure of the projected effect of continuing inflation.

15.9 While the employee remains a member of Scheme X his G.M.P. entitlement is increased annually in line with increases in average earnings (which we are assuming to be at the rate of 8 per cent. p.a.) under the provisions of section 21 of the 1975 Act. His entitlement at the end of the year 1980/81, before the increase of April 1981, is thus expected to be the 1979/80 amount of £17.46 increased by 8 per cent., added to the 1980/81 amount which is calculated as £20.04, giving the rounded total of £39 shown in column (7) of the Table. The figures in column (7) are obtained by repeating this revaluation process for all subsequent years, and these figures are used in the following discussion of the position for each main benefit.

Member's pension on age retirement

The quality test

15.10   The members' pensions are on the scale of 1/80ths of the average annual salary during the three years preceding retirement for each year of pensionable service. In the outline of Scheme X in Chapter 13 we have not included a definition of 'salary' but we will assume that this means the full taxable earnings of the members. The pension formula satisfies the quality test and no extra cost therefore arises in this connection.

The G.M.P. requirements

15.11   In Scheme X members may retire with an immediate pension at any time after attainment of age 60 subject to the consent of the employer. The following further details of the G.M.P. arrangements now need to be noted.

(i)   In the G.M.P. calculation there is a distinction between

    (a)   members of an occupational scheme who retire during the tax year in which State pensionable age is reached, and

    (b)   members of an occupational scheme who leave (which term includes early retirement) before the start of the tax year in which State pensionable age is reached.

(ii)   For a member who retires in the tax year during which State pensionable age is reached, the figures of relevant earnings on which the G.M.P. is based are those up to the end of the tax year preceding the one in which the member retires, revalued under the section 21 Orders which came into force before the end of the tax year preceding the one in which the member reaches State pensionable age. The employee receives no credit as far as the amount of the G.M.P. is concerned for any relevant earnings in the year in which he attains State pensionable age.

(iii)   For an employee who leaves before the start of the tax year in which State pensionable age is reached, the G.M.P. at the date of leaving is based on the relevant earnings in all the tax years concerned up to and including the tax year in which leaving takes place. The section 21 Order for this tax year does operate, and the amount of the relevant earnings for this tax year is included in the calculation of the G.M.P. In both these respects the calculation differs from that described in (ii) above.

(iv) For an early leaver in (iii) above, fixed-rate revaluation of the G.M.P. at 8½ per cent. per annum, which is to be used for Scheme X, applies for each complete tax year after the tax year of termination of membership up to and including the tax year before attainment of State pensionable age.

15.12 These complicated rules are illustrated for the retirement on grounds of age of an employee in Group D of Table 1 by the calculations shown in Table 19. Comments on these figures are given in the following paragraphs, but we deal first with a logical difficulty which the reader may have noticed. This relates to the fact that secton 21 Orders are assumed to be at the rate of 8 per cent. per annum (because this is the rate of escalation of general pay levels used in our basis) whereas the administrators of Scheme X have elected for the G.M.P.s of early leavers to be revalued at the fixed revaluation rate of 8½ per cent. per annum. It might be argued that they should have opted for section 21 revaluation since this is at a lower rate, or alternatively that it is unrealistic to assume that the rate of 8½ per cent. per annum would remain unchanged in long term conditions of 8 per cent. per annum pay increases. On the other hand, it might be argued that the certainty of 8½ per cent. per annum revaluation might be preferred, even in the conditions implied by the basis, to the uncertainty of section 21 Orders. We will not pursue the matter here and will ignore the apparent difficulty. We now turn to the discussion of the age retirement figures.

Retirement at age 65

15.13 It will be seen from item (ii) of paragraph 15.11 that the G.M.P. on retirement at age 65 (which takes place just before the end of a tax year since the birthday is assumed to be 1st April) is made up as follows.

(i) Nil in respect of relevant earnings during the tax year of retirement.

(ii) The G.M.P. earned in the tax year preceding that of retirement taken at its face amount, i.e. without any further indexing.

(iii) The total G.M.P. earned in all previous tax years of contracted-out membership of the scheme as revalued by section 21 Orders up to and including that coming into effect during the tax year preceding the tax year of retirement.

15.14 The G.M.P. on retirement at age 65 for the employee concerned in the example is therefore made up as follows, using the three sub-divisions of the previous paragraph and drawing on figures from columns (6) and (7) of Table 18.

Period	G.M.P. at retirement in respect of period
	£
Tax year 2013/14	−
Tax year 2012/13	521
Earlier tax years ....$12{,}351 \times 1.08 =$	13,339
Total (small discrepancy in addition results from rounding of separate elements)	£13,861

The multiplier of 1.08 in this calculation represents the effect of the section 21 Order for the tax year 2012/13. The figure of £13,861 appears as the last entry in columns (2) and (4) of Table 19.

15.15 We next calculate the G.M.P. at age 65 of those who retire at age 64 last birthday. Since the birthdays of all employees fall on 1st April, virtually all retirements at age 64 last birthday from the employees in Group D will take place in the tax year 2013/14. This is the tax year in which State pensionable age is attained, so that the G.M.P. regulations outlined in item (ii) of paragraph 15.11 apply in this case in exactly the same way as to retirement at age 65. The accrued G.M.P. on retirement is thus £13,861 per annum, as in the previous paragraph, and this appears in column (2) of Table 19 against age 64.

15.16 We will assume that retirements dealt with in the previous paragraph take place on the average half way through the tax year at age 64½. There are no complete tax years falling within the definition of item (iv) of paragraph 15.11 so that the figure of £13,861 is not increased by revaluation at 8½ per cent. p.a. and £13,861 p.a. is therefore the amount of the G.M.P. when age 65 is reached; this figure appears in column (4) of Table 19 against age 64.

15.17   We turn to retirement at age 63 last birthday, assumed to take place at age 63½ half way through the tax year 2012/13. This case falls under item (iii) of paragraph 15.11 and the G.M.P. on retirement at age 63½ is made up as follows.

Period	G.M.P. at retirement in respect of period
	£
Tax year 2012/13	$521 \times 0.5 =$ 261
Earlier tax years ....$12,351 \times 1.08 =$	13,339
	£13,600

The multiplier of 1.08 in this calculation represents the effect of the section 21 Order for the tax year 2012/13. The total figure of £13,600 appears in column (2) of Table 19 against age 63.

15.18   The number of complete tax years falling within the definition of item (iv) of paragraph 15.11 (i.e. between the assumed date of retirement of 5th October 2012 and the 65th birthday on 1st April 2014) is nil. The figure of £13,600 is therefore not increased by revaluation at 8½ per cent. p.a. for the period between the date of retirement and the date of attainment of age 65. The amount of the G.M.P. when age 65 is reached is therefore £13,600, and this figure appears in column (4) of Table 19 against age 63.

15.19   Similar considerations (but with the effect of fixed-rate revaluation entering the picture) apply to retirements between the 60th and 63rd birthdays, giving rise to the other figures shown in columns (2), (3) and (4) of Table 19.

15.20   As far as the retirement on grounds of age with a normal scale pension of the employees in Group D of Table 1 is concerned, the figures in column (4) of Table 19 will form the basis of our answers to the questions posed in items (ii) and (iii) of paragraph 15.2, namely whether the G.M.P. requirements will lead to extra cost and the extent of the savings in cost resulting from the absence of pension increases on the G.M.P. We deal first with the question of extra cost.

Additional costs

15.21   If the employee remains in Scheme X until attainment of age 65 his annual pay averaged over the final three years is expected to be

$$£3,000 \times z_{65} (686)/s_{29} (22.5) = £91,467$$

His annual pension on retirement at that age will be based on 2.5 years of pensionable service in respect of pre-scheme employment and 35 years of contributory membership, and is thus expected to amount to

$$37.5/80\text{ths of } £91,467 = £42,875$$

This greatly exceeds the amount of the G.M.P. at age 65, calculated in Table 19 as £13,861 p.a., so that for an employee in Group D retiring at age 65 the requirements of the quantity test are not expected to impose costs additional to those calculated in the previous chapter. This was obvious from general reasoning, firstly because the pension fraction is much greater than the G.M.P. fraction for this employee and secondly because the pension is based on final average salary which includes a large promotional element (as is seen from the scale in Table 2) in addition to the escalation rate common to both salary and section 21 Orders.

15.22   We turn to the other extreme of age retirement on normal scale pension, namely the case of retirement at age 60 last birthday. On his retirement at assumed age 60½ the annual pay averaged over the final three years of the employee in Group D is expected to be

$$£3,000 \times z_{60½} (467)/s_{29} (22.5) = £62,267$$

His annual pension on retirement at that age will be based on 2.5 years of pensionable service in respect of pre-scheme employment and 30.5 years of contributory membership, and is thus expected to amount to

$$33/80\text{ths of } £62,267 = £25,685$$

When the pension is in payment it will be increased at the rate of 3 per cent. per annum and until the employee reaches age 65 there is no G.M.P. element in payment to receive increases from the State pension scheme. The whole of the pension from Scheme X will therefore be increased at 3 per cent. per annum and we will assume that the first such increase is granted at the end of the fiscal year of retirement and is based on one-half of a year as a pensioner. The amount of pension in payment in the year of age 65 to 66 is therefore

$$£25,685 \times 1.03^{4\frac{1}{2}} = £29,342$$

This amount is substantially greater than the amount of the G.M.P. at age 65, calculated in Table 19 as £12,204, so that the requirements of the quantity test are not expected to impose costs additional to those calculated in the previous chapter.

15.23 The above calculations represent the type of investigation which in principle has to be made to establish the combinations of circumstances, if any, in which the requirements of the quantity test will impose costs additional to those calculated in the previous chapter. The calculations shown indicate that for the employees aged 30 at entry there are unlikely to be any such additional costs. This is essentially because the G.M.P. fraction at those ages is much lower than the pension fraction of 1/80th on which Scheme X is based. This indicates that if there are any circumstances in which the quantity test will lead to extra cost these are more likely to be associated with employees in the older age groups of Table 1, because for these employees the G.M.P. fraction as well as the pension fraction of Scheme X is 1/80th. A further factor tending to increase the G.M.P. in relation to the scheme pension is that each year's G.M.P. is dynamised up to age 65, whereas the scheme pension is averaged over the final three years and is to this extent on a less favourable basis than the G.M.P.

15.24 There is, however, an important factor acting in the other direction, namely the fact that the employees at the older ages in Table 1 have very long periods of pre-scheme service which will count, albeit at the half rate, for pensionable service. Under the quantity test the whole of the scheme pension is to be compared with the amount of G.M.P., even though much of the scheme pension arises in respect of periods which were not contracted-out employment, and this has the effect of raising the scheme pension well above the level of the G.M.P. We will assume without further investigation that over the whole of the potential initial membership summarised in Table 1 the requirements of the quantity test will not impose costs additional to those calculated in the previous chapter. The reader will perhaps notice that in this paragraph we state that the whole of the pension at age 65 of a man who retired at, say, age 60 with an immediate pension may be taken into account for the purpose of the G.M.P. test at age 65, whereas in paragraph 4.52 we illustrate the anti-franking provisions of the 1984 Act which prevent a somewhat similar practice in the case of an early leaver with preserved rights. This would not be accepted by all commentators as a genuine anomaly; the reader need merely note the situation.

The saving in cost on pension increases

15.25 We turn to the third matter dealt with in paragraph 5.2, namely the saving in cost arising from the fact that pension increases after the pensioner attains State pensionable age are not to be provided from Scheme X on the G.M.P. content of each pension. We shall have to consider later the points that arise in assessing this saving in cases where the G.M.P. exceeds the normal scale amount of a pension at age 65, but as noted in the conclusion to the previous paragraph the calculations made for age retirements indicate that in all cases the G.M.P. at age 65 is expected to be less than the pension calculated on the normal pension scale of Scheme X. It follows that in order to place a value on the saving in costs now under consideration all that is necessary is to value the G.M.P. content of each age pension from age 65 firstly on the assumption of 3 per cent. increases and secondly as a flat pension, the difference between these two figures representing the saving under consideration.

15.26 We shall again base the discussion on the example of the employee in Group D of Table 1. It will be recalled that the expected amount of the G.M.P. at age 65 is shown, for the various ages at which age retirement with a normal scale pension can take place, in column (4) of Table 19. The most straightforward way of making the calculation described in the previous paragraph is to construct a commutation function based on the values of C_x^r already calculated in column (3) of Table 5, adding the probability that the employee, having retired, will survive to age 65, together with a discounting function for the period from the date of retirement to attainment of age 65. We shall incorporate the difference between a flat and an increasing pension as an end-piece to the calculation. We therefore need to calculate

$$C_x^r \frac{D_{65}}{D_{x+\frac{1}{2}}}$$

for x from 60 to 64. This process, and the incorporation of the amount of the G.M.P. at age 65, is shown in columns (5), (6) and (7) of Table 19. The D functions are calculated on a(55) mortality at 9 per cent. The values in column (7) are summed to produce a function for division by D_{30}. Below the table we show this process; allowance for the fact that 30 employees are involved leads to the calculation of a capital value at age 30 of a single payment at age 65 equal to the annual amount of the G.M.P. Multiplication by the appropriate annuity shows that for the Group D employees the value at age 30 of the G.M.P. following age retirement with a normal scale pension is £89,800 if the pension increases at 3 per cent. p.a. and £74,100 if it remains fixed, a saving of £15,700.

15.27 It will be noted that the annuities used incorporate a five year guarantee. It is not obvious that this is appropriate for the G.M.P. element of a pension; it flows from benefit specification 7(i) in Chapter 13, but more detailed consideration of this apparently simple point indicates how complex a full theoretical treatment of the G.M.P. arrangements would be. The capital sum payable on death during the first five years after retirement is to be equal to 'the amount of the pension which would otherwise have been payable during the remaining balance of the five-year period'. This implies that in the calculation of the capital sum, pension increases that the member would have enjoyed had he survived for the full five years (namely nil on the G.M.P. content and 3 per cent. p.a. on the excess) are to be allowed for. Thus the precise value of the guarantee per unit of pension depends on the age at retirement, since a retired employee's pension begins to have a G.M.P. content only when he attains age 65. For a member who retires at age 65 with pension P of which the G.M.P. content is G, the benefit valued at the instant of retirement in Chapter 14 is

$$P \, \bar{a} \, _{\overline{65\,\,5|}} \text{ at } 5.825\%$$

whereas it now appears that (except for the fact that the guarantee is in the form of an immediate capital sum rather than continuing annuity payments) the benefit that should be valued is

$$(P - G)\, \bar{a}\, \frac{}{_{65\,\overline{5}|}}\, \text{at } 5.825\%, \text{ plus}$$

$$G\, \bar{a}\, \frac{}{_{65\,\overline{5}|}}\, \text{at } 9\%$$

This indicates that the saving is approximately as calculated in Table 19 for retirement at age 65. This is not, however, the case at other retirement ages. We shall use five year guaranteed annuities for present purposes, but the proposed form of the guarantee would be administratively burdensome and in practice it would be modified. The calculation of the savings in costs over the whole range of the potential initial membership, corresponding to those in Table 19, are not shown in this book but the results are set out in columns (2) to (4) of Table 23.

Member's pension on ill-health retirement

The quality test

15.28 The conditions for contracting-out do not require the payment of a pension before attainment of the State pensionable age of 65 for men and 60 for women. They do not prohibit the use of earlier ages as the normal retirement ages of the scheme for men and women, nor a facility for retirement on pension before attainment of those ages, but there is a requirement that if early retirement with an immediate pension is permitted the rate of any actuarial reduction as described in paragraph 5.42 must not (unless otherwise certified by an actuary) exceed 6 per cent. for each year by which the age at retirement precedes the normal retirement age of the scheme. We are dealing now with the particular case of early retirement on grounds of ill-health, and the amount of the pension is to be the full amount of the pension accrued under the normal scale of Scheme X at the date of ill-health retirement without any actuarial reduction. The quality test is therefore satisfied and gives rise to no cost additional to that calculated in the previous chapter.

The G.M.P. requirements

15.29 As noted earlier, the test as to whether the pension payable from Scheme X is at least equal to the amount of the G.M.P. is imposed when the retired employee attains State pensionable age. An employee retiring early with an ill-health pension is regarded as an early leaver as far as the State scheme records are concerned, so that his G.M.P. is revalued under whichever system of G.M.P. revaluation for early leavers is chosen, for the years from the date of his retirement until the date that he attains State pensionable age. We are assuming that G.M.P.s are revalued at the rate of 8½ per cent. per annum, while pensions in payment under Scheme X are increased in payment at the rate of only 3 per cent. per annum; there is thus on the face of it a possibility that the G.M.P. rights included in a pension granted on ill-health retirement at an early age will have increased by the time that the retired employee reaches age 65 to an amount greater than the scale pension then in payment.

15.30 We will investigate the position using the employee in initial Group D covered in the previous example and we will assume that he retires in the year of age 35 to 36. His pension will be based on averaged pay equal to

$$£3,000 \times z_{35\frac{1}{2}} (38.8)/s_{29} (22.5) = £5,173$$

His pensionable service at retirement consists of 2.5 years in respect of pre-scheme employment and 5.5 years (assuming retirement half way through the year of age) in respect of contributory membership of Scheme X, a total of 8 years. The ill-health pension is therefore equal to

$$8/80\text{ths of } £5,173 = £517.3$$

The pension is increased at 3 per cent. per annum during payment, the first such increase being assumed to be granted (at the rate for one half of a year) at the end of the scheme year (assumed to be the same as the tax year) of retirement. The pension amounts in the year of age 65 to 66 to

$$£517.3 \times 1.03^{29\frac{1}{2}} (2.392) = £1,237$$

15.31 The accrued G.M.P. at the date of ill-health retirement may be calculated from Table 18. It is equal to the G.M.P. accrued up to age 35 increased by 8 per cent., plus one-half of the G.M.P. for the year of age 35 to 36. The total amount is therefore equal to

$$£132 \times 1.08 + £33 \times 0.5 = £159.1$$

This amount is increased by 8½ per cent. per annum for the 28 complete tax years between that of retirement and that of attainment of age 65 and the pension required to be paid under the quantity test is therefore equal to

$$£159.1 \times 1.085^{28} \ (9.818) = £1,562$$

15.32 On the assumptions used for the projections it will therefore be necessary to increase the scale ill-health pension upon attainment of age 65 to satisfy the quantity test. It will be seen that this position arises from the interaction of the following three factors.

(i) The G.M.P. fraction is small, because the member was comparatively young on 6th April 1978. This in itself would lead to a G.M.P. which was small compared with the scale pension.

(ii) The member is comparatively young at the assumed date of ill-health retirement. The period over which 8½ per cent. p.a. increases on the G.M.P. have to be provided is therefore comparatively long and the excess of such increases over the increases of 3 per cent. p.a. on the scale pension outweighs the effect of (i).

(iii) The period of credited pensionable service in respect of pre-scheme membership is comparatively short so that there is no substantial margin from this source to absorb the excess effect of (ii) over (i).

15.33 If we consider the ill-health retirement of the same employee at age 45 instead of 35, the expected final average salary is

$$£3,000 \times z_{45\frac{1}{2}} \ (112)/s_{29} \ (22.5) = £14,933$$

The initial level of annual pension is

$$18/80\text{ths of }£14,933 = £3,360$$

This will have risen in the year of age 65 to 66 to

$$£3,360 \times 1.03^{19\frac{1}{2}} \ (1.780) = £5,981$$

The G.M.P. at the date of retirement is calculated from Table 18 as

$$£1,071 \times 1.08 + £101 \times 0.5 = £1,207$$

This will have increased at age 65 to

$$£1,207 \times 1.085^{18} \ (4.342) = £5,241$$

which is less than the normal ill-health pension. In this case the G.M.P. test does not therefore necessitate any special increase at age 65 to the scale pension.

15.34 Turning now to employees at the older ages, the probability of the G.M.P. exceeding the scale pension is less. The G.M.P. fraction is 1/80th and is therefore equal to the normal pension fraction of the scheme, so that this feature on its own would make it more likely that the operation of the G.M.P. test would lead to additional cost. On the other hand the period up to attainment of age 65 during which the rate of increase in G.M.P. of 8½ per cent. p.a. exceeds the rate of pension increase of 3 per cent. p.a. is shorter than in the examples above. Furthermore, the retiring member is likely to have a substantial credit of pensionable service in respect of pre-scheme employment, thus increasing the initial excess of scale pension over G.M.P. It is found by trial calculations that there are comparatively few cases at this end of the age range in which the G.M.P. test leads to extra cost.

15.35 To what extent should we make precise calculations in this connection? Such calculations would clearly be complex and it is necessary to consider how significant they would be in the overall financial assessment. The capital values in respect of ill-health pensions and the associated widows' pensions as shown in Tables 15 to 17 represent only a small proportion of the total benefit values, and this would be the case even if the ill-health retirement rates underlying the service table were in line with current general experience. The element of the contribution rate in respect of ill-health pensions will therefore be modest. Furthermore, the above examples indicate that the G.M.P. test will have more effect in cases of retirement at younger ages than at older ages, and the incidence of ill-health retirement at these younger ages is very small. General reasoning therefore indicates that the additional cost resulting from the operation of the G.M.P. test as far as ill-health retirement is concerned will involve only a small addition to what is in any event a modest element in the total contribution rate. We shall not make any further detailed calculations but will bear this factor in mind in the final settling of the contribution rate.

The saving in cost on pension increases

15.36 Had the G.M.P. at age 65 been less than the ill-health pension payable at that age in all cases of ill-health retirement, the calculations in respect of the saving in cost arising from the fact that pension increases after the pensioner attains State pensionable age are not to be provided from Scheme X on the G.M.P. content of each pension would follow the method used in the context of age pensions as described earlier. The theoretical complications arising from the fact that the G.M.P. may exceed the normal scale pension are considerable. The discussion above indicates, however, that most of the calculated liabilities arise from expected ill-health retirements which will give rise to a scale pension at age 65 in excess of G.M.P. We will therefore assess the saving in exactly the same way as for age pensions and accept the small inaccuracy involved. The calculations are essentially similar to those for age retirements before age 65 (but using annuity values without a guarantee period, on the grounds that many ill-health pensions will have little or no guarantee period remaining when the G.M.P. element comes into the reckoning at age 65) and are not illustrated by examples. The figures are shown in columns (5) to (7) of Table 23.

Preserved pensions of early leavers

The quality test

15.37 Early leavers who satisfy the conditions of the law relating to the preservation of pensions are to be provided with preserved pensions payable upon attainment of age 65. The scale of member's pension satisfies the quality test for contracting-out so that there will be no extra cost in this connection.

The G.M.P. requirements

15.38 As noted previously, the G.M.P. requirement is that if an employee has a period of contracted-out employment by virtue of his membership of an occupational pension scheme, his pension payable from that scheme after he has attained State pensionable age must not be less that the amount of the G.M.P. which arose during that period of contracted-out employment, revalued up to his attainment of State pensionable age. The anti-franking provisions of the 1984 Act have to be allowed for, as do the provisions of the 1985 Act relating to the revaluation of the non-G.M.P. element of the pension. Under specification 9(ii) of Scheme X the G.M.P. element and the whole of the non-G.M.P. element of a preserved pension are regarded as separate entitlements and they are accumulated separately during the period before the pension comes into payment. The provisions of Scheme X thus go somewhat further than the legislation in that the past service as well as the future service element in that part of an early leaver's preserved pension which is not G.M.P. are to enjoy increases at 5 per cent. p.a. during the period of preservation.

15.39 In these circumstances the cost in addition to that calculated in the previous chapter is likely to be substantial. We shall again use the example of the Group D employee discussed earlier in this chapter to illustrate the position. We shall project the expected withdrawal benefits for this employee, looking separately at the G.M.P. and non-G.M.P. elements of the preserved pension.

15.40 The detailed calculations are shown in Table 20; comments on the build up of this table are as follows.

Column (2) This column shows the normal C function on withdrawal, which will be needed for both the G.M.P. and the non-G.M.P. constituent of the preserved pension. Some of these values have already appeared in Table 7.

Columns (3) and (4) Further items that are common to the valuation of both constituents of preserved pensions are the probability that the early leaver will survive to age 65 and a discounting factor at 9 per cent. p.a. for the period between the date of leaving and the date of attainment of age 65. Column (3) incorporates these two items.

Columns (5), (6), (7) and (8) We shall calculate the amount of the pension on the normal scale which has arisen in respect of contributory membership of Scheme X at the date of leaving, and these columns show the calculation of the average salary and duration on which the pension is based and hence the amount of the pension. It will be noted that we are not including allowance for the period of pensionable service credited for pre-scheme employment in this calculation. The reason for this is that in the general assessment of the situation it is more useful to look at the

G.M.P. liability as part of the overall liability arising from the period over which the G.M.P. has accrued, i.e. the future service liability, rather than as part of the total liability.

Columns (9) and (10) The amount of the accrued G.M.P. at the date of leaving, calculated by the method explained in paragraph 15.11(iii) and illustrated in paragraph 15.31 in the context of ill-health pensions, is shown in column (9). The am ount of the non-G.M.P. element of preserved pension at the date of leaving, obtained by deduction of the figure in column (9) from that in column (8), is shown in column (10).

Columns (11) to (15) Table 17 shows the present capital value of the expected withdrawal benefits arising from future membership before allowance for contracting-out at a rounded figure of £4,900. It may be calculated from item (33) of Table 14 that the figure before rounding is £4,927. As a check on the present calculations we shall first value the excess of the preserved pension over the G.M.P. at the date of leaving and the G.M.P. itself as if both were normal constituents of a preserved pension; the total should agree with the above figure. This will of course involve our ignoring at this stage the special characteristics of the G.M.P. Columns (11) to (15) of Table 20 show the calculations, the capital values being arrived at by an end-piece multiplication by the annuity value at age 65. It will be seen that the total value of £2,185 plus £2,773, i.e. £4,958, differs somewhat from the figure quoted above, due to the slight differences between manual and computer methods mentioned earlier, but the result represents a satisfactory check.

Columns (16) to (18) In columns (16) and (17) we allow for the fact that the accrued G.M.P. is in fact to be revalued during the period of preservation at 8½ per cent. in accordance with the method outlined in paragraph 15.11(iv). In column (18) we introduce the valuation function excluding the annuity value at age 65. The end-piece multiplications in column (18) lead to the capital value of the G.M.P. without pension increases.

15.41 It will be seen from Table 20 that in place of the future service liability expressed as £4,900 in Table 17, we have in fact to provide for the following liabilities.

	Capital Liability
	£ 000s
G.M.P. content of preserved pension (col. (18))	3.9
Balance of preserved pension (col. (15))	2.8
Total	6.7

The figures for the whole of the potential initial membership are shown in columns (17) to (19) of Table 23.

15.42 The liability involved is comparatively small, so that although the effect on the entitlement of individual early leavers is substantial the effect on the contribution rate calculations will not be great. In practice the matter is of more importance; the withdrawal rates in the actual calculations would probably be much greater than those underlying the service table in Table 2 and the liabilities in respect of withdrawal benefits would consequently be much greater.

Widows' pensions

15.43 We now consider the effects of the contracting-out requirements and of the absence of pension increases on the G.M.P. element of Scheme X pensions in the context of widows' pensions. It will be recalled that in the calculations of Chapter 14 we used a proportion married of 90 per cent. for all ages and for all the different types of widows' pensions involved. We stated in paragraph 14.12 that we would take this proportion as covering widows' pensions arising from post-leaving and post-retirement marriages. We shall use the same proportion in the present calculations. We first consider the widow's pension on the death of a member of Scheme X after he had retired on grounds of age. The points are discussed under the three headings of paragraph 15.2.

Widows' pensions on death after age retirement

The quality test

15.44 As noted in paragraph 4.24 the quality test of contracting-out requires that the pension provided to a widow must not be less than 1/160th of final average salary provided that the definition of salary and the length of the averaging period are satisfactory for contracting-out. This is the case in Scheme X, so that the quality test is satisfied.

The G.M.P. requirements

15.45 In principle the G.M.P. requirement in respect of widows' pensions on death after retirement is that the pension provided to the widow must not be less than one-half of the member's G.M.P. The implementation of this principle is somewhat complex, as will be shown in paragraph 15.53, but for immediate purposes the principle can be taken as stated. It was shown in paragraph 15.11 et seq that the member's pension on age retirement is expected, on the actuarial projections used, to exceed the amount of the G.M.P. in all cases. It follows that the amount of the widow's pension is likely to exceed the amount of the widow's G.M.P. and we will therefore assume that no extra cost will arise in this connection.

The saving in cost on pension increases

15.46 We turn to the assessment of the saving in cost, compared with the figures calculated in the previous chapter, arising from the fact that no increases will be paid from Scheme X on the G.M.P. content of a widow's pension payable on death after retirement. If we consider a member of Scheme X who retires before age 65 and dies before age 65 the position is reasonably clear. The employee's G.M.P. rights have continued to grow during the period that his pension was in payment before age 65, because as far as the State scheme is concerned he is classed during this period as an early leaver (whose pension must not, after the date of his attainment of age 65, be less than his G.M.P. rights as revalued up to that date). When he dies, the administrator of Scheme X would be informed by the Department of Health and Social Security of the amount of the widow's G.M.P., which subject to technicalities of calculation is equal to one-half of the amount to which the member's G.M.P. had grown by the effect of revaluations up to the date of his death.

15.47 The widow's pension that would be put into payment in Scheme X would be one-half of the pension that was payable to the retired employee, and subsequent increases in the pension to the widow would be based on that amount less the amount of the widow's G.M.P. The saving in cost is therefore conceptually straightforward; it is the difference between the value of the widow's G.M.P. with 3 per cent. annual increases and the value without such increases.

15.48 Matters become somewhat less straightforward if the employee, having retired at or before age 65, dies after having attained age 65. Some readers may find the following analysis up to paragraph 15.51 to be of unnecessary length, but it is hoped that others will find it helpful. We consider a retired employee who, on attaining age 65, is in receipt of a pension of P from Scheme X. We do not need to specify whether this pension has just come into payment by virtue of retirement at age 65 or whether it was a pension that came into payment earlier and has been increased to the level P by the time the pensioner reached age 65. Upon attainment of age 65 there is introduced into the situation a G.M.P. entitlement of G.

15.49 In the calculations of Chapter 14 we costed the member's pension as if 3 per cent. increases were subsequently payable on the whole of the pension P. We have considered earlier in this chapter the adjustment to the liabilities resulting from the fact that increases after age 65 are to be provided only on the excess of the member's pension over the amount of his G.M.P. Suppose that at some date after the member's attainment of age 65 the effect of 3 per cent. increases each year has been to multiply the amount of pension payable to him at age 65 by a factor of $(1 + k)$. In the calculations of Chapter 14 the amount of the member's pension at the later date now being considered was assumed to be

$$P(1 + k)$$

In fact, because of the absence of pension increases on the G.M.P. content, the amount of the pension will be

$$G + (1 + k)\ (P - G)$$

The difference between these two expressions is

$$kG$$

This represents the amount of increases on the G.M.P. In the discussion earlier in this chapter we have taken the saving in cost by virtue of the absence of pension increases on G.M.P.s as simply the difference between the value of a G.M.P. increasing while in payment and the value of a flat G.M.P., and the above discussion indicates the logic of this.

15.50 Suppose that the retired employee dies at the time that pension increases have amounted to a total multiplier of $(1 + k)$ as indicated above. Under the rules of Scheme X a widow's pension starts to be paid at a rate equal to one-half of the member's pension. We now consider the position some years later when the 3 per cent. annual increases in Scheme X pensions since the date of the retired employee's death amount to a total multiplier of $(1 + j)$. In the previous chapter we have costed the pension to the widow as if it would amount at the instant now under consideration to

$$\tfrac{1}{2} P\,(1 + k)\,(1 + j) \dotfill \quad 15.50.1$$

15.51 As noted in the previous paragraph the pension payable to the retired employee at the date of death was

$$G + (1 + k)\,(P - G) \dotfill \quad 15.51.1$$

The widow's pension starts at one-half of this amount, i.e. at

$$\tfrac{1}{2} G + \tfrac{1}{2}\,(1 + k)\,(P - G) \dotfill \quad 15.51.2$$

Subsequent increases are provided only on the excess of her pension over her G.M.P. (i.e. only on the second term in expression 15.51.2) so that at the later time now under consideration her pension amounts to

$$\tfrac{1}{2} G + \tfrac{1}{2}\,(1 + k)\,(P - G)\,(1 + j) \dotfill \quad 15.51.3$$

The difference between this expression and expression 15.50.1 is

$$\tfrac{1}{2} G\,[(1 + k)\,(1 + j) - 1] \dotfill \quad 15.51.4$$

This expression clearly represents the difference between a half-G.M.P. allowing for all the 3 per cent. annual increases after the retired employee attained age 65 (both during his own lifetime and that of his widow) and a half-G.M.P. with no increases after the member's attainment of age 65. It follows that in calculating the saving in the cost of widows' pensions resulting from the absence of pension increases on G.M.P.s, compared with the costs calculated in the previous chapter, we shall need to evaluate the difference between two reversionary annuities to the widow calculated at the date of the member's 65th birthday, namely the difference between

$$\bar{a}_{65/f} \text{ at } 5.825 \text{ per cent.}$$

and

$$\bar{a}_{65/f} \text{ at } 9 \text{ per cent.}$$

15.52   The various points are again illustrated by considering the employees in Group D of Table 1, the calculations being shown in Table 21. Comments on the table are as follows.

Columns (1), (2) and (3)   We have to deal with the various ages at which retirement in normal health with a normal scale pension can occur and columns (1) and (2) show the tax years and assumed average ages at retirement concerned. Column (3) shows the commutation functions which have already been calculated in Table 5.

Columns (4) and (5)   We have to cover the various ages at which the death of the retired employee may take place. Deaths before age 65 have to be dealt with year by year because the employee's G.M.P., and hence that of the widow, continues to be revalued up to the age of death. As will be gathered from the discussion above, death after age 65 is dealt with by the use of a reversionary annuity calculated at age 65. Column (4) shows the tax year during which death before attainment of age 65 occurs or during which age 65 is reached and column (5) shows the assumed age of the retired employee on the happening of the event concerned.

Column (6)   This column shows the amount of the member's G.M.P. upon death before age 65 or upon attainment of age 65 as the case may be. The figures underlying this column have already been produced in Table 18 but for convenience they are shown in the following statement.

Tax year beginning 6th April	Age at beginning of year	G.M.P. earned during year	Total revalued G.M.P. at end of year
(1)	(2)	(3)	(4)
		£	£
2008	59	383	8,656
2009	60	414	9,762
2010	61	447	10,990
2011	62	483	12,351
2012	63	521	13,861
2013	64		

15.53   In order to arrive at the figures in column (6) of Table 21 it is necessary to apply the detailed rules for the calculation of the

amount of a widow's G.M.P. according to various circumstances.
These rules are essentially as follows.

Event	Amount of widow's G.M.P.
Early leaver dies in tax year in which his service terminated.	One half of the employee's G.M.P. calculated up to the end of the tax year before the employee's death.
Early leaver dies after tax year in which service terminated but before his G.M.P. comes into payment	One half of the employee's G.M.P. at termination of service as subsequently revalued. In Scheme X this revaluation is at the rate of 8½ per cent. for each complete tax year between the date of leaving and the date of death.
Early leaver dies after his G.M.P. comes into payment.	One half of the employee's G.M.P. in payment.

The figures in column (6) of Table 21 are obtained by the
application of these rules (except for the halving of all amounts,
which is brought in as an end-piece calculation) to the data in the
table above.

15.54 *Column (7)* The figures in column (7) show the probability
of the event concerned on a(55) male mortality. For instance, in
the first line we are dealing with retirement at age 60½ and death
before attainment of age 61. The probability of death (the
probability of such retirement having been separately allowed for
in column (3)) is taken as

$$\tfrac{1}{2}d_{60} \div l_{60\frac{1}{2}}$$

Similarly the probability of death in the next complete year, i.e. at
average age 61½, is

$$d_{61} \div l_{60\frac{1}{2}}$$

The probability of survival to age 65 is

$$l_{65} \div l_{60\frac{1}{2}}$$

Column (8) This column introduces the probability that the
member, having been married at the date of retirement, will have
a surviving wife at the date of death resulting from that marriage.

It also introduces the appropriate discounting factor at 9 per cent. per annum, and is therefore of the form D/D at the appropriate ages. The mortality basis is a(55) female unadjusted. We have obviously not allowed for post-retirement marriages in this factor; these are assumed to be allowed for in the proportion married included in the end-piece calculations.

Column (9)   The figures in this column represent the product of the various relevant earlier columns as shown in the column heading.

Columns (10) to (13)   Columns (10) and (11) show the annuity values required on the basis of the reasoning set out above. For the various cases of death before age 65, column (10) shows the value of the annuity to the widow allowing for pension increases and column (11) shows the value of the annuity to the widow with no pension increases, as mentioned in paragraphs 15.46 and 15.47. For the rows corresponding to attainment of age 65 by the member, the annuities are reversionary annuities to the wife should she survive her husband, calculated with allowance for increases at 3 per cent. p.a. (i.e. at a rate of interest of 5.825 per cent.) in column (10) and without increases (i.e. at 9 per cent.) in column (11). Columns (12) and (13) show the application of the annuity values to the figures in column (9). The calculations at the foot of columns (12) and (13) convert the calculated figures to capital values at age 30 and introduce the fact that there are 30 members and that the widow's G.M.P. is equal to one-half of the employee's G.M.P. It will be seen that the saving in costs compared with the figures calculated in the previous chapter is represented by the difference between £15,300 and £10,300.

15.55   The corresponding savings in cost over the whole range of potential initial membership are shown in columns (8) to (10) of Table 23.

Widows' pensions on death after ill-health retirement

The quality test

15.56   As in the case of death after age retirement (see paragraph 15.44) the requirements of the quality test are met and this test will not therefore give rise to additional cost.

The G.M.P. requirements

15.57 The discussion of members' pensions on ill-health retirement ending at paragraph 15.35 led to the conclusion that the requirements of the G.M.P. test would not impose any material costs in addition to those calculated in the previous chapter. We will assume without further investigation that the same conclusion applies in respect of widows' pensions on death after ill-health retirement.

The saving in cost on pension increases

15.58 The calculations of the saving in cost, compared with the figures calculated in the previous chapter, arising from the fact that no increases will be paid from Scheme X on the G.M.P. content of a widow's pension payable on the death of an ill-health pensioner are similar in principle to the calculations relating to the death of a pensioner who retired on grounds of age. This will be clear if we consider the first block of figures in Table 21 relating to retirement on grounds of age at age 60 last birthday. The calculations would have followed exactly the same course had the retirement been on grounds of ill-health and not of age, although the figures would have been different. The calculations are, of course, much more lengthy. In Table 21 we are dealing with a group of employees aged 30 but as the age retirement decrement does not enter the service table until age 60, Table 21 deals only with retirement at ages 60 and over, the final results being discounted back to age 30. The ill-health retirement decrement, on the other hand, begins at age 31 (as shown in the service table in Table 2) so that calculations corresponding to those of Table 21 would have to deal separately with the probability of ill-health retirement at each age from 31 to 64 inclusive and with the widows' pensions flowing from death at each age after the age of retirement.

15.59 In view of the extensive nature of the calculations, and the fact that no new points of principle are involved, specimen figures are not shown. The savings in cost over the whole range of the potential initial membership as calculated by computer are shown in columns (11) to (13) of Table 23.

Widows' pensions on death after withdrawal with a preserved pension

The quality test

15.60 The pension payable to a widow upon the death of a person who has ceased to be a member of an occupational scheme by reason of withdrawal with a preserved pension must satisfy essentially the same test as that mentioned in paragraph 15.44, namely that the pension must not be less than 1/160th of final average salary for each year of service. The outline specification of Scheme X does not specify the scale of the widow's pension payable on the death of an early leaver but it was stated in paragraph 14.16 that the calculations would be made on the assumption that the death benefit was a half rate widow's pension whether the early leaver died before or after attainment of age 65. This scale of widows' pensions satisfies the quality test and we will assume that no costs will arise in this connection additional to those calculated in Chapter 14.

The G.M.P. requirements

15.61 The specification of Scheme X provides for the G.M.P. element and the non-G.M.P. element of the preserved pension of an early leaver to be regarded as separate entitlements. We will assume that the same applies to the widow's pension.

15.62 The widow's pension payable upon the death of a member who has left with a preserved pension may therefore be regarded as the sum of the following two separate entitlements.

(i) An amount equal to one-half of the early leaver's G.M.P. at the date of his death. If he dies before attaining age 65 the pension is equal to one-half of the amount to which his prospective G.M.P. entitlement has grown under the effect of revaluation at the date of death; if he dies after having attained age 65 the amount is equal to one-half of the fixed amount G.M.P. in payment to him. The simplicity of the 'one-half' relationship is of course modified by the detailed rules mentioned in paragraph 15.53.

(ii) An amount equal to one-half of the amount to which the early leaver's non-G.M.P. preserved pension had grown at the date of death. Since a rate of increase of 5 per cent. p.a.

applies before the pension comes into payment and a rate of 3 per cent. p.a. after payment has started, the valuation of this part of the widow's pension involves the points that arose for Table 11.

15.63 As far as the G.M.P. element is concerned, the calculations are (as in the case of the death of an ill-health pensioner) similar to those of Table 21. The first block of figures in that table relates to age retirements at age 60 but the same type of calculation would apply to withdrawal with a preserved pension at some earlier age. The underlying benefit to the member is, of course, different in the two cases, since in the circumstances of Table 21 the member has left early with an immediate pension whereas in the circumstances now under consideration the member has left early with a pension entitlement which will not come into payment until he attains age 65. This difference does not, however, affect the calculations shown in Table 21 because these calculations flow from the amount of the widow's pension entitlement at a given age at death. As in the case of ill-health pensions, the calculations are very extensive and specimen calculations are not shown.

15.64 Turning to the non-G.M.P. element of the widow's pension, the calculations are the same as those illustrated in Table 11, except that we are now dealing only with that part of the widow's pension which represents the excess of the scale pension over the G.M.P. at the date of the member's withdrawal, and not with the whole of the scale widow's pension at that date. Apart from this difference, the calculations proceed as in Table 11, and it has not been thought necessary to set out a further example.

15.65 The values of these two separate entitlements have been calculated over the whole range of the potential initial membership on the basis of 90 per cent. proportions married at the date of leaving and the results are shown in columns (20) to (22) of Table 23.

Widows' pensions on death in service

The quality test

15.66 The quality test relating to widows' pensions on death in service is essentially similar to that mentioned previously in respect of the death of a current pensioner or an early leaver with a preserved pension and as before we will assume that the quality test will not give rise to additional cost.

The G.M.P. requirements

15.67 As noted in Specification 6(ii) of Scheme X the widow's pension on death during employment is to be equal to one-half of the pension to which the member would have been entitled had he retired on grounds of ill-health at the date of his death. In the discussion of the member's ill-health pension earlier in this chapter we decided to assume that the G.M.P. requirement would not give rise to any material costs in addition to those calculated in the previous chapter. The widow's pension is equal to one-half of the deceased member's notional ill-health pension, and the widow's G.M.P. is in principle equal to one-half of his G.M.P.; we will therefore assume that the G.M.P. requirement will not give rise to extra cost in respect of widows' pensions on death in service.

The saving in cost on pension increases

15.68 As noted above, the widow's pension on death in service which was costed in the previous chapter is equal to one-half of the member's notional ill-health pension at the date of his death. The existence of the widow's G.M.P. will not (save in exceptional cases) affect the opening amount of her pension, but it will affect the amount of the increases subsequently granted since these are based only on the excess of her pension over her G.M.P. and not on the full pension from Scheme X. The saving in cost is therefore calculated as the difference between the amount of her G.M.P. with increases and the amount without such increases.

15.69 Table 22 shows the calculations in this connection for the member in group D used in the previous examples. The calculations are straightforward and do not require further explanation. The end-piece calculations proceed as follows.

	Column (6)	Column (7)
	£	£
Total	20,213	15,284
× Number of members	30	30
× for widow's G.M.P.	0.5	0.5
× proportion married	0.9	0.9
÷ 1% of D_{30}	26.884	26.884
	£10,150	£7,675

It will be seen that the saving in costs on the basis of 90 per cent. proportion married is equal to the difference between £10,200 and £7,700, namely £2,500. The corresponding amounts over the whole range of the potential initial membership are shown in columns (14) to (16) of Table 23.

Other benefits

15.70 The benefits dealt with in this chapter represent the major benefits payable and account for the bulk of the liabilities. The contracting-out requirements impinge on the benefit specification outline in Chapter 13 in various ways which we have not so far covered, generally representing restrictions on the operation of various options rather than additional costs. For the calculation of the contribution rates for Scheme X we will assume that the figures calculated in this chapter represent the important factors in the situation, and these are the figures used in the next chapter to adjust the values calculated in Chapter 14 for the purpose of the settling of the contribution rates.

Calculations in practice

15.71 It will be evident from this chapter that the G.M.P. requirements and the widespread practice of not providing pension increases on the G.M.P. element of a pension in payment from a scheme have greatly increased the complexity of the calculation of pension scheme costs. In practice, the extent of calculation required is a matter of judgement. Approximate assessments are difficult, not only because of the general complexity of the G.M.P. arrangements but also because when the amount of a benefit is to be the greater of two amounts calculated in different ways (such as the scale pension and the G.M.P.) it is not satisfactory, in the calculation of cost, simply to compare the total values of the two separate benefits over a group of members. This will underestimate the cost, because it does not reveal the effect of taking the larger of the two benefits in each individual case. We have not needed to consider this point in the artificial circumstances of Scheme X.

CHAPTER 16

SCHEME X: CONTRIBUTION RATES

SCHEME X: CONTRIBUTION RATES

16.1 The figures calculated in Chapters 14 and 15 are summarised in Tables 15, 16 and 24, which provide the basic material for the settling of the contribution rates for Scheme X. Table 15 shows the capital liability in respect of the pensionable service credits granted to the initial entrants. Table 16 shows the estimated cost of the benefit rights expected to arise in the year following the Commencement Date in respect of the initial entrants, except that at this stage no allowance has been made for G.M.P.s. In Table 24 we show the future service values of Table 17 adjusted to allow for G.M.P.s in accordance with the figures of Table 23. Thus, for instance, column (2) of Table 24 is obtained from column (2) of Table 17 by deduction of the figures in column (4) of Table 23. For most benefits the values of Table 24 are less than those of Table 17, because of the absence of pension increases on the G.M.P. content of a pension after it comes into payment. The Table 24 values of the benefits to early leavers and the associated widows' pensions do not differ greatly from those of Table 17, because the saving arising from the absence of pension increases is offset by the extra cost of providing 8½ per cent. instead of 5 per cent. annual increases on the G.M.P. content during the period of preservation. The following miscellaneous points have now to be dealt with.

Withdrawal benefits

16.2 A matter which was left for reconsideration as far as the calculation of liabilities is concerned is the benefit on withdrawal. It was noted at the end of paragraph 14.10 that, since the withdrawal benefit was to be valued as a preserved pension in all cases, it might be necessary to make an appropriate adjustment to allow for any cases of leavers during the early years of membership for whom a return of contributions would be a more valuable benefit than the preserved pension with its G.M.P. content.

16.3 We can use some of the calculations in Table 20 to obtain a comparison of the value of the two alternative benefits on withdrawal. It will be recalled that in Table 20 we calculated the value, for an initial entrant in Group D, of the preserved pension on withdrawal arising from his contributory membership of Scheme X. We ignored the fact that the member concerned would have a pensionable service credit in respect of pre-scheme employment and that this credit would count towards the calculation of a preserved pension on withdrawal. The exclusion of this past service is convenient for our present purposes, since we shall be using the calculations to arrive at contribution rates for future new entrants (who would have no past service credit) as well as for the initial entrants.

16.4 The first row of figures in Table 20 shows that for an entrant at age 30 the initial amount of the preserved pension in respect of the first half year's contributory membership is £18, of which £9 is G.M.P. and £9 is non-G.M.P. Column (13) shows that the amount of the non-G.M.P. element is expected to have grown at age 65 to £48 per annum under the effect of increases at the rate of 5 per cent. p.a. during the period of deferment. Column (17) shows that the G.M.P. element is expected to have grown at age 65 to £133 per annum under the effect of 8½ per cent. p.a. revaluation during that period. The capital value of these two entitlements has to be calculated separately, since the first will enjoy 3 per cent. p.a. increases in payment while the G.M.P. element will not attract such increases. The calculation of the total capital value proceeds as follows.

Non-G.M.P.

£

$$£48 \times \frac{D_{65}}{D_{30\frac{1}{2}}} \ (9\%) \ \times \ \bar{a}_{\overline{65\,5|}} \ (5.825\%)$$

$$= \ £48 \times .0409 \times 9.309 \qquad\qquad = \quad 18$$

G.M.P.

$$£133 \times \frac{D_{65}}{D_{30\frac{1}{2}}} \ (9\%) \ \times \ \bar{a}_{\overline{65\,5|}} \ (9\%)$$

$$= £133 \times .0409 \times 7.679 \qquad\qquad = \quad \underline{42}$$

$$\underline{£60}$$

16.5 This is the value of the benefit in respect of contributory membership to a member of Group D withdrawing at age 30½ calculated at the instant of leaving. We have to compare this with the amount that the member has paid in contributions. We have not yet, however, arrived at the members' contribution rate, and it is therefore necessary to make a preliminary estimate of what this might be. A first indication may be derived from Table 24 which shows that the total future service benefits as shown in that table have a value of £3.639m. and that a contribution of 1 per cent. of pensionable pay payable throughout the expected future membership of the initial entrants has a value of £281,900. Thus on one particular funding plan (and we shall look at a number of alternative plans later in this chapter) the joint contribution rate required to cover the year by year accrual of benefits (but not covering the credits of pensionable service in respect of pre-scheme employment, which are to be paid for by special contributions from the employer) is calculated at

$$3,639,000 \div 281,900 = 12.9 \text{ per cent.}$$

It was stated in the specification in Chapter 13 that the employer is to pay a contribution of between 1½ times and twice the total contributions of the members and this suggests that the members' contribution may be of the order of 5 per cent. of pensionable pay.

16.6 If we assume this rate of members' contribution, the amount of contributions paid by the initial entrant in Group D during the first half year of his membership would be 5 per cent. of his pensionable pay in that half-year, i.e.

$$0.5 \times .05 \times £3,000 \times s_{30} (25.7)/s_{29} (22.5) = £85.7$$

These calculations show that the value, calculated on the valuation basis, of the preserved pension in respect of the period of contributory membership concerned is materially less than the amount of the member's own contributions during that period. A somewhat similar relationship will hold at other young entry ages.

16.7 To the extent that the initial entrants have past service credits these will increase the value of the preserved pension relative to the amount of the member's contributions, so that there may not be many cases in which we have valued a withdrawal benefit less valuable than the member's own contributions. If, for instance, we allow in the above example for the fact that the scale pension on withdrawal would be based on pensionable service of 3 years instead of one-half year this leads to a preserved pension of initial amount £106 per annum of which £9 as before is G.M.P. and £97 non-G.M.P. The total capital value of these rights (calculated as in paragraph 16.4) is considerably more than the amount of the member's contributions.

16.8 An adjustment is certainly required for entrants in Group A who have no past service, and for future new entrants, but in view of the comparatively small extra liabilities involved we will not make a recalculation but will bear the point in mind in the settling of the contribution rate.

Retirements in the early years

16.9 We turn to another matter which needs consideration. It will be seen from Table 1 that five of the potential initial entrants are at age 65 and would therefore be expected to retire immediately if they joined Scheme X, while others are at ages at which voluntary retirement on grounds of age is possible. Furthermore, other benefits will in the normal course of events become payable during the opening years of Scheme X. This raises a difficulty in that pensions are based on the average pay during the three years preceding the event concerned, so that the amounts of salary in years before Scheme X was set up will have to be used in the calculation of certain benefits. We will assume that these amounts are available, so that provided the detailed rules of Scheme X are drawn up satisfactorily there will be no administrative difficulty.

16.10 A point arises, however, on the financing of Scheme X. We have implicitly assumed, in valuing all prospective pensions by formulae involving the normal 'z' function, that pay levels before the setting up of Scheme X will have changed from year to year in line with the salary scale shown in Table 3, whereas in fact the salary progression of individuals will have been different from this. Thus, the benefit calculation for a member retiring at age 65 immediately upon the setting up of Scheme X will not correspond to the calculation implied by the z function in the final column of Table 3. The theoretical adjustment for this feature was mentioned in paragraph 9.60. We will ignore this point in the initial costing of the scheme although it may feature in the analysis of profit and loss made in connection with the first regular actuarial valuation of the scheme.

The settling of contribution rates

16.11 We turn from these miscellaneous points to the main matters with which we shall be concerned in this chapter. These may be summarised as follows.

(i) We will have to consider which of the funding plans outlined in Chapter 8 is to be used. Broadly we have to decide whether the normal contribution rate, i.e. the rate to cover the cost of the year-by-year accrual of benefit rights in future, should be settled mainly on the basis of the cost of the accrual of benefit in the first year (the implication being that the age distribution of the workforce from time to time will always be much the same) or whether we should have regard to the flow of benefits expected to arise from the whole future membership of the initial entrants, or from the whole future membership of a typical new entrant in the future.

(ii) We will have to settle how the initial liability is to be dealt with.

(iii) We will have to consider the part of the total contribution that the members will be required to pay, an aspect of the discussion that has of course been briefly anticipated in paragraph 16.5. In this connection it will be necessary to bear in mind that immediately before the establishment of Scheme X the employees are members of the State earnings-related scheme. The procedure mentioned in paragraph 17.11 which has to be followed when it is proposed that an employment should become a contracted-out employment does not call for the consent of the employees concerned. However, consultation with any recognised trades union is required, and in any event the employer would wish to carry his employees with him in a matter of such importance. It is therefore highly desirable that the benefit and contribution arrangements being offered to the employees should appear attractive when compared with their contributions and benefits in the State scheme. The decision on the contribution rate to be charged to the members in Scheme X is central to this question.

(iv) It will be recalled from paragraphs 4.42 and 4.43 that another condition for contracting-out is the production of a solvency certificate. The contribution and other arrangements will therefore need to be such that the actuary will be able to issue this certificate.

16.12 Another point which is of theoretical interest, although it does not impinge on the figures, arises from the fact that in Chapter 15 it was necessary to settle the date as at which the initial calculations were made (taken as 5th April 1979) because this established the ages of the employees concerned at 5th April 1978 and hence determined the G.M.P. fractions. If similar calculations were made at some future date on the basis of membership information drawn up as at that future date which was identical to that of Table 1 the G.M.P. adjustments would be different, because the ages at 5th April 1978 of the persons concerned, which determine the G.M.P. fraction, would be different. Thus we have the curious position that a scheme used for contracting-out cannot reach a theoretically stable condition until all the members are persons who attained age 16 after 5th April 1978.

Funding criteria

16.13 It will be recalled from Chapter 8 that a particular funding plan may conveniently be examined from the following points of view.

(i) *Security* The question is whether the accumulating assets represent reasonable security for the growing pension rights of the members, independent of the employer.

(ii) *Stability* The question is whether, if the scheme is assumed to continue unchanged for a long period, the financial burden on the employer is expected in the normal course of events to remain reasonably stable in terms of his payroll from time to time in the future.

(iii) *Durability* The issue here is how well the funding method is likely to serve its purpose in the face of some unexpected event, which we have taken as a cessation of the flow of new entrants with the scheme remaining in full force for the existing members.

Funding plans

16.14   We shall look at the application of Funding Plans C, D, E and F of Chapter 8 to the circumstances of Scheme X in the light of the above criteria. We shall not consider funding plans which are intended to cover only the cost of benefit rights based on present levels of pay, since these would not provide the employer with a realistic indication of cost.

Plan C

16.15   Under this Plan (which was discussed in paragraphs 8.46 et seq) the aim is that the fund in hand at any time should match the past service liabilities allowing for expected future pay increases. It follows that the normal contribution rate in a particular year is that required to cover the cost of the accrual of benefits in that year, allowing for expected future pay increases. The values of Table 16 were calculated from salaries in the year ended on the Commencement Date, but we are now seeking to establish the contribution rate payable in the year which started on that date. We therefore need to estimate the amount of a contribution of 1 per cent. of payroll in the year following the Commencement Date. We will make the broad assumption that total payroll in that year is equal to the payroll of £1,363,000 in the previous year (see Table 1) increased by 8 per cent., i.e about £1.47 m. Clearly this assumption implies that the distribution by age and seniority of the workforce in the year is much the same as in the previous year, under the combined effect of new entrants, promotions and exits. This is not a realistic assumption but will serve our purpose.

16.16   The calculation of the contribution rate for the normal contributory benefits is based on the figures of Table 16.

(1)   Value of benefits in respect of year of membership following Commencement Date (Table 16) £193,000

(2)   Approximate amount of 1 per cent. contribution in the year, 1 per cent. of say £1.47 m. £14,700

(3)   Approximate contribution rate required in the year, before allowance is made for contracting-out (1) ÷ (2) .... 13.1 per cent.

In the artificial circumstances of Scheme X there is inconsistency in this calculation in that the salaries of members at age 65 have been brought in with no corresponding liabilities being allowed for. We do not attempt to allow specially for this point.

16.17 We will not make the extensive calculations required to assess the precise adjustment to this figure in respect of the absence of pension increases on the G.M.P. part of the pension rights accruing in the one year concerned, and the other effects of contracting-out. It will be seen from the column (10) totals of Tables 17 and 24 that the overall effect of these factors as far as the whole expected future service liabilities are concerned is to reduce the Table 17 figure of £3,913,200 by about 7 per cent. to the Table 24 figure of £3,639,000. If we take this as representing a reasonable adjustment (representing an average effect over a long future period) to the figure calculated in the previous paragraph we arrive at a reduction of some 1 per cent., giving a contribution rate of 12.1 per cent.

We will use this figure as representing the first year contribution rate under Plan C.

16.18 One point calling for special comment relates to the costing of the capital sum benefit on death in service as shown in column (9) of Table 16. The method of calculation was illustrated in item 42 of Table 14. The other benefits are in the form of rights which accrue, for each year of pensionable service, to the extent of some defined fraction such as 1/80th or 1/160th. The contribution paid in a particular year is in principle the amount needed to fund the part of an eventual pension benefit arising in respect of that year's membership. There is no comparable concept in the case of the capital sum benefit on death in service, since this is a fixed multiple of salary. It is partly for this reason that the cost of the latter benefit is usually taken in this method of funding as simply the expected cost of claims in the year concerned.

16.19 There is, however, a further aspect to this question. This is that it is prudent to fund for pension benefits because even if the pension scheme concerned is wound up at some future date, assets will still be required to provide preserved pensions and contingent widows' pensions in respect of the period of membership of the scheme. This is not the case, however, in respect of cover for substantial capital sum payments on death in service, since such cover would normally cease if the scheme were terminated.

This is therefore a second reason to regard capital sum benefits as temporary life assurance to be met by an element in the contribution rate at the time that the benefit is paid. It will be noted that this argument holds irrespective of the funding plan for the pension benefits, so that in the calculations for any of the different funding methods discussed in this chapter there may be used this 'risk premium' method of meeting the cost of the capital sum benefit on death in service.

16.20 One advantage of this approach is that under it the element of the contribution rate covering the benefit will probably not differ greatly from the amount of the premium which the trustees would be asked to pay if they decided to insure this risk by means of term assurance with a life office. In the funding methods discussed later in this chapter under which the existing members are followed through their subsequent progress as a closed group, the element of the contribution rate covering the capital sum benefit on death in service is comparatively large (since mortality rates at older ages are brought in) and it is difficult to explain to scheme trustees why the cost of the cover should be more than the current cost.

Comments on Plan C

16.21 We have so far discussed only the normal rate of contribution under Plan C, i.e. the contribution required to cover the cost of the year-by-year accrual of benefit rights. There is also the question of how the initial liability of £1,597,800 shown in Table 15 is to be met. Since this is a separate question, we will first comment briefly on the normal contribution rate, according to the usual criteria.

16.22 Comments are as follows.

Security

The cost of each year's accrual of normal contributory benefits is in principle met as it occurs, expected future pay increases being allowed for. The position is therefore satisfactory in respect of the security of the year-by-year accrual of benefit rights for contributory service.

Stability

The contribution rate will vary as the distribution by age of the numbers and pay of the members varies. In order to examine this we need in principle to estimate the pay in the year starting on the Commencement Date for each age group separately, so that we can make calculations similar to those of paragraph 16.16 for each such group. Since, however, we are concerned only with the variability of the rate with age, and not its absolute amount, we will for simplicity use pay in the previous year. The figures do not therefore represent true contribution rates, but merely provide an indication of variability. They are as follows.

Age at Commencement Date	Total Salary in previous year	Figures from Table 16 column (10)	(3) as % of (2)
(1)	(2)	(3)	(4)
	£ 000	£ 000	%
20	72	10.7	14.9
25	161	23.8	14.8
30	90	13.1	14.6
35	149	22.2	14.9
40	104	15.3	14.7
45	206	29.3	14.2
50	295	41.0	13.9
55	110	15.7	14.3
60	141	21.9	15.5

The figures of column (4) vary little with age, and this is likely to be also the case for the accurately calculated contribution rates, so that the overall rate is likely to be stable. The figures are of course a function of the valuation basis, in particular the service table, salary scale and difference between the rate of interest and rate of pay escalation. Our conclusion on stability therefore relates to this particular case and is not of wider relevance.

Durability

The run of the figures in column (4) of the table above is such that the contribution rate will remain reasonably stable even if the age distribution of the membership changes greatly.

The initial liability

16.23 Under Plan C the aim is that the past service liabilities allowing for future pay increases should be matched by the funds in hand. Upon the setting up of Scheme X these liabilities amount to £1,597,800 as shown in Table 15. There are no funds in hand, and it must be assumed that whatever funding plan is involved it will not be possible to clear this liability very quickly. If Scheme X were to be wound up shortly after its inception as a result of some unexpected development, the liabilities would be much less than the figure noted above, because the prospective benefits would be preserved pensions increasing at 5 per cent. p.a. (with small amounts of G.M.P.) instead of benefit rights linked to pay which is projected to grow at 8 per cent. p.a. Nevertheless, the assets in hand would be very much less than the liabilities, and pensions in payment and G.M.P.s would form a first charge on these assets; it would thus not be possible to provide the members with preserved pensions reflecting their expectations under the rules. The situation could hardly be otherwise, and this should not be accepted as a valid criticism of a funding plan. It will be recalled from paragraph 3.14 that the fact that there may be an insufficiency of funds on the winding up of a pension scheme is accepted in the law relating to the preservation of pensions.

16.24 Nevertheless, because of the need to build up security of the benefits at a reasonable speed it is necessary to consider how quickly a particular contribution arrangement relating to the past service liability would clear this liability. The figure representing the initial liability may be thought of as the amount which, if paid into Scheme X immediately and invested to yield 9 per cent. p.a., would meet the benefits arising from pre-scheme service as they fell due, assuming that the experience was in accordance with all the other features of the actuarial basis. It follows that if no action is taken to clear the initial liability it will grow at the rate of interest of 9 per cent. p.a., again assuming that all the other features of the basis are borne out in fact. If therefore we consider the position at the end of the first year of existence of Scheme X, the initial liability would be expected on the valuation basis to have grown, in the absence of any payments to clear it, by 9 per cent. of £1,597,800, i.e. by about £144,000.

16.25 We will consider the following three arrangements to meet the initial liability.

(i)   A fixed annual payment over a period of 20 years.

(ii) A contribution assessed as a fixed percentage of total pensionable payroll over a period of 20 years.

(iii) A contribution assessed as a fixed percentage of total pensionable payroll over a period of 10 years.

16.26 The rates of contribution required under these three arrangements are calculated as follows.

Arrangement (i)

The fixed annual amount is equal to

$$£1,597,800 \div \bar{a}_{\overline{20}|} \,(9\%)\,(9.53) = £167,700$$

Arrangement (ii)

We will assume that the total payroll of the persons who are members of Scheme X from time to time in the future will be equal to the initial payroll increased at 8 per cent. p.a. It will be noted that we are dealing here with the expected payroll of all members of the scheme from time to time, not merely the survivors of the initial entrants. The value of a one per cent. contribution will be calculated using an annuity certain at a rate of interest of 1 per cent., on the grounds that 1.09/1.08 is approximately equal to 1.01. The value of a one per cent. contribution payable for 20 years is

$$.01 \times £1,363,000 \times \bar{a}_{\overline{20}|} \,(1\%)(18.14) = £247,200$$

The percentage of payroll required is therefore equal to

$$1,597,800 \div 247,200 = 6.5 \text{ per cent., say.}$$

The amount in the first year is 6.5 per cent. of £1.47m., i.e. £95,500.

Arrangement (iii)

The value of a one per cent. contribution payable for 10 years is

$$.01 \times £1,363,000 \times \bar{a}_{\overline{10}|} \,(1\%)(9.52) = £129,800$$

The percentage of payroll required is therefore equal to

$$1,597,800 \div 129,800 = 12.3 \text{ per cent., say.}$$

The amount in the first year is 12.3 per cent. of £1.47m., i.e. £180,800.

Comments on these arrangements are as follows.

Fixed annual payment over 20 years

Security

16.27   The annual payment of £167,700 is not very much greater than the first year interest of £144,000 mentioned in paragraph 16.24. Thus in the early years the contribution is largely absorbed in meeting interest on the liability, and only a small balance remains to be used to reduce the outstanding amount of the liability. The period of 20 years taken to extinguish the liability is long in modern conditions. The final column of Table 15 shows that the bulk of the initial liability relates to members aged 45 and over, so that the total period of payment of the contribution broadly matches the total period during which most of the liability is expected to come into payment. However, a substantial part of the liability would still be outstanding after say 15 years under this arrangement, whereas the members giving rise to the bulk of the liability would have retired by then. The arrangement is not very satisfactory from the point of view of security.

16.28   Another aspect of security is the question of how well the funding method would deal with divergences of pay progression from that expected. A contribution that is expressed as a percentage of payroll will rise or fall if pay increases exceed or fall short of those expected, and the value of the contribution will therefore tend to some extent to move in sympathy with the liabilities. This is not the case with a contribution of fixed amount, so that in principle a contribution of this type is somewhat less attractive to the members, from the point of view of security, than is a pay-related contribution.

Stability

16.29   On the face of it this method offers stability, since the burden on the employer is of known and fixed amount for a period of 20 years. However, the employer may well prefer a burden which is a fixed percentage of payroll, and is therefore stable in real terms. The contribution under consideration represents a diminishing percentage of payroll, because payroll is expected to increase from year to year under the effect of continuing inflation whereas the contribution remains of fixed amount. The method therefore has disadvantages from the point of view of stability.

Durability

16.30 No particular points arise from the consideration of a closed and ageing membership, since the contribution is not related to the membership from time to time.

Additional contribution equal to 6.5 per cent. of total pensionable payroll payable for 20 years

Security

16.31 The additional contribution arising under this method is intended to extinguish the initial liability over 20 years, the same period as for the fixed additional contribution considered above. However, the first year amount of £95,500 is much less than the first year's interest of £144,000, so that the initial liability would grow in the early years and would be cleared more slowly than under the fixed amount arrangements. This aspect of the proposed method is not therefore very attractive from the members' point of view in respect of security.

16.32 The amount that will in fact be received under this method depends directly on the amount of the payroll from time to time. If the employer prospers the number of employees may increase and the payroll may grow faster than anticipated. A percentage of payroll would then bring in more money to Scheme X than expected, and although this would lead later to a revision of the percentage, this aspect of security might appear attractive to the members if they expect the employer's business to progress.

Stability

16.33 The proposed contribution is satisfactory from the point of view of stability since it represents a burden which is stable in real terms.

Durability

16.34 The method is open to criticism from the aspect of durability. If the flow of new entrants dwindles the total pensionable payroll, and hence the amount of the contribution, will fall, but the liabilities in respect of the initial entrants will not be diminished. The employer might thus be asked to pay an increased percentage contribution at a time when he might find it difficult to do so.

Additional contribution equal to 12.3 per cent. of total pensionable payroll payable for 10 years

Security

16.35 The first year amount of £180,800 is a reasonably substantial payment and the total projected period of 10 years for the extinguishing of the initial liability is not unduly long. The arrangement is therefore reasonably attractive to the members from the point of view of security.

Stability

16.36 The contribution is satisfactory on the grounds of stability, since it represents a stable burden on the employer expressed as a percentage of payroll. Whether the employer can afford to pay so large a contribution in addition to his share of the normal contribution is, of course, for him to consider.

Durability

16.37 Comments similar to those made in respect of the corresponding 20 year contribution apply here, but the risk referred to in paragraph 16.34 is diminished by the shortening of the period of payment.

Plan D: New entrant contribution rate

16.38 Under this plan, which was discussed in paragraph 8.53 et seq, the normal contribution rate is that which, if payable throughout the membership of a new entrant at the normal entry age, would be expected to cover the cost of the benefits. It appears from the distribution of ages and past service in Table 1 that entry to the employment has tended in the past to be at ages between 20 and 30. We therefore need to investigate the contribution rates required for new entrants at those ages on the basis of the figures in Table 24. The results are as follows.

Age at Commencement Date	Table 24: future service contribution rate = column (10) ÷ column (11)
	per cent.
20	13.6
25	13.3
30	13.0
35	12.9
40	12.6
45	12.3
50	12.4
55	13.2
60	14.2

These calculations indicate that the normal joint contribution rate for new entrants, as indicated by the first three figures in the table, is about 13.3 per cent. Since contribution rates are often rounded to ¼ of one per cent. we shall assume a rate of 13.25 per cent.

16.39 If we assume that this rate is to be adopted as the normal contribution, the initial liability at the Commencement Date is evidently calculated as follows.

	£ 000
Past service liability (Table 15)	1,597.8
Future service liability (Table 24)	3,639.0
	5,236.8
Value of contribution of 13.25 per cent. during expected future membership of initial entrants	
13.25 × £281,900 (Table 24)	3,735.2
Initial balance of liability	1,501.6

The initial liability of £1,501,600 needs to be cleared, and the issues that arise in the settling of the contribution arrangements for this purpose are the same as those discussed under Plan C.

16.40 We leave it mainly to the reader to consider this and subsequent plans in the light of the usual criteria; the main characteristics were mentioned in Chapter 8, and no special points arise in the present example.

Plan E: Attained age contribution rate

16.41 Under this plan, which was discussed in paragraph 8.71 et seq, the normal contribution rate is that required to meet the future service liabilities. From columns (10) and (11) of Table 24 this rate is equal to

$$3,639.0 \div 281.9 = 12.9 \text{ per cent.}$$

It was pointed out in paragraph 8.73 that, provided the initial liability is cleared separately, the normal contribution rate would be expected to move at successive valuations towards the new entrant level. In the particular case under consideration this implies a small increase from the above figure of 12.9 per cent. to the rate of 13.25 per cent. mentioned in paragraph 16.38. This is an unusual position; normally the new entrant rate is somewhat lower than the attained age rate. The position in respect of the initial liability is the same as that under Plan C.

Plan F: Aggregate contribution rate

16.42 Under this plan, which was discussed in paragraph 8.74 et seq, the contribution rate is that which, if payable throughout the expected future membership of the existing members, would be sufficient, on the actuarial basis used, to meet the liabilities. The calculation is shown below; for clarity we divide the liabilities into past service and future service elements, but this is not an essential part of the plan.

16.43 The calculations are as follows.

	Capital value of benefits	Contribution required = (1) ÷ 281.9 (Table 24)
	(1) £ 000	(2) per cent.
(1) Pre-scheme employment benefit rights (Table 15)	1,597.8	5.67
(2) Contributory service benefit rights (Table 24)	3,639.0	12.91
	5,236.8	18.58

Under this funding plan the joint contribution rate required initially is thus 18.58 per cent., which we will round to 5.7 plus 12.9 = 18.6 per cent.

16.44 It will be recalled from paragraph 16.17 that the contribution rate required to cover the cost of the accrual of benefit rights in the year beginning on the Commencement Date is 12.1 per cent. If the contribution of 18.6 per cent. calculated above is in fact paid, a balance of 6.5 per cent. is available in the first year in respect of the initial liability. It will be recalled from paragraph 16.24 that interest on this liability amounts in the first year to £144,000. The contribution paid towards the initial liability would be 6.5 per cent. of £1.47 m. (from paragraph 16.15), or approximately £96,000. It is therefore clear that the initial liability outstanding at the end of the first year would be a considerably greater cash sum than the figure at the Commencement Date. It would be only after a lengthy period, when the pay related contribution had grown with the effect of the escalating payroll (offset by the diminishing number of survivors out of the initial membership) that the amount of the outstanding initial liability would gradually begin to fall. It is therefore clear that this particular funding plan represents a slow way of paying off the initial liability.

Stability

16.45 We are concerned under the heading of stability with the question of whether the financial burden on the employer is expected in the normal course of events to remain reasonably stable in terms of his payroll from time to time in the future. In the particular circumstances of Scheme X this principle obviously cannot be carried too far, because it is an integral part of the situation that the employer is to pay not only his share of the normal contribution to cover the cost of contributory benefits but also contributions to meet the cost of the past service credits on the setting up of Scheme X. In the long term the second element of the contribution will run off and the first will tend to the new entrant rate; overall stability of the financial burden is therefore not the aim. Thus stability is best thought of in this context as relating separately to these two constituents of the employer's contribution.

Security: a general comment

16.46 Despite the differences between the various funding plans discussed above, they are all satisfactory in respect of the security offered to the members in respect of the year-by-year accrual of their pension rights for contributory service. The degree of security in respect of pensionable service credits for pre-scheme employment varies according to the speed with which funds are built up. If Scheme X were assured of a permanent life, the level of funding and hence of security would not be an important issue. As noted in Chapter 8, it may be extremely important if a scheme is wound up or if a part of the membership moves to another scheme, taking with it an appropriate share of the first scheme. The issues that arise in the latter circumstances are illustrated in respect of Scheme X in Chapter 31.

Further issues involved

16.47 We will assume that after discussions the employer decides that he is likely to be able to afford a total contribution rate of 20 per cent. in addition to the indirect cost on him represented by the employees' contributions, and that a contribution pattern on the following lines is being contemplated.

	Percentage of payroll per cent.
Normal joint contribution rate:	
employees	5
employer	8
Employer's additional contribution in respect of initial liability, payable for approximately 10 years	12
Total	25

We now consider the suitability of this contribution plan from the other aspects which have to be taken into consideration.

Solvency certificate A

16.48 It will be recalled that one of the requirements for contracting-out is that the scheme should attain the necessary level of solvency. For a scheme such as Scheme X the Occupational Pensions Board has to be satisfied in this respect by the production of the solvency certificate shown at the end of Chapter 4. In this certificate the actuary has to certify that in his opinion the resources of the scheme are likely, in the normal course of events, to be sufficient at all times over the five years following the date of the certificate to meet in full, in the event of the winding up of the scheme, certain specified liabilities of the scheme. We now have to consider whether payment of contributions at the rates contemplated would enable the actuary to issue this certificate.

16.49 For the purposes of Scheme X the liabilities referred to above are as follows.

(i)   G.M.P.s, both in payment and prospective, on the basis that the liabilities in this connection would be met by the payment of premiums to the State scheme.

(ii) Pensions in course of payment.

(iii) Any other liabilities of Scheme X which are accorded in a winding up a priority equal to or higher than that accorded to items (i) and (ii) above.

(iv) Expenses of administration.

16.50 We will assume that the trust deed and rules of Scheme X will be drawn up in such a way that items (i) and (ii) above enjoy a priority higher than any of the other liabilities arising on a winding up. The main implication of this is that the rights arising from the credit of pensionable service in respect of pre-scheme employment would, on an early winding up, be funded only to the extent that the resources were not required to meet G.M.P.s and pensions in course of payment. We are thus concerned with the question of whether the growing funds are likely, during the first five years of existence of Scheme X, to cover the liabilities for pensions in course of payment, including the G.M.P. element, and the prospective G.M.P.s of active members.

16.51 It will be noted from Table 1 that a number of employees were already at the latest retirement age of 65 at the time of preparation of the initial data. It must be assumed that these employees would act in their own best interests and would therefore join Scheme X, and retire immediately, upon the setting up of the scheme. It is thus necessary to estimate the liabilities in respect of these employees on the assumption that they would so retire. The initial amount of their pensions on this assumption would have been, as a first approximation,

$$1/80\text{th of one-half of } £1,155,000 = £7,200 \text{ per annum}$$

This amount is calculated using the figure of 'salary × duration' from the final column of Table 1 and is an approximation because the three-year averaging period has not been allowed for. The annuity factor at age 65, allowing for a half rate reversionary pension to the widow, is approximately 11, so that the immediate liability in respect of current pensions for the employees concerned would total some £80,000.

16.52 We are envisaging a contribution rate of 25 per cent. so that on an assumed first year payroll approaching £1.5m. the total contributions in the first year would be of the order of £375,000. It is necessary to form a view as to the amount which would be required for State scheme premium payments in order to buy back G.M.P. rights in the State scheme if Scheme X ceased to be contracted-out at, say, the end of its first year of existence. It will be recalled from paragraph 4.38 that such premiums would be calculated by applying the State scheme premium tables to the amounts of the G.M.P.s. As a first approximation to this amount we take the total amount of the State scheme contribution abatement in the first year. This is 7 per cent. of relevant earnings (this being the rate for the year 1979/80 in accordance with the assumed Commencement Date), which will be of the order of

7 per cent. of (£1.5m. – number of members times lower earnings limit)

This sum would be of the order of £80,000. It thus appears that subject to satisfactory arrangements as to details of cash flow, perhaps involving an acceleration of the employer's contributions to cover the liability for immediate retirements, and a control of policy as to early retirements, the position in the first year is likely to be satisfactory by a considerable margin for the purposes of the solvency certificate.

16.53 In considering how matters will develop over the first five years for the purpose of the certificate the actuary will probably assume that the various events giving rise to a flow of benefits will be in accordance with the probabilities assumed in his basis. If he has reason to suppose that exceptional rates of early retirement or other events will occur he will seek to allow for these, but the wording of the certificate refers to the 'normal course of events' and this might well be taken as implying that circumstances will unfold in the way anticipated in the actuarial basis. The actuary will, however, bear in mind that he has to allow for any exceptional experience which might precede a winding up.

16.54   The requirement is that pensions in course of payment, including the G.M.P. element, and the prospective G.M.P.s of active members should be likely to be covered by the resources available on a winding up of Scheme X. The contribution rate includes a large element in respect of the pre-scheme liabilities which do not figure in the prior charges on a winding up, so that it is to be expected that in the ordinary way the position on a winding up as far as the solvency certificate is concerned would further improve rather than deteriorate. The actuary might well make approximate calculations as to the amount of the prior liabilities in say three years' time. We will make these calculations as part of the first normal actuarial valuation of Scheme X three years after its Commencement Date.

16.55   We will assume that the rates of contribution contemplated in paragraph 16.47 will enable the solvency certificate to be signed, subject to any special arrangements as to the incidence of the employer's contributions in the first year as mentioned above.

Rate of members' contributions

16.56   It will be recalled from Chapter 13 that membership of Scheme X is to be voluntary for those persons who were employees at the Commencement Date. It is desirable on general grounds that the scheme should appear attractive to these employees and we now consider from their point of view the proposition that they should join Scheme X. The alternative is to remain in the State earnings-related pension scheme. The attraction of membership of Scheme X will depend to a considerable extent on immediate cost to the members.

16.57   Contracting-out will reduce the State scheme contributions of the employees concerned by 2½ per cent. of relevant earnings, i.e. the band of earnings between the lower and upper earnings limit of the State scheme. This was the figure in force in April 1979, which is assumed to be the date of our calculations. Contributions to the State scheme are paid out of after-tax income. Members will be required to pay a contribution of 5 per cent. to Scheme X and this contribution is allowed as an expense as far as the personal taxation of the employees is concerned. We will take into consideration only the standard rate of income tax, namely 30 per cent.; the effective cost to the employee is thus 70 per cent. of 5 per cent., i.e. 3.5 per cent.

16.58 An employee included in Table 1 would therefore have to consider comparative costs as outlined in the following table. It is assumed that the comparison would be made in advance of April 1979 on the basis of 1978/79 figures. As stated in paragraph 15.6, the lower and upper earnings limit for State scheme purposes in 1978/79 were £910 and £6,240 p.a. respectively, so that the maximum figure for relevant earnings in that year was £5,330.

Salary in 1978/79	Relevant earnings in 1978/79	2½% of (2)	5% of (1)	70% of (4)
(1)	(2)	(3)	(4)	(5)
£	£	£	£	£
2,400	1,490	37	120	84
3,000	2,090	52	150	105
4,000	3,090	77	200	140
6,000	5,090	127	300	210
8,000	5,330	133	400	280
10,000	5,330	133	500	350

Some of the lower paid employees might not in fact be subject to tax, depending in part on their personal circumstances, and for these employees the comparison would be between columns (3) and (4) rather than columns (3) and (5).

16.59 The employees are therefore being asked to pay a substantially increased amount out of after-tax earnings in respect of pensions. For this additional payment they become entitled to the range of benefits under Scheme X; on the other hand their State scheme benefits will be reduced by the amount of G.M.P.s earned during contracted-out employment in Scheme X. The proposition will probably look attractive to some employees and not to others. They will need to consider the following factors amongst others.

(i) Substantial past service credits will be provided to many of the initial entrants to Scheme X.

(ii) The pension fraction of Scheme X is 1/80th at all ages, whereas the effective pension scale of the State scheme and hence of the G.M.P. is less than this except for those within 20 years of State pension age in April 1978.

(iii) Full scale pensions are available from age 60 with the employer's consent in Scheme X but not earlier than age 65 in the State scheme.

(iv) The facility in Scheme X for retirement with a reduced immediate pension from age 55 has no counterpart in the State scheme.

(v) Scheme X provides better benefits on premature retirement due to ill-health than does the State scheme.

(vi) The capital sum death in service benefit in Scheme X is substantial and is not matched in the State scheme.

(vii) The pension from Scheme X is commutable for a cash sum on retirement within Inland Revenue limits; there is no corresponding feature in the State scheme.

(viii) Contributions to Scheme X can be seen to be invested in a fund and are in certain circumstances returnable. Contributions to the State scheme, on the other hand, are used immediately in the payment of benefits.

16.60   We will assume that it is decided to set up Scheme X on the lines contemplated, and in succeeding chapters we follow the progress of the scheme up to the first three-yearly actuarial valuation. As to the initial membership, it is commonly found that younger employees faced with the choice of joining an occupational pension scheme or not are influenced more by questions of immediate contribution cost than by long term benefits. It is highly unlikely that all the employees in Table 1 would choose to join Scheme X even if it could be shown that membership represented an attractive bargain in the long term. For simplicity of calculation, however, we will assume that all these employees do in fact join.

Actuarial basis

16.61   In making the calculations in respect of the initial entrants to Scheme X we have used the service table in Table 2 simply because this was readily available. In practice it would be necessary to consider, when making the calculations for a new scheme, whether the fact that the initial entrants were existing employees (rather than persons entering the employment and entering the scheme at the same time) had implications as to the service table to be used.

16.62 The initial entrants to a new scheme such as Scheme X are likely to be 'select' in two respects. In the first place they are persons who have exercised an option. In the second place, many such entrants will be employees who have been with the employer for some years and may be expected to experience lower rates of withdrawal than would new employees at the same age. The selective effect of the option will reduce the expected withdrawal rates still more, since an employee who expects to leave the employer fairly soon has little to gain by joining the scheme.

16.63 In principle the actuary should use a basis suitable for new entrants to the employment when calculating the normal contribution rates and a basis appropriate to the existing workforce when making the calculations of initial liability. For Scheme X we shall not make any further adjustments in this connection.

Negative values

16.64 In the actuarial theory of life assurance important issues arise in connection with negative values. These arise when the present value of the future premiums expected to be received by the life fund concerned in respect of a particular contract exceeds the present value of the liabilities under the contract. If the contract is capable of being terminated by the policyholder concerned it may be necessary to make a special adjustment in an actuarial valuation of the life fund in order to ensure that the contract is not taken in as an asset, since the asset will not be realised if the policyholder terminates the policy.

16.65 At first sight it may appear that similar considerations apply in pension schemes. In Scheme X, for instance, the joint contributions payable are intended to cover not only the normal accrual of benefit rights but also the initial liability; it will be recalled that a contribution of 12 per cent. of payroll is to be paid for approximately ten years in this latter respect. Since no past service liability will arise for a new entrant to Scheme X shortly after the Commencement Date, the present value at entry of the flow of contributions expected to arise from his membership of the scheme will greatly exceed the present value of the expected flow of future benefits to and in respect of him. Should any special action be taken in respect of this 'negative value' in the calculations?

16.66 The answer to this question is that it is comparatively unusual for the concept of the 'elimination of negative values' to have any validity in pension scheme calculations. The theory of the matter starts from the fact that, if the experience is exactly as expected, the contribution theoretically required from the employer in respect of each individual member of a scheme is the excess of the joint contribution theoretically required for that individual over the contribution payable by him; we shall call this excess the 'employer's theoretical contribution'. The total contribution actually payable by the employer may be expressed for convenience as a single percentage of total pensionable pay. It is fixed at such a level that the total employer's contribution is of much the same amount as the total of the 'employer's theoretical contribution' for each individual. The employer's contribution is thus defined and valued as a percentage of pensionable payroll because this is much less trouble than defining, valuing and paying the balance of the theoretical joint contribution for each individual, and by definition gives much the same answer in total. It is therefore in effect the total of the 'employer's theoretical contributions' that is being valued, and a negative – or indeed a positive – value at entry does not arise. It is meaningless to compare the value of the expected benefits and of a specific joint contribution for an individual member.

16.67 It may be objected that, whatever the theory of the arrangement may be, a given member gives rise to his own contribution and to the employer's contribution. Whilst an employee is a member of Scheme X a joint contribution of 25 per cent. is payable, which was not paid before he joined and will cease to be paid if he leaves, so that it is realistic to value a 25 per cent. contribution for him. A part of the employer's contribution in respect of him is required for other purposes (if he is at an age requiring a smaller theoretical contribution rate) and since this part will not be received if he leaves it is unwise to take credit for it in advance; negative values should therefore be eliminated.

16.68 Against this objection can be advanced two arguments. Firstly, as mentioned above, the employer's contribution is a global contribution to keep the scheme in financial balance and is not hypothecated to individual members; this is the essential way in which the position differs from that of an individual life assurance policy in a life office. The general suitability of the contribution rate will be looked at as part of each valuation of the scheme, and the argument in terms of the movement of individual members is not a helpful way of considering the matter. Another way of expressing this is to say that even if withdrawals are more numerous than expected the employer is in general expected to replace each employee who leaves by a similar employee, so that the contribution to the scheme which gives rise to the 'negative values' will be continued, albeit in respect of a different individual.

16.69   The second objection to the argument of paragraph 16.67 is that withdrawal rates will have been included in the basis; if withdrawals do not exceed those expected the 'asset' represented by the value of the balance of the contribution over that theoretically required is a good asset and can reasonably be taken credit for.

16.70   In pension scheme work an excess of the present value of contributions over the present value of benefits is a relevant factor in the general position, to be considered with all the other relevant factors, rather than a feature requiring automatic action corresponding to the 'elimination of negative values' in life office work. In a pension scheme it is not uncommon for the joint contributions to be at a higher level than is required to support the promised benefits even if there is no element in the contribution rate in respect of past service liabilities such as has been discussed in the previous paragraphs. For instance, the rules of a private sector scheme may promise only a modest level of increase on pensions in course of payment, with provision for further discretionary increases, and the contribution rates payable may be such as will, it is hoped, enable a higher level of increase to be provided. In making a valuation the actuary will have to decide between a number of possibilities including the following.

(i)   Value the promised benefits and the full contribution rates, permit the consequent excess of contribution value to produce a surplus but explain that this surplus really represents the present value of further pension increases which it is hoped to grant over future years.

(ii)   Include in the valuation of the benefits a rate of pension increase higher than that in the rules with the intention of producing a valuation in broad equilibrium and thus demonstrating the rate of pension increase expected to be sustainable in future.

16.71   One case where it may be prudent not to take credit for an excess of contribution values over benefit values is where it is expected that the membership of a scheme may decline because of exceptional circumstances such as redundancies, which have not been allowed for in the service table. If there are employees whose continued membership of the scheme would give rise to a contribution flow which is looked to for the clearance of a particular liability, and there is a possibility that those employees may not continue as members because of enforced withdrawal, it is obviously imprudent to take credit for the contribution margin in respect of them. The adjustment to be made in the actuarial valuation would be similar to the elimination of negative values in a life office valuation.

CHAPTER 17

STARTING A SCHEME: PROCEDURE

STARTING A SCHEME: PROCEDURE

17.1 Although this book is concerned with principles rather than the complexities of everyday practice, it will be useful to the reader to be aware of some procedural matters that arise when a new scheme is being established. In this chapter we touch on the following.

(i)   Approval by the Inland Revenue authorities.
(ii) Submission of the scheme details to the Occupational Pensions Board.
(iii) The obtaining of a contracting-out certificate if the scheme is to be used for contracting-out.
(iv) The setting up of the constitutional framework.

It is also necessary to establish methods and tables in connection with the individual calculations that will arise in the day to day running of the scheme and to deal with the formation and implementation of investment policy. These subjects are dealt with in Chapters 18 to 20.

Inland Revenue approval

17.2 The procedure by which application for approval of a scheme is to be made to the Inland Revenue is laid down in paragraph 6 of Part II of schedule 5 to the Finance Act 1970, which reads as follows.

An application for the approval for the purposes of the principal Chapter of any retirement benefits scheme shall be made in writing by the administrator of the scheme to the Board before the end of the first year of assessment for which approval is required, and shall be supported by

(a)   two copies of the instrument or other document constituting the scheme; and
(b)   two copies of the rules of the scheme and, except where the application is being sought on the setting up of the scheme,

two copies of the accounts of the scheme for the last year for which such accounts have been made up; and

(c) such other information and particulars (including copies of any actuarial report or advice given to the administrator or employer in connection with the setting up of a scheme) as the Board may consider relevant.

17.3 The practical interpretation of these provisions by the Inland Revenue Superannuation Funds Office is laid down at the time of writing of this book in Part 22 of the Practice Notes and in Memorandum No. 65 of the Joint Office of the S.F.O. and O.P.B.

The Interim Deed procedure

17.4 The following gives the wording of two of the Practice Notes concerned, slightly changed in the interests of clarity. It covers the setting up of a scheme under an Interim Deed, definitive documentation being dealt with later.

Practice Note 22.5 Application for approval of a new scheme is to be supported by a copy of each deed, board resolution or other instrument constituting the scheme, the scheme rules, all announcements made to employees about the scheme, and in appropriate cases actuarial reports or advice received by the administrator or employer.

Practice Note 22.6 Where the rules and other documents are complicated and cannot be executed in their final form before the date on which the scheme is to come into operation, the Inland Revenue will normally accept that the scheme is effectively established by an interim deed or declaration creating an irrevocable trust in relation to the monies or policies to be held thereunder, and setting out the main purposes of the scheme. Immediate tax relief on a provisional basis will be allowed in respect of contributions being made by employees, provided the Inland Revenue are satisfied that all the essential features of the scheme have been communicated in writing to every member. The employer will not obtain tax relief in respect of his contributions nor will any repayment of income tax paid on investment income be made until the scheme is formally approved but such relief and repayment will then be given from the effective date of approval. A preliminary notice to employees on broad lines will be satisfactory provided that the main features of the scheme are covered and are supplemented as necessary before formal approval is given. The notice should make it clear that formal approval under the Finance Act 1970 will be dependent on the final documents and scheme rules meeting in full the Inland Revenue requirements in this respect.

17.5 In Practice Note 22.10 it is noted that the employees concerned must be given written particulars of all essential features of the scheme (as laid down in section 19 of the 1970 Act to which reference is made in paragraph 2.5 of this book) and there is provided the following list of the matters which should be covered.

(a) Main benefits, including those
> on normal retirement
> on death whilst still in employment
> on death after retirement
> on withdrawal before retirement (including any optional methods of preserving benefits and the extent to which the value of preserved pensions is protected against inflation during the period of deferment)
> on early retirement (e.g. for ill-health) if provision is made for this
> on late retirement if provision is made for this
> on any options at retirement (e.g. to surrender part of pension and take in lieu a dependant's pension or lump sum);

(b) Basis of any contractual provisions for increasing pensions in payment or deferred benefits;

(c) Basis of contributions by members where the scheme is contributory, and administrative arrangements for collection. Any provisions governing the effect of temporary absence should be explained;

(d) How the scheme as a whole is financed and the basis on which the employer contributes to it (e.g. that the employer pays the balance of the cost of the benefits or contributes a stated proportion of the members' contributions);

(e) The legal constitution of the scheme including reference to the enactment under which it is or will be approved by the Inland Revenue;

(f) Particulars of the administrator, trustees and, where appropriate, any committee of management, including methods of appointment and replacement;

(g) Broad details of powers of amendment of benefits or rules and how changes can be effected.

These matters would normally be dealt with in a scheme booklet.

The Form of application for approval

17.6 The Inland Revenue authorities have laid down as Appendix 1 to Memorandum No. 65 the form in which they desire the application for Inland Revenue approval of a new scheme open to more than one employee to be submitted to them. Although the details are not important for present purposes, this Appendix is reproduced as Attachment 17.1 at the end of this chapter in order to convey the type and scope of the information for which the Inland Revenue ask. Some points of interest on this form are as follows.

Administrator

As shown in paragraph 2.5 of this book, section 19(2)(c) of the Finance Act 1970 requires there to be a person resident in the United Kingdom to act as the administrator of the scheme. Item 3 of the form requires the name and address of this person to be provided.

Funding method

In item 7 of the form the Inland Revenue ask for details of the funding method to be employed. This requires an outline of some of the matters dealt with in the preceding chapters of this book.

Other schemes

Item 8 requires details of all other schemes of the employer. The reason for this is that Inland Revenue control is exercised over the aggregate benefits which an employee may receive from all pension schemes with which he is involved, so that information about other schemes is required when a specific scheme is being considered for approval.

Submission of scheme details to the O.P.B.

17.7   The O.P.B. have to be satisfied that the rules of a scheme satisfy the statutory requirements in respect of preservation (see Chapter 3) and equal access (see paragraph 4.48). Thus although the bulk of the work of the O.P.B. is currently to do with contracting-out, the rules of a scheme have to be submitted to the Board whether or not the scheme is to be used for that purpose.

Contracting-out procedure

17.8   The next matter which we consider is the procedure which has to be followed in order that some or all the members of an occupational pension scheme may be contracted-out of the State earnings-related scheme by virtue of their membership of the occupational scheme. The statutory authority for the procedure is set out in sections 30 and 31 of, and schedule 2 to, the Social Security Pensions Act 1975, and the various statutory instruments issued under the Act. On the authority of this legislation the Occupational Pensions Board issue detailed guidance on procedure from time to time, and the guidance current at the time of writing of this book is contained in Memorandum No. 66 of the Joint Office of the S.F.O. and O.P.B.

17.9   An employer's authority for paying national insurance contributions at the lower contracted-out rate is the contracting-out certificate issued by the Occupational Pensions Board. Memorandum No. 66 provides as appendices a specimen of the notice of intention to elect to contract-out which the employer must give to his employees, the form of election for the issue of a contracting-out certificate which must be completed by the employer and a specimen of a contracting-out certificate. These various forms are shown as Attachments 17.2, 17.3, and 17.4 at the end of this chapter. Brief comments on them are as follows.

Specimen notice to employees

17.10   Attachment 17.2 is a specimen of the notice of intention to elect to contract-out which has to be conveyed to all employees in all the employments to which the scheme relates. It will be seen that item 4 effectively requires a brief outline of the scheme to be provided, and that in item 5 the employer is required to set out any changes to be made to the benefits and contributions of an existing scheme as a consequence of contracting-out. In the context of a new scheme item 5 does not of course arise. The matters covered in item 4 would normally be similar to those contained in the outline of the scheme which must be provided when application is being made to the Inland Revenue for approval under the interim deed procedure. Thus in the case of a new scheme this outline normally serves both purposes.

The employer's election for the issue of a contracting-out certificate

17.11   The content of this election requires little comment but the following points may be noted.

(i)   The required effective date of contracting-out must be inserted in item 1 of the election and the O.P.B. suggest that the employer should apply well in advance of the desired effective date because the heavy workload of the O.P.B. officials makes it impossible to process applications quickly.

(ii)   An employer in making his election may discriminate between employees only within closely controlled guidelines. Broadly, employees who would not be able to complete a specified minimum length of service (not exceeding 5 years) as members of the scheme before they reach the scheme's normal retirement age may be excluded, but an employer may not otherwise discriminate between employees on any grounds other than their employment. This matter is provided for in item 2 of the form of election.

(iii)   It will be seen that in item 5 of the form the employer is required to state the way in which the necessary notice to employees has been conveyed to them.

(iv)   The employer is required to consult recognised trades unions in connection with his intention to contract-out some or all of his employees, and this is dealt with in item 7 of the form.

The contracting-out certificate

17.12   Attachment 17.4 to this chapter is a specimen contracting-out certificate. Although we are not concerned with administrative details the reader may note that there are two numbers associated with this certificate, namely the employer's contracting-out number ('ECON') and the scheme contracted-out number ('SCON'). The reason for this is that in correspondence with the authorities in respect of the G.M.P.s arising under the scheme the authorities are concerned with the scheme, as being the financial entity that is to provide the G.M.P., and the scheme contracted-out number is the reference number in such correspondence. The employer's contracting-out number, on the other hand, is required in connection with the return which the employer makes to the Inland Revenue authorities at the end of each tax year in respect of his normal tax affairs. This tax return also serves as the source document for the setting up of G.M.P. data by the D.H.S.S., the date being derived from the details of the national insurance contributions of individuals shown on the tax return.

Initial procedure

17.13 The documents which have to be submitted to the O.P.B. with an employer's election for the issue of a contracting-out certificate are as follows.

(i) A copy of the notice given to employees, to trades unions and to the others concerned.

(ii) A copy of all the documents constituting the scheme (with rules that meet the contracting-out, preservation and equal access requirements) unless these are already held by the Joint Office of the S.F.O. and O.P.B.

(iii) An actuarial certificate A in relation to the solvency of the scheme. The provision of the actuarial certificate for Scheme X was discussed in the previous chapter. The reader will note from the specimen Certificate A at the end of Chapter 4 that item 4 of the certificate relates to an undertaking by the principal employer. As this is usually submitted as part of the data for a valuation the matter is discussed in paragraph 21.16.

(iv) Certain additional statements if the scheme is based on insurance contracts.

Annual statements

17.14 We have so far been concerned in this discussion with the procedures and forms involved when application is made for the first time for a scheme to be used in connection with contracting-out. The O.P.B. also require an annual statement to be submitted and a copy of this annual statement is shown as Attachment 17.5 to this chapter. Comments are as follows.

(i)   It will be seen that a statement has to be made to the effect that the accounts of the scheme for the year concerned and the balance sheet have been audited. The form does not ask for a copy of the accounts and indeed the O.P.B. have stated that they do not normally wish to see copies of scheme accounts.

(ii)   Self-investment and concentration of investments are dealt with in item 4 of the annual statement.

(iii) Item 5 of the statement requires the person completing the form to state that the appropriate actuary has been given the opportunity of considering any change which might affect the scheme's current actuarial certificate. This is an important point in practice, since otherwise the actuary might not be aware of such changes.

Constitutional and administrative points

17.15   As explained earlier in this book an occupational pension scheme is normally set up as a trust. Unless the members are few in number the scheme will in due course involve substantial financial operations which will have to be soundly administered. Some implications of this are as follows.

Trustees

17.16   If individual trustees are to be appointed it will be necessary to settle the procedure for appointment and replacement. It is not a legal requirement that some of the trustees should be drawn from the membership of the scheme, but this is not unusual; the method of selection or election of these 'member' trustees is a matter of some importance, since it may impinge on the general personnel policy of the employer. There is a wide variety in the way schemes are run; there may be a trustee company instead of individual trustees, in which case the directors of the trustee company are for all practical purposes the trustees. Another variation is for a scheme to have not only trustees (individual or corporate) but also a committee of management. In this case responsibilities are divided between the two bodies and it is often the committee of management which exercises any discretionary powers in such matters as the destination of capital sum death benefits where this is discretionary. The trustees remain responsible for the investment of funds.

Administrator

17.17 As noted earlier, a pension scheme must have an 'administrator'. This term is defined in section 26(1) of the Finance Act 1970 as 'the person or persons having the management of the scheme'. The identity of the administrator is thus a question of fact; it is not permitted for the trustees to nominate as the administrator a person who does not in fact manage the scheme.

Accounts

17.18 As mentioned in paragraph 17.14, the O.P.B. require that the accounts and balance sheet of a scheme used for contracting-out should be audited. Even if a scheme is not used for contracting-out there will usually (but not invariably) be a requirement in the trust deed that proper books of account should be kept and audited annually. The subject of accounting procedures is outside the scope of this book but it is obviously essential that accounting systems should be properly set up and run.

Ill-health retirement

17.19 Ill-health retirement is an area in which the trustees need to take particular care to ensure that they are soundly advised, particularly in a scheme which provides ill-health pensions based on pensionable service greater than that actually completed. The financial risks involved in granting ill-health retirement benefits which should not have been granted are obvious. It is, however, worth noting that the existence of this risk does not imply any unprofessional conduct or improper certification of ill-health by the medical adviser of the individual member concerned. It is rather that a medical adviser's view that his patient's health might be helped by retirement on pension may be correct, but may not constitute a cause for ill-health retirement under the specific terms of the trust deed. It is therefore often desirable for the trustees to have their own medical advice, directed towards the proper implementation of the relevant provisions of the trust deed and rules.

17.20 The provisions governing ill-health retirement vary widely from one scheme to another. Scheme rules may provide that entitlement to an ill-health retirement pension is dependent on 'disability', or 'total disability', or 'a breakdown in health which prevents the member from following his normal employment' or one of a large number of other definitions. Furthermore, a particular illness may be such as to compel retirement from one occupation but not from another. It is therefore not possible to generalise to any extent in this complex area.

Communication of information to members and others

17.21   Employers and trustees usually find it difficult to stimulate interest in a pension scheme amongst the members of the scheme, and members usually find it difficult to understand the scheme. Many employers and trustees have made considerable efforts in the past to convey information about a scheme to its members, and this has now become a legislative requirement and will therefore have to be provided for in future in the constitutional arrangements of a scheme when it is being set up. Schedule 2 to the Social Security Act 1985 introduced a new section 56A to the Social Security Pensions Act 1975 covering the disclosure of information about a scheme to members, other prospective beneficiaries and recognised trade unions, together with a framework for a registry of occupational pension schemes.

17.22   The details of the legislation are to be the subject of regulations so that a full discussion of the subject is not yet possible, but it seems likely at the time of writing, in the light of a consultative document, that some main requirements will be as follows.

(i)   A scheme leaflet giving basic information should be provided automatically to every new member (as already required under S.F.O. practice) and each recognised trade union.

(ii)   Statements should be provided automatically to individuals when benefits become payable or certain rights in connection with such matters as options have arisen.

(iii) A copy of the annual report should be provided automatically to each recognised trade union.

(iv)   In addition to the above provisions for automatic disclosure, a wide variety of other documents, to be specified by regulation, should be provided on request.

ATTACHMENT 17.1.

SCHEME OPEN TO MORE THAN ONE EMPLOYEE

1 Title of scheme.

INFORMATION ABOUT EMPLOYER(S)

2 (a) Name of employer or principal employer.

   (b) Status (eg limited company, partnership, sole trader).

   (c) Address (registered office if a company, or principal place of business if an individual or a partnership).

   (d) Nature of business.

   (e) Name of tax district (HM Inspector) dealing w th employer's liability to corporation tax or income tax Schedule D — a Collector of Taxes office should *not* be named here.

   (f) Employer's reference in that district.

 *(g) Name of tax district(s) (HM Inspector(s)) dealing with employer's PAYE for employees who are members of the scheme — a Collector of Taxes office should *not* be named here.

 *(h) Employer's reference in that/those district(s).

   (i) Date to which employer's trading accounts are made up.

> NOTE: If the scheme is a centralised scheme for a group of associated employers (see PN 16.7-9), please —
>
>   (a) give information as at 2 for all participating employers (set out as at 2(a) — (i), and
>
>   (b) give brief details of the financial or other connections of all other participating employers with the principal employer.

INFORMATION ABOUT SCHEME

3 Administrator:

   (a) Name.

   (b) Address.

4 (a) Commencing date, or original commencing date in conversion cases.

   (b) Date of conversion (conversion cases only).

5 Number of initial members.

6 Insured scheme:

   (a) Type of policy used and whether with profits or investment linked.

   (b) Will the policy be in a standard form appropriate to the scheme and agreed, or in course of being agreed, with the Inland Revenue as satisfying section 323(4)(aa) Income and Corporation Taxes Act 1970?

                                                                            YES/NO

   (c) If "No", a copy of the policy(ies) will be required by the Superannuation Funds Office.

This information is readily available from the employer's PAYE tax deduction cards.

7   Funding:

   (a)   Method (eg whether controlled funding, or level annual premiums, or, in self-administered schemes, whether employer's ordinary contributions are calculated as a percentage of salaries, or as level annuity sums; ignore this question if a separate actuarial report gives the required information).

   (b)   Initial ordinary annual contribution.

   (c)   In self-administered schemes, a copy of the actuarial report relating to the setting-up of the scheme or its conversion to new code.

   If any special contributions have been paid by the employer(s), particulars of —

   (d)   the amounts and dates of the special contributions, and

   (e)   the total of the employer's ordinary annual contributions to all exempt approved schemes in the accounting year in which each payment was made, and

   (f)   the total of the employer's special contributions to all exempt approved schemes in the accounting year in which each payment was made.

   NOTE: If a special contribution, although not yet paid, is proposed in the near future, and its amount is known, please give such particulars as are available.

8   In respect of all other schemes of all participating employers, including individual arrangements, discretionary schemes and service agreements, under which any employee who is eligible for membership of the new scheme can or may benefit:

   (a)   Name of employer.

   (b)   Name of scheme.

   (c)   Superannuation Funds Office reference number.

   (d)   How the scheme will be affected by the setting-up of the new or converted scheme.

   NOTE: If this information is given in the members' announcement about the new scheme, it will suffice merely to say "see announcement".

   (e)   Copies of documentation for the discontinuance (by winding up or making paid up) of existing schemes or amendments to make them compatible with new code approval of the new or converted scheme and, where appropriate, a copy of any form of waiver or agreement for the surrender by employees of existing rights in exchange for rights under the new or converted scheme.

   NOTE: It is appreciated that the information at (e) can be produced only where the current practitioner also dealt with the existing scheme.

9   New schemes in which the membership and the benefits are at the employer's discretion:

   (a)   The date, or respective dates, on which the first employee was nominated as a member and written notification of his rights under the scheme was given to him.

   (b)   The date on which the first contributions were paid, or the life office accepted risk.

   (c)   The minimum proportion of the total cost which will be borne by the employer in relation to any member (this will only be required in contributory schemes where the level of the employees' contributions is determined on a discretionary basis).

10   (a)   Name of person paying pensions.

    (b)   If payer is other than the employer as administrator or the life office:

       (i)   Address.

       (ii)   Name of tax district (HM Inspector) dealing with PAYE on pensions — a Collector of Taxes office should *not* be named here.

       (iii) Reference in that district.

INFORMATION ABOUT EMPLOYEES

11 Name of each director joining the scheme who is within A or B below. (State whether A or B applies.)

A   A director who either alone or together with his/her spouse and minor children is the beneficial owner of shares which, when added to any shares held by the trustees of any settlement to which the director or his/her spouse has transferred assets, carry more than 20% of the voting rights in the company providing the pension or in a company which controls that company.

B   A director who at any time before 6 April 1973 has been a controlling director as defined in section 224(1) Income and Corporation Taxes Act 1970.

12 If any member has suffered a reduction in remuneration of more than £2,000 per annum in connection with the setting-up of this scheme, please furnish details of the reduction, with copies of correspondence etc in which it was recorded. (See Memorandum No 54.)

ATTACHMENT 17.2.

SPECIMEN NOTICE OF INTENTION TO ELECT TO CONTRACT-OUT

1   This notice is given to employees of .... *(name of employer)*
     in the employments shown at item 3(a).

2   I/We .... *(name of employer)* give notice that, in
     accordance with Part III of the Social Security Pensions Act 1975/Part IV of the Social Security Pensions
     (Northern Ireland) Order 1975, I/we/the company intend to apply to the Occupational Pensions Board
     for a contracting-out certificate which will be effective from .... *(date).*

3   The employees to be covered by the certificate are those who qualify for pension benefits at the
     level required for contracting-out under the .... *(name of scheme)* in —

         (a)   *(i)   all employments to which the scheme relates.

               *(ii)   (any other description of the employments).

         *(b)   Members who are unable to complete ...... (5 or less) years' pensionable service
                before the scheme's normal pension age have been excluded.

4   †The benefits provided by, and any employee contributions payable to, the scheme are —

     ....

5   *†The changes to be made to scheme benefits and contributions as a consequence of contracting-out are as
     follows:—

     ....

     *No changes have to be made to scheme benefits or contributions as a consequence of contracting-out.

                                                                    (continued overleaf)

NOTES

1   *In the case of a holding company election, the name of the direct employer should be shown here.
     The notice should be given to all employees in the employments stated unless the election relates to a
     closed scheme in which case it need not be given to employees who could not become members.*

2   *In the case of a holding company election, the name of the holding company should be entered, followed
     be "on behalf of your employer".*

3   *(a)   Any employee should see clearly whether he will be covered by the election. Where the employer
             differentiates within employments — eg between part-time and full-time staff, the description at
             (ii) should be readily identifiable. If any scheme members will not be contracted-out because they
             are in a category which does not qualify them for benefits at the requisite level, this should also
             be explained at (ii).*

4   *Reference may be made to an existing booklet which has been issued to employees, who should be
     told where copies can be obtained. Where the election is in respect of a new scheme this should be
     made clear and item 5 omitted.*

5   *This need be completed only in the case of an existing scheme. Provision of the information will also
     satisfy the SFO requirement that every employee must be given particulars of all essential changes in the
     scheme that concern him.*

*Delete or complete as appropriate
†Alternatively, reference may be made if preferred to a relevant document

6   The effect of the election on NI contributions and state scheme benefits should be explained, adapting whichever of the following paragraphs is appropriate.

    (a)   If the employees' previous employment was not contracted-out:

       As a result of your being contracted-out, you will pay National Insurance contributions at a lower rate — currently *2½% less than the rate you have been paying on earnings between *£ ...... and *£ ...... a week. This is because the pension scheme is taking over from the state the responsibility for providing an additional pension for the period you are contracted-out.

       The pension which the scheme provides must not fall below a minimum level related to your earnings in contracted-out service — the "guaranteed minimum pension" (GMP). When you reach 65 (60 for a woman) the Department of Health and Social Security will calculate the amount of the state additional pension to which you would have been entitled had you not been contracted-out and will increase this in subsequent years to meet rises in prices. If this figure exceeds the GMP which your scheme is paying, the difference will be paid with your state pension. In this way, your combined pensions will never be less than they would have been had you never been contracted-out. For further information about current rates of National Insurance contributions and pensions contact .... *(appropriate officer of the company)* or your local DHSS office.

    (b)   If the employees' previous employment was contracted-out:

       As you will still be contracted-out, there will be no change in the rate of your National Insurance contributions or in the way that your state scheme benefits are calculated.

7   Between .... *(date of issue)* and .... *(date of expiry of notice)* representations about this election may be made by or on behalf of those affected by this notice to —

....

....

8   Representations about this election may also be made by or on behalf of those affected by this notice direct to the Occupational Pensions Board, Apex Tower, High Street, New Malden, Surrey KT3 4DN, who will not issue a contracting-out certificate until at least 14 days have elapsed from the date of the expiry of the notice. The Occupational Pensions Board may defer the issue of a certificate beyond the 14 days to enable the employer's decision to elect to contract-out to be further considered by those concerned if, in the light of any representations made to them, this seems appropriate.

9   The Occupational Pensions Board may refuse to issue a contracting-out certificate if they are not satisfied that consultations have been undertaken with all independent trade unions recognised to any extent for the purpose of collective bargaining in relation to the employees concerned.

               Signature ....

               Position in firm ....

               Date ....

NOTES

6   (a)   *Employers may provide greater detail than is given in this explanation — in a separate document if preferred.*

7   *The date of expiry should be at least 3 months later than the date on which the notice is issued. See paragraph 18 if a shorter period is to be considered.*

9   *This item must be included whether or not any such union exists.*

The current percentage difference and the current amount of the lower and upper earnings limits should be entered.

ATTACHMENT 17.3.

OCCUPATIONAL PENSIONS BOARD
LYNWOOD ROAD
THAMES DITTON
SURREY KT7 0DP

ELECTION FOR THE ISSUE OF A CONTRACTING-OUT CERTIFICATE

1　　I/We

　　　of

(name and address of employer)

hereby elect that with effect from the start of .... *(required effective date)* the employment(s) described below, service in which qualifies the earners employed in it/them for requisite benefits under the

(name of occupational pension scheme and address of scheme authority liable for the payment of guaranteed minimum pensions)

shall be contracted-out employment(s) by reference to that scheme for the purposes of Part III of the Social Security Pensions Act 1975/Part IV of the Social Security Pensions (Northern Ireland) Order 1975.

Employments to be covered by the contracting-out certificate

*(a)　all employments with .... *(name of employer)*

*(b)　all employments with .... *(name of employer)*
　　　except...
　　　... *(employments not to be covered)*

*(c)　In holding company cases if subsidiaries are to be included in the coverage of the certificate, please state the names of the subsidiaries here or attach a list.

　　　...
　　　...
　　　...

　　　*All the subsidiaries included at (c) above or on the attached list are subsidiaries within the meaning of section 154 of the Companies Act 1948.

　　　*Not all the subsidiaries included at (c) above or on the attached list are subsidiaries within the meaning of section 154 of the Companies Act 1948 and an employer's undertaking is enclosed.

2　　*Members who are unable to complete 5 years' pensionable service before the scheme's normal pension age have been excluded.

　　　*Members who are unable to complete .... years' pensionable service before the scheme's normal pension age have been excluded.

　　　*No members are excluded on the grounds that they are unable to complete a specified period of pensionable service (not exceeding 5 years) before the scheme's normal pension age.

Delete or complete as appropriate

OP 3 *(Rev 3/84)*

Men   Women

3   The approximate numbers of employees expected to be
covered by the contracting-out certificate will be:

4   The following are the names and addresses of —

the trustees of the trust(s), if any, under which benefits will be paid

....

....

the insurance company or friendly society (if any)

....

....

the scheme administrator

....

....

5   A copy of the notice in respect of this election is enclosed. The notice has been given to all employees in
(the) employment(s) to which the election relates —

*Please tick the
appropriate box*

by sending or delivering it in writing to each of them ☐

by exhibiting it conspicuously at the place of work or employment
and drawing each employee's attention to it in writing ☐

in some other manner already approved by the Board ☐

6   Copies of the notice have also been sent (or delivered) to —

the trustees ☐   the scheme administrator ☐

the insurance company ☐   the friendly society ☐

7*(a) I/We confirm that all independent trade unions recognised to any extent for the purpose of collective
bargaining in relation to the earners concerned have been given a copy of the election notice †and that
consultations with them have been undertaken. *As the notice of intent ran for less than 3 months
we also confirm that before the notice was issued all such trade unions assented to the date of expiry
specified in the notice.

*(b) There is no independent trade union recognised to any extent for the purpose of collective bargaining
in relation to the earners concerned.

8*(a) I/We confirm that a scheme bank account, separate from that of the employer, exists for the pension
scheme named at 1 overleaf.

*(b) There is no scheme bank account because —

(i)   the scheme is an individual arrangement/based on earmarked policies*;

(ii)   other arrangements have been approved by the OPB (Ref ....)∂

(This item is not applicable in the case of public service schemes.)

9   I/We apply to the Occupational Pensions Board to determine the question whether the employment(s)
described in paragraph 1 is/are to be treated as contracted-out employment(s) and if so from what date.
I/We ask the Occupational Pensions Board to issue a contracting-out certificate accordingly.

Signed ....

(by or on behalf of employer)

Position in firm ....

Date ....

*Delete as appropriate

†The rest of this sentence is irrelevant and should be deleted if the election is one to which regulation 10A of
the Certification of Employments Regulations applies and for which a notice of explanation is appropriate.
∂The reference to such approval must be quoted.

ATTACHMENT 17.4.

OCCUPATIONAL PENSIONS BOARD

CONTRACTING-OUT CERTIFICATE

(Issued under Part III of the Social Security Pensions Act 1975/Part IV of the Social Security Pensions (Northern Ireland) Order 1975)

Employer's contracting-out number (To be inserted later when notified by DHSS)	E							
Scheme contracted-out number	S							

Issued to

It is hereby certified that, with effect from the start of   the undermentioned employments, in respect of earners who qualify for requisite benefits* under

and except to the extent (if any) specified below, are to be treated as contracted-out employments by reference to the scheme for the purposes of Part III of the Social Security Pensions Act 1975/ Part IV of the Social Security Pensions (Northern Ireland) Order 1975.

Employments:

Date

R. W. ABBOTT
Chairman

* Requisite benefits are benefits which are provided in accordance with the requirements of sections 33 and 36 of the Social Security Pensions Act 1975/Articles 35 and 38 of the Social Security Pensions (Northern Ireland) Order 1975.

Issued by the Occupational Pensions Board, Lynwood Road, Thames Ditton, Surrey KT7 0DP

OP1 (7/85)

ATTACHMENT 17.5.

> This statement must be submitted annually to the OPB within 3 months of the end of the scheme's year.
>
> If any item on the statement cannot be completed, the statement should not be withheld — it should be submitted at the required time with an explanation regarding the uncompleted item. The OPB will then say if additional information is required.

OCCUPATIONAL PENSIONS BOARD

Self-administered schemes — annual statement for the purposes of the Social Security Pensions Act 1975 and the Social Security Pensions (Northern Ireland) Order 1975

Name of scheme ....

Statement following scheme year ending ....

I, the undersigned, hereby state that:—

1   The accounts of the scheme for the year ended .... and the balance sheet as at that date have been audited.

2   (i)   The auditor's report was not qualified in any way.

   (ii)   The auditor's report was qualified. A copy of the qualified report is attached.

3   I have obtained sufficient information from the employers and I am satisfied that contributions at the appropriate rate have been paid to the scheme for the year ended.. .

4   On the date shown in item 3 above, the position relating to self-investment and concentration of investment was as follows:—

   (a)   *With regard to self-investment:*

      (i)   there was no self-investment;

      (ii)   self-investment, in aggregate, did not exceed 10% of the scheme's total resources;

      (iii)   self-investment exceeded 10% of the scheme's total resources and a statement is attached giving the type and value of each item of self-investment;

      (iv)   it cannot be decided whether or not self-investment exceeded 10% of the scheme's total resources and a statement is attached giving full information about the self-investment.

   (b)   *With regard to concentration of investment:*

      (i)   there was no concentration of investment;

      (ii)   there was a concentration of investment and a statement is attached giving details.

5   The appropriate actuary has been given the opportunity of considering any change which might affect the scheme's current actuarial certificate.

Signature ....
Name ....
Capacity
in scheme ....
Date ....

(The statement must normally be signed by a trustee, the scheme administrator or the scheme's auditor. If it is proposed that it should be signed by any other responsible member of the scheme's administration, the OPB should be consulted in advance.)

For notes on completion, see overleaf

OP 21 *(Rev 3/84)*

Notes on completion of form OP 21

ITEM 1 – AUDITED ACCOUNTS

(a)   For every year of contracting-out the OPB will want to be assured that there have been audited scheme accounts. They accept that the audit of accounts for the scheme year to which the statement relates will not necessarily have been completed by the time that form OP 21 is due to be submitted (3 months after the end of the scheme year). But they consider that audited accounts should be available 15 months after the end of the scheme year. The appropriate date to be entered at item 1 is, therefore, the end of either the scheme year to which the statement relates or the scheme year previous to that. If, exceptionally, audited accounts are not available for either of those years, an explanation for the delay in having the accounts audited and an estimate of when audited accounts will be available should accompany the OP 21.

(b)   The OPB do not normally wish to see copies of scheme accounts and these should not be submitted.

ITEM 2 – AUDITOR'S REPORT

(a)   This item relates to the scheme year inserted at item 1.

(b)   The statement which does not apply should be deleted.

(c)   If the auditor qualified his report on the accounts, a copy of the qualified report only should be enclosed with any additional comments you may wish to make. The OPB may then make further enquiries.

ITEM 3 – CONTRIBUTIONS TO THE SCHEME

(a)   This item must always relate to the last scheme year — that is, the year to which the statement relates. It is not necessary to have audited accounts for the purpose of certifying that contributions at the appropriate rate were paid in respect of that year; a knowledge of the pattern and rate of payments should be sufficient to establish this. It would be acceptable to the OPB if scheme authorities complete item 3 on that basis, adding a suitable footnote if desired.

(b)   The "appropriate rate" for contributions to the scheme is the rate considered by the actuary as satisfactory for the scheme as a whole. This will normally be the rate entered by the actuary on Certificate A. Exceptionally, the actuary may have chosen to make a separate calculation of the rate necessary to cover only the liabilities listed on Certificate A and has entered this lower rate on the certificate; in such a case the lower rate is *not* the "appropriate rate" for contributions to the scheme for the purpose of item 3 (see paragraphs 5 and 10 of Memorandum No 76). It should also be noted that there are no circumstances where the appropriate rate for the scheme as a whole will ever be lower than the rate entered on Certificate A.

(c)   Contributions to the scheme on the basis of the appropriate rate should, as necessary, take account of increases of employer's and employees' contributions to the scheme in respect of any changes since the actuary's certificate was given and, for the purpose of item 3, the scheme authorities must be satisfied that sufficient information relating to new entrants and changes in earnings and total membership has been supplied by the employer.

(d)   If contributions at the appropriate rate have not been paid, a statement on the latest position should be supplied indicating:—

   (i)   The total contribution due for the year in question, ie the last scheme year.

   (ii)   The amount of the unpaid contributions.

   (iii) The amount, if any, of the unpaid contributions represented by employees' contributions.

   (iv) The proposals for paying the contributions.

ITEM 4 – SELF-INVESTMENT AND CONCENTRATION OF INVESTMENT

(a)   This item must show the position as at the end of the last scheme year, ie the year entered at item 3.

(b)   The statements which do not apply should be deleted.

(c)   Self-investment means investment of part or all of the resources in the business of the employer or that of an associated company. In assessing self-investment the market price of quoted securities and the estimated current value of other investments should be used. If self-investment exceeds or might exceed the 10% level, details must be supplied. If the self-investment included:—

   (i)   Ordinary shares, preference shares or unsecured loans — clearly identify these and give full details.

   (ii)   Mortgages, debentures or other secured loans — give full details, including the nature of the security.

   (iii) Freehold and leasehold property — state the nature of the property and the terms of the lease.

   (iv) Unpaid interest, dividends or rents on any of the above — give full details.

   If a statement of self-investment has to be supplied it should also show the amount of the total contribution due to the scheme for the last scheme year, and the value of the total resources of the scheme.

(d)   Concentration of investment means investment (other than in the employer's own undertaking) of more than 10% of the scheme's total resources in one undertaking and in any associate of it, or in one property. For the purpose of this statement, concentrations of investment in British Government securities, and possible concentrations arising out of investments in managed funds, deposit administration arrangements, unit trusts or investment trusts should be disregarded. If there is any other concentration of investment, details must be supplied.

(e)   Where statements are being provided as at (c) and (d) above, these should include details of any substantial change in the position which may have occurred since the end of the last scheme year.

ITEM 5 – SCHEME CHANGES

The OPB's guidance provides that, when there is any substantial alteration of a scheme, the OPB require either a new actuarial certificate or an actuarial statement to the effect that the scheme's current certificate is not invalidated by the change. A substantial alteration might involve, for example, a general improvement in benefits, a reduction in contributions or a change in the scheme's financial arrangements. Employers are also required to give an undertaking to the actuary to notify him if certain events occur during the currency of the certificate. If, for any reason, the actuary has not been given the opportunity to consider any changes which might affect the validity of the scheme's current actuarial certificate, item 5 should be deleted and details of the change involved should be sent to the OPB together with the OP 21.

CHAPTER 18

STARTING A SCHEME: DETAILED PROVISIONS: MISCELLANEOUS CALCULATIONS

STARTING A SCHEME: DETAILED PROVISIONS: MISCELLANEOUS CALCULATIONS

18.1 In the outline of Scheme X in Chapter 13 some of the benefit scales are precise; the amount of the pension on retirement at normal pension age, for instance, could be calculated from Spec. 4 given the data in a particular case. There are a number of benefits, however, for which points of principle and detail will have to be considered, and actuarial tables and procedures settled, before the amounts of benefit can be calculated. This is almost always the case when a scheme is being set up. The points which arise in respect of early leavers in various circumstances are of particular interest and are discussed separately in Chapter 19. In the present chapter we deal with various other matters and we shall consider them in the order in which they arise for an employee joining a scheme and proceeding through his career. We shall use the provisions of Scheme X to illustrate these.

Receipt of transfer values

18.2 As mentioned in paragraphs 3.12 and 6.39 et seq, the rules of pension schemes must now provide for the trustees to pay transfer values. Payment is discussed in the next chapter; we consider here the nature of the additional benefits which may be provided in respect of a transfer value received. There are two broad alternative approaches. The first is the granting of additional benefits defined as fixed money amounts. The second is the granting of an additional period of pensionable service, so that when a benefit is subsequently calculated the total pensionable service taken into account includes that credited in respect of the transfer payment. Various points which need to be considered in connection with these alternatives are now considered. The regulations under the legislation mentioned in paragraph 3.12, and professional Guidance Note GN11, have come to hand as this chapter goes to the printer. Their main significance for the immediate discussion is that the actuarial basis for converting a transfer value received into benefit rights must be consistent with the basis used for calculating transfer values payable. It is not thought that anything in the present discussion offends against this principle.

Fixed amount credit

18.3 The main reason advanced in favour of fixed amount credits is that the trustees of the receiving scheme ought to be in the position of giving broadly value for money in respect of the benefits which they offer in return for a cash amount received. If the amount is converted into pensionable service which will give rise to benefits based on final average pensionable pay the trustees are not in this position, since the final pay of the individual concerned cannot be predicted.

Pensionable service credit

18.4 The principal argument advanced in favour of a credit of pensionable service is that the main benefits to the new member will be based on final average pensionable pay; this is the type of benefit scale that the member is looking for, and the extra rights arising from the transfer payment received should be of the same type. In this way the transfer value benefits are largely protected against inflation if the member remains until retirement. If the member is granted additional fixed benefits these may seem large at the time but they will subsequently be eroded in value if inflation continues.

Discussion

18.5 The issues are not straightforward. The first point to be noted on the issue of value for money is that even if a fixed amount credit is to be granted the actuary will have to assume a rate of interest in order to make his calculations, and deviations of the investment experience from that assumed may in themselves lead to substantial profit or loss to the scheme. These deviations may arise not only in the long term but also in respect of market conditions at the time that the transfer payment is received (unless the terms of conversion of a transfer payment into fixed additional benefits are linked closely to market conditions at the time that the money is received, which may flow from Guidance Note GN11).

18.6 A further aspect of the same point is that, at least in respect of the period before a benefit starts to be paid, the main assumption in a calculation of fixed amount credits is the average future rate of interest, whereas the main assumption in a calculation of pensionable service credits is the difference between the future rate of interest and the future rate of increase in general pay levels. As indicated in Chapter 11, many actuaries would feel more confident in suggesting a likely range for the latter assumption than for the former. The value to an individual of service credit also depends on his individual pay progression, although we might assume that taking one case with another the average pay progression is in line with the scale used. The comparative likelihood of fair value for money being provided under the two methods is not easily assessed.

18.7 Another relevant factor is whether or not the employer undertakes to meet the 'balance of cost' as mentioned in paragraph 8.86. If he does, this is an argument for his having a strong voice as to the type of benefits to be granted for a transfer value received, since any deviations from the expected cost to the scheme arising from the conversion of transfer payments will in principle be reflected in the employer's contributions.

18.8 A quite different but equally important element in the discussion emerges when the matter is looked at from the member's point of view in relation to the benefits that may emerge in various different circumstances under the two methods. Suppose, for instance, that a transfer payment would purchase a fixed amount pension of £100 p.a. payable in addition to the normal pension whenever that pension became payable, but that the pensionable service credit which a transfer payment of the same amount would purchase would give rise to only say £50 p.a. of additional pension rights on the basis of the new member's pensionable pay at entry. The relationship between the two amounts is perfectly possible because, as explained below, expected future progress of pensionable pay has to be allowed for in the calculation of a pensionable service credit. Suppose that the member retires on grounds of ill-health after only a few years of membership. Had he had a fixed amount credit the ill-health pension would be increased by £100 p.a. With a pensionable service credit the extra pension might be only say £60 p.a. (growth of pensionable pay since entry having raised the original figure).

18.9 Advocates of the service credit method would assert that this apparent anomaly is in fact acceptable, for the following reasons.

(i) The service credit granted will represent reasonable value for money taking into account all the various different ways in which benefits may eventually become payable under the scheme.

(ii) The member will probably not be given the option of the two different types of credit at entry so that the anomaly will not in fact present itself in the way described.

(iii) The new member will probably have the option of leaving a preserved pension in his previous scheme instead of applying for the payment of a transfer value, so that the different implications of the fixed pension of £100 p.a. (regarding this as an indication of the amount of preserved pension which could be left in the previous scheme) and the service credit are factors that he will take into account in deciding whether to ask for a transfer payment in the first place.

18.10 Whether these arguments are accepted or not, the service credit method gives rise to particular difficulties if a member who brought a transfer value into a scheme leaves after comparatively short membership with payment of a transfer value from the scheme. The point is mentioned in paragraph 4.2 of Guidance Note GN11. An arrangement sometimes used is the provision of additional pensionable service but with a guarantee that the preserved pension will not be less than a specified money amount. This ensures that the problems discussed above are largely solved. The method has the disadvantage of added administrative complexity and it is also often found confusing by the member concerned.

Contracting-out

18.11 A new factor in this debate arises from contracting-out. The arrangements which held during the opening years of contracting-out required that if G.M.P. rights were passed over from one scheme to another as part of the entitlement contained in a transfer payment, those G.M.P. rights would subsequently have to be fully indexed by Section 21 Orders within the new scheme. This presented schemes whose policy was to grant an additional fixed amount benefit with a difficulty, since the G.M.P. entitlement was necessarily dynamised. For this reason many schemes refuse to accept G.M.P. entitlements as part of the benefits conveyed by a transfer payment. Although the Inland Revenue authorities in general do not permit a dual type of withdrawal benefit in which part of the total entitlement is conveyed as a transfer payment and part dealt with in some other way they did agree in the circumstances under discussion to permit a leaver's rights net of the G.M.P. entitlement to be conveyed from one contracted-out scheme to another by means of a transfer payment, with the G.M.P. entitlement being dealt with in some other way. Matters have subsequently been advanced by the introduction of the transfer premium mentioned in paragraph 4.35A for use when the receiving scheme is not contracted-out.

18.12 In schemes which provided additional pensionable service for a transfer payment received, on the other hand, there was little difficulty in principle in including the G.M.P. rights in the general pattern of additional benefits granted. It was, however, necessary in such a scheme to establish whether the transfer amount would in fact be likely to be sufficient to support the G.M.P. entitlement with its compulsory dynamisation. Clearly this might not necessarily be so, since the receiving trustees have no knowledge of the way in which the proposed transfer payment had been calculated.

18.13 The requirement that G.M.P. rights taken on in connection with a transfer value received must be increased under Section 21 Orders was subsequently changed and the difficulty mentioned in paragraph 18.11 has largely disappeared.

Calculation of pensionable service credit

18.14 To illustrate some of the calculations involved in this area we will assume that the policy in Scheme X is to accept transfer payments involving G.M.P. obligations and to provide in exchange an additional period of pensionable service. In principle the method of calculation is to divide the amount available by the cost of the benefit rights arising from one additional year of pensionable service in order to arrive at the period of such service to be credited. There are, however, two preliminary points to be considered.

18.15   The first point is that if the new member is at an age less than the age at which withdrawal decrement in the service table terminates it is necessary to make an assumption in the calculations about the benefit that would be payable, in respect of the transfer value received, on subsequent withdrawal. For the reasons explained in the next chapter we will assume that this benefit, of whatever form, will be equal in value to the amount of the transfer value received accumulated with interest in respect of the period between entry and exit. The function $^{j}\bar{A}_{x}^{w}$ which appears in paragraph 9.95 might well feature in the calculation, even though this is open to criticism on the grounds that the rate of interest accumulation to be added to a transfer value received in order to arrive at the corresponding element in a transfer value payable might well in practice be higher than the effective rate of interest addition of 4 per cent. p.a. mentioned in Spec. 8(i) of Scheme X (see Chapter 13) which would be incorporated in the calculation of $^{j}\bar{A}_{x}^{w}$.

18.16   The second point relates to any G.M.P. element to be taken on in respect of a transfer value received. It will be recalled from Spec. 9(i) that pension increases are not to be provided on the G.M.P. element of a pension in payment when such increases are provided from the State scheme. Thus the cost of providing the pension rights in respect of the additional pensionable service granted will be less than would have been the case had no G.M.P. element been involved.

18.17   We will assume that the amount of the capital sum payable from Scheme X on the death of a member in service is not affected by the amount of any transfer value brought in at entry, so that this death benefit does not enter into the present calculation. The main function we require to value the benefit rights in respect of one year of pensionable service is therefore of the form

$$\frac{^{z}M_{x}^{ra}}{^{s}D_{x}} \quad \text{(relating to the member's pension on age and ill-health retirement)}$$

$$+ (0.5)\frac{^{z}M_{x}^{wa}}{^{s}D_{x}} \quad \text{(relating to the widow's pension on death in service or after retirement)}$$

The factor of 0.5 reflects the half-rate widow's pension. A proportion married is included in the factor. The application of this function to

1/80 (salary at entry)

produces the cost of the pension rights in respect of one year of credited service.

18.18 Thus in principle the calculation of the period to be granted proceeds as follows, x being the age at entry.

(1) Amount of transfer value received
(2) $1 - {}^{j}\bar{A}_{x}^{w}$
(3) (1) × (2)
(4) Amount of accrued G.M.P. accepted on transfer
(5) Function to value saving arising from absence of pension increases on G.M.P. content when this eventually comes into payment
(6) (4) × (5)
(7) (3) + (6)
(8) Salary at entry
(9) 'M/D' function as noted in paragraph 18.17
(10) 1/80 × (8) × (9)
(11) Additional pensionable service to be credited = (7) ÷ (10)

The sign in item (7) is a plus rather than a minus because the cost of a credited year in item (10) includes the cost of increases on the whole of the pension, so that for calculation purposes it is correct to add to the transfer value received the amount of the saving resulting from the absence of pension increases on the G.M.P.

18.19 Were it not for the pension increase saving on the G.M.P., the calculation would be of the form

$$\frac{TV(1 - {}^{j}\bar{A}_{x}^{w})}{1/80 \times \text{Salary} \times \text{'M/D' function}}$$

$$= \frac{TV}{\text{Salary} \times f(x)}$$

The calculation of $f(x)$ at specimen ages is shown in Table 25. The functions in columns (2), (3) and (4) are obtained from those in Table 13, combining where necessary those relating to age retirement and ill-health retirement into one total value. The values of ${}^{j}\bar{A}_{x}^{w}$ are calculated on the same basis as the other factors although this calculation is not shown in this book. The values of $f(x)$ as revealed in the final column of Table 25 are not in themselves important, since they are a function of the actuarial basis used and we have noted earlier in this book that the service table employed was chosen only because it was already available in published tables. Nevertheless, the following point arising from consideration of the numerical values of $f(x)$ should be noted.

18.20 The values of $f(x)$ are the factors which, applied to the salary of the new entrant, give the capital cost of providing a pensionable service credit of one year. The reader may recall that one of the funding plans discussed in Chapter 16 was very similar to this, in that the contribution paid in a particular year was intended to cover the cost of the benefit rights accruing in that year. The overall contribution rate arrived at in paragraph 16.16 before allowing for contracting-out was 13.1 per cent. The values of $f(x)$ would appear to lead to a much higher average cost of a year's benefit rights than this, and it is instructive to consider why this is so.

18.21 The first reason is that in paragraph 16.16 we made an adjustment to ensure that the salary on the basis of which the contribution rate was being calculated was the salary appropriate to the year in which the benefit rights were accruing. In our present calculations, however, we have made no such adjustment, so that the values of $f(x)$ as they stand are factors applicable to the salary which the new entrant would have expected to receive had he been a member of the scheme in the year preceding his date of entry. This is obviously a highly artificial concept; what is required in practice is a factor to apply to the rate of salary at the date of entry, since this is the only salary figure available for the new entrant.

18.22 The adjustment to be made to the values of $f(x)$ to make them applicable to a rate of salary at entry would be one for consideration in individual circumstances. A more important point for present purposes is that in the calculation of $f(x)$ it is assumed that if the member bringing in the transfer value subsequently withdraws, the whole amount of the transfer value accumulated with interest will be paid out. Thus in respect of the credited years the withdrawal benefit is broadly speaking the full cost of these credited years. In the contribution rate calculation, on the other hand, the withdrawal benefit allowed for is simply the scale deferred pension which would arise in respect of the year concerned and this is of much lower value than the full cost of the year. At age 25, for instance, the probability of future withdrawal is very high, as is shown by the very large value $^{j}\bar{A}\,^{w}_{k}$ in column (6) of Table 25, so that this point assumes great importance at this particular age. On this reasoning it would be expected that at the ages at which there is no withdrawal decrement in the basis the figures in column (7) of Table 25 would not differ very greatly from the contribution rates as calculated for that age by the method of paragraph 16.16 and this is indeed the case.

18.23 It remains to be considered whether the values of $f(x)$ in the final column of Table 25 should be used in our calculations for Scheme X or whether they should be subject to adjustment. The principle underlying the method is that the additional pensionable service to be provided in respect of a transfer value should be such that on the average no profit or loss arises from the acceptance of such payments. Many trustees of schemes would regard this as an important principle which should not be departed from to any great extent. Nevertheless it would be difficult to explain to trustees and members why the figures run as they do in this particular case, despite the explanations given above, and this would be a factor in the actuary's consideration of the figures to be employed. Furthermore, administrative simplicity is an important factor to be considered. A broad approach might, for instance, involve the use of the contribution rate for the ordinary accrual of benefits (excluding the cost of the capital sum benefit on death in service if it is appropriate to do so) as a reasonable measure of the cost of a year's pensionable service credit. The decision would depend partly on an assessment of the ages at entry at which the bulk of transfer payments would be received. On this basis it might be decided in Scheme X to take 12 per cent. of salary at entry as the cost of a year's accrual of benefit rights in cases where complexities arising from contracting-out are not involved. At the time of writing it is not clear whether this broad approach would be permissible under Guidance Note GN11. This ends our discussion of the points involved in the receipt of transfer payments.

Capital sums on death during employment

18.24 We have already modified the original provisions of Spec. 6(i) of Scheme X because of the arguments set out in paragraph 13.3. When a capital sum death benefit is to be related to salary it is necessary to settle whether this should be salary at the rate payable at the date of death, salary in the year ended on the date of death, salary in the last full scheme year or some other definition. We will assume that in Scheme X the salary concerned is the rate of salary payable at death. This is the assumption underlying the calculation of the factors in Table 12.

Capital sums on retirement

18.25 It was mentioned in Spec. 5 of Scheme X that there is to be provision for the commutation of pension upon retirement for a capital sum within Inland Revenue limits. It is therefore necessary to settle the terms on which £1 per annum of pension coming into payment may be converted into capital sum. It will be recalled from Spec. 9 of Scheme X that the part of a pension in course of payment which represents the excess over G.M.P. is to be increased at 3 per cent. p.a. As mentioned in paragraph 2.22, the terms of commutation permitted under Inland Revenue rules vary according to the extent to which pensions are to be increased in course of payment, and a pension which is to be increased at 3 per cent. p.a. may under those rules be valued at a rate of interest of 5 per cent. in arriving at the terms of commutation.

18.26 It does not follow, however, that the terms in Scheme X should be as favourable as this. The finances of the scheme have been settled on the basis of a rate of interest of 9 per cent. per annum so that if lump sum is to be equivalent to annual pension on this basis the annuities should be calculated on the rate of interest of 5.825 per cent. used in the calculations outlined in preceding chapters. This would lead to commutation factors at various ages as follows, allowing for the five year guarantee of the annuity.

Age at retirement in normal health	Capital value of a pension of £1 per annum at date of retirement
	£
55	11.81
60	10.60
65	9.31

18.27 A point that should be carefully noted is that even if the terms of conversion are precisely those of the actuarial basis used for the financing of the scheme, it does not follow that commutation leads to no financial gain or loss to the scheme. If a particular commutation payment is made from Scheme X on the basis of the previous paragraph at a time when high yields are available on investments, then the trustees have lost that higher yield, and not merely the valuation rate of interest, on the amount involved.

18.28 As noted in paragraph 2.22, the Inland Revenue rules permit an overall figure of £9 to be used for all male members as an alternative to a scale such as that indicated above. Both types of arrangement are encountered in practice. If a fixed multiplier is used for all ages this may introduce complications in the actuarial valuation, to make some allowance for the fact that part of the pension may be taken in a form which has a value different to that implicit in the valuation. To avoid this complication we will assume that a scale based on the above figures is to be used in Scheme X. In practice it would be necessary to construct a scale for all the ages which might be involved.

18.29 Retirement from Scheme X in normal health will not take place before age 55, but retirement on grounds of ill-health may take place at any age and it is necessary to consider whether the provisions for commutation in Spec. 5 should be open to members retiring on grounds of ill-health, and if so the terms on which commutation should be granted. It could be argued that commutation should not be automatically available to a member of Scheme X retiring on grounds of ill-health because the scale of ill-health pensions is not over-generous; it does not, for instance, include any grant in respect of potential future years of membership such as was mentioned in paragraph 5.53 and the ill-health pensions provided from Scheme X in the early years will not be very large even allowing for the grants of pensionable service to be made in respect of pre-scheme employment. If it is thought that an ill-health pensioner's greatest need will be for continuing income, this is an argument for not providing a facility to give up this income for an immediate cash payment which may not be used wisely.

18.30 On the other hand it may be argued that a provision which is available to a member retiring in normal health should not be denied to one retiring on grounds of ill-health, not only because of general questions of equity but because ill-health retirement will normally imply an unexpected change in circumstances where a modest capital sum may be very useful. We will assume that commutation is to be permitted in Scheme X in respect of ill-health pensioners. This raises the question of the terms which should apply for such commutation, and in particular whether and to what extent these terms should take account of the particular nature of the ill-health in each case.

18.31 The effect of allowing for ill-health would of course be to reduce the capital sum in respect of each £1 of pension, since expected mortality is increased and the annuity value therefore reduced. We will assume that commutation of an ill-health retirement pension will be on terms assessed as if the member were in normal health, so that the terms of paragraph 18.26 will apply. In principle this will involve a small adjustment in the valuation, but since only a proportion of a benefit representing a modest part of the liabilities is to be increased in value to a comparatively small extent the point would probably be allowed for in practice, if at all, by a roughly calculated adjustment to the total liabilities.

Guarantee of pension

18.32 We have already discussed in paragraph 15.27 the practical difficulties arising from the apparently simple definition of the guarantee of the pension set out in Spec. 7 of Scheme X. The calculations of initial liability and contribution rates have been made using an annuity with payments guaranteed to continue for 5 years. We will assume for simplicity that the final arrangement in Scheme X is that on death during the period of five years following the start of payment of a pension the capital sum payable is equal to the outstanding part of the five year period in years and fractions of a year, multiplied by the annual amount of pension in payment at the date of death.

STARTING A SCHEME: DETAILED PROVISIONS: EARLY LEAVERS

Attachment: Guidance Note GN11

STARTING A SCHEME: DETAILED PROVISIONS: EARLY LEAVERS

19.1 In this chapter we deal with various actuarial calculations in connection with the benefits to an individual whose membership of a pension scheme terminates (other than by death) before attainment of normal pension age. The points are dealt with at some length because the discussion throws light on the financial structure of schemes. The scale benefits to an early leaver with a preserved pension or an ill-health retirement pension are specified in Chapter 13, and we are more concerned in the present chapter with cases where actuarial tables or advice are required. The question of bulk payments from a scheme when a group of members transfer to another scheme in connection with the termination or disposal of part of the employer's business raises different issues and is discussed in Chapter 30.

Payment of transfer values

19.2 Spec. 8 of Scheme X provides for an early leaver to receive a refund of contributions or, if the preservation legislation applies, a preserved pension. The specification does not provide for the possibility of transfer payments, but as mentioned in paragraph 3.12 the Social Security Act 1985 has introduced a leaving member's right to a transfer value as an alternative to a preserved pension and we will assume that such provisions are to be included in Scheme X. The relevant regulations and Guidance Note GN11 flowing from the Act have come to hand as this chapter goes to the printer, and it has not been possible to scrutinise the text of this chapter in the light of these documents. The text of GN11 is reproduced at the end of this chapter and the reader should note its main points. It deals with minimum requirements and does not prevent payment of higher values.

The principle of calculation

19.3 In the following paragraphs we discuss the calculation of transfer values as a matter of principle. The principle underlying the calculation of a transfer value to be paid out of a scheme is normally that this should be actuarially equivalent in value to the preserved pension which would otherwise be granted. The principle rests on the notion that individual early leavers whose pension rights are to be preserved will include some persons who are able to transfer an amount to the pension scheme of their new employers and others who are not able to do so, and who therefore have to retain preserved rights in the first scheme. The aim is to arrive at reasonable equity in the treatment of these two groups. What is involved is therefore the preparation of tables and standard methods to be applied to the amount of the preserved benefits which would otherwise be granted, in order to arrive at an equivalent transfer payment.

Public sector transfers

19.4 The principle that the pension rights of an early leaver should enjoy a high degree of preservation in real terms is widely applied in public sector schemes in the United Kingdom, either by the provision of preserved pensions which (except for the G.M.P. element) are increased in line with prices both during the period of preservation and after they come into payment, and are therefore of high quality, or by the payment of transfer values. As noted in paragraph 6.40 there is a widespread network of arrangements in the public sector for the payment and receipt of transfer values on a common scale. The factors used in this common scale to convert preserved rights into cash transfer payments are comparatively high, reflecting the quality of the preserved benefits.

19.5 The use of a common scale of factors is possible because many public sector schemes provide a generally similar package of benefits. For the same reason the public sector transfer arrangements involve the general concept of 'year-for-year' transfers, i.e. that a credit of pensionable service equal to that which the transferring member had accrued in his previous scheme should be provided in his new scheme in respect of the transfer payment received. This pensionable credit does not represent strict value for money in respect of the transfer payment received in each individual case; the intention is that taking one case with another, and assuming a flow of movements both ways between any two schemes, the transfer values passing should represent a reasonable financial backing for the 'year-for-year' arrangement.

Private sector transfers

19.6   The passage of transfer payments is much less widespread in the private sector of the United Kingdom economy and there is no generally accepted table of factors for the conversion of preserved rights into transfer payments. The diversity of private sector scheme militates against a system similar to that of the public sector. For example, the preserved benefits to a male early leaver may differ from one private sector scheme to another in the following respects, amongst others.

(i)   The age at which the pension becomes payable.

(ii)   The provisions if any for increases in excess of the 1985 Act revaluation requirements to be granted on the preserved rights (other than any G.M.P. content) before they come into payment.

(iii)   The provisions if any for increases to be granted on the preserved rights (other than any G.M.P. content) after they come into payment.

(iv)   The treatment of any G.M.P. content in respect of the revaluation option chosen before the G.M.P. comes into payment.

19.7   Despite this diversity it is not impossible to conceive of a common scale of transfer value factors for private sector schemes if there was a strong feeling that such a scale was desirable. There is, however, little evidence at the time of writing of such a desire. Private sector employers are in general in competition with each other, so that the whole approach to the question of early leavers differs from that in the public sector.

19.8   Even if a common scale of transfer value factors for application to the amount of preserved benefits were to be available in the private sector, the provision of 'year-for-year' pensionable service in the receiving scheme in respect of pensionable service in the previous scheme is not a practicable aim in the private sector because of the wide diversity of pension scales. Furthermore, the notion that the benefit granted should not be linked to the amount of the transfer payment received is not suitable to the private sector. It rests on the assumption that there will be substantial two-way traffic in respect of transfer payments amongst broadly similar schemes, and although this may have some validity in the public sector it is by no means the case in the private sector. In private sector schemes therefore the general principles that apply are that it is for those concerned with a particular scheme to settle the provisions for the preserved benefits of early leavers, and for the conversion of these rights into transfer payments, and that the benefits to be provided in the receiving scheme in respect of a transfer payment should represent value for money. Within the limitations of the system as a whole this allows automatically for the differing pension scales and other features of different private sector schemes.

Transfer payments: benefit or share of fund?

19.9 In addition to the various complexities discussed above there is a further aspect of transfer value payments which it is useful to discuss. This involves the question of whether a transfer payment made from a scheme represents the 'share of the fund' of the leaving member or is more properly regarded as a benefit payment. The 'share of fund' approach theoretically requires each transfer amount calculation to include an adjustment reflecting the market values of the scheme's investments at the time. In practice the total market value of these investments is recorded only at intervals, so that a rigorous application of the theory would be impracticable. Furthermore it may be argued that a transfer payment should be regarded as simply one of the benefits provided from the scheme; since the other benefits do not vary in amount according to market conditions, neither should the transfer payment. In practice it is comparatively unusual for an individual transfer payment to be so adjusted, although this may well be introduced as a consequence of the 1985 Act provisions. As noted in Chapter 30, the position is quite different in the case of bulk transfer payments.

19.10 Even if a market value adjustment is not to be included, there remains the question of whether the level of funding should be taken into account. The effect may be to reduce the payment or to justify a more generous basis of calculation. We may illustrate the points involved by considering what transfer payment should be made from Scheme X if one of the initial entrants with considerable past service leaves the scheme shortly after its inception. Funding of the initial liabilities has only just begun, so that virtually no assets have been accumulated in respect of the past service rights of the leaving member. The question is whether the transfer payment should be a very small amount, or nil, in token of this fact, or whether it should represent the full value of the past service rights at the date of leaving or some intermediate value.

19.11   The argument for paying only the small amount which has been funded is that if, in the event, the employer is unable to meet his obligations in respect of the contribution payments to clear the initial liability, the initial members who continue in Scheme X may not receive the past service benefits promised to them. A transfer payment which includes the full value of past service rights therefore conveys on the leaving employee a security which the 'staying' members do not enjoy. The specific provisions of the Trust Deed and Rules are also of course relevant.

19.12   A somewhat similar point arises when the funding plan of a scheme incorporates allowance for increases on pensions after they start to be paid greater than the rate of increase (if any) guaranteed in the rules. The point then is that a transfer payment calculated on the valuation basis will give the leaving employee the value of future pension increases that the staying members may not in the event enjoy. These issues have to be settled on their merits in individual cases, although broadly speaking the tendency is for the full preserved rights to be valued on the bases used for the actuarial valuation in the calculation of a transfer payment.

19.13   We will assume that transfer values payable from Scheme X will be actuarially equivalent to the preserved rights that would otherwise have been provided to the leaving member. The rules of Scheme X convey upon each member the past service rights granted at the Commencement Date even if the member leaves shortly after that date. We will therefore assume that a transfer payment is to represent the full value of the preserved rights of an early leaver, no regard being had to the fact that the corresponding assets are not in the fund.

Minimum transfer payments

19.14 It may happen that the calculation of a transfer payment produces a sum smaller than the amount of the member's own contributions to the scheme accumulated at a (usually modest) rate of interest. In this case it is usually provided that this latter amount should be payable as a transfer payment. This provision is made for the obvious reason that this latter amount is the benefit (before deductions on account of tax and any C.E.P.) to which the member should have been entitled in the absence of the preservation provisions. In the past, and particularly before contracting-out, this situation was quite common. It will be seen, for instance, from the centre column of the table in paragraph 8.31 that the value of a fixed preserved pension is less than a typical members' contribution rate of say 5 per cent. at ages up to about 40 in the particular circumstances of that example. In such a case a procedure essentially similar to a transfer value calculation would have to be followed even if the leaving member opted for a preserved pension, and even if the 'value for money' provisions mentioned in paragraph 3.5 cease to be a legislative requirement. The preserved pension would be increased sufficiently to give rise to a notional transfer value equal to the accumulated contributions. It will be seen from the corresponding figures of the table in paragraph 8.44 that the point is not so likely to arise if the preserved pension is increased during deferment.

Domestic transfer payments

19.15 Turning to another aspect of private sector transfer values, it is widely, though not universally, accepted that special considerations apply when transfer values pass between two pension schemes of the same company or the same group. This may happen, for instance, when an employee is transferred from a wages grade scheme to a salaried staff scheme upon promotion, or when an employee transfers from one company to another within the same group and the two companies concerned have different pension schemes. In such cases it is often considered that as far as possible the accrued pension rights of the person concerned should be maintained in real terms. This would not be the case if the transfer payment was equivalent to a preserved pension with entitlement to no, or only low, increases during the period of deferment, because in respect of his pensionable service up to the date of transfer the member would lose the benefits of expected future pay increases. Thus a system of transfer values more closely linked to the full actuarial reserve including allowance for expected future pay increases may well be used for such domestic transfers, even though the scales for transfer payments in respect of an employee moving to entirely separate employment may be less generous.

19.16 We conclude this brief discussion of the principles of transfer value calculation by reminding the reader of the point mentioned in paragraph 3.8 about the criticism voiced in recent years of the rights of early leavers from occupational schemes. The matter has been discussed at length by financial and other commentators, but the discussion has often been less than adequate because of the complexities of the subject. For instance, there has sometimes been an implication that a transfer value is necessarily a more favourable way of dealing with the pension rights of an early leaver than is the preservation of pension rights in his former scheme. This is obviously not so if the principle of financial equivalence mentioned in previous paragraphs is applied rigorously.

19.17 In practice it is usually not possible to advise a leaving member whether he would be better off with a transfer payment or with the retention of preserved rights in his former scheme. A transfer value calculated on the long term rate of interest used for the purpose of an actuarial valuation of a pension scheme may indeed appear to be a more valuable benefit than a preserved pension, particularly if market rates of interest are high at the time. The use of a transfer amount to provide a Section 32 annuity (see paragraph 6.43) is seen by some early leavers as attractive in these circumstances. On the other hand, the provision of regular increases on preserved pension rights during the period before they come into payment will certainly grow, partly because of legislation and partly under the stimulus of good practice, so that a leaving member retaining preserved rights in his former scheme may find that those rights are increased over the years to a greater extent than he had anticipated.

Calculation of transfer payments

19.18 We shall illustrate the principles discussed above by considering the factors and procedures appropriate for the calculation of transfer values payable in respect of male early leavers from a scheme with a normal pension age for males of 65, used for contracting-out. The various elements of preserved benefit which have to be valued in order to arrive at the transfer payment are conveniently considered under the following headings.

(i) The G.M.P. element of the early leaver's preserved pension.

(ii) The non-G.M.P. element of the early leaver's preserved pension.

(iii) The G.M.P. element of the contingent pension payable to a widow on the early leaver's death before or after his attainment of age 65.

(iv) The non-G.M.P. element of the contingent pension payable to a widow on the early leaver's death before or after his attainment of age 65.

(v) Any capital sum payable on the death of the early leaver before age 65.

(vi) Any capital sum payable on the death of the early leaver after age 65.

Marital status

19.19 The presence of widow's pension rights in the above list raises the question of whether the calculation of the transfer payment should differ, in the methods or factors employed, according to marital status at the date of leaving. The probability of payment of a pension to a widow at some future date is different according to whether the leaving member is married or not at the date of exit. There are, however, strong arguments in favour of not making any distinction in practice. In the first place it will be recalled from paragraph 4.25 that in a contracted-out pension scheme the widow's pension rights which form part of the preserved benefits of an early leaver must (save in exceptional circumstances) be payable even if the marriage takes place after the person concerned has left the scheme. Thus we are concerned in principle with proportions married at the date of death rather than the date of leaving the scheme, so that even if persons who were single at the latter date had a transfer payment calculated accordingly, the calculation would have to allow for the probability of subsequent marriage and the final value might differ little from that for a married member. The scheme receiving the transfer payment will usually provide rights to a widow's pension as part of the package of benefits provided in exchange for the transfer payment (and will have to do so if the rights transferred contain a G.M.P. element) and it might be to the member's disadvantage if the transfer value contained no element in respect of widow's pension rights, even if the member was not married at the date of transfer.

19.20 A further argument in favour of not making any distinction on grounds of marital status arises from practical points such as the need for simplicity in the calculation procedures. In many cases transfer payments are calculated in the office of the pension scheme concerned rather than by submission of each case to the adviser, and in these circumstances it is obviously necessary that the procedure should be as simple and straightforward as possible, since the calculations will very probably be made by staff with no actuarial knowledge. A further point which may be important in practice is that not all members may wish to reveal the precise details of their personal relationships. A scale not depending on marital status helps in both these respects.

19.21 A further factor pointing to a scale independent of marital status arises if matters are considered from the member's point of view. Two members of a scheme who have identical data except that one is married and one single will have paid the same contributions (unless the scheme is exceptional in having members' contribution rates that vary with marital status) and it will probably seem unreasonable that their transfer payments should be different. We will assume that the factors to be calculated are not to be dependent on marital status at the date of leaving.

19.22 We therefore need to assume appropriate proportions married to apply to male early leavers. As noted earlier, the passage of transfer payments between private sector pension schemes in the United Kingdom is not widespread. This raises the possibility that early leavers for whom transfer values are paid are in some respects a select class, and one way in which they may be so is in relation to proportions married. In most schemes, however, the number of cases is not sufficiently large for this to be fully investigated, so that the question of proportions married for present purposes cannot be approached from a firm statistical basis. The reader may note in passing that the whole question of selection in this area is relevant to the discussion on the use of the valuation basis for transfer calculations, as mentioned in paragraph 19.12.

19.23   As an illustration of a simple approach which will be adequate for present purposes we will consider transfer tables to value a member's pension, capital sum death benefits and a half-rate widow's pension payable on death before or after the member's pension date, as follows.

(i)   Normal pension age of 65.

(ii)   Member's pension guaranteed for minimum period of five years.

(iii)   A capital sum payment on death before attainment of age 65 equal to twice the annual amount of the member's prospective pension at the date of death.

We will assume a proportion married of 100 per cent. at the date that the early leaver attains age 65, or date of death if earlier than 65. In the initial calculations for Scheme X we used a proportion married of 90 per cent. which for an early leaver was the proportion at the date of leaving, with the probability of survival of the wife to the date of her husband's death allowed for explicitly (see, for instance, column (3) of Table 11(a)). The present calculations incorporate a slightly different basis largely to emphasise that the main basis should not be followed automatically.

19.24   Despite the aim of simplicity, the need to deal separately with the G.M.P. and non-G.M.P. elements of the preserved benefits is unavoidable, because these two elements differ fundamentally. We will assume that, as in Scheme X, the G.M.P. and non-G.M.P. elements of preserved benefits are to be regarded as separate entitlements, with the G.M.P. element being increased at 8½ per cent. for each complete tax year of deferment but with no increases in payment, while the non-G.M.P. element increases at 5 per cent. p.a. during deferment and at 3 per cent. p.a. in payment. The factors to be applied to the amount of the member's non-G.M.P. and G.M.P. pension entitlements respectively for exact age x at leaving are evidently as follows, using the actuarial basis employed for Scheme X, i.e. 9 per cent. interest and a(55) mortality. G.M.P. increases in deferment are assumed to number one less than the difference between the age at leaving and 65 (to reflect the position described in paragraph 15.11(iv)).

Non-G.M.P. benefits

Member's pension: $\dfrac{D_{65}}{D_x} \overset{9\%}{(1.05)^{65-x}} \overset{5.825\%}{\bar{a}_{\overline{65\,5|}}}$

Widow's pension:

$$0.5 \left[\sum_{y=x}^{64} \frac{d_y}{l_x} \overset{9\%}{v^{y-x+\frac{1}{2}}} (1.05)^{y-x+\frac{1}{2}} \overset{5.825\%}{\bar{a}_{y-3+\frac{1}{2}}} \right.$$

$$\left. + \frac{D_{65}}{D_x} \overset{9\%}{(1.05)^{65-x}} \overset{5.825\%}{\bar{a}_{65/62}} \right]$$

G.M.P. benefits

Member's pension: $\dfrac{D_{65}}{D_x} \overset{9\%}{(1.085)^{65-x-1}} \overset{9\%}{\bar{a}_{\overline{65\,5|}}}$

Widow's pension:

$$0.5 \left[\frac{d_x}{l_x} \overset{9\%}{v^{\frac{1}{2}}} \bar{a}_{x-3+\frac{1}{2}} + \sum_{y=x+1}^{64} \frac{d_y}{l_x} \overset{9\%}{v^{y-x+\frac{1}{2}}} (1.085)^{y-x-\frac{1}{2}} \right.$$

$$\left. \overset{9\%}{\bar{a}_{y-3+\frac{1}{2}}} + \frac{D_{65}}{D_x} \overset{9\%}{(1.085)^{65-x-1}} \overset{9\%}{\bar{a}_{65|62}} \right]$$

Capital sum on death before age 65

Formulae as that part of widow's pension formulae relating to death before member reaches age 65 but with the number 4 instead of $\bar{a}_{y-3+\frac{1}{2}}$. The combination of the number 4 with 0.5 outside the square brackets leads to a benefit of twice the amount of the member's pension rights at the date of death, as required.

19.25   Would tables drawn up on this basis be suitable for Scheme X? Points that need to be considered are as follows.

(i)   We have not specified what, if any, capital sum is to be paid from Scheme X if an early leaver with preserved pension rights dies before his pension comes into payment at age 65.

Since we are assuming 100 per cent. married at death before age 65 the reserve in respect of the widow's pension is available to provide a capital sum if the ex-member dies leaving no widow, in addition to the explicit capital sum provided for in all cases.

(ii) The member's pension in Scheme X is guaranteed for five years after it comes into payment. The formula allows for this guarantee.

(iii) We will assume that the reversionary annuity to the widow at male age 65 in the formulae of paragraph 19.24 is based on mortality alone and contains no allowance for remarriage. The assumption of 100 per cent. married at age 65 with no allowance for remarriage has to be considered against the lower proportion that would in fact be encountered in Scheme X at age 65 but with allowance for widows' benefits in respect of marriages after age 65, as required under the contracting-out law.

Factors for the calculation of transfer values payable often involve simplifications in the interests of presentation and administration similar to those for factors in connection with transfer values received as noted in the previous chapter. In view of this, factors calculated on the lines under discussion might be found suitable for Scheme X.

19.26 We will show as an example the calculation of factors in accordance with the above formulae for age 55 at leaving. The fact that the service table in Table 2 does not provide for a withdrawal decrement at age 55 is of course irrelevant; it is normally necessary to provide transfer value factors for all ages, even though the number of cases involved at some ages may be small. Table 26 shows the part of the calculations relating to widows' pensions in accordance with the formulae of paragraph 19.24. Columns (2) and (3) represent the elements $(1.05)^{y-x+\frac{1}{2}}$ and 1.000 or $(1.085)^{y-x-\frac{1}{2}}$ respectively, as used in the non-G.M.P. and G.M.P. formulae of paragraph 19.24. The other columns follow from those formulae. The small addition required for the capital sum benefit on death before age 65 can be made as an adjustment to the values in Table 26. In effect the annuity values in columns (6) and (7) relating to male ages up to 64 have to be increased by 4. The effect of this is to increase the calculated figures of 1.61 and 1.36 to 1.82 and 1.59 respectively.

19.27 The calculations required in respect of the member's pension are as follows.

Non-G.M.P. pension

$$\frac{D_{65}}{D_{55}} \overset{9\%}{(1.05)^{10}} \quad \overset{5.825\%}{\ddot{a}_{\overline{65\ 5|}}}$$

$$= \frac{2911}{7928} \ (1.629)\ (9.309) \qquad\qquad = 5.57$$

G.M.P. pension

$$\frac{D_{65}}{D_{55}} \overset{9\%}{(1.085)^{9}} \quad \overset{9\%}{\ddot{a}_{\overline{65\ 5|}}}$$

$$= \frac{2911}{7928} \ (2.084)\ (7.679) \qquad\qquad = 5.88$$

The values of the factors at age 55 including death benefits are therefore as follows.

Non-G.M.P. benefits

$$5.57 + 1.82 = 7.39$$

G.M.P. benefits

$$5.88 + 1.59 = 7.47$$

19.28 Factors calculated on this basis at specimen ages are as follows.

Age x	Factor for valuation of:	
	Non-G.M.P. element	G.M.P. element
25	2.61	6.30
35	3.68	6.65
45	5.21	7.03
55	7.39	7.47

It is interesting to note that the G.M.P. factors exceed the non-G.M.P. factors at all these ages. This is because, in value terms, the absence of increases in payment on the G.M.P. is more than offset by the high rate of revaluation in deferment. We will assume without further discussion that factors calculated on this

424 CHAPTER NINETEEN

method and basis are suitable for Scheme X and we will use them in constructing the financial experience for the first three years of Scheme X later in this book.

Special cases

19.29 We end this discussion of transfer value payments by discussing two particular aspects of the subject. The first arises in connection with the fact that not all pension scheme trustees are willing to take on a G.M.P. liability as part of the benefits in respect of a transfer value received. There may therefore be occasions when it will be desired to pay a transfer value but to retain in the paying scheme the liability for the G.M.P. The form of the transfer value tables in Scheme X is well suited to this eventuality, since the values of the G.M.P. and the non-G.M.P. elements are separately calculated and it is only the latter value which is paid over if the receiving scheme will not accept the G.M.P. liability.

Transfer out after transfer in

19.30 The second particular aspect is concerned with a case that normally requires special treatment, namely that of a member who brings in a transfer payment to a scheme and subsequently leaves with payment of a transfer value to his new scheme. It will be recalled from Chapter 18 that if a period of pensionable service was granted in the first scheme in respect of the transfer value received, the cost of providing each year of such credited service will normally be calculated allowing for expected future pay increases, in order to represent a fair assessment of this cost. When the member concerned becomes an early leaver, however, the preserved pension would be based on current pensionable pay and not projected final pensionable pay. The transfer value calculation would allow for any increases that the preserved pension would enjoy during deferment, but even so it is clearly likely that there will be an anomaly between the amount of a transfer value brought in and the element of a transfer subsequently payable which relates to the period of pensionable service granted in respect of the transfer value received.

19.31 The point may be made clearer by an example, in which for simplicity we will ignore G.M.P.s. If we take the cost of a year's pensionable service on entry to Scheme X to be 13 per cent.

of pay, then for each £1,000 p.a. of pay at entry a transfer value of £130 will purchase one added year. If an employee at age 35 entered and left again immediately, a year's service credit would give rise to a transfer value calculated as follows.

Preserved pension: 1/80th of £1,000 = £12.5 p.a.
Transfer value: £12.5 × 3.68 (from paragraph 19.28)
                                                      = £46

A transfer payment in of £130 gives rise to a transfer payment out of only £46.

19.32   In comparing £130 with £46 it may be said broadly that on entry the member was charged for future pay increases at 8 per cent. p.a. but on exit he receives only the benefit of future pension increases in deferment at 5 per cent.; the loss of value is therefore roughly measured as the effect of increases at about 3 per cent. p.a. for some 30 years, and this is indeed the broad magnitude of the difference between the two amounts. A special procedure often used to remove this anomaly is to calculate that part of a transfer value payable which arises in respect of the service credited at entry by some method which represents the transfer value at entry accumulated at an appropriate rate of investment yield.

19.33   The anomaly under discussion is an obvious one, and it is usually thought that special treatment is required. However, few issues in pensions are straightforward. The reader should bear in mind that the leaving member is essentially in much the same position as a member who has paid contributions in the normal way in respect of the period concerned. If one employee enters a scheme with a transfer value which purchases additional pensionable service of, say, three years, and an otherwise similar employee has been a member of the scheme for three years, the contributions which the latter member had himself paid during that period and that part of the employer's contributions required to provide the balance of his actuarial reserve (assuming that this reserve includes allowance for expected future pay increases) will in the normal case amount to much the same sum as the transfer value. On the other hand, the transfer value received was in no part the money of the current employer. The issues are not straightforward and it should not be accepted without any consideration that the member who brought in a transfer payment merits special terms on subsequent exit. Nevertheless as a practical matter this point is usually conceded. Paragraph 4.2 of GN11 refers to this matter. This ends the discussion of individual transfer payments.

Early retirement with an actuarially reduced pension

19.34 We turn to another type of early cessation of normal membership of a scheme. It will be recalled from Spec.3 of Scheme X that members normally retire at age 65, may retire between the ages of 60 and 65 with the consent of the employer with an immediate pension based on the normal scale, and may retire at any age between 55 and 65 without the consent of the employer with an immediate pension adjusted for early payment. We now consider the adjustment to be made to the normal scale pension in cases of early retirement without the consent of the employer.

19.35 A member leaving Scheme X on his own initiative would normally become entitled to a preserved pension (provided that the preservation requirements were met). This suggests that one line of approach to the problem now under consideration would be that the immediate pension should be so calculated as to be equivalent in actuarial value to the preserved benefits which could otherwise have been granted. The calculations involved in the application of this principle are clearly somewhat similar to those mentioned earlier in this chapter in the calculation of transfer payments, except that the capital value of the preserved benefits would be converted into an immediate pension rather than paid to the trustees of another scheme as a capital sum.

19.36 In order to investigate the results of such a calculation we will suppose that an early leaver from Scheme X at age 55 has preserved pension rights of £100 per annum at the date of leaving (calculated by applying the normal pension scale to pensionable service and final average pensionable salary at that date) and we will investigate the amount of the immediate pension that could be provided in place of these rights. The presence of a G.M.P. element in these rights leads to complications and we will assume that there are no such rights. From paragraph 19.28 the capital value of the preserved rights at the date of retirement is

$$£100 \times 7.39 = £739$$

An immediate pension at age 55 to the member with a half-rate reversionary pension to the widow, both with increases at 3 per cent. p.a., is valued on a basis consistent with the figures of paragraph 19.28 (which involves a proportion married of 100 per cent) as follows.

$$\bar{a}_{\overline{55\,5|}} + 0.5\,\bar{a}_{55\,|\,52} \qquad @ \quad 5.825\%$$
$$= 11.814 + 0.5(2.631) \qquad = \quad 13.130$$

The immediate pension at age 55 equivalent to the preserved pension of £100 p.a. would therefore amount to

$$£739 \div 13.130 = £56.3 \text{ p.a.}$$

19.37 Accrued pension rights of £100 p.a. must therefore be reduced to £56.3 p.a. if the benefit is to be taken in the form of an immediate pension without extra cost to the scheme. This reduction amounts to a compound rate for the 10 year period by which the age at retirement falls short of age 65 of 5.6 per cent. p.a. (i.e. the scale pension is multiplied by 0.944 for each year by which retirement is early). This represents the effect of the following three main factors.

(i)   Upon early retirement the assets of the scheme are called upon to finance the retirement benefits earlier than they would otherwise have been, so that the benefit of investment accumulation in the meantime is lost.

(ii)   The benefits are payable on the average for a longer period than would have been the case on retirement at the normal age.

(iii) The preserved benefit rights would have increased at 5 per cent. p.a. until they came into payment at age 65, but the immediate pension increases at only 3 per cent. p.a. This moderates the rate of actuarial reduction.

19.38 The provision of increases during the period of deferment and in payment and the provision of widow's pension rights complicate the position, and it may be helpful to some readers to consider a special simplified example. Suppose that an annuity of 1 p.a. is due to come into payment in 10 years' time and then to be paid for a fixed term of 15 years, mortality being ignored over the whole period involved, and that it is desired to convert this into an immediate annuity payable for 25 years certain having the same present value. We will use a rate of interest of 9 per cent. and we will first suppose that the annuities are of flat amount. The calculation, in which all the elements are at 9 per cent. interest, is evidently as follows.

$$v^{10} \left(\frac{\bar{a}_{\overline{15|}}}{\bar{a}_{\overline{25|}}} \right)$$

$$= (0.917)^{10}(0.821)$$

To help with the subsequent analysis we may choose to write this as

$$(0.917)^{10}(0.980)^{10}$$

$$= (0.899)^{10} = 0.347$$

The reduction in the amount of the annuity from 1 to 0.347 if payment is taken 10 years early may thus be expressed as a compound rate of reduction of about 10 per cent. p.a. for the ten year period, of which loss of interest for each year by which the start of payment is accelerated accounts for about 8 per cent. and the reduction because of the longer period of payment about 2 per cent.

19.39 If we now suppose that the amount of the original deferred annuity increases at 5 per cent. p.a. in deferment and 3 per cent. p.a. in payment, and that the amount of the equivalent immediate annuity is also to increase at 3 per cent. p.a. in payment, the calculation evidently becomes as follows, with the 'v' function at 9 per cent. and the annuity functions at 5.825 per cent.

$$v^{10} (1.05)^{10} \left(\frac{\bar{a}_{\overline{15|}}}{\bar{a}_{\overline{25|}}} \right)$$

$$= (0.917)^{10}(1.05)^{10}(0.756)$$

$$= (0.963)^{10}(0.972)^{10}$$

$$= (0.936)^{10} = 0.516$$

The reduction from 1 to 0.516 represents a compound rate of reduction of 6.4 per cent. p.a. for the ten year period by which payment is taken early. The introduction of annual increases has had the effect of reducing the rate of reduction for early payment. The two sets of figures may be compared as follows.

(i)   As far as the respreading of payments is concerned, the introduction of a rate of increase in payment increases the effect of respreading (0.980 becomes 0.972 in the example). This is because the lower the effective rate of interest (i.e. interest rate minus increase rate) the more important financially are payments in the more distant future.

(ii)   As far as the acceleration of the start of payment is concerned, the introduction of a rate of increase during deferment moderates the effect (0.917 becomes 0.963 in the example).

These comments continue to be broadly valid in practical cases.

Early retirement factors for Scheme X

19.40   In considering whether a table of early retirement factors based on the above principles should be used in Scheme X there are two points to be borne in mind. The first of these relates to legislation. The contracting-out arrangements permit early retirement with an immediate pension adjusted in the way now under consideration but the rate of reduction is not to be greater than 6 per cent. for each year by which retirement is early, unless on a basis which has been certified as reasonable by an actuary. Although certification by an actuary is a possibility, most scheme administrators would attach importance to the rate of 6 per cent. This is a simple and not a compound rate, so that a 60 per cent. reduction would be permitted if retirement was 10 years early.

19.41   Another point which is not of universal relevance but needs to be dealt with in the context of Scheme X relates to the two types of early retirement which may occur between the ages of 60 and 65, namely retirement with and without the consent of the employer. Spec. 3(i) provides that if such retirement is with the employer's consent there is to be no actuarial reduction. It might be thought natural that retirements between the ages of 60 and 65 without the employer's consent should suffer a reduction in pension based on the number of years by which the age at retirement is less than 65, but the practical implications of the dual retirement provisions at these ages would need careful consideration as part of the personnel relations policy of the employer. On early retirement at age 60 under such provisions, for instance, the question of whether such retirement was with or without the consent of the employer would have a substantial effect on the amount of the pension, and this might not be thought desirable on general grounds. Management might therefore wish to ease the rate of reduction for ages between 60 and 65 or even, in practice, to remove the reduction altogether even in cases where the retirement is without the consent of the employer, although the question of extra cost would then arise.

Early retirement reduction: an alternative principle

19.42 The above discussion has been based on the assumption that the immediate pension and the associated death benefits should be broadly equivalent in actuarial value to the benefits which would have been provided had the early leaver elected to take a preserved pension. This may seem an obvious principle to employ, particularly in view of the preceding discussion about transfer payments. In fact, however, it is not the principle most widely used in these cases in directly invested schemes, although it is employed in some insured schemes where the member's rights at any time are more closely linked to the amount of deferred annuity purchased for him at that time. An alternative and more generous approach involves the provision of an immediate pension equivalent to the full actuarial reserve which was held in respect of the early leaver as an active member just before the date of early leaving, rather than the reserve held for him as an early leaver with a preserved pension.

19.43 This method often arises because of a desire on the part of trustees and employers to be reasonably generous to an employee who is retiring a few years early and wishes to take an immediate pension. Normally such an employee may well be a long-serving employee who is not moving to other work and the attitude of the employer is not that implied in paragraph 19.7 in relation to an early leaver at a younger age who may be joining a competitor. An additional factor which makes generous treatment desirable is that, since the State pension is not payable until the early leaver attains age 65, the period up to that date will be one in which he will probably suffer a quite severe loss of income and a generous approach will be appreciated.

19.44 A further point on the financial side is that at the ages leading up to normal pension age it is almost certain that the service table underlying the financial structure of the scheme will not include any expected withdrawals. Thus the full actuarial reserve as a continuing member is available for each individual, and the provision of an immediate pension and associated benefits equal in value to this full reserve does not place a strain on the fund, but merely reduces profits which would have arisen if the member retiring early had been granted only benefits equivalent in value to preserved pension rights.

The actuarial reserve

19.45 Introduction of the full 'actuarial reserve' into the discussion makes it necessary for us to settle what we mean, for the particular purpose in hand, by this term. As an illustration we will take the initial membership data for a member of Group P in Scheme X as shown in Table 1. We will make the calculation of the immediate pension that could be provided for this member if he retired with an immediate pension on the Commencement Date and the full actuarial reserve was used to provide the pension. We will consider three different ways of defining the actuarial reserve. The factors that we shall need for the calculations are derived from Table 13 and are set out below.

		$\dfrac{^{z}M_{55}}{^{s}D_{55}}$	$\dfrac{^{z}R_{55}}{^{s}D_{55}}$
(1)	Member's age and ill-health pension	8.10	64.8
(2)	Widow's pension on death after member's age or ill-health retirement	2.40	19.5
(3)	Widow's pension on death in service	1.12	5.5
(4)	$(1) + 0.50\,[(2) + (3)]$	9.86	77.3
(5)	Lump sum on death in service	0.11	
(6)	Contributions: $^{s}\bar{a}_{55}$	8.23	

19.46 The member had salary of £6,000 p.a. in the year preceding the date at which the calculation is being made, and has pensionable service equal to one-half of actual past service, i.e. 14 years. It will be recalled that the joint contribution rate payable is 13 per cent. for the normal accrual of benefit and 12 per cent. in respect of the initial liability.

Various present capital values are as follows; we regard the lump sum benefit on death in service each year as provided from an element in that year's contribution rate, so that nothing is included for this benefit in the past service reserve.

Past service benefits

$$\frac{14}{80} \times £6,000 \times \frac{{}^{z}M}{{}^{s}D} \text{ function (9.86)} \qquad = £10,353$$

Future service benefits

Pension:

$$\frac{1}{80} \times £6,000 \times \frac{{}^{z}R}{{}^{s}D} \text{ function (77.3)} = £5,797$$

Lump sum on death in service:

$$2 \times £6,000 \times .011 \qquad = \underline{£1,320}$$

$$£7,117$$

Normal joint contributions

$$0.13 \times £6,000 \times 8.23 \qquad\qquad = £6,419$$

Additional contributions

$$0.12 \times £6,000 \times 8.23 \qquad\qquad = £5,926$$

Past and future service reserves

19.47   The first method which we will use for the calculation of the actuarial reserve of the member regarded as an active member takes into account both the past and the expected future pensionable service of the member together with the full rate of joint contribution payable, as follows.

	£
Past service benefits	10,353
Future service benefits	7,117
	17,470
Future contributions	12,345
Reserve	£5,125

Since the widow pension factors underlying this calculation involve a proportion married of 90 per cent. we will for consistency use the same assumption in the annuity function to convert this amount into an immediate pension. Using the figures of paragraph 19.36 the annuity value is

$$11.814 + 0.45 \, (2.631) = 12.998$$

This method would therefore lead to an immediate pension of

$$£5,125 \div 12.998 = £394 \text{ p.a.}$$

19.48 We need to calculate the accrued pension rights of the member concerned at the Commencement Date and for this purpose we need to refer to Table 32, which is used at a later stage in this book and which includes the assumed salary progression of the initial members during the three years preceding the setting up of Scheme X. The calculation proceeds as follows.

	£
Salary over preceding three years	4,800
	5,200
	6,000
	16,000
Average annual salary	5,333

Accrued pension

$$\frac{14}{80} \times £5,333 \qquad = 933$$

The accrued pension therefore amounts to £933 p.a.

19.49 It will be seen that on this basis of calculation the immediate pension payable at age 55 is of the order of 42 per cent. of the accrued scale pension of £933 at that age, which is less favourable than the proportion in paragraph 19.36 even though the present method is intended to represent a more generous approach. A feature of the present method of calculation is that the values of the future service benefits and the future joint contributions combine in the reckoning of paragraph 19.47 at a substantial negative value, and thus reduce the final value compared with what it would have been had only the member's past service rights been taken into account. It will be recalled that the high contribution rate payable includes a 12 per cent. contribution intended to fund the past service rights over a 10 year period, so that under the method of calculation now being contemplated the member is being charged for the fact that Scheme X is losing an expected asset (namely the employer's special contributions in respect of past service) as a consequence of the early retirement of the member. This would normally be regarded as unfair, on the grounds that the particular funding arrangements of the scheme should not impinge to a greater degree than necessary on the benefits of individual members.

19.50 We therefore turn to a second method of calculation which is similar to the first except that the joint contribution rate taken into account is that required to fund the normal year by year accrual of benefits over the membership as a whole but does not include the employer's contributions in respect of the initial past service liability. The calculation proceeds as follows.

	£
Past service benefits	10,353
Future service benefits	7,117
	17,470
Future normal joint contributions	6,419
	£11,051

Immediate pension: £11,051 ÷ 12.998 .... = £850 p.a.

19.51 This calculation indicates that an immediate pension equal to 91 per cent. of the scale pension of £933 could be paid on early retirement at age 55. The element in the total actuarial reserve resulting from future benefits and future joint contributions is a net positive value of £7,117 minus £6,419, i.e. £698 and the inclusion of future benefits and contributions therefore has a much smaller effect than was the case in the first method of calculation, although it remains the case that the funding plan impinges to some extent on the benefit calculation. Methods such as these which involve future service considerations are in practice very uncommon.

Past service reserve

19.52 The small future service value suggests a further method of calculation, namely that only the past service reserve should be taken into account. The calculation proceeds as follows.

Past service benefits	£10,353
£10,353 ÷ 12.998 =	£797

This pension amounts to 85 per cent. of the accrued pension rights. Both this percentage and that of the previous paragraph might be thought reasonably attractive by a member; the 'penalty' for early retirement is small.

19.53 As noted in paragraph 19.40, O.P.B. guidance envisages a rate of reduction of 6 per cent. for each year by which the age at retirement precedes normal pension age. For this purpose normal pension age is the earliest age at which the member can become entitled to receive a normal scale pension under the scheme (apart from any special provisions, for example on grounds of ill-health). We will interpret normal pension age as being age 65 in the context of Scheme X, since retirement in normal health with a full scale pension at an age less than this may take place only with the consent of the employer. A rate of reduction of 6 per cent. for each year by which the age at retirement precedes normal pension age would involve a reduction of 60 per cent. at age 55, leaving an immediate pension equal to 40 per cent. of the scale pension. This compares with the figure of 85 per cent. calculated by the third method outlined above.

19.54 The figures calculated in previous paragraphs are specific to Scheme X and are not of wider relevance. They are in particular much affected by the extent to which ill-health retirement, and retirement in normal health before age 65, are allowed for in the service table and by the assumed rate of pay escalation. These two factors largely account for the fact that the reduction calculated above is much less severe than that based on actuarial equivalence to a preserved pension. As to the first of these, the preserved pension is payable only at age 65 so that payment at age 55 is ten years early, but it is less than ten years early compared with the average age at retirement based on the age and ill-health retirement decrements in the service table. As to the second influence, the reserve as an active member brings in the value of projected pay increases equal to the promotional scale of Table 2 with 8 per cent. annual increases superimposed, whereas the reserve for a preserved pension incorporates only 5 per cent. projected annual increases during the period of deferment. The effect on the reduction factor of an allowance for increases at 5 per cent. p.a. was noted in item (ii) of paragraph 19.39 as a moderation of the actuarial reduction factor, and the effect of allowing for pay increases is to diminish the reduction further.

Early retirement factors: two further considerations

19.55 These calculations give an indication of the rate of actuarial reduction that may be appropriate. We shall use the past service reserve, but there are two aspects that call for further comment. The first is that whereas the various actuarial reserves considered in the preceding paragraphs are essentially functions of the actuarial basis, the accrued pension rights of £933 p.a. in the example as calculated in paragraph 19.48 depend on the actual salary progression in the three years preceding the date as at which the calculation is being made. Had the pay progression been different over that period, because of different levels of inflation from time to time in the past, the accrued pension rights would no longer be £933 p.a. The actuarial reserve calculations would, however, be the same. We would therefore have arrived at a different percentage reduction.

19.56 In order to eliminate any distortions arising on this account it is desirable to repeat the calculations of previous paragraphs but using for the calculation of the salary progression the salary scale of column (4) of Table 3 rather than the actual experience. The calculation proceeds as follows.

(1)	Salary scale s_x year of age 54 to 55	311
(2)	Salary scale year of age 53 to 54	284
(3)	Salary scale year of age 52 to 53	259
(4)	Actual salary year of age 54 to 55	£6,000 p.a.
(5)	(4) × (2) ÷ (1)	£5,479 p.a.
(6)	(4) × (3) ÷ (1)	£4,997 p.a.
(7)	Average of (4), (5) and (6)	£5,492 p.a.
(8)	Accrued pension $= \dfrac{14}{80}$ times (7)	£961 p.a.

The figure of £961 p.a. is not very different from the figure of £933 p.a. used in the examples and in this instance the percentage has not therefore been materially distorted by the particular salary experience of the preceding three years. The percentage in paragraph 19.52, for instance, falls from 85 to 83 on the basis of an accrued pension of £961 p.a.

19.57 The second aspect of the calculations that calls for comment is that we have so far looked only at the early retirement reduction factor for age 55 which is the earliest age at which early retirement under Spec. 3(ii) of Scheme X is permitted. It is tempting to suppose that the rate of reduction should be fixed over the whole range of retirement ages between 55 and 65 by interpolation between the calculated factor at age 55 and unity at age 65. This may not, however, be the best method. It is very likely in practice that early retirements under Spec. 3(ii) will take place mostly during the two or three years before attainment of age 65. Interpolation from age 55 may not give a reasonable result at later ages and calculations therefore need to be made for these ages.

19.58 Calculations on the lines of those in paragraph 19.52 proceed as follows for each £1,000 of annual salary at the age shown. The function in line (2) covers both the member's pension and the widow's pension as in item (4) of paragraph 19.45. Salaries are calculated as in paragraph 19.56. The annuity values in line (8) are calculated in the same way as that in paragraph 19.47.

		60	63
(1)	Age x		
(2)	$\dfrac{{}^{z}M_x}{{}^{s}D_x}$	9.91	9.69
(3)	Salary age $x-1$ to x	£1,000	£1,000
(4)	Salary age $x-2$ to $x-1$	£ 914	£ 919
(5)	Salary age $x-3$ to $x-2$	£ 838	£ 843
(6)	Average of (3), (4) and (5)	£ 917	£ 921
(7)	1/80th of (6)	£11.46	£11.51
(8)	Annuity at age x	11.936	11.239
(9)	$\dfrac{1,000}{80}$ (2) ÷ (8)	£10.38	£10.78
(10)	(9) as percentage of (7)	90.6	93.7

These figures indicate no clear pattern for the scale of reduction and we will look at a further aspect before settling the scale.

Widows' pensions on early retirement

19.59 The various methods discussed above of arriving at the actuarial reduction in a member's pension on account of early retirement have an implication for widows' pensions which needs to be considered. Whichever detailed method is used, the general effect is that a member leaving at an age less than 65, who could have had a preserved pension of P per annum coming into payment at age 65 (with 5 per cent. p.a. increases in deferment and 3 per cent. p.a. increases in payment) with a half-rate widow's pension, may have instead an immediate pension of kP per annum where $k < 1$, with 3 per cent. p.a. increases in payment and with a half-rate widow's pension. If a member who left at age x ($x < 65$)

with a preserved pension dies at age $x + t$ leaving a widow, her pension is initially at the rate of 0.5 P increased at 5 per cent. p.a. for the period while the member was aged less than 65 and 3 per cent. p.a. for any period while the member was aged over 65. Had the member elected for an immediate pension the amount of the widow's pension coming into payment at time t would be 0.5 $kP(1.03)^t$. Since $k < 1$ the widow's pension in the second case is smaller than in the first case.

19.60 Is it equitable to the wife that her cover for a widow's pension should be affected by the way in which the member elects to distribute his own income in retirement? In the past, opinion has tended to vary on this point. Some have taken the view that it is wrong for the widow's rights to be so reduced, and the calculation of the early retirement factor has been amended to provide for the widow's rights to remain unchanged. If the actuarial reserve in respect of the member's accrued pension P p.a. in the previous paragraph amounts to r, then in the most straightforward case the calculation of the early retirement proportion k is changed from

$$kP(\bar{a}'_x + 0.5(p)\,\bar{a}_{x|y}) \quad = R$$

to

$$P(k\bar{a}'_x + 0.5(p)\,\bar{a}_{x|y}) \quad = R$$

where p is the proportion married, and y the age of the wife, for member's age at retirement x.

19.61 We illustrate the effect of this change by considering the figures of paragraph 19.52. The initial level of the member's immediate pension is £797 p.a. and of the widow's contingent reversionary pension £399 p.a. If the widow's rights are to remain unchanged the calculation proceeds as follows.

(1)	Reserve	£10,353
(2)	Member's accrued pension rights (from paragraph 19.56)	£961 p.a.
(3)	Value of half-rate widow's reversionary annuity (from paragraph 19.47)	
	0.45 × 2.631	1.184
(4)	Value of widow's reversionary annuity	
	(2) × (3)	£1,138

(5)	Value available for member's pension	
	(1) − (4)	£9,215
(6)	Member's immediate annuity (from	
	paragraph 19.47)	11.814
(7)	Member's immediate pension	
	(5) ÷ (6)	£780
(8)	(7) as percentage of (2)	81

A point on contracting-out

19.62 It will be seen that in this case the effect of retaining the widow's pension rights at the original level is to reduce the initial amount of the member's pension from £797 p.a. to £780 p.a. This comparatively small effect is typical. A new factor was introduced by contracting-out in that in respect of any period of contracted-out service the widow must be entitled to a pension of at least 1/160th of the appropriate minimum definition of pensionable earnings for each year of contracted-out pensionable service. This is an absolute requirement, irrespective of whether or not the member takes his pension early. The extent to which this would impinge on the widow's pension fraction in cases of early retirement depends on the circumstances of each contracted-out scheme. It should be noted that this requirement is in terms of a minimum definition of pensionable earnings as laid down in the legislation. The effect of this may be illustrated by considering a scheme which provides widows' pensions on a scale of only 1/180th but on a definition of pensionable earnings larger than that required under the legislation. The rules of the scheme would have to provide for the minimum contracting-out requirement referred to above but if in practice the minimum widow's pension under the contracting-out requirements was less than that on the normal scale of the scheme no adjustment would be called for. This is why we state above that the effect of this provision depends on the circumstances of each contracted-out scheme.

Settling the scale of reduction

19.63 In settling the scale of actuarial reduction for immediate pensions on early retirement we will consider the results of earlier calculations and the further points relating to widows' pensions. The calculations in paragraphs 19.56 and 19.58 give the following values for the proportion of the accrued rights which may be paid immediately, to the nearest whole percentage point.

Age at retirement	Percentage
55	83
60	91
63	94

These figures present a somewhat confused picture. As in other areas of our calculations, the figures depend heavily on the service table in Table 2; in particular the decrements for retirement in normal health between age 60 and 65 have an important bearing on the fluctuations of the actuarial reserve with age.

19.64 In this as in other aspects of pension schemes simplicity of administration is important, and this will influence our views in deciding whether a scale should follow the rather irregular course of the above percentages or should represent a more smooth progression. In a typical scheme the number of cases arising under this provision will normally be comparatively small, so that the financial effect of using a scale which departs from the calculated figures is not very great. In most schemes a simple scale is used producing a reduction directly proportionate to the period by which retirement is early.

19.65 It is again stressed that the figures which have emerged in our calculations are a function of the actuarial basis, in particular the age retirement decrements in the service table and the relation between the rate of interest and the rate of salary escalation. We will use a rate of reduction of 1 per cent. for each complete half year by which the age at retirement is less than age 65, the widow's reversionary pension being equal to one-half of the member's reduced pension before any commutation for a lump sum. The scale of reduction does not differ too markedly from the theoretical figures calculated above, although in practice such a scale would be very generous, a reduction of less than one per cent. per quarter year being comparatively rare. We mentioned in paragraph 19.41 that on retirement immediately after attainment of age 60 the question of whether the retirement was with or without the consent of the employer would have a material effect on the pension, because under Spec. 3(i) and 3(ii) of Scheme X there would be an actuarial reduction in the second case but not in the first. On the scale of reduction now contemplated the immediate pension in the second case would be payable slighty less than five years early and would therefore be of an amount of 9 per cent. less than the accrued scale pension. Although this reduction is less severe than might sometimes be encountered in practice it is nevertheless a substantial amount. The personnel department of the employer might well have an interest in the formulation of policy as envisaged in paragraph 19.41.

The member's G.M.P.

19.66 An aspect of the contracting-out requirements in the context of early retirement which needs to be mentioned relates to the implications of the G.M.P. test under which the pension payable to a retired member of a pension scheme after attainment of State pensionable age must not be less than the amount of the G.M.P. in respect of his contracted-out employment in the scheme concerned. We have already discussed this general issue in the context of ill-health pensions (see paragraph 15.29 et seq). We now consider the G.M.P. requirements in the following cases.

(i) The case of a male member entitled to retire at an age less than age 65 (e.g. between age 60 and 65) with an immediate pension calculated on the normal scale of the scheme without any actuarial reduction for early payment. Such an entitlement may arise because the rules of the scheme confer an unfettered right to this or because, as in Scheme X, the necessary employer's consent has been granted.

(ii) The early leaver retiring with an actuarially reduced immediate pension as discussed earlier in this chapter.

19.67 We consider first case (i) above, i.e. early retirement with an immediate pension where no actuarial reduction for early payment is involved. Suppose that a male member of Scheme X retires at age 60 with an immediate pension of £1,000 p.a. and that his G.M.P. calculated at the date of retirement is £850. It will be recalled that the G.M.P. test does not operate until the member attains age 65. Because the revaluation of G.M.P.s in deferment operates only for complete tax years in the period of deferment we will assume that the G.M.P. rights will have grown at age 65 to

$$£850(1.085)^4 = £1,178 \text{ p.a.}$$

Under the effect of increases at the rate of 3 per cent. p.a. provided for in the specification of Scheme X, the pension would have grown at age 65 to

$$£1,000(1.03)^5 = £1,159 \text{ p.a.}$$

The quantity test of contracting-out has no effect on the amount of the pension until age 65 is reached, but at that time the pension must be increased from £1,159 p.a. to £1,178 p.a.

19.68 In this case the contracting-out requirements therefore lead to extra cost. At the time of writing cases of this type are rare, because G.M.P. rights have been accruing only since April 1978 while the pensions of members retiring in normal health at, or in the period of a few years preceding, normal pension age are usually based on pensionable service with a substantial pre-April 1978 element. The scale pension is therefore considerably larger than the G.M.P. Even where this is not so, it is unlikely that any extra cost involved in cases such as that of the previous paragraph would inhibit the use of the early retirement provision in Spec. 3(i) of Scheme X. Early retirement on full scale pension with the employer's consent would probably be regarded by management as an important part of personnel policy and small extra cost arising from the G.M.P. requirements would be only a peripheral factor.

19.69 Early retirement under Spec. 3(i) of Scheme X is allowed for in the service table included in Table 2 and the expected cost (apart from any G.M.P. cost) was allowed for in settling the employer's contribution rate. The issues are rather different if early retirement is taking place under Spec. 3(ii). In this case the event is not taking place with the consent of the employer and he has not provided any resources (by way of an element in the contribution rate) to fund additional cost. There is therefore a difficulty if a member's desire to retire early looks likely to place a financial strain on the scheme.

19.70 If we consider the member in the example of paragraph 19.67 but now as a case of early retirement without the employer's consent, the operation of the early retirement reduction rate of 9 per cent. (assuming that retirement takes place shortly after attainment of age 60, i.e. nine complete half-years early) would lead to an immediate pension of 91 per cent. of £1,000, i.e. £910 p.a. As in paragraph 19.67, the G.M.P. rights will amount to £1,178 p.a. when age 65 is reached. The immediate pension, however, will have increased to only

$$£910(1.03)^5 = £1,055 \text{ p.a.}$$

at that time. There will thus have to be a material increase in the amount of the pension when the member attains age 65, in order to satisfy the G.M.P. requirements.

19.71 The essence of the difficulty caused by this situation may be expressed as follows, in the framework of the above example.

(i) We are concerned here not with the case where the member has a right to retire early with an immediate pension calculated on the normal scale, but with the case where he retires early in circumstances where the normal benefit would be a preserved pension payable at age 65, and he accepts an actuarial reduction in the amount of his pension in token of the fact that it is to be paid immediately.

(ii) The trustees and members of Scheme X will probably regard the reduction of 1 per cent. for each half year by which payment is accelerated as leading to an amount of immediate pension taken early which gives equivalence in value to the preserved pension that the member could otherwise have had (although as we have seen the immediate pension is in fact more valuable than the preserved pension because the former is based on the value of the full reserve).

(iii) In the absence of the G.M.P. requirements the member in the example under consideration could have left with a preserved pension of £1,000 p.a. (which would increase at 5 per cent. p.a. before it came into payment and 3 per cent. p.a. while in payment) or an immediate pension of £910 p.a. increasing at 3 per cent. p.a. while in payment. These figures might seem a sensible interpretation of the principle in (ii) above.

(iv) If the member takes the preserved pension this will have grown to £1,276 p.a. by the time that it comes into payment at age 65 under the effect of increases at 5 per cent. p.a. in the meantime. The G.M.P. test requires a pension of £1,178 to be payable as from that age, so that no extra cost to the scheme is involved.

(v) If an immediate pension is taken the initial amount is £910 p.a. This is payable, with regular 3 per cent. p.a. increases until attainment of age 65, at which time the amount has to be increased to £1,178 p.a. because of the G.M.P. test, with consequent extra cost to the scheme.

(vi) The costs to the scheme of (iv) and (v) therefore differ, even though it was intended that the member's option should be financially neutral as far as Scheme X is concerned.

19.72   The trustees of Scheme X will have to consider what policy to follow in the face of this difficulty. As noted earlier, at the time of writing the G.M.P. is not normally so large a proportion of the total rights as in this example and the problem does not therefore arise in many cases. Nevertheless the difficulty is a growing one and trustees may find it necessary to include in the rules a provision limiting the extent to which the option to retire early with an immediate pension may be exercised.

19.73   The interaction of the G.M.P. requirements, the other relevant legislation and the various types of benefits for early leavers has led to many difficulties which it would not be appropriate to discuss in this book. The resolution of these difficulties is a matter of arriving at the arrangements which seem most suitable and equitable in the circumstances of the particular pension scheme concerned, rather than of principle. The matter has been mentioned here mainly to alert the reader to the fact that the contracting-out requirements have added a new layer of complexity to the subject of early leavers' benefits and although it is hoped that this chapter will provide an introduction to some of the points involved it does not purport to represent a guide for dealing with practical problems.

GN 11

INSTITUTE OF ACTUARIES

STAPLE INN HALL,
HIGH HOLBORN,
LONDON, WC1V 7QJ

Telephone: 01-242 0106
Telegraphic Address: Actinst London WC1

FACULTY OF ACTUARIES

23 ST. ANDREW SQUARE,
EDINBURGH,
EH2 1AQ

Telephone: 031-557 1575

December 1985

GUIDANCE NOTE GN11

RETIREMENT BENEFIT SCHEMES - TRANSFER VALUES

Preamble

This Guidance Note must be read in conjunction with Part II, Schedule 1A of the Social Security Pensions Act 1975 (which was inserted by Section 2 of, and Part II of Schedule 1 to, the Social Security Act 1985) and with Regulations (The Occupational Pension Schemes (Transfer Values) Regulations 1985 SI 1985/1931) made thereunder, to which reference is made in this Note.

Introduction

1.1   These guidelines apply to the basis of calculation of individual transfer values from retirement benefit schemes (whether to other retirement benefit schemes or to individual annuity contracts) and to the assessment of benefits in such schemes in respect of incoming transfer payments.

1.2   The guidelines apply whether the actuary is acting as an individual, as a partner, as a director of a corporate body or in the course of his employment.

1.3   The guidelines relate to United Kingdom requirements and conditions.

Purpose of the Guidelines

2.1   The purposes of the guidelines are (a) to ensure that members of retirement benefit schemes exercising a right to a transfer value can be assured that it fairly reflects their reasonable expectation of benefits otherwise available on withdrawal and (b) to ensure that incoming and outgoing transfers are dealt with consistently.

2.2   The actuary needs to bear in mind that his advice may be made available to third parties who can reasonably be expected to rely on it.

- 2 -

Normal Basis of Calculation

3.1   It is a fundamental requirement, stemming from the legislation, that a transfer value should represent the actuarial value of the benefits which would otherwise have been preserved.

3.2   Such actuarial value should be assessed having regard to market rates of interest. One of the ways in which a market value assessment may be made is on the basis of market redemption yields on British Government Stocks of appropriate duration and type at the time of transfer with allowance for investment of future interest receipts at such rates as the actuary considers reasonable. In valuing benefits which are subject to revaluation in accordance with the general index of retail prices, yields on index-linked gilts will be an appropriate criterion.

3.3   Guaranteed or statutory increases, both in deferment and after retirement, should be valued as part of the preserved benefit. The actuary should establish with the Trustees whether and to what extent it is considered appropriate to make any addition for future discretionary increases to the preserved benefit when calculating its value for transfer. This will be particularly important if there has been any recent practice of granting benefits beyond those prescribed in the rules or where there is a margin in the funding basis allowing for future increases. The actuary should also bear in mind the requirements of Regulation 4(1).

3.4   In calculating benefits in respect of transfer values received by a retirement benefit scheme the actuary should use methods and assumptions which are reasonable and consistent with the methods and assumptions (including any allowance for future discretionary increases) used for outgoing transfers from that scheme (subject to adjustment, in respect of incoming transfers, to take account of expected salary increases in cases where "added years" are to be credited).

3.5   In the case of both incoming and outgoing transfers, allowance for expenses may be made where appropriate e.g. to reflect administrative costs incurred, the saving in cost of paying pensions and any relevant costs of sale or purchase of investments.

Departures from the Normal Basis

4.1   If in the actuary's opinion the scheme's assets would be insufficient to cover liabilities (as defined in paragraph 3.1.9 of the guidance note entitled "Retirement Benefit Schemes - Actuarial Reports (GN9)" and if the immediate payment of a transfer value would further reduce the security for the benefits of other members, the actuary should advise the trustees as to any reduced transfer value which would be appropriate having regard to the provisions of Regulation 4(3) or that the member's interests might be better served by deferring the taking of a transfer value until a later date.

4.2   In cases where an outgoing transfer value is under
      consideration in respect of a withdrawing member in
      respect of whom a transfer value has already been
      received, special care may be needed in the choice of the
      basis of calculation - particularly where "added years"
      have been credited - to ensure that the outgoing transfer
      value is, subject to paragraph 4.1, both equitable in
      relation to, and consistent with, the transfer value
      received.

4.3   If in the actuary's opinion an incoming transfer value
      would be insufficient to provide minimum statutory
      benefits (e.g. a "guaranteed minimum pension"), the
      actuary should advise the trustees accordingly.

4.4   This guidance is not intended to inhibit trustees from
      paying higher transfer values which may arise under
      Transfer Club arrangements or otherwise.

Presentation

5.1   It is not necessary for each transfer value to be
      authorised separately by the actuary. The actuary may
      supply   tables,   for   use   by   the   trustees   and
      administrators, for calculating the amount of any
      transfer value payable and the pensionable service or
      other benefit to be credited for an incoming payment. The
      actuary should specify the circumstances (e.g. changes in
      investment conditions) in which adjustments to the tables
      or revised rates would apply.

5.2   The actuary should inform the trustees of the basis on
      which benefits have been brought into account in
      assessing transfer values. The actuary should also inform
      the trustees of the basis of calculation of transfer
      values - and, where applicable, of crediting pensionable
      service - in a form suitable for possible transmission to
      members.

Money Purchase Benefits

6.1   Where all or part of the member's benefits depend
      directly on the proceeds of an earmarked investment, the
      corresponding transfer value will be the realisable value
      of that investment, e.g. the amount of a building society
      deposit or the cash value of a policy of insurance
      earmarked for the member. Similarly, if all or part of an
      incoming transfer value is to be applied to an earmarked
      investment, the benefit to be granted will depend on the
      proceeds of the investment.

CHAPTER 20

STARTING A SCHEME:
INVESTMENT POLICY, PROCEDURE
AND PERFORMANCE

STARTING A SCHEME: INVESTMENT POLICY, PROCEDURE AND PERFORMANCE

Introduction

20.1 We have described in previous chapters the steps leading up to the establishment of a new scheme. With the scheme in existence the flow of contribution income will begin, and the trustees will need by this stage to have decided on their investment policy and the procedures by which it is to be carried out. The general subject of institutional investment is dealt with elsewhere in the course of reading for the examinations of the Institute and the Faculty, but for convenience we mention in this chapter some points of particular interest in pension scheme investment. We confine the discussion to exempt approved schemes providing benefits based on final average pensionable pay.

The background

20.2 Someone becoming a pension scheme trustee for the first time and seeking a broad indication of normal investment policy would find a number of sources of information available to him, notably the official publications mentioned in paragraph 1.6, booklets of stockbrokers, merchant banks and other investment advisers specialising in pension scheme investment and articles in the technical press. The Government Actuary's surveys do not cover this matter. Over a period of 15 years up to the time of writing the distribution of the assets of directly invested schemes has tended to be in the ranges indicated in the following table. We do not show typical holdings of index-linked gilts, because these are of comparatively recent introduction, or of cash for the reason mentioned in paragraph 20.3(ii).

Type of investment	Proportion of total portfolio
	per cent.
'Real' assets:	
United Kingdom ordinary shares and convertibles	45 to 60
Overseas investments	5 to 20
Direct holdings of property	0 to 15
Property and other units	0 to 10
Index-linked gilt-edged securities	
Money assets:	
Fixed-interest gilt-edged and other securities	20 to 25
Cash	

We refer to the first group as 'real' assets because (except for index-linked gilts) they represent participation in real activities and their worth in money terms is therefore likely to increase if the value of the unit of money diminishes. The same characteristic is guaranteed in the case of index-linked gilts, as noted later in this chapter.

20.3 The proportions for a particular scheme are likely to vary from time to time. The following are examples of the influences that lead to change.

(i) The proportion held in overseas ordinary shares was modest while such investments were the subject of exchange control regulations but grew markedly when these were abolished. A typical proportion at the time of writing is 15 to 20 per cent.

(ii) Cash balances may sometimes form a substantial part of the total if trustees and their advisers anticipate a fall in market values of investments, and are sufficiently confident of their judgement to leave accumulating cash flows uninvested or to make a positive decision to sell other investments and hold cash. This is the main reason for accumulating cash, and we do not consider cash further as a major constituent of investment strategy.

(iii) Fixed-interest gilt-edged securities may also form a substantially greater part of the total if trustees expect a rise in the market value of such investments which will not be matched by a rise in ordinary share prices.

(iv) Only the larger schemes have direct holdings of property, so that the percentage would be zero for a large proportion of schemes.

The questions underlying policy

20.4 It will be seen that these examples mainly reflect legislative controls (example (i)) or tactical positions (examples (ii) and (iii)). The distribution ranges of the previous paragraph remain a reasonable indication of typical policy and we now consider the reasons underlying this. In formulating their investment policy the trustees will in principle ask the following questions.

(i) When will the investment proceeds be needed?
(ii) What amounts of investment proceeds will be needed?
(iii) Is it important that the investments should be readily marketable?
(iv) What are the risks?

We shall consider matters from these viewpoints.

When will the money be needed?

20.5 If upon the setting up of a pension scheme no credits of pensionable service are granted in respect of the previous periods of employment of the initial entrants, there will be a very long period of growth before pensions in respect of a full working lifetime begin to be paid and the scheme attains a measure of maturity. If pensionable service credits are given for pre-scheme employment the pension outgo will build up more quickly and so will the fund, because contributions will be paid to fund the initial liability. In either case there will normally be a long period during which the accumulating funds will grow, i.e. income, being the total of contributions and investment income, will exceed outgo with a balance remaining for investment. In the planning of the investment policy there will be no specific dates within this period at which capital amounts are expected to be required to meet the benefit outgo, since the period is one during which normal income is expected to exceed outgo.

The mature scheme

20.6 The previous paragraph relates to a scheme whose funds are growing because the scheme is young. Turning to the position of a pension scheme which has attained maturity, we first consider a scheme which has attained a stationary condition over a long period during which the rate of inflation has been zero and general levels of earnings have remained unchanged. By a stationary condition we mean that there is a steady flow of new entrants and exits and the membership statistics do not vary with time; the information produced for an actuarial valuation is always the same irrespective of the date of the valuation. We will suppose that the experience of the scheme is exactly in line with expectation, so that there is neither surplus nor deficiency, and that the assets of the scheme consist of a cash balance placed on deposit at a stable rate of interest.

20.7 Since there is neither surplus nor deficiency the fund is equal to the sum of the past service liabilities for active members and the liabilities for ex-members with preserved pensions and retired members and dependants in receipt of pension. The membership statistics do not vary with time. The liabilities, which are obtained by applying actuarial factors to the membership data, are constant, and so therefore is the fund. It follows that the income from contributions and interest is equal to the benefit outgo.

20.8 We consider now a scheme which has reached a state of maturity similar to that defined above except that we assume that there have been increases in the general levels of earnings at rate e per annum for an indefinitely long period. The numbers and age distribution of the persons with an interest in the scheme do not vary with time. The annual amounts of pensionable earnings, pension etc. included in the data for an actuarial valuation do, however, vary with time, because of the increasing level of pensionable earnings. For each person aged x included in a valuation at time t, a valuation at time $(t + 1)$ would include a person then aged x with particulars identical to those of the first person except that any item which depends on pensionable earnings will be greater by a factor $(1 + e)$ than the corresponding item for the first person. It is assumed that pensions in course of payment are increased by a fixed percentage each year, but it is not necessary to specify what this percentage is. We ignore in this discussion the decline over time of the average G.M.P. fraction.

20.9 The liabilities at time $(t + 1)$ are equal to the liabilities at time t multiplied by a factor $(1 + e)$, because the pensionable earnings and pensions in the data at time $(t + 1)$ are themselves greater by a factor $(1 + e)$ than the corresponding figures in the data at time t. Since the fund is equal to the liabilities, the fund at time $(t + 1)$ is greater by a factor $(1 + e)$ than the fund at time t. The fund therefore continues to grow with time, i.e. the income from contributions and investment income together is sufficient to provide the benefit outgo and to provide a balance for investment.

20.10 The trustees of a scheme usually have no grounds for expecting anything other than a continuing flow of new entrants and they may well believe that some degree of inflation is likely to persist. The above examples indicate that in these circumstances the funds will continue to grow both during any period while the scheme is attaining maturity and thereafter, i.e. that benefits can be paid from income throughout the foreseeable future. It follows that there is no date at which it is expected that investments will have to be realised, or at which it is desirable that investments should mature, to pay benefits. This indefinite term is one important characteristic of the investment position of the typical pension scheme open to new entrants.

20.11 A subsidiary point arising from this discussion is that there is usually no need to choose investments so as to achieve the maximum possible immediate income. Contributions together with a reasonable level of investment income are likely to exceed outgo, so that investments which provide part of the yield in the form of growth in capital value (as explained for ordinary shares in paragraph 11.6) are perfectly satisfactory.

20.12 A number of points may occur to the reader in respect of this discussion, and we now consider two of these. The first relates to the theoretical model as a whole; what, it may be asked, is the validity of a theory which involves an ever accumulating fund which will never be needed, since income is assumed to exceed outgo in perpetuity? This question was answered, in essence, in the discussion on the security of pension rights in Chapter 8. The trustees of a scheme never know when the question of the extent to which the benefit expectations are funded will become important, so that all they can normally do is to plan as if the scheme had an indefinite life. They will nevertheless be aware that, because companies and even public undertakings do not in fact have an indefinite life with a workforce of constant number, the existence of a fund accumulated on a rational basis may become an important factor at any time.

The matching of assets to liabilities on the assumption of a closed scheme

20.13 A second point which merits discussion arises from the fact that, as will be seen later in this book, the actuarial valuation of a pension scheme is almost always made on the basis of the data relating to members and beneficiaries at the valuation date. Persons who may become members in the future are not allowed for explicitly in the calculations. In some cases this is justified on the straightforward grounds that the contributions paid by and in respect of future new entrants will be roughly equivalent to the cost of their benefits, so that the inclusion in the valuation of a projected stream of future new entrants would be pointless. Scheme X provides an example of a case where this is not so, because the 25 per cent. contribution rate mentioned in paragraph 16.47 will be paid for future new entrants as well as for initial entrants but will be much more than is required to meet the cost of the benefits for the former. Even in this case the special asset so constituted will be valued by assuming a continuation of total payroll at a certain level rather than by complex calculations involving a projected stream of new entrants.

20.14 In these circumstances it might be argued that investments should be chosen as if the scheme was to be closed immediately to new entrants, the intention being to match the investments to the liabilities in respect of the existing members and pensioners, and to demonstrate in the actuarial value that assets and liabilities are well matched by term in respect of the persons included in the valuation. At the time of writing it seems likely that further discussion and evaluation of this approach will be stimulated by a paper by A.J. Wise entitled 'The Matching of Assets to Liabilities' submitted to the Institute on 26th March 1984. The concept of a scheme closed to new entrants is fundamental to any theory of matching, since only on the assumption of closure to new entrants does the future lifetime of a scheme become finite. The author introduces the notion that the assessment of the extent to which the investments of a scheme are matched to its liabilities will serve as a technique of valuation, as an alternative to the traditional method of valuation by comparison of present capital values dealt with later in this book. For present purposes we shall leave the discussion as to when the investment proceeds of a typical scheme open to new entrants will be needed at the point we reached in paragraph 20.10, namely that there is no specific date; the term of the investments is indefinite.

What amounts of investment proceeds will be needed?

20.15 We turn to the second question of paragraph 20.4, concerning the amounts of investment proceeds needed in the future. The cost of pensions linked to final pay, and indexed to prices when in payment, cannot be predicted with certainty, and trustees will be aware that although actuaries make the best estimates that they can, there is always the possibility that outgo will be greater than anticipated. In a scheme where pensions are not linked to final pay, or pension increases are not linked to price increases, the scale benefits may prove to be inadequate, and it will be an advantage if surplus resources are available from which those benefits may be augmented. Even if the benefits are wholly satisfactory in all respects it will be advantageous if surplus resources are available, since these may be used to reduce the costs to the members or the employer or both.

20.16 All these considerations point to the second important characteristic of pension scheme investment. This is that the trustees must give a high priority to the general aim of securing the maximum possible return on the investments at all times. There is no specific figure of yield which may be taken as representing success, and which the trustees and their investment advisers need not strive to surpass.

20.17 Trustees will be aware that the feature most likely to give rise to unexpected increases in the liabilities of a pension scheme is a rate of inflation greater than that anticipated. This is likely to lead to higher levels of earnings and hence higher initial amounts of pension, and will also make desirable higher rates of increase in pensions in course of payment than would otherwise have been the case. In their search for the maximum investment yields trustees will therefore bear in mind the effect, if any, on the various types of investments if the rate of future inflation is higher than anticipated. Ideally the investments should be such that increased inflation is likely to raise the investment proceeds and thus cover wholly or in part any increased liabilities.

Is it important that the investments should be readily marketable?

20.18   As to the third question of paragraph 20.4, the expectation of trustees of a pension scheme is normally that it will continue in existence indefinitely. Nevertheless, in view of the uncertainties of commercial and industrial life the possibility that the whole or part of the scheme may need to be wound up or transferred to another scheme at comparatively short notice is always present. The implications of this for investment policy are that the investments should be capable of realisation or of transfer to other trustees without difficulty if circumstances so require, so that the security afforded to the members is not prejudiced. The assets should therefore be readily marketable and likely to be generally acceptable to other trustees.

What are the risks?

20.19   As to the fourth question of paragraph 20.4, we shall not be concerned in this book with the complex issues of risk and return that arise in portfolio theory. We shall limit our comments on risk to the observation that the investments should be spread over different types of asset, and over a number of separate holdings within each type, rather than being concentrated in large units, the failure of any one of which might jeopardise the position of the whole fund.

The investment aims

20.20   The preceding discussion suggests the following as important features of the investments of a pension scheme.

(i)   The investment policy is not normally linked to specific future dates at which resources will be required; the term is indefinite.

(ii)   The general aim is to produce the maximum possible resources at all times.

(iii) In furtherance of (ii) there is attraction in investments which are likely to produce increased resources in inflationary conditions.

(iv) The investments should be conventional and should be marketable reasonably easily.

(v) Investments should be diversified so as to achieve a spread of risks.

The main types of investment

Stable conditions

20.21 We will comment on the main types of investment for funded occupational pension schemes in the United Kingdom in the light of these criteria. In order to remind the reader of the differing characteristics of different types of investment we will start with an example, in which it is first assumed that during a long period market conditions are as follows.

Rate of interest	9.00 per cent.
Immediate yield on ordinary shares	5.00 per cent.
Rate of growth of dividends on ordinary shares	3.68 per cent.
Immediate yield on index-linked gilt-edged securities	3.00 per cent.
Rate of increase in R.P.I	5.78 per cent.

The figures of immediate yield on equities and index-linked securities are chosen as being reasonable assumptions. The dividend growth rate and R.P.I. increase rate are chosen so as to give a total yield of 9 per cent. according to the main formula of paragraph 11.7. Thus

$$\delta_{(9\%)} = \delta_{(3.68\%)} + .05$$

and

$$\delta_{(9\%)} = \delta_{(5.78\%)} + .03$$

20.22 We will assume that 100 units of currency are invested in three types of investment. The first is a 15 year fixed-interest security with a 9 per cent. coupon issued at par, and for simplicity we will assume that interest is paid in one amount at the end of each year. The second is an ordinary share, and we will assume that the dividend is paid in one amount half-way through the year concerned. An investor purchasing an ordinary share at a yield of 5 per cent. will receive half-way through the first year a dividend equal to $5 \times (1.0368)^{\frac{1}{2}} = 5.09$. The third type of investment is an index-linked gilt-edged security with 15 years to run to maturity.

On the basis of assumptions and reasoning corresponding to the case of the ordinary share the index-linked interest will amount to $3.0 \times (1.0578)^{1/2} = 3.09$ half-way through the first year.

20.23 Table 27 shows the flow of the cash proceeds from these investments over the 15 year period. Column (2) of the table shows the fixed-interest income each year and the capital amount of 100 on maturity at time 15. Accumulation (a) is the figure obtained by accumulating to time 15, at the rate of interest of 9 per cent. p.a., each item of cash received, including the maturity proceeds of 100. For simplicity this accumulation is assumed to occur in a deposit account rather than by re-investment in the same stock. This process of accumulation is not shown; it merely involves multiplication of cash received at time $n + 1/2$ by the factor $(1.09)^{15-n-1/2}$ and addition of the maturity proceeds. The figure of 364 is, of course, simply $100(1.09)^{15}$.

20.24 Column (3) of the table shows the growth of the initial dividend of 5 at the rate of increase of 3.68 per cent. p.a. The figure of capital at time 15 is the assumed amount of the proceeds of sale at that time, ignoring expenses, and by repeated use of the reasoning of paragraph 11.6(i) is equal to $100(1.0368)^{15}$. The figure of accumulation (a) is the same as for the gilt-edged security, confirming the equivalence in value of the two investments in the conditions postulated.

20.25 Similarly, column (5) of the table shows the growth of the interest on the index-linked gilt at the rate of increase of 5.748 per cent. p.a. The maturity proceeds of 232.30 represent the initial value of 100 increased at 5.78 per cent. p.a. over the whole term. The amount of accumulation (a) is the same as for the other two investments.

Changing conditions

20.26 As noted in paragraph 20.17, the feature most likely to lead to unexpected increases in the liabilities of pension schemes is a rate of inflation greater than anticipated. This will increase the liabilities, but it is also likely to increase the rates of interest available in the market so that investment proceeds are likely to rise. We will examine the effect on the three types of investment under discussion if immediately after the end of the seventh year market conditions change to the following pattern.

Rate of interest	12.00 per cent.
Immediate yield on ordinary shares	5.00 per cent.
Rates of growth of dividends on ordinary shares	6.54 per cent.
Immediate yield on index-linked gilt-edged security	3.00 per cent.
Rate of increase in R.P.I	8.69 per cent.

As before, the figures of dividend increase and R.P.I. increase are chosen so as to produce a yield of 12 per cent. on equity shares and on indexed gilts. We will assume that the income received from various investments is accumulated in a deposit account which provides a return of 9 per cent. p.a. for the first seven years and 12 per cent. p.a. for the next eight years, the resulting total being shown as accumulation (b) in the table.

20.27 Accumulation (b) for the fixed-interest security amounts to 416, the excess over accumulation (a) resulting from the more favourable rate of interest earned on the deposit account in the second part of the period.

20.28 Column (4) of the table shows the flow of dividends on the new assumption. The figures are the same as those of column (3) for the first seven years but the rate of increase then becomes 6.54 per cent. p.a. The assumed market value at sale is equal to $100(1.0368)^7 (1.0654)^8$. The figure of 453 for the accumulation (b) is obtained by accumulating the figures of column (4) at 9 per cent. p.a. for the first seven years and 12 per cent. p.a. for the next eight years. This total figure is in fact equal to $100(1.09)^7 (1.12)^8$. It will be noted that the amount of accumulation (b) exceeds the figure for the fixed- interest gilt-edged security. The reason for this is essentially that the income from the investment, as well as the rate of interest at which it may be reinvested, is increased in the changed conditions, reflecting characteristic (iii) of paragraph 20.20.

20.29 Column (6) shows the figures for the index-linked gilt corresponding to those of column (4). The amount of accumulation (b) is the same as that for the equity investment. Some of these features are referred to in the subsequent text.

Types of investment

20.30 We now turn to a brief discussion of the main types of

pension scheme investment in the United Kingdom and we will
consider these, in the order in which they are set out in paragraph
20.2, in the light of the points set out in paragraph 20.20.

United Kingdom ordinary shares

Term

20.31   The ordinary shares of United Kingdom companies do not
have any definite date of redemption or maturity. The companies
whose ownership is represented by these shares have an indefinite
life and the investments are usually traded on the assumption that
the flow of dividend income from them will continue in perpetuity.
This general position accords well with the needs of pension
scheme trustees.

Long term yield

20.32   As noted in paragraph 20.2, the ordinary shares of United
Kingdom companies form a large proportion of the investments of
occupational schemes in the United Kingdom. These shares are
advocated as suitable investments for pension schemes on the
grounds that they are matched to the liabilities, in the sense that
dividend levels (and therefore capital values taking one year with
another) will tend to be affected in a reasonably predictable way
by the general economic conditions which also affect earnings
levels and hence the liabilities of schemes. The argument of
Chapter 11 is based on this assumption.

20.33   Thus the most important characteristic of an ordinary
share for the present purposes is the expectation that the dividends
will grow at a speed related to prevailing inflationary conditions
from time to time, as illustrated by the divergence of the figures in
column (4) of Table 27 from those in column (3) when general
economic conditions are assumed to change after seven years. To
repeat the point, it is hoped that the proceeds from an investment
in ordinary shares will grow if the rate of inflation increases not
only because of the more favourable reinvestment opportunities
but also because the actual amount of each dividend is increased.
The long term performance of equities in the past, leading to the
future expectation noted in paragraph 11.20, has in general been
superior to that of other types of investment.

Marketability and risk

20.34   An investment portfolio consisting of the ordinary shares of a wide spread of companies listed on the United Kingdom stock exchange would be wholly satisfactory as far as general acceptability, marketability and spread of risk are concerned.

Investment in the employer's business

20.35   A particular point in the area of risk that arises in ordinary share investment is the extent to which a pension scheme should invest in the business of the employer concerned (usually referred to as 'self-investment'). The law impinges on this matter only in connection with contracting-out. It will be noted that item 5 of Certificate A at the end of Chapter 4 covers the point. The O.P.B. have provided detailed guidance on the matters that must be considered if self-investment exceeds 10 per cent. of the scheme's resources. On general grounds there is obviously no objection to investment in the employer's business to the extent dictated by the normal requirements of a balanced portfolio, but it is in principle undesirable that too large a part of the scheme should be so invested, because the accruing benefits would not then be backed by assets independent of the prosperity of the employer. The member would be relying on the employer both for his continued employment and for the security of his pension benefits, and this is clearly undesirable. An investment in the premises or other assets of the employer might not be open to such strong objection provided that these assets were, in the last resort, marketable and would be equally valuable in other hands.

Investment in the employer's business: small self-administered schemes

20.36   Although this book is mainly concerned with the generality of pension schemes it is necessary to mention here the so-called 'small self-administered scheme', a term used by the S.F.O. to denote a particular kind of arrangement. In recent years there has been considerable growth in the numbers of such schemes, which are associated in the main with small companies whose tax advisers have emphasised the potential financial advantages of being able to pay contributions to a tax-exempt pension scheme, the scheme then being able to lend some of these contributions back to the company.

20.37 The membership of such a scheme will normally not include ordinary employees who are at arm's length from the employer. It may consist entirely of the directors of a family owned and run company. Because of this the disadvantage of 'self investment' noted in paragraph 20.35, while remaining true, will not be so important in the minds of the members. They will be more concerned with the advantage noted above.

20.38 It is not necessary for small schemes to include in the trust deed any special restrictions on the investment powers of the trustees, except that loans to members of the scheme or to any other individuals having a contingent interest in the scheme will probably be prohibited. Furthermore, it is an Inland Revenue requirement that any loans granted to the employer must be transacted on commercial terms and must not exceed 50 per cent. of the assets. This ends the discussion of UK ordinary shares as pension scheme investments.

Overseas investments

20.39 In the past it was comparatively unusual for United Kingdom pension schemes to invest to any substantial extent in overseas assets. This was partly due to exchange control regulations in the United Kingdom, and the so-called 'dollar-premium' which arose from the existence of a limited pool of currency which could be used for overseas investment. Upon the abolition of exchange control this obstacle was removed and United Kingdom pension schemes subsequently invested to a considerable extent in the ordinary shares of overseas companies and to a more modest extent in overseas property and various overseas fixed-interest securities.

20.40 As far as the ordinary shares of overseas companies are concerned, these have the virtue that they may enable a pension scheme to invest in areas which are not available in the United Kingdom (such as certain areas of advanced technology and private medicine). Overseas investments furthermore represent an extension of the principle of the spreading of risks, since they represent an opportunity to invest in other economies. There is automatically introduced the uncertainty of the long term relation between sterling and other currencies; the liabilities of United Kingdom pension schemes are defined in sterling so that the proceeds of overseas investments will eventually have to be translated back into sterling when the investments are realised to provide benefits.

20.41 A further aspect of overseas investment which sometimes causes difficulty is the need to obtain reliable advice on individual companies. Some countries operate in a way reasonably familiar to United Kingdom institutions both as regards the general economic framework and the market in ordinary shares. Other countries, however, differ markedly from the United Kingdom both in their economies and in their methods of trading ordinary shares, and this sometimes presents pitfalls to the overseas investor.

20.42 In general the comments made on United Kingdom ordinary shares apply also to overseas ordinary shares. It is not, however, possible to generalise about the long term return to be expected upon such investments. The addition of currency variations to the other uncertainties associated with ordinary shares has led in recent years to returns on overseas ordinary shares which have fluctuated greatly from one year to another, and from one country to another. No clear picture has emerged.

Direct holdings of property

20.43 In considering property as a pension scheme investment it is necessary to distinguish clearly between shares in a quoted property company and direct holding of property. Shares in a property company may well play their part in the general spread of ordinary shares held by a pension scheme, but the asset which is being purchased represents the residual profit, after corporation tax, obtained by the skill of the managers of the property company. This skill may well be exercised by using borrowed finance to purchase properties, the return on which provides an excess over the cost of borrowing. In our discussion of property we shall not be referring to this type of investment but rather to the direct holding of property.

20.44 The direct holding of property is confined to large pension schemes. The trustees will look ideally for a property with an established tenant on a long lease with frequent rent reviews (perhaps at intervals of not more than five years) and with reasonable certainty that the tenant will be able to afford the increased rents from time to time. The trustees will of course also be much concerned with the position and fabric of the building, since they will need to attract another tenant if the first is unable to meet his obligations, or upon the expiry of the lease. The property, whether shops, offices or industrial buildings, will be viewed in this light. The immediate returns available on these three types of property often differ markedly from each other and vary from time to time with market conditions. The term of the investment is represented by the expected useful life of the building and, more immediately, by the outstanding term of the lease of the existing tenant.

Return

20.45 In assessing the expected long term return on a property the period between rent reviews is obviously of crucial importance. Dividend increases on ordinary shares are normally looked for each year, whereas a rent review may well take place only at intervals of five years or sometimes of three years. The intervals may be a good deal longer than this under leases which have been in force for many years but a higher return will then be required if the purchase of such a property is under consideration because of the diminished value arising from the longer period between rent reviews.

Marketability and risk

20.46 Property investments involve particular difficulties as far as marketability, general acceptability to other trustees and risks are concerned. As to marketability, the sale of even a modest property is obviously a much more involved matter than the sale of a holding of gilts or ordinary shares. There may not be a demand for the particular property at the time at which disposal is desired. Furthermore the proceeds are unlikely to be known in advance, at least with the accuracy possible with stock exchange securities.

20.47 As to acceptability to other trustees this also may pose problems. If for instance a scheme is transferring some of its members to another scheme in connection with the sale of part of the operations of a group of companies, with the transfer of the appropriate part of the funds which is to include properties, it may be a matter of some difficulty to arrive at agreement on the particular properties to be transferred, or even on the value of the properties for the purpose of arriving at the total market value of the funds to be split. Each property holding cannot be split as could be the case with a holding of stock exchange securities.

20.48 As to general spread of risks, an individual property is a substantial investment and this is another reason why only large schemes are direct investors in property; a smaller scheme could not own a sufficient number of properties to provide a reasonable spread of risks.

20.49 This brief discussion has been more concerned with the difficulties of property investment than with its advantages. It should be said that properties have over long periods proved to be highly satisfactory long term investments of pension schemes.

Agricultural land

20.50 A particular case of property is represented by agricultural land, a market which has been entered by some United Kingdom pension schemes in recent years. One argument advanced for buying farm land is that this is a valuable commodity of which there is only a finite supply so that it should in principle represent a good store of value. It remains a rather specialised market.

Property and other units

20.51 There are in the United Kingdom many different organisations offering various sorts of units exclusively to fully approved pension schemes. Such funds offer, for instance, units in ordinary shares or in properties, or a unit in which the fund managers make the decisions as to the disposition between various markets. A particular case of units is represented by the managed funds associated with many life offices, as mentioned in Chapter 32. The characteristics of units in general follow those of the underlying investments, although the point made in paragraph 8.16 about liquidity when investment income is accumulated within units should be noted.

Index-linked gilt-edged securities

20.52 The introduction of these securities was mentioned in paragraph 11.21 et seq in which it was pointed out that the interest represents a yield in excess of increases in the Retail Price Index and the maturity proceeds are linked to increases in this index over the term of the stock, so that the return available in the market on these investments from time to time represents a guaranteed yield in excess of prices, except to the extent that the yield that will be obtained on the reinvestment of the comparatively small income is unknown. Except for this point, these investments therefore have the unique characteristic that they provide a guaranteed return in excess of prices. If it is assumed that the percentage excess of increases in pensionable earnings over price increases will vary within only a narrow range, these investments may be regarded as well matched to the requirements of pension scheme trustees.

20.53 Since the introduction in March 1981 of the first index-linked gilt-edged security further issues have been made, and such securities covering a wide range of terms are now available, although it is not clear at the time of writing whether successive governments are likely to continue to fund their borrowing in this way. In general, considerations of term, marketability and risk are similar to those for conventional gilts as mentioned below, except that the effective term is longer than that for a conventional gilt as will be seen from the large proportion of the total proceeds represented by the capital proceeds in columns (5) and (6) of Table 27 compared with the amount of 100 in column (2). As a particular aspect of risk it may be noted that the guaranteed return referred to in the previous paragraph is certain only if the stock is held to redemption. Until that time the price at which it may be sold in the market will depend on market conditions. At the time of writing the performance of these securities has been disappointing, i.e. market values are not as high as would have been the case had the securities remained on their initial yield basis. This, of course, adds to the attractions of the investment to a potential purchaser, since the guarantee of linkage of the eventual redemption proceeds to price increases over the whole term (in addition to price-indexed income) remains.

20.54 It will be seen from the table in paragraph 20.2 that index-linked gilts form only a small part of the investments of many pension schemes. The reader may find this puzzling, given the attractions of the stock as noted above. Although the feature may be partly to do with the comparatively recent introduction of such stocks, and the fact that the supply has grown only gradually, it is nevertheless the case that many trustees and investment advisers have so far shown little enthusiasm for these investments. This is partly due to the fact that there is a general expectation that long term yields on ordinary shares should be in the region of 3 to 5 per cent. p.a. in excess of prices, as noted in paragraph 11.27, whereas indexed gilts have tended to provide only 2 to 3 per cent. over price increases. Little attraction is therefore seen when such investments are compared with ordinary shares, despite the much greater degree of certainty of the indexed yield relative to prices. A further point is that although by their nature indexed gilts are best compared with ordinary shares, many trustees and advisers compare them with conventional fixed-interest gilts. For much of the period since the introduction of indexed gilts the yield on fixed-interest gilts has greatly exceeded the rate of price increases expected in the short term, so that indexed gilts have been overshadowed by the apparently more favourable yields on conventional gilts. The fact that future returns on the latter are of fixed money amounts and are therefore vulnerable to future inflation in the longer term has not been given great weight.

Fixed-interest gilt-edged securities

Term

20.55   The discussion earlier in this chapter led to the conclusion that the term of the liabilities of an open pension scheme is indefinite. The market in gilt-edged securities in the United Kingdom is vast and covers a wide range of unexpired terms. It might therefore be thought that a range of gilt-edged securities of varying outstanding terms would be reasonably suited to the needs of a pension scheme. The matter is not, however, straightfoward, because in interpreting the term of a dated investment we are concerned with the incidence of the whole expected cash flow from the investment, including both income and capital proceeds, and not simply with the maturity date. It will for instance be seen from column (2) of Table 27 that although the security used in the example has a term of 15 years, the maturity proceeds represent only 100 out of a total 9 per cent. accumulation of 364. It is evident from this that the weighted term of the proceeds from the security is much less than 15 years, and indeed it may readily be shown that at the 9 per cent. accumulation rate the income payments received in the first five years accumulate at the end of the term to 128 out of the total of 364. The first five years' income payments are thus much more important than the whole of the capital proceeds when allowance is made for the incidence of the payments and the effect of reinvestment. A characteristic of the typical fixed-interest gilt-edged security is therefore that a high level of income is produced and has to be reinvested; the terms on which this is possible are therefore more important than in the case of assets which produce less income.

Return

20.56 The conclusion of the previous paragraph has led into the discussion of the investment yield. A figure of yield which is normally available for all fixed-interest gilt-edged securities is the yield to redemption, and this is often compared by some commentators with the rate of price increase at a particular time, the implication being that the difference represents a yield in excess of price increases which will be obtained on the security until its maturity date. It will be seen from the preceding discussion, however, that this provides only a partial assessment, for two main reasons. The first of these is that the proceeds of the investment are fixed in amount, so that a change in the rate of price increases changes the yield relative to prices. Thus although the redemption yield is a reasonable measure of the apparent real yield at the time that the calculation is being made it has limited significance as far as the long term future is concerned. The second point is that the yield to redemption is not an accurate measure of the yield which will eventually be obtained on the security even if it is held to redemption, because this figure will depend on the rate at which reinvestment of the income is possible over the years.

Marketability and risk

20.57 As to general acceptability, marketability and spread of risk, fixed-interest gilt-edged securities are completely satisfactory in all respects. They can be bought and sold in large quantities with minimal dealing costs and there is, for practical purposes, no risk; it is assumed that the government will be able to meet its commitments.

Investment procedure and machinery

20.58 The trustees of a scheme will normally be responsible under the terms of the deed for the investment of the assets of the scheme. The means by which trustees receive advice on investments and by which they implement their chosen policies vary very widely from one scheme to another. The trustees of a large scheme may well employ a full time investment manager with his own staff. The trustees of a smaller scheme may use the services of an expert such as a stockbroker or merchant bank, while others may set up an investment panel which might typically include representatives of stockbrokers or a merchant bank, other independent experts often including the actuary, and those of the trustees who are themselves versed in investment matters. However the trustees are advised, the ultimate responsibility for major policy decisions rests with them. The degree to which the day-to-day implementation of policy is delegated varies widely, but it is usually thought best to give the maximum freedom to those operating the policy.

Investment performance measurement

20.59 Many trustee bodies wish to have regular assessment of whether their policies have been correct and have been carried out efficiently. Even where the trustees do not deal in specific investments but proceed by way of purchase of units they will wish to have an indication of the performance of the investments underlying the units. Equally, it is in the interests of the investment manager, stockbroker or merchant bank to know whether his performance is satisfactory. He may also wish to assess the extent to which he is impeded by any limitations imposed as a result of policy decision by the trustees on his freedom of action in day-to-day transactions. For all these reasons the regular measurement of investment performance has grown greatly in recent years and is now a feature of many schemes. The subject is a specialised one but the following discussion deals with some of the major points which arise when trustees wish to have the investment performance of their scheme monitored over periods of one year.

The meaning of performance

20.60 It is necessary when discussing investment performance to be clear as to what is being measured. One interpretation might be that the question is whether the investment performance in a particular year is such as is likely to have led to an improvement or a deterioration in the position which will be revealed when the next actuarial valuation is made. This is not, however, a practicable approach, because it would hinge on the relationship between investment yields and rates of increase of pensionable pay and pensions in course of payment assumed in the previous actuarial valuation and whether the performance of the investments in the year concerned has exceeded or fallen short of the performance implied by the rates of increase in pensionable pay and pensions in the year. A further complication arises from the fact that, as will be shown later, the assets may well be taken into the actuarial valuation at a calculated value rather than their book value or market value and this would be a difficult concept to bring into an annual performance measurement procedure.

20.61 Another important point is that an investigation of investment performance based on the interpretation referred to in the previous paragraph would not be solely a measure of the skill with which investment policy has been formed and implemented. It might be that investment conditions as a whole had been unfavourable during a particular year, when compared with the growth in the liabilities of pension schemes arising from the increases in pensionable pay and pensions in payment during that year. In this case the investment policy might have been well conceived and executed but the result for the year in question would still be unfavourable in terms of the outcome of the next actuarial valuation.

Comparative performance

20.62 The question is therefore normally approached from a different direction. The issue under this approach is whether the trustees' policy and its implementation has been more or less successful than that of other pension scheme trustees. In this case trustees are no longer concerned with the question of whether the investment experience of the particular year has or has not been favourable in its long term implications; the question is one of comparison with other schemes.

20.63 Since the schemes whose performance is being compared are virtually all free of tax the accumulation to be measured represents the joint effect of income and changes in capital values.

For this reason comparative measures of investment performance are based on the concept that the market value of the fund concerned at the beginning of the year and the net cash flowing into the fund from outside sources (i.e. represented by contributions less benefits but not including the income generated from the investments themselves) have accumulated to the observed market value of the fund at the end of the year and this accumulation may be expressed as a rate of interest.

20.64   The matter is not, however, as simple as might be gathered from the preceding paragraph because the two schemes may perform exactly in line with the market but may have different calculated returns because of the timing of their cash flows. This can be readily illustrated if we consider two schemes both of which hold only a single stock. We will assume that the income under this stock is reinvested continously so that the worth of the stock is fully represented by a market value from time to time, this market value being assumed to be 100 at 1st January of a particular year, 80 at 30th June and 120 at 31st December. Pension Scheme A has £100 invested at the beginning of the year and no cash flows. The assets will therefore amount to £120 at the end of the year so that the rate of interest earned on the fund has been 20 per cent. Scheme B also has £100 invested at the beginning of the year but receives a further £40 of contributions less benefits on 30th June which is immediately invested in the stock. The market value at the end of the year will be £120 in respect of the initial amount plus £60 in respect of the new investment at the half year, a total of £180. The rate of return achieved by Scheme B is the rate of interest which, applied to £100 for a full year and £40 for a half year, gives a total of £180 at the end of the year and this rate of return is 33.7 per cent. This example shows that a straightforward measurement of return achieved by the two schemes would be misleading as an indication of the skill of the investment managers concerned, since both funds have merely followed the market but the two rates of return are greatly different.

20.65   Because of this feature the return calculated by the method of the previous paragraph, which is known as a money weighted return, is faulty as a method of comparison. What is required is a measurement of return which removes the effect of differing cash flows. One widely used example of such a measure is the time weighted return which in effect represents a compounding of the rate of return achieved between the dates of differing cash flows. We illustrate this rate of return by comparing the two schemes in the previous example. The return on Scheme A is the same as previously calculated. The return on Scheme B is calculated as follows. The first period between cash flows is the first six months of the year. During this period the investment fell from 100 to 80 so that the time weighted return was -20 per cent. The second period between cash flows was the second half of the year, during which the assets of £120 immediately after the half yearly payment increased to £180. The percentage time weighted return for the whole of the year is therefore calculated as follows.

$$100 \ [\ \frac{80}{100} \ \cdot \ \frac{180}{120} - 1 \ ] \ = \ 20 \, \text{per cent.}$$

The time weighted return for Scheme B is 20 per cent., i.e. the same as for Scheme A. Since the managers of the two schemes performed in the same way by merely moving in line with the market a proper method of comparison would produce the same result, as is the case using the time weighted return.

20.66 The time weighted return is very widely used in measurements of investment performance. The accurate calculation of this measure does in principle require the market value of the fund concerned to be known at the date of each cash flow. This requirement is of course almost always unattainable in practice, so that various methods are used to approximate to the accurately calculated return. Some of the complexities of the subject flow from this point and we will not pursue them further. The reader should merely note the essential distinction between the money weighted return and the time weighted return and the reason why the latter is almost universally used for comparative purposes.

The investment aim reconsidered

20.67 It can be argued that if comparative performance may reasonably be assessed by consideration of market values at the end of a short period, the aim of pension scheme investment might best be expressed for practical purposes as the obtaining of the highest possible market value at some date in the near future, such as one year hence. This is in fact what an active policy usually amounts to. The investment manager or other adviser will not be looking too far into the future in deciding on his tactics, since in the nature of things he will be more sure of his judgement over the shorter term. He will be thinking of long term performance as the resultant of continuing short term performance. Trustees and investment advisers are sometimes accused of being too greatly influenced by the prospect of immediate gain; this accusation is usually made in specific cases where control of a company is being contested and shares are being bought and sold in the market on a large scale. Pension schemes and other institutional holders are often involved, as substantial holders of stock. The question of whether an attractive offer for the holding should be rejected on longer term grounds is one of judgement in each individual case.

CHAPTER 21

THE ACTUARIAL INVESTIGATION: PURPOSE, METHOD AND DATA

Attachment: Employer's undertaking

THE ACTUARIAL INVESTIGATION: PURPOSE, METHOD AND DATA

Frequency of the investigation

21.1 A condition of tax approval of an occupational pension scheme is that the trust deed and rules must provide for regular actuarial investigations of the scheme. Typically the reference is to an 'actuarial investigation' or an 'actuarial valuation'; we shall regard these as synonymous. The Inland Revenue require the period between investigations to be not more than five years, but there has been a trend over many years for investigations to be made at periods of three years rather than five years, on the grounds that five years is too long a period in rapidly changing economic conditions. The Solvency Certificate A required by the O.P.B. in connection with the supervision of the resources of occupational schemes used for contracting-out as mentioned in paragraph 4.43 has to be renewed at a date not later than six months after the end of the three year period starting on the date on which the previous certificate was signed, even though the certificate itself relates to a five year period from the date of signature. There is no formal requirement for the carrying out of three-yearly actuarial valuations, but in practice most actuaries would wish to make a full investigation of the scheme before renewing the Solvency Certificate and this has accelerated the trend towards a three- year period. Some schemes are valued even more frequently, but generally a three year period has become customary. We will assume in following the progress of Scheme X that the first actuarial investigation is to be made three years after the setting up of the scheme, i.e. as at 5th April 1982.

Nature of the actuarial investigation

The short term position: discontinuance solvency

21.2 Normally, one purpose of the actuarial investigation is to establish whether, if the scheme had been discontinued at the valuation date, the assets in hand would have been sufficient to continue to honour the benefits already in payment and the preserved rights of ex-members, and to secure the preserved benefits to which the employee members would have been entitled had they left the scheme on the valuation date. This aspect of solvency first came into prominence in the United Kingdom towards the end of 1974 when market values of investments were exceptionally low and economic conditions appeared to be in crisis; trustees became much concerned with the question of whether the funds of their schemes would be sufficient to purchase discontinuance benefits if the employer was forced to wind up. Although investment values subsequently recovered it has become common for the annual statements of trustees, or the annual report and accounts of pension schemes, to have annexed to them a statement of the actuary's opinion concerning the level of discontinuance solvency.

21.3 Such actuarial statements vary greatly in length, and in depth of treatment. An example of a statement of moderate length covering a year when a full valuation had not been made is as follows. It will be seen that the opportunity is taken to outline the financial structure and long term position of the scheme as well as the short term position. The words 'discontinuance' or 'winding up' do not appear in the second main paragraph and the final paragraph because in the particular scheme from which this example is adapted the trustees thought that such references would unduly alarm the membership. The reference to 'the rates of contribution specified in the rules' would not be appropriate if the rate of employer's contribution was not in fact so specified.

ACTUARY'S REPORT

Scheme A

The last full actuarial review of the Scheme was made as at (date).

The way in which the Scheme operates is that the contributions received in respect of employee members are invested over their working lifetime and are used in due course to pay for their benefits when they come to retire. This arrangement provides the members with security for the eventual payment of their pensions. The current pension payments from the Scheme arise from the contributions paid over many years in the past when the members now retired were in employment.

In the first part of our review we investigated whether the accumulated funds were sufficient to cover the pensions already in course of payment for the remainder of the lives of the present pensioners, together with the pension rights earned to date by employee members based upon their present level of pensionable pay and past periods of membership of the Scheme, and the pension rights retained in the Scheme by former members. Widows' pension rights were also brought into account. The result of this part of our review was to show that the assets were sufficient to provide these benefits.

The main purpose of our review was to investigate whether the assets and contribution rates of the Scheme were likely to be adequate in the long run, allowing for the fact that when employee members finally retire their pensions will be based on their pensionable pay levels and periods of membership at retirement and not at (date). The result of this part of the review was to show that, as far as could be foreseen on the basis of the information available and our view of likely future long term economic conditions, the Scheme would be able to meet its future commitments on the basis of the rates of contribution specified in the rules, and that there was a surplus of assets over long term liabilities in respect of membership already accrued at the valuation date.

We have also made an approximate assessment of the solvency of the Scheme two years later, i.e. as at (date). Taking into account the results of the full actuarial review and the accounts of the Scheme for the following two years we are of the opinion that the assets of the Scheme would have been adequate at (date) to purchase in the open market pensions for current beneficiaries equal to the amounts which they were then actually receiving, and deferred pensions for the current employee members equal to their accrued entitlements, together with the deferred pensions already granted to former members of the Scheme.

The long-term position

21.4 The main part of the actuarial investigation, however, is concerned with the long-term financial transactions of the continuing scheme. It involves projections of expected future income and outgo in respect of the employee members, persons in receipt of pension and other persons with an interest in the scheme at the date of the valuation. The investigation not only provides an assessment of the long-term prospects of the scheme at a particular date but it is also the principal means by which the actuary renews and deepens his knowledge of the scheme and its workings, and so equips himself to advise his client generally and to answer any questions which the client may put to him in connection with the investigation, or indeed at any time before the next investigation is made.

21.5 Within this general purpose the formal nature of the actuarial investigation depends on the specific provisions of the trust deed and rules of the scheme. In some schemes the rates of contribution of both the members and the employers are defined in the rules, as are the scales of benefit. This is logically an absurd position, since it is not possible to predict the cost of final pay benefits with accuracy. The actuarial investigation, which involves a valuation of future benefits and contributions, will always (except for a chance equality of assets and liabilities) show a long-term surplus or shortfall. The unfolding experience of the scheme will always differ from the expectations on which the previous actuarial investigation was based. The trust deed and rules will specify the action then to be taken by way, for instance, of an adjustment to benefits or contribution rates or the carrying forward of a surplus or deficiency within the bounds of prudence and the limits allowed by the Inland Revenue rules.

21.6 A reader coming to this subject from life office work may assume that the emergence of a shortfall (sometimes called a deficiency) at a particular valuation is something which should if possible be avoided. This is not, however, necessarily so. At the previous valuation date the actuary may well have given his best estimate of the future progress of the scheme; experience in the meantime will have differed in very many ways from his expectation, so that a surplus or a shortfall are broadly speaking equally likely at the present investigation. A somewhat different case that may be mentioned arises when a scheme is financed in such a way that valuations are expected to show surpluses from which the benefits may be increased. A particular example of this arises when pension increases are not promised in the rules, or are promised only to a modest extent, but the scheme is funded with the specific aim of providing resources from which non-guaranteed pension increases can be granted. In this case the hope is that the actuarial valuation will show surpluses which will be used to provide pension increases.

Regulation of the pace of funding

21.7 The provisions of the trust deed and rules of a scheme are not usually as described in the previous paragraphs. More commonly the employer's contribution is defined as the rate required to provide the benefits after taking account of the assets and the future contributions payable by the members. In such circumstances the purpose of the actuarial investigation is to arrive at the employer's contribution rate. The investigation is carried out by valuing

(i)   the liabilities, and
(ii)   the fund in hand and the contributions expected to be paid in the future by the members.

The residual liability (i) minus (ii) obviously represents the value of the employer's contributions required, and the valuation proceeds by the translation of this liability into a recommended employer's contribution rate.

Valuation method

21.8 Although the precise purpose of the actuarial investigation varies from one case to another, the method of valuation is essentially the same in all cases. It is a development of the method shown in the example of paragraph 9.9 et seq. We will suppose that when projections are made of the expected future income and expenditure of a scheme these reveal the following situation.

(i)   The only obligation of the scheme is to make a single payment of £8,674 in 20 years' time.
(ii)   The scheme has only one asset, namely a document which promises a payment of £50 at the end of each future year from the first year to the twentieth year inclusive and a payment of £1,000 at the end of that twentieth year.
(iii) Contributions to the scheme are payable at the rate of £100 at the end of each year from the first year to the twentieth year inclusive.

We will suppose that all payments into and out of the scheme are certain to take place. The example is, of course, far removed from reality and its purpose is solely to illustrate principles. In particular the pattern of proceeds in item (ii) is that of a typical fixed-interest gilt-edged security, but this is not meant to imply that such a security is a desirable type of investment. The pattern was chosen simply to ensure that the arithmetic in the example was straightforward. The pattern of income from the holding and sale of an ordinary share would have been more appropriate but would have added an irrelevant complication to the calculations.

21.9   We are now to make a valuation of the scheme to establish whether it is in balance or not in the long term. The statement of projected income and outgo does not show whether the scheme is in balance, because we have to allow for the fact that the income received during the 20 year period will be invested. We therefore need to make an assumption about the average rate at which the new money received by the scheme will be invested during this period. We will assume a rate of 9 per cent. p.a. The amount to which the resources of the scheme will accumulate at the end of the 20 year period is evidently as follows.

	£
Income from contributions:	
100 $s_{\overline{20\rvert}}$ (51.160)	5,116
Investment proceeds:	
income 50 $s_{\overline{20\rvert}}$	2,558
capital	1,000
	£8,674

The accumulated amount after 20 years is exactly equal to the amount of the benefit payment then to be made, so that the scheme is exactly in balance.

21.10   This is in principle the method of investigation followed in the valuation of pension schemes. In practice it would be impossible to set out the results in exactly this way because there is not a unique defined date at which all the benefits become payable and to which the accumulation should therefore be made. It is therefore more convenient to discount expected income and outgo to the date at which the valuation is being made. The statement of capital values summarising the position of the scheme is then as follows.

Present capital values at 9 per cent. interest

	£	£
Liabilities:		
8,674 v^{20} (0.17843)		1,548
Assets:		
Future contributions		
100 $a_{\overline{20}\rceil}$ (9.129)	913	
Fund 50 $a_{\overline{20}\rceil}$ + 1,000 v^{20}	635	
		1,548

This valuation therefore correctly reflects the expected position of an equality of assets and liabilities.

21.11 It is important to note that the validity of this process of summarising by discounting to present capital value depends on the rate of discount being equal to the expected rate of investment yield on new money during the period concerned. Had we drawn up the statement in the previous paragraph on the basis of a rate of interest different from the average rate expected to be earned on new investments made in the future the valuation would not have shown an equality of assets and liabilities, even though the figures of paragraph 21.9 show that this is the position.

An important point

21.12 Although this example is greatly simplified it illustrates an important point. This is that the market rate of interest at the time that the valuation is being made has not entered into the discussion, nor has the book value or market value of the investments of the scheme at that date. The calculation is based on the long term rate of interest which will be obtained on the investments which will have to be made, under the normal working of the scheme, for the period of 20 years involved, and the value of the asset for the purpose of the statement in paragraph 21.10 is the value obtained by discounting the expected future proceeds. In practice some practitioners think it appropriate to include the assets at their market value, or an amount representing a 'smoothed market value', and to frame the interest assumptions accordingly. What is involved in such an approach is an interpretation of the rate of interest different to that which we are employing. We comment again in paragraph 24.27 on methods involving market values. The main discussion in this book will be in the framework discussed in the preceding paragraphs.

The data for the actuarial investigation

21.13 We now consider the information needed for the regular actuarial investigation of a pension scheme. In principle the information needed for a typical scheme is as follows; in practice information about the wives, husbands and other dependants of employee members may not be available, or if submitted may not be reliable.

(i)   An up-to-date copy of the trust deed and rules and, for contracted-out schemes, the undertaking by the principal employer referred to in item 4 of Certificate A and mentioned in paragraph 21.16 below.

(ii) A copy of the accounts and balance sheet of the scheme for each of the years since the previous investigation.

(iii) Details of each investment of the scheme at the date of the investigation.

(iv) Details of each employee member, ex-member with preserved pension rights and current pensioner of the scheme at the investigation date and of any other persons who at that date are contingently entitled to benefit from the scheme, e.g. the wives and husbands of members and ex-members if they are contingently entitled to widows' or widowers' pensions.

(v)   Details of all persons who were in one of the categories in (iv) at the date of the previous investigation or at some time between the two investigation dates but are not included in (iv) at the present investigation date. This information is needed for the investigation of the experience.

We shall illustrate the discussion under each of these headings except heading (i) by reference to the first three-yearly investigation of Scheme X. In this case the 'previous investigation' means the calculations for the setting up of the scheme.

Trust Deed and Rules

21.14 An up-to-date copy of the deed and rules is needed because this document governs the working of the scheme in all important respects. Unless the actuary is newly appointed as adviser to the scheme he will normally have copies of the deed and rules in his own office and will have been consulted about any important changes. He may therefore need to ask at the investigation date only for confirmation that no changes have been made of which he has not been informed. If the actuary is newly appointed he will need to study the up-to-date deed and rules before he can define the information needed for the investigation.

21.15 The actuary will normally wish to base his work on the most up-to-date information available. If, for instance, he is aware that a significant change in the provisions of the trust deed and rules was made with effect from a date shortly after the investigation date he may well decide to make his investigation on the basis of the amended provisions, even though they were not in force at the investigation date. It may be noted in passing that this applies also to other aspects of the position; if for instance the actuary is aware of an exceptional pay increase or pension increase or exceptional investment performance that occurred shortly after the investigation date he may wish to bring this into account in his calculations. The extent to which account should be taken in an investigation of events after the investigation date is one of professional judgement.

The undertaking from the principal employer

21.16 Item 4 of Certificate A refers to an undertaking from the principal employer. This arises because the O.P.B. were concerned to ensure that an actuary preparing Certificate A would be in possession of all relevant facts. An actuary is not necessarily in close touch between valuation dates with every scheme with which he deals and he relies to some extent on the trustees and the employer to keep him informed. A standard form of the undertaking issued by the O.P.B. is shown at the end of this chapter, but it is the actuary's responsibility to add such further items to the form of undertaking as he considers necessary in each particular case.

The accounts and balance sheets

21.17 The actuary may or may not have received a copy of each year's accounts and balance sheet as it was issued. In any event he will require for the purpose of the valuation a copy of these documents for each year since the previous valuation date. The need for this information hardly requires further explanation; it establishes the financial history of the scheme since the previous valuation date and, in broad terms, the position as to the assets at the valuation date. Although a year-by-year examination of the financial progress of the scheme is illuminating, the actuary will also wish to consider the period since the last valuation as a whole and for this purpose he will normally prepare a consolidated revenue account. The accounts may also serve as the basis of valuable checks of the data submitted for the valuation. The actuary will, for instance, be able to investigate from the accounts the trend of the contribution income and pension outgo of a scheme and hence to arrive at estimated annual amounts of contribution income and pension outgo in force at the investigation date, to check against the amounts in force as calculated from the membership data. A further type of check is possible if, as is often the case, the annual accounts are accompanied by a trustees' report giving details of the numbers of members and beneficiaries in various categories. This information may serve as a valuable check on the individual membership data under headings (iv) and (v) of paragraph 21.13.

21.18   The accounts for each of the first three years of Scheme X, and the consolidated figures for the whole of the period, are shown in Table 46. Except for the amounts of investment income the figures have been constructed from the individual membership data, and the calculation of some of the amounts is illustrated in the discussion of membership data later in this chapter.

The investments

21.19   It is clearly necessary for the actuary to have full details of the investments of the scheme at the investigation date. The information for our investigation of Scheme X is shown in Table 47. The investments are shown in a highly simplified form, since no important points of principle would be illustrated by a more extended treatment.

Details of individuals with an interest in the scheme at the investigation date

21.20   Information about employee members, ex-members with preserved rights, persons in receipt of pension and other prospective beneficiaries is required for the investigation. The information is required for each individual because the liabilities depend on the way in which pensionable service, pensionable salary, age and other important factors combine for each individual. The way in which this information is submitted varies widely from one scheme to another; the data for small schemes may be submitted in the form of manuscript cards while the data for large schemes may be contained on magnetic tape. The practical details of data transmission are highly complex and are not dealt with in this book.

Summarised data

21.21 There is, however, one aspect of data transmission which is worthy of note. This concerns the question of whether it is advantageous for scheme officials with ample data processing facilities to carry out part of the data manipulation involved in the valuation process and to present the actuary with summarised information rather than with details of individuals. This course may seem to have attractions to both the client and the actuary but in fact it has disadvantages.

21.22 The most important disadvantage flows from the fact that, as noted in paragraph 21.4, the regular actuarial investigation is not simply a self-contained arithmetical exercise but is also the means by which the actuary equips himself with a deeper knowledge of the scheme and its workings, the better to answer further questions from his client. If the actuary is presented with information which has already been summarised, important aspects of the workings of the scheme may be concealed. Furthermore, the client may subsequently ask questions which the actuary may not be able to answer if he is not able to look into the working of the scheme below the surface of summarised data. For instance, a question about a possible change in the provisions of the scheme may necessitate calculations based on the valuation data organised in a different way, or perhaps the investigation of each individual separately. In these circumstances it may not be convenient for the client's data processing staff to turn again to pension scheme matters, particularly if new computer programs are involved. If the actuary has received information in individual form the data might have to be reprocessed in his office to deal with such queries but his staff will be experienced in such tasks and the matter will cause less difficulty.

21.23 A further significant disadvantage of the submission of data in summarised form is that the checks and tests of the data are made much more difficult since errors may be concealed in group total figures. The actuary will normally seek to reconcile the membership numbers with the numbers at the previous investigation date, allowing for new entrants, and this may be made difficult if information is summarised. Thus a part of the investigation which is essentially an aspect of the actuary's professional responsibilities is taken outside his control. In practice most data processing continues to be carried out in the actuary's office.

G.M.P. information

21.24 A particular aspect of the membership data for contracted-out schemes relates to guaranteed minimum pensions. The actuary will need to have details about the G.M.P.s of the various classes of persons concerned, not only because of the direct effect on the projected liabilities of the scheme but also because the valuation will probably be used as the basis of renewal of the Solvency Certificate and the position as to G.M.P.s is an essential part of the data for this.

21.25 G.M.P. statements are automatically issued by the Department of Health and Social Security ('D.H.S.S.') upon a contracted-out employee's attainment of State pension age, i.e. age 65 for men and 60 for women, and on the death of a married man. It will be recalled that the employee's or widow's G.M.P. comes into payment on the happening of one of these events and the amount does not subsequently change, so that information about G.M.P.s for pensioners over State pension age and for widows is normally already available at a valuation date. Accrued amounts of revalued G.M.P.s in respect of employee members, and in respect of persons who have left the scheme but for whom benefits with a G.M.P. element are being preserved, will not however normally be available in the records of the scheme. The D.H.S.S. therefore provide a service by means of which the G.M.P. information necessary for the valuation of a scheme may be obtained.

21.26 Although we are not primarily concerned in this book with practical details the following brief description of the position in this connection may be of interest. The basic data from which the D.H.S.S. calculate G.M.P. entitlements is the amount of the employee's national insurance contributions paid at the contracted-out rate on earnings between the lower and upper earnings limit, and this information appears on the tax deduction card for the employee concerned. The information in respect of a particular tax year is transmitted to the computer records of the D.H.S.S., but normally it cannot be assumed that contributions paid during a particular tax year will be fully into the computer records until December following the end of that tax year.

21.27 Depending on the date of an actuarial investigation the accrued G.M.P. entitlements at the end of a particular tax year of employee members of a scheme and early leavers who have preserved benefits in the scheme may be requested from the D.H.S.S., the particular tax year concerned depending on the investigation date. If it is desired to make calculations based on fully up-to-date amounts of accrued G.M.P. at the investigation date this is possible provided that the scheme authorities submit to the D.H.S.S. the necessary data in respect of national insurance contributions relating to the current tax year, and also to the preceding tax year if the latter information is not already on the D.H.S.S. computer.

21.28 The D.H.S.S. will provide G.M.P. information free of charge if the pension scheme authorities concerned do not make use of the D.H.S.S. service more frequently than is required for the purpose of providing the Solvency Certificate to the O.P.B. and provided that the full up-to-date G.M.P. information mentioned above is not required. If the up-to-date information is required, or a scheme makes use of the D.H.S.S. service more frequently than is strictly needed for certification purposes, a charge is made for the service. The D.H.S.S. service for the provision of G.M.P. information for actuarial valuation purposes does not appear to be greatly used; actuaries often make their own estimates of accrued G.M.P.s although this may become less common as G.M.P. amounts increase.

Changes in membership

21.29   The final item of paragraph 21.13 relates to persons who had an interest in the scheme at some time at or after the previous investigation date but do not give rise to liabilities at the present investigation date. Information about such persons is needed for the investigation of the experience, for the reconciliation of the information at the previous valuation date with that at the present valuation date and for the broad reconciliation of the membership data with the financial data shown in the accounts.

Source data for Scheme X

21.30   The basic information relating to the membership of Scheme X during the first three years, from which we shall construct the membership data, the experience and the revenue accounts, is summarised in Tables 28 to 32. Tables 28, 29 and 30 relate to the initial entrants and show according to membership group the salary during each of the years concerned, the numbers who ceased to be employee members according to each cause of cessation during each year and the numbers remaining at the end of the year. As to entrants after the Commencement Date, the numbers are shown in Table 31 according to membership group. The salaries at any time of the new entrants are taken for simplicity as identical to the salaries at that time of the initial members in the group concerned. The following points as to the application of this basic data should be noted.

(i)   It has been assumed that all new entrants in a particular year remain in the scheme until the end of that year and that any subsequent leavers from this group before the valuation date are all withdrawals with return of contributions. The assumption that there are no persons who entered the scheme and subsequently left during the scheme year of entry is an artificial one but simplifies the calculations.

(ii)   All events are assumed to occur half way through the scheme year concerned except that the persons in Group T, who were aged almost exactly 65 on the Commencement Date, are assumed to have retired immediately the scheme was set up.

(iii) In general money amounts are shown rounded to whole pounds but unrounded figures are taken to subsequent calculations. This sometimes results in apparent minor inaccuracies but these are of no importance.

21.31   Table 32 shows the salary progression of the individuals in each group in the three years before the Commencement Date (some of these figures being required in connection with the calculation of various benefits) and during the three year period ended on the investigation date. The table also shows the Relevant Earnings (i.e. the part of full earnings that lies between the lower and upper earnings limits as mentioned in paragraph 4.5) of each individual during each of the three years, these figures appearing in the columns headed 'RE'. It will be recalled from paragraph 15.4 that in order to quantify the G.M.P. elements in the initial calculations for Scheme X it was necessary to specify the Commencement Date of the scheme and this was fixed at 5th April 1979. The amounts of the lower and upper earnings limits of the State pension scheme for the three years concerned are shown in the following statement.

Fiscal year	Lower earnings limit	Upper earnings limit
	£	£
1979/80	1,014	7,020
1980/81	1,196	8,580
1981/82	1,404	10,400

21.32   The calculation of the accrued G.M.P.s at the investigation date of the employee members of Scheme X at that date involves the revaluation of Relevant Earnings in accordance with the appropriate Section 21 orders and the application of the appropriate G.M.P. fractions to the total amount of revalued Relevant Earnings. In order to carry out this process it is necessary to know the revaluation factors laid down for the fiscal year 1981/82 in respect of the two preceding fiscal years and these are as follows.

Fiscal year	G.M.P. revaluation factor for 1981/82
	%
1979/80	42.9
1980/81	19.4

In some cases of exits from employee membership of Scheme X we shall need to calculate a G.M.P. for a cessation of contracted-out employment taking place in fiscal year 1980/81. In this case the revaluation factor to be applied to Relevant Earnings in the year 1979/80 is 19.7 per cent. It will be appreciated that the compounded effect of this factor and the factor of 19.4 per cent. above leads to the factor of 42.9 per cent. above.

Individual data at the investigation date

21.33 The remainder of this chapter is concerned with the creation of the revenue accounts for the first three years of Scheme X and of the data referred to in items (iv) and (v) of paragraph 21.13 in respect of the first actuarial investigation of Scheme X. We consider first the information under (iv) and we begin with details of each employee member of the scheme at the investigation date. The first part of Table 33 shows the assembly of the salary and service data in respect of the members in Group D and it is thought that the various items will be self-explanatory. The second part of the table shows the calculation of the accrued G.M.P. rights in respect of this group of members. The progress of Relevant Earnings for the initial entrants is drawn from Table 32 and the figures for subsequent entrants are the same except that only one-half of a full year is allowed for in the year of entry. Relevant Earnings are then revalued in accordance with the factors of paragraph 21.32 and the resulting figures are multiplied by the appropriate fraction to calculate the accrued G.M.P. per head (and hence total accrued G.M.P.s for the group) at the date concerned. For an explanation of why the G.M.P. fraction for members in Group D is 1/140th the reader should refer to paragraph 15.5. The result of carrying out these processes for each of the membership groups involved, and amalgamating the figures for different groups of the same age, is shown in Table 34. The information in this table forms the basic valuation data in respect of the employee members.

Preserved and current pensions

21.34 We turn to the data in respect of preserved and current pensions. Spec. 9 of Scheme X provides for annual increases in the non-G.M.P. elements of pensions in payment and preserved pension rights at the rate of 3 per cent. p.a. and 5 per cent. p.a.

respectively. We will assume that the detailed provisions of the scheme provide for the trustees to give greater increases should they consider this possible after taking the advice of the actuary and that, in view of the comparatively small cost involved in the early years, the actuary agreed to the provision of an increase of 5 per cent. in the non-G.M.P. element of pensions in payment instead of 3 per cent. at the end of year 1, year 2 and year 3. The cost of the excess increase will emerge as an item of financial strain in the investigation. We will incorporate the third of these increases in the data at the investigation date.

Ex-members with preserved pension rights

21.35 It will be seen from Tables 28, 29 and 30 that 13 initial entrants withdrew with entitlement to preserved benefits during the three years. All these persons survived to the date of the investigation. The preserved pension of each is calculated at the date of leaving and we show in Table 35 the calculation of the amount of the preserved rights at the investigation date in respect of the member in Group H who left in the third year. The calculations are straightforward and are not thought to require explanation, except to note that, in accordance with Spec. 9(ii) of Scheme X, the G.M.P. and the excess over G.M.P. are treated as separate entitlements. Calculations of this type in respect of all the early leavers concerned lead to the figures shown in Table 36. The information contained in other tables will enable the reader to check these amounts if desired.

Current pensioners

21.36 The persons in receipt of pension from Scheme X at the investigation date fall into the following categories.

(i) Five members of Group T who were aged 65 at the Commencement Date. All retired immediately upon the inception of the scheme and all survived to the investigation date.

(ii) Persons who retired before age 65 with a pension calculated on the full scale in accordance with Spec. 3(i) of the scheme. It will be seen from Tables 28 to 30 that there were 7 such cases; all survived to the investigation date.

(iii) Five members who retired with an immediate pension which had been reduced for early payment in accordance with the scale of paragraph 19.65. All survived to the investigation date.

(iv) Nine persons who retired on grounds of ill-health. The member in Group K who retired in year 1 died in year 3; the others survived to the investigation date.

(v) Widows in receipt of pension. There are 9 such cases, 8 arising upon the deaths of members during employment and 1 from the death of the ill-health pensioner referred to in (iv) above. Tables 28 to 30 show that there were 9 cases of death in service, but the member in Group J who died in year 1 did not leave a widow. All widows who started to receive pension during the three years survived to the investigation date.

21.37   These various categories of pensioner not only represent liabilities at the investigation date but also gave rise to benefit outgo during the three year period. In the following paragraphs each category is discussed in turn and we deal both with the benefit outflow and the valuation data. It should be noted that under Spec. 7(ii) of Scheme X the initial amount of the pension to a widow upon the death of a pensioner is equal to one half of the annual pension which would have been payable to the retired employee had he not given up any pension in exchange for a lump sum. We will therefore need to include this notional gross amount of pension, as well as the amount of pension in fact payable, in the data for the investigation.

Retirements at age 65

21.38   We deal first with the benefits to the members of Group T who retired at age 65 immediately on the setting up of the scheme. There is of course no G.M.P. element in their entitlement, since they retired without having completed any membership as contracted-out employees. Each member commuted £1,000 of initial annual pension. The calculations of benefit outflow and the creation of valuation data are shown in Table 37. It has not been thought necessary to set out the sources of the various items of information where these have been obtained in a wholly straightforward way from earlier tables.

Early retirements in normal health

21.39 We turn to the benefits in respect of the persons who retired in normal health before attainment of age 65, i.e. those in groups (ii) and (iii) of paragraph 21.36. Table 38 shows the calculation of the initial amount of pension payable in the twelve cases concerned before commutation. It has been assumed that in the five cases of retirement involving an actuarial reduction factor the member would have timed his retirement so as to minimise the effect of the reduction scale. Since this is framed in terms of the number of complete half years by which the age at retirement is less than 65 this implies that the members will have retired immediately after the attainment of the half age. Thus the employee in Group P who retired early in year 1 is assumed to have done so immediately after attainment of age 55½ so that the reduction factor operates for only eighteen complete half years, giving the figure of 18 per cent. shown in column (7) of Table 38. It has not been thought necessary to set out in detail the calculation of the average annual salary shown in column (3) of the table. The only point which may need comment is that, as each member is assumed to retire half way through a scheme year, the salaries from Table 32 taken into account in the present calculations involve half years, as in the calculations of Table 35.

21.40 The amounts of pension shown in column (8) of Table 38 are carried to Table 39 which shows in column (4) the amount of pension given up at retirement for a capital sum. The scale used for the conversion of pension into capital sum is calculated on the basis outlined in paragraph 18.26. The table shows the amounts of lump sum so calculated in each year, the total figures being carried to the revenue accounts. The table also shows the amounts of pension payable in each year. In the year of retirement the amount payable is assumed to be one half of the initial annual amount after commutation. In subsequent years the amount is equal to the initial annual amount after commutation with increases at 5 per cent. p.a. The amount so increased is the full amount in payment; the G.M.P. does not affect the increases until the pensioner attains age 65.

21.41 The valuation data in respect of the members' pensions include the 5 per cent. increase granted on the valuation date. The valuation data in respect of contingent reversionary widows'

pensions are based upon one half of the amount of the members'
pensions which would have been included in the valuation data
had no pension been commuted for a lump sum. It is necessary to
include in the valuation data the G.M.P. rights of each pensioner
as at the investigation date because, as will be recalled from Spec.
9(i), no pension increases are provided from Scheme X on the
G.M.P. element of a pension in payment after the pensioner's
attainment of age 65. As an example, the calculation of the
accrued G.M.P. entitlement at the investigation date of a member
of Group P who retired in year no. 2 as listed in Table 39 is shown
below.

Relevant Earnings:
year no. 1	£5,586
half-year no. 2	£3,052

Revalued Relevant Earnings at date of retirement:
$$£3,052 + 1.197\,(£5,586) \quad = \qquad £9,738$$

G.M.P. at date of leaving:
$$£9,738 \div 80 \qquad\qquad = \qquad £121.73 \text{ p.a.}$$

Number of complete tax years between date of retirement and
investigation date = 1

G.M.P. at investigation date:
$$£121.73 \times 1.085 \qquad\qquad = \qquad £132 \text{ p.a.}$$

The calculations for the other members proceed in the same way
and are not shown in detail. The full data for the valuation in
respect of these 12 persons is shown in Table 40.

21.42 The reader may have noted the following difference in
treatment.

(i)   When dealing with preserved pension rights we increase the
       G.M.P. element and the non-G.M.P. element separately
       until the leaver attains age 65, at which time a pension equal
       to the total of the two amounts will come into payment.

(ii)   When dealing with an immediate pension on early retirement
       the whole pension is increased at the 'normal Scheme X rate'
       (i.e. 3 per cent., 5 per cent. or whatever rate is decided on by
       the trustees from time to time). The G.M.P. amount at
       retirement is dynamised at the statutory rate but this amount
       does not affect the total amount of pension payable unless

the revalued G.M.P. exceeds the normal scale pension after the pensioner attains State pensionable age. Except for such cases, the G.M.P. amount merely defines the part which is not to receive increases from Scheme X after the member's attainment of age 65.

This apparent anomaly does not raise an important point of principle; indeed it can be argued that it is not even a true anomaly. It is, however, an example of the complex points for discussion that arise in schemes used for contracting-out.

Ill-health retirements

21.43 We turn to the pensioners mentioned in item (iv) of paragraph 21.36. The calculations of the initial amount of pension are similar to those for the persons in group (ii) and are not shown in detail. The resulting figures are shown in column (3) of Table 41. The amount of pension payable after the pensioner's attainment of age 65 must not be less than the G.M.P. We noted in paragraph 15.29 that if an ill-health retirement took place at an early age the period during which the G.M.P. rights would grow under the effect of revaluation would be long. The effect might be that when the pensioner attained age 65 the revalued G.M.P. rights might exceed the amount to which the pension in payment had increased under the effect of the normal pension increases of Scheme X, in which case the pension would have to be increased accordingly. The discussion of that paragraph was in terms of the liabilities of the scheme, and we shall have to consider matters from this point of view in making the valuation of these pensions, but there is a more immediate point that needs to be considered.

21.44 This is to do with the extent to which these individuals should be permitted to give up pension for lump sum on retirement. There is obviously a risk that if commutation is permitted to the full extent allowed by Inland Revenue rules the residual pension may be so small that it will be much less than the G.M.P. when the pensioner attains age 65. The pension would have to be increased and there would be a financial strain on the funds. We will consider the case of the first person shown in Table 41. He retired from Group E in year 3 and was therefore aged 37.5 at retirement. If it was assumed when he retired that future pension increases would be at the rate of 3 per cent. per annum, his pension would be expected to have grown under the effect of increases up to and including that at age 65 to

$$£262 (1.03)^{28} = £599$$

21.45 The calculation of the amount of the G.M.P. at the date of ill-health retirement proceeds on the same lines as the calculation in paragraph 21.41. The results for the ten individuals shown in Table 41 are as follows.

Group	Amount of G.M.P. at retirement
	£ p.a.
E	72
J	60
J	115
K	19
M	21
M	21
N	186
N	186
Q	122
S	274

21.46 The amount of the G.M.P. for the pensioner from Group E will increase under the effect of revaluations to

$$£72 (1.085)^{26} = £600$$

at age 65. Thus, by chance, the full amount of the ill-health pension is almost exactly sufficient to meet the G.M.P. requirement when the time comes. It would probably not be thought prudent to take credit in advance for the possibility that pension increases in Scheme X would exceed 3 per cent. p.a., and the consequence is that the member concerned is not permitted to take any of his entitlement as a lump sum. In all the other cases in Table 41 a modest degree of commutation would be possible. It is assumed that the detailed rules of Scheme X provide for ill-health retirement pension to be given up in exchange for lump sum on the same terms as apply for a retirement in normal health. The amounts of pension given up and lump sum provided are shown in Table 41. The various pension amounts as at the investigation date as required for the calculation of the liabilities, i.e. including the appropriate number of 8½ per cent. increases for the period up to the investigation date on the G.M.P. and 5 per cent. increases (including that on the valuation date) on the total pension, are shown in Table 42. There are only nine cases because of the death in year no. 3 referred to in item (iv) of paragraph 21.36.

Benefits on death in service

21.47 The widow's pension arising upon the death of an employee member is defined in Spec. 6(ii) of Scheme X as one half of the pension to which the member would have been entitled had he retired on grounds of ill- health at the date of his death. The calculation of the widow's pension on death in service is therefore very similar to the calculation of the member's pension on ill-health retirement, and the resulting figures are shown in Table 43. The widow's G.M.P. is equal to one half of the member's G.M.P. at the end of the tax year before the tax year of death. No account is therefore taken of any Relevant Earnings of the employee during the tax year of death. This point was not mentioned in paragraph 15.67, since it is essentially one of mechanics rather than principle; it is mentioned here only because any reader wishing to check the G.M.P. figures in column (4) of Table 43 will need to allow for the feature. It is this point that gives rise to the fact that widows of employees who died in year 1 have no G.M.P.; the deceased members were not contracted-out in the preceding tax year, because Scheme X was set up only at the end of that year. The calculations are not shown in detail; the figures for the accounts and for the valuation data are shown in Table 43 and, as in other cases, the information in the various tables is sufficient for the reader to check any amounts if this is desired. It is assumed that all widows are in receipt of State benefits (although this would not necessarily be so in practice) so that pension increases on the G.M.P. are being provided from the State scheme. The widow's G.M.P. therefore remains constant in payment, 5 per cent. increases being provided only on the excess over G.M.P.

21.48 The following statement shows the data as at the investigation date in respect of the widows in Table 43, allowing for the 5 per cent. increase provided at that date on the excess of pension over G.M.P.

	Widow's pension at investigation date:-	
Member's group	total	G.M.P.
(1)	(2)	(3)
	£ p.a.	£ p.a.
G	171	25
J	333	17
K	385	42
K	385	42
O	1,088	
Q	775	
R	819	83
S	1,513	38

Benefits on death after retirement

21.49   The calculation of the widow's pension which arose upon the death in year 3 of the ill-health pensioner in Group K is shown in the following statement, which also shows the outflow on death benefits and the valuation data.

Rate of ill-health pension at date of death had member not given up pension for lump sum

$$£507 \ (1.05)^2 = £559 \text{ p.a.}$$

Initial rate of widow's pension

$$0.5 \times £559 = £279 \text{ p.a.}$$

Amount of widow's pension paid in year 3

$$0.5 \times £279 = £139$$

Amount of widow's pension in force at investigation date including 5 per cent. increase on that date

$$1.05 \times £279 = £293 \text{ p.a.}$$

Widow's G.M.P., equal to one half of husband's G.M.P. up to end of tax year before tax year of death

$$0.5 \times £20 = £10 \text{ p.a.}$$

Amount of lump sum benefit on death after retirement, paid in year 3

Outstanding balance of five year guarantee period = 3 years

Rate of pension at death   =   £338

Lump sum = 3 × £338 = £1,014

Leavers before the investigation date

21.50 Paragraphs 21.33 to 21.49 were concerned with persons giving rise to liability at the valuation date. We now turn to persons in group (v) of paragraph 21.13, i.e. persons who had an interest in Scheme X at some earlier date but are not included in the valuation data. They fall into the following categories.

(i) Early leavers who left with a refund of their own contributions to the scheme, subject to payment of a C.E.P.

(ii) Early leavers in respect of whom a transfer value was paid to the pension scheme of their new employer.

(iii) Members who died during employment.

As noted above, these various groups of persons do not give rise to liabilities at the valuation date but they gave rise to items in the revenue accounts. The benefit expenditure arising from category (iii) has already been dealt with.

Early leavers with refunds of contributions

21.51 Early leavers who did not satisfy the qualifying requirements for the preservation of benefits, and were therefore entitled only to a refund of contributions subject to appropriate payments to the State scheme, were comparatively numerous. Tables 28 to 31 show that there were 70 such cases amongst the initial entrants and 140 amongst subsequent entrants. Table 44 shows the calculation of the payments in respect of the early leavers in this category during year 1. As stated in item (i) of paragraph 21.30, we have assumed that no persons entering Scheme X left in the scheme year of entry, and the persons covered by Table 44 are therefore all initial entrants. Column (5) represents a half year's contribution at the member's contribution rate of 5 per cent. and column (6) represents the total C.E.P. in respect of the assumed half year of membership in each case. The C.E.P. is shown as 3½ per cent. of Relevant Earnings for a half year because as noted in paragraph 4.28 the contracting-out contribution abatement amounted in total to 7 per cent. of Relevant Earnings in the years concerned. The totals of columns (5) and (6) allow for the number of cases involved. In year 2 and year 3 matters are slightly more complicated because interest on contributions paid has to be allowed for but apart from this the calculations are similar to those of Table 44. The C.E.P. is paid by the employer. It was noted in paragraph 4.30 that the 1975 Act gives the employer power to recover, from a refund of contributions due to a member, the member's share of a C.E.P. We will assume that the employer exercises this power and also adjusts his contributions to the scheme so that his part of the C.E.P. is effectively met from the scheme. The calculation of the amounts to be shown in the revenue account for year 1 arising from Table 44 is as follows.

Gross refund to members		£2,487
Members' shares of C.E.P.s		
£2,436 × 2½/7	=	£ 870
Net refund to member including tax		£1,617
Total C.E.P. payments		£2,436

These sums appear in the revenue account for year 1.

Early leavers with transfer payments

21.52   The calculations in respect of the 11 early leavers for whom transfer values were paid during the first three years are summarised in Table 45. The calculations of the preserved pension at the date of leaving, and the G.M.P. element of that preserved pension, are similar in principle to those for other groups and are not shown in detail; the resulting figures are shown in columns (3) and (4) of the table. The transfer value factors used to convert these preserved rights into an equivalent cash payment are calculated on the same basis as those of paragraph 19.28 and their application leads to the various amounts shown in columns (7), (8) and (9) of the table. It is assumed in all cases that the receiving scheme is a contracted-out scheme taking on the G.M.P. liability, so that the transfer value payable is the combined value of the G.M.P. and non-G.M.P. constituents of the preserved benefits.

Contribution income

21.53   The preceding discussion deals with the benefit outgo of Scheme X under the various headings during the three years and with the valuation data. It remains to establish the amounts of contribution income of the scheme, and the investment income, during the three years. As to contribution income, it will be recalled that new entrants in a particular group are assumed to have the same salary as the surviving initial entrants. The calculation of contribution income therefore involves merely the mean number of members in each group, and the salary figure for the group, in each of the three years concerned. The calculations are entirely straightforward and are not illustrated.

Investments

21.54 We will assume that the investment policy of the trustees of Scheme X during the first three years was that about one-tenth of the money becoming available should be invested in long term fixed-interest gilt-edged securities, that there should be modest investment in property units, index-linked gilt-edged securities and the ordinary shares of various overseas companies and that the balance of the money becoming available should be invested in United Kingdom ordinary shares. The amounts of investment income as shown in Table 46 have been arrived at on this basis, and the assets at the valuation date are summarised in Table 47.

APPENDIX 9

UNDERTAKING FROM THE PRINCIPAL EMPLOYER OF

....

.... **(NAME OF SCHEME)**
TO THE ACTUARY AT THE TIME OF THE ISSUE OR RENEWAL OF CERTIFICATE A

I undertake on behalf of the employer to notify you as soon as practicable if there is a proposal to wind up the scheme or if any of the events at (a) to (e) below occur in the period up to ....(date specified by the actuary):—

   (a)   Any changes in the rules of the scheme affecting contribution or benefit levels or the degree of
          priority accorded to benefits in the event of the winding up of the scheme.

   (b)   Any change in the definition of pensionable pay and any unexpected change in the general
          remuneration levels of scheme members.

   (c)   Any unexpected increase or decrease in the number of members or pensioners resulting, for example,
          from the acquisition or sale of participating companies or through early retirement.

   (d)   Any discretionary augmentation of benefits on early, normal or late retirement or on the death
          of a member.

   (e)   Any discretionary increases to pensions in payment and/or preserved pensions.

I give this undertaking subject to the modifications agreed with you as shown in your letter dated ....*

Signed ....
(for and on behalf of employer)

Name ....

Position with employer ....

Date ....

Delete if not applicable

CHAPTER 22

THE ACTUARIAL INVESTIGATION: EXPERIENCE AND BASIS

THE ACTUARIAL INVESTIGATION: EXPERIENCE AND BASIS

The previous basis

22.1 When checks on the data have been completed and any errors corrected the actuary will proceed to the next stage of his work, namely the settling of the actuarial basis of his calculations. Assuming that he is concerned with the regular actuarial investigation of an existing scheme, the natural starting point is the basis used for the previous investigation. That basis was thought suitable at the time; the experience of the scheme, and of the economy as a whole, will have unfolded over the intervening years, and the question is whether any of the assumptions need to be changed in the light of this further experience. Even if the scheme is so large that the experience statistics would support the construction of new rates of decrement and mortality, these statistics relate to only a short period and it remains likely that the actuary will approach the matter by considering whether the previous assumptions need to be changed rather than by constructing new rates from the experience irrespective of what has gone before.

The theoretical procedure

22.2 In principle therefore the procedure is to analyse the various respects in which the experience has differed from that expected on the basis of the previous assumptions. The actuary is principally concerned with the financial importance of these deviations, and the full procedure for this stage is theoretically as follows.

(i)   A valuation of the present data is carried out on the actuarial basis used on the previous occasion, and the result of this valuation compared with the result shown on the previous occasion.

(ii) The various features of the experience during the intervaluation period, such as numbers of decrements and rates of pay increase, are compared with those expected on the basis used in the previous valuation.

(iii) The financial effect of each of the items in (ii) is calculated, and the actuary satisfies himself that the totality of these effects accounts for the shift from the previous to the present valuation result.

(iv) The actuary decides on any changes needed in the previous actuarial basis for the purpose of the present valuation in the light of the financial items in (iii) and his views on the broader economic factors.

In practice the experienced actuary would not normally follow this full procedure but would probably decide on any changes in the basis in the light of (ii) alone, as we will do for Scheme X. He would be able to estimate the financial importance of each of these items from his general experience. He will certainly need at a later stage to carry out a process similar to (iii) as a check on the valuation result, as described in chapter 25.

The assumptions in detail

22.3 It will be recalled from Chapters 11 and 12 that the main elements that may be involved in the actuarial valuation of a pension scheme fall under two headings as follows.

Economic assumptions

(i) The average future dividend yield on ordinary shares, i.e. the initial yearly rate of dividend flow resulting from unit investment in ordinary shares.

(ii) The average annual rate of growth in the yearly amount of the dividend stream from a holding of ordinary shares.

(iii) The average long term yield which will be obtained on new investments made in the future.

(iv) The average annual rate at which general levels of pay will increase in the future

(v) The average annual rate at which prices will increase in the future.

(vi) The average annual rate at which the amount of the State scheme lower earnings limit will increase in the future.

Statistical assumptions

(i)   The various elements in the service table or tables which will be used for the calculations for active members.

(ii) The mortality rates of members after retirement.

(iii) The mortality rates of dependants of members.

(iv) Other statistical elements.

(v)   The salary scale before allowing for escalation.

In addition it will be necessary to take into the calculations an assumed rate of increase of existing and future pensions in payment, and of the preserved rights of early leavers during the period of preservation (except to the extent that these rates are specified in the rules, or under legislation, and it is not desired to fund for a higher rate).

Weight to be given to experience of scheme

22.4   It will be clear that in settling these assumptions the weight to be given to the experience of the scheme will depend on which assumption is under consideration. In general the economic assumptions reflect a particular view about future economic conditions, and will therefore not be greatly influenced by the experience of the scheme during the comparatively short period since its commencement or the previous investigation date. On the other hand it is obvious that the ill-health retirement experience of the scheme concerned during the period under analysis will be highly relevant in the consideration of ill-health retirement rates. This experience will reflect conditions in the employment concerned, the general level of health of the employees, the conditions which have to be met under the trust deed and rules of the scheme before an ill-health pension can be granted, the way in which the trustees interpret those conditions, the attractiveness of the ill-health benefit scales and other features peculiar to the scheme. In the settling of the statistical assumptions the actuary, while drawing on his general experience, will be influenced to a greater or lesser degree by the emerging experience of the scheme provided that the volume of statistics is sufficient. We now discuss various elements of the basis in more detail, using the data of Scheme X for purposes of illustration. The economic assumptions were discussed in Chapter 11 and we shall deal here only with any further subsidiary points on these elements of the basis. The with-escalation salary scale involves both economic and statistical assumptions and we will consider the salary experience of Scheme X under both headings.

Economic assumptions

The valuation rate of interest

22.5   The valuation rate of interest is the assumed long term yield which will be obtained on new investments made in the future. As noted above, the recent investment performance of a scheme at a particular investigation date is of little relevance to the consideration of this future yield. Furthermore, although it may be useful to express the flow of investment income into a scheme as a rate of interest based on mean book or market values for use in the analysis of surplus, the figure has little wider significance, since it represents only a part of the totality of the investment return (capital growth being the other major constituent) over only a brief period.

22.6   If the actuary has at his disposal the results of investment performance measurements for the scheme concerned during the period between valuations this will indicate to him the relative success or otherwise of the formulation and implementation of investment policy. Even if this shows that the performance differed significantly from the average performance of pension schemes during the period it does not necessarily follow that the actuary would think it appropriate to take this into account in settling his assumption as to long term investment yields. He might think it imprudent to take credit for investment performance better than that of the generality of pension scheme investors over a long future period, simply because of success in the recent past; equally he might think it wrong to increase assessed costs by assuming that any lack of success in recent investment performance would continue in the long-term future.

The salary experience

22.7   The salary experience represents the combined effect of the 'salary scale' element in each individual's pay progression, and escalation of general levels of pay. The volume of data relating to earnings is usually sufficient even in a pension scheme of only modest size to support a detailed investigation of the experience.

In Scheme X, for instance, although the expected and actual numbers of deaths in service and ill-health retirements during the first three years as shown in Table 50 are too small to justify detailed analysis, information about earnings is available for several hundred members. An investigation of pay progression is therefore commonly made, but it is usually confined to persons who were active members throughout the intervaluation period. New entrants are excluded not only because statistics relating to pay during early or probationary periods of employment might distort the picture but also because the amount of earnings in the year of entry represents in most cases only a part of a year's pay and would therefore need to be adjusted before being compared with an annual figure at a later date. These adjustments might involve much work while adding only marginal information of doubtful validity to the data. Similar adjustments would be involved in respect of the year of exit for leavers during the period. Even if only those persons who were members throughout the period are included in the experience a similar adjustment may be needed for those who joined during the year immediately before the start of the period.

22.8 In previous paragraphs we have referred in general terms to the 'salary experience'. It might be thought that the 'salary' to be investigated is that on which pension scheme contributions and benefits are based, but as mentioned in paragraph 9.25 et seq. this is not necessarily so. It will be recalled from Chapter 5 that a common type of integrated scheme is that in which contributions and benefits are based on pensionable pay equal to pay less a 'discard', often equal to a multiple of the lower earnings limit. Using an obvious notation for pay, pensionable pay and this limit in the year of age x to $x + 1$, the arrangement in a scheme where this multiple is unity may be expressed as

$$PP_x = P_x - L$$

The first element in the right hand side of this expression is expected to increase on account of both individual progress and earnings escalation but the second element will increase only in line with the single person's State flat-rate pension. Expected pensionable salary in t years' time is therefore given by

$$PP_{x+t} = P_x \; \frac{s_{x+t}}{s_x} - L(1+j)^t$$

where j is the assumed rate of escalation of the lower earnings limit (which rate, as noted in paragraph 11.28, is not necessarily equal to the assumed rate of escalation of earnings) and the salary scale incorporates a promotional scale with escalation superimposed as in Table 3.

22.9 In the investigation of the salary experience it would not in this case be correct to compare

$$PP_x$$

with

$$PP_{x+t}$$

because the expected relationship between these two amounts of pensionable pay is the more complex one shown in the previous paragraph. In such a case the appropriate procedure is clearly to compare

$$P_x$$

with

$$P_{x+t}$$

and to make a separate comparison of the actual and expected amounts of the lower earnings limits. It may be that the pay of individuals which is included in the data is in fact pay before deduction of the lower earnings limit, in which case these pay amounts are taken into the experience. It is often the case, however, that the scheme records show amounts of pensionable pay. In this case it is necessary to add back the appropriate multiple of the lower earnings limit (or whatever 'discard' amount has been used) to arrive at the pay whose progress is to be analysed. Scheme X is not an integrated scheme so that our illustration using the data of this scheme will not involve this complication.

22.10 We will confine our investigation of the salary experience amongst members of Scheme X to those persons who were employees throughout the period; there were 215 such members and the earnings figures for them are summarised in Table 48. Column (2) of the Table shows the total salaries of the persons concerned in the year ended on the Commencement Date, all these representing a full year's salary. Column (3) shows the expected increase in earnings during the subsequent three years, the ratios being derived from the figures in column (4) of Table 3.

It will be appreciated that these ratios represent the combined effect of the increases which would be expected to arise on account of promotions and other normal progress of individuals if overall pay levels remain stable (as shown in column (2) of Table 3) and, superimposed upon these increases, growth at the rate of 8 per cent. per annum. The expected amounts of salary in the year preceding the investigation date are shown in column (4) of Table 48. Column (5) shows the actual amounts of salary in that year and column (6) shows the comparison of actual with expected amounts.

22.11 The figures in column (6) indicate that the actual salaries are much as expected in the central range of ages. They are somewhat less than expected at the younger ages and there is a slight excess at the older ages. This suggests that the basis represented the experience reasonably accurately during the period except at the youngest ages, but it will be appreciated that the figures do not show whether this is true in respect of promotional increases and increases on account of salary escalation separately. It is not necessary to look into this question for the purpose of the analysis of surplus, since we are there concerned with the overall salary experience. It is nevertheless desirable as a general principle that the actuary should have as complete an understanding as possible of the working of the scheme, and he may therefore wish to look more deeply into the two separate constituents of the salary experience. How may he do this?

22.12 An item of information available from Table 48 which has not yet been used is the profile of average salaries from age to age in the year preceding the Commencement Date and in the year preceding the investigation date. We consider the use of this data in the discussion of the promotional salary scale in paragraph 22.39 et seq; at this stage the reader should merely note that although an average salary profile may throw some light on the pattern of promotional increases it cannot be relied upon to do so.

22.13 As to the investigation of the rate of increase in general levels of earnings, the actuary has the following lines of approach.

(i) He will have the results of an investigation of the total experience as in Table 48. If he is able to satisfy himself by an investigation on the lines indicated in the previous paragraph, or by information from the employer about promotional scales, that the basic salary scale is a reasonable measure of 'promotional' increases, then the balance of the experience is a measure of the rate of escalation. If, for instance, actual salaries in Table 48 had been 109 per cent. of expected salaries then (assuming the suitability of the basic scale) the actuary might reasonably conclude that escalation of pay levels during the period had been at a rate of approximately 11 per cent. p.a., equal to the rate of 8 per cent. p.a. included in the basis and the further 3 per cent. p.a. indicated by the experience.

(ii)   A variation on (i) arises if the actuary considers that the promotional scale in his basis is too shallow, or too steep, in the light of his interpretation of the profiles mentioned in the previous paragraph and any other information on salary scales. If, for instance, the experience is as in (i) but the actuary considers that promotional increases amount on the average to 1 per cent. more at each age than allowed for in his basic scale, he might then conclude that escalation had been at the rate of about 10 per cent. p.a., i.e. the rate of 11 per cent. mentioned in the previous paragraph less the rate of 1 per cent. mentioned above.

(iii) The actuary will be aware of the progress of the various indices of national average earnings and these may give him some guidance on what to expect as far as pay escalation is concerned in his investigation of the experience. The relevance of these indices to his purpose will depend partly on whether pensionable earnings in the scheme are similar in kind to those taken into national statistics. It might not, for instance, be appropriate for him to compare his estimated figure of earnings escalation in a scheme where pensionable earnings did not include overtime and bonus payments with a national earnings index which did include such payments.

22.14   As indicated earlier, the assumption as to the future escalation of general levels of earnings to be included in the actuarial basis of the investigation hinges on the view taken about general economic conditions in the future. The recent pay escalation experience of a scheme is not of crucial importance, since it merely reflected passing economic conditions. There is, however, one respect in which the actuary may find the experience of particular interest. This relates to his assessment of whether increases in general levels of earnings in the company concerned, or perhaps in the whole industry concerned, have been markedly different from the average for the economy as a whole. In some areas of economic activity in the United Kingdom in recent years rates of pay increase have tended to be consistently above the national average, and in other areas consistently below. The actuary may conclude from the evidence of his investigation and from his general knowledge and views that the experience that he is investigating is indicative of one or other of these categories. In this case he will have to decide whether his assumption as to future pay escalation should involve a conscious adjustment of the figure which represents his view for the average rate across the whole economy.

Pension increases

22.15 The assumption as to the rate at which present and future pensions will be increased in payment is not normally a straighforward 'economic' assumption. It depends upon both the provisions of the trust deed and rules of the scheme and the actuary's knowledge of what has happened in practice. Some possible cases and the ways in which they might be provided for in the valuation assumptions are now discussed.

Full indexing

22.16 The rules of many public sector pension schemes in the United Kingdom provide for pensions in payment to be increased in line with increases in the Retail Price Index. Since this is a formal provision of the rules it is allowed for fully in the valuation and the economic assumption about price increases covers the point.

No increase

22.17 At the other extreme, it is possible to envisage a scheme in which no increases in pensions in payment are provided for under the scheme and the trustees have no power to increase such pensions on a discretionary basis. Such a situation is comparatively rare in practice but if it is encountered the actuary has to bear in mind a requirement of the Inland Revenue rules that no advance provision for pension increases may be made if these could not occur under the trust deed and rules of the scheme. Thus the valuation would have to be made without explicit provision for pension increases, even if the actuary thought it likely that the rules would be changed to provide for or permit such increases.

Discretionary increases funded by the employer

22.18   A case which is encountered in private sector schemes is where the rules and funding levels of a scheme provide for no pension increases or only a modest rate of pension increase but there is a power of discretionary augmentation and it has been the employer's policy to make specific payments into the scheme in years when his resources permit, to fund the capital cost of special increases on pensions in course of payment. The actuary may wish to have discussions with the trustees and the employer to establish whether it is intended to continue this policy. If this is the position then it may well be appropriate to take into the valuation merely the rate of increase, if any, provided for in the trust deed and rules of the scheme. The assumption is that the employer will continue to make special payments in respect of the capital cost of extra pension increases as this cost is incurred.

Discretionary increases from scheme surplus

22.19   As mentioned earlier, a situation which is common in private sector schemes in the United Kingdom is that a modest rate of pension increase such as 3 per cent. per annum is guaranteed under the rules but the trustees have a power of discretionary augmentation, and they seek to provide a better rate of increase subject to resources being available from the assets of the scheme concerned. In some cases this policy is carried out only at each triennial valuation, a part or the whole of any surplus then revealed being used to provide special pension increases intended to restore to some extent the loss of purchasing power experienced by pensioners since the previous increases were given. Alternatively trustees may ask for an approximate actuarial assessment of the position of the scheme year by year and give pension increases where possible in the light of these annual assessments. In either case the course which the actuary will follow in his valuation will be a matter of his judgement and usually for discussion with the trustees and the employer. If for instance a guaranteed rate of only 3 per cent. per annum is incorporated in the rules with a power of discretionary augmentation, the valuation may be made using this rate, the implication being that the emergence of surplus from which a higher rate could be provided may or may not occur in practice. On the other hand there may be an understanding by the trustees and the employer that the financing and valuation of the scheme should be based on the assumption of 5 per cent. pension increases even though only 3 per cent. is guaranteed. This stronger basis obviously leads to a greater likelihood that it will in practise be possible to provide pension increases in excess of the guaranteed rate of 3 per cent. from the assets of the scheme.

Pension increases: conclusion

22.20 It will be clear from the above discussion that it is not possible to generalise about the assumption in respect of pension increases in a valuation. Each has to be considered in the light of the particular circumstances. The matter is further complicated by the fact that although in private sector schemes in the United Kingdom many trustees and employers would aim to grant a reasonable level of increases in pensions in course of payment there is no statutory requirement to do so, whereas the 1985 Act revaluation provisions require increases to be provided on a part of the preserved pension rights of early leavers during the period of preservation. It is currently a matter of speculation whether trustees will feel a moral obligation to provide, on pensions in payment, at least the rate of increase required by law on the preserved rights of early leavers.

Statistical assumptions

22.21 We turn to those elements of the actuarial basis which are more specific to the scheme concerned. The distinction between these and the economic assumptions is not absolute; for instance, the rates of withdrawal experienced amongst members of a pension scheme will reflect the circumstances of the particular employer and industry but they will also be affected by general economic conditions during the intervaluation period, because the extent to which employees change jobs is greatly influenced by these general conditions. Similarly the extent to which a provision for members to retire early with a full scale pension (such as that of Spec. 3(i) of Scheme X) is exercised from time to time may be bound up with economic conditions and the employer's circumstances, in particular his policy as to redundancy. This policy may be implemented through the retirement of older employees if this is helped by the provisions of the pension scheme. The following discussion is mainly in terms of the statistical experience but the actuary will bear the wider points above in mind when settling the basis.

The investigation of the experience

22.22 The techniques that the actuary will use to analyse the movements of membership of a scheme will depend partly on the size of that membership. In a large scheme three or five years' experience will yield a considerable volume of statistics; the process of investigating the experience may well be based on the use of a computer with the data being transmitted by way of magnetic tape or some other medium directly accessible to the computer. In this case the assembly of the population exposed to risk may well involve the conceptually simple method of treating each member separately and aggregating the resulting years of exposure. At the other extreme the investigation of the experience of a small scheme will not merit so accurate an approach, since the number of decrements experienced under the various headings will be very small. Even in this case however a comparison of actual to expected movements for each type of decrement will be needed for the analysis of surplus.

22.23 The experience should be investigated in membership groups which are expected to be reasonably homogeneous with respect to the rates being investigated. The first sub-division is almost always according to sex, since the two sexes typically have different experience in such matters as decrement rates in service, promotional salary scales and mortality after retirement. It may also be necessary to separate manual from clerical grades in a scheme which covers both and, possibly, outside staff from inside staff and technical from non-technical staff.

22.24 As in other fields of his work, the actuary will be faced with the problem of how far to carry the process of sub-division. The extreme would be to examine separately the experience of each group which exhibited or was likely to exhibit distinctive characteristics as regards one or more of the decrement rates or the salary scale. Movements between sub-groups, if numerous, might have to be allowed for as new entrants and exits of each sub-group. In practice the number of sub-divisions will depend upon the volume of data available, since if the data in each sub-group are scanty the results will be unreliable. It is not sound to increase the volume of data by extending the investigation over a longer period, since this may conceal secular change.

22.25 If the rates derived from the experience of a heterogeneous group are used in the valuation of the liabilities for members of that group at a valuation date the tacit assumption is that the proportions of the different sub-groups of the membership have remained unchanged during the period under investigation and will continue to remain unchanged. If these assumptions turn out to be incorrect, the rates experienced by the group in future will differ from those in the past even if there is no variation in the rates experienced by the underlying homogeneous sub-groups.

22.26 In principle the aim is to produce a multiple decrement service table for each homogeneous sub-division of the active membership. This service table is based on crude probability ratios (not rates in the strict sense) for each type of exit at each age. For each type of exit these ratios are equal to the number of exits during the year of age x to $x + 1$ divided by the number of members entering that year of age.

The calculation of the exposed to risk

22.27 The probabilities with which we are concerned therefore represent the number of exits during a particular year of age divided by the number of members entering that year of age. An employee who passes through the whole of the year of age concerned as a member of the scheme obviously contributes one year of exposure at the age concerned; an employee who is a new entrant to the scheme during that year contributes on the average one-half of a year of exposure to the total. The construction of the total years of exposure to risk at each age has traditionally involved the use of 'continuous' formulae by means of which the exposure at a certain age is derived from that at the previous age by allowance for entrants and exits. The particular formula involved depends on the way in which the various ages are defined. With the growing use of computers in the administration of pension schemes and the carrying out of actuarial calculations it has become practicable for the years of exposure to risk at each age to be accumulated directly from the data relating to each individual. We shall not therefore consider examples of continuous formulae for the building up of the exposed to risk in this book.

The experience of Scheme X

22.28   We shall illustrate the points that arise in the investigation of the experience by considering the first three years of Scheme X. In the artificially simple movement of membership of this scheme the creation of exposed to risk is a straightforward matter and the first part of Table 49 shows the calculations for the employees in Group D. There were 30 such employees at the Commencement Date, all aged 30, so that their contribution to the exposed to risk for year of age 30 to 31 is 30 years as shown in column (2) of the Table. There were 16 entrants in this group during year no.1 and since each of these contributed only one-half of a year of exposure during the year of age concerned their contribution is as shown in column (3) of the Table. There were no other members in year of age 30 to 31 during the first three years of Scheme X so that the total exposed to risk for that year is 38 years as shown in column (6) of the Table. As to exposure in year of age 31 to 32, the initial entrants numbered 25 at the beginning of the second year of Scheme X and therefore contribute 25 years to the exposed to risk. The entrants in year no. 1 were all assumed to remain in Scheme X until the beginning of year no. 2 and therefore in that year contribute 16 years to the exposed to risk from age 31 to aged 32. The new entrants in year no.2 numbered 16 and contribute one-half of a year each as shown in column (4) of the Table. The total exposure at year of age 31 to 32 is therefore 49 years as shown in column (6) of the Table.

22.29   In the remainder of the Table the exposed to risk for Group D is operated on by the probabilities of withdrawal, death in service and ill-health retirement to obtain expected numbers, and these are compared with actual numbers. We have not had cause to show earlier in this book the probabilities involved, because our work has proceeded on the basis of the service table in Table 2. It will readily be seen, however, that the service table incorporates these probabilities; thus the withdrawal decrement rate of 0.046 shown at age 31 in column (7) of Table 49 is equal to 1,557 ÷ 33,839 as shown at age 31 in the service table in Table 2.

22.30 We do not show the detailed calculations corresponding to those of Table 49 over the whole range of ages concerned, since no points of particular interest are involved. The resulting totals of expected and actual numbers are summarised in Table 50 and we now comment on these results.

Rates of withdrawal

22.31 It will be recalled from paragraph 14.10 that the contribution rates for Scheme X were calculated on the assumption that all withdrawing members would be entitled to a preserved pension. We discussed in paragraph 16.2 et seq the allowance, if any, which needed to be made for the fact that many withdrawing members were likely to be entitled to, and to prefer, a benefit equal to a refund of their own accumulated contributions to the scheme after allowing for the necessary payment back into the State scheme and tax. Table 50 shows that the number of withdrawing members was very large and it will be seen from Table 51, which shows the numbers of early leavers according to benefit on leaving, that most of them received a refund of contributions.

22.32 A substantial excess of the number of members withdrawing from a pension scheme over the number expected was a feature of the experience with which actuaries in the United Kingdom became familiar in the years up to 1980 because the comparatively full employment position which held up to the mid-1970s led to high mobility of labour. Actuaries tended over the period to increase the withdrawal rates used in the service tables of pension schemes, but even so the rates were normally set at a much lower level than indicated by the experience, for the reasons discussed in paragraph 12.19. At the time of writing rates of withdrawal experienced have in many cases tended to diminish, reflecting the greater stability of the workforce in a time of high unemployment. Nevertheless the general comparison of actual and expected numbers of withdrawals indicated by Tables 50 and 51 is not wholly exceptional.

22.33 What does this imply in respect of the withdrawal rates to be used in a valuation? Table 51 shows that although most of those withdrawing were leavers at the younger ages with a return of contributions, a modest proportion were members who left over the whole range of ages with a preserved pension or a transfer payment. The gradual, if slow, improvement in the benefits to leavers flowing from the preservation law, the G.M.P. entitlement in schemes used for contracting-out and the growth of dynamisation of preserved rights is likely to lead to a continuing growth in the number of leavers with preserved pensions, or transfer payments of equivalent value. This implies that the withdrawal rates should be extended further up the age range, and this has tended to occur in practice. There is difficulty, however, even in larger schemes, in arriving at rationally assessed withdrawal rates at the older ages. The alternative is not to anticipate withdrawals at these ages, and this is a reasonable course of action since typically an unanticipated withdrawal at such ages leads to a profit to the scheme even allowing for the gradual improvement in leavers' benefits. In the circumstances of Scheme X we shall leave the rates unchanged.

Rates of mortality in service

22.34 It will be seen from Table 50 that the number of deaths of members in service was 9 compared with an expected number of 4.3. The experience was therefore very heavy and it is necessary to consider whether the rates of mortality should be changed. The numbers involved are comparatively small and the evidence relates to only one inter-valuation period; on both these counts it is unlikely that the actuary would change the rates of mortality which he orginally thought, on the basis of his general experience, to be reasonable although he might well wish to assess whether a marked divergence of actual from expected numbers was statistically significant.

Rates of ill-health retirement

22.35 Table 50 shows that the number of ill-health retirements during the three-year period was 10 compared with an expected number of 1.1. The experience was therefore exceptionally high. One plausible explanation of this is that, since the employer did not have a pension scheme before the setting up of Scheme X, it was impossible on financial grounds for some employees to retire for reasons of ill-health even though they would have been justified in doing so if an ill-health benefit had been available. It was therefore to be expected that upon the setting up of a scheme in which pre-scheme employment counted as pensionable service, even if only at the half rate, these members would take advantage of the provisions. The heavy experience may therefore be a temporary feature and we shall not change the rates at this stage.

Early retirement in normal health

22.36 It will be recalled that members of Scheme X are able to retire before attainment of age 65 under the provisions of Spec. 3. Retirement with an immediate pension equal to the accrued scale pension may take place with the consent of the employer while early retirement with an immediate pension but without the consent of the employer involves the actuarial reduction mentioned in paragraph 19.65. This scale of reduction is intended to ensure that this type of early retirement does not, on average, place a financial strain on the scheme, the value of the benefit being approximately equivalent to the actuarial reserve held for the member as a continuing member. For the reason explained in paragraph 12.6 there is no need to include allowance for this decrement in the service table. We are therefore concerned, in the analysis of the experience, with the expected and actual numbers of members retiring between the ages of 60 and 65 with an immediate pension calculated on the full scale.

22.37 We have not shown in Table 50 the number of members expected to retire in this way during the three-year period but the calculation is made in exactly the same way as those underlying Table 50. The comparison of the numbers expected to retire at each age with those actually retiring at these ages during the three-year period is as follows.

Age at beginning of scheme year of retirement	Numbers retiring:-	
	expected	actual
60	4.00	4
61	2.25	
62	1.30	3
64		
65	5.00	5

The numbers are too small to enable any positive conclusions to be drawn, but they give no grounds for changing the asssumptions.

Pensioners' mortality

22.38   The number of persons in receipt of pension is obviously much too small for there to be any significant experience in connection with mortality after retirement and we will assume that the mortality table used in the initial calculations to represent mortality after retirement and during the period of deferment of preserved pensions is to be retained.

Salary progression

22.39   We return to the consideration of the earnings experience, and the desirability of analysing the total progression of earnings into that representing the progress of individuals if overall levels of earnings remained stable and that representing escalation of earnings levels. We are here concerned with the first of these.

22.40   It will be recalled that Table 48 was based on the salaries of those persons who were contributing members of Scheme X throughout the period involved, new entrants being omitted on the grounds referred to in paragraph 22.7. The Table shows how the earnings of each age group increased during the period concerned under the combined effect of individual progress and escalation. If the former factor could be isolated and the results at all ages combined in sequence, a progression theoretically corresponding to column (2) of Table 3 would be obtained.

22.41   In practice the investigation of the basic salary scale is usually conducted by an examination of the profile of average salaries at given dates. This is not theoretically sound; in principle it is necessary to follow the earnings of the survivors in service from time to time of a given cohort of members as they progress through their career. A profile of average salaries at a given date does not give the equivalent of such a 'cohort analysis' because, for example, the average earnings of members at age 40 at a given date may represent the effect of status, past history and other factors quite different from those which will hold at age 40 for members now aged 35. An investigation of average salaries is based on the assumption that such differences do not wholly invalidate the comparison.

22.42   Because the average salary profile method is widely used we illustrate it in Table 52. This Table shows the profile of average earnings at the Commencement Date and at the first valuation date (on different scales) of the persons covered by Table 48, together with the progression represented by the assumed salary scale before escalation, i.e. the salary scale in column (2) of Table 3. It will be seen that the comparison does not inspire confidence that the salary scale in the basis is suitable for its purpose. The observed average salaries show comparatively little change until the age of approximately 45 but then show a steep rise. If the profile of average salaries could be regarded as representing the expected average progress of individuals apart from escalation, the figures imply that, for entrants at the younger ages, contributions will be received over the middle part of the career on earnings lower than those indicated by the salary scale in the basis, but that this scale may give a reasonable indication of the eventual salary on which an age retirement pension would eventually be based. Thus the basis may represent too optimistic a pattern of income and outgo.

22.43 On the other hand, the figures of Table 48 column (6) show that over the central range of ages the salary scale with escalation did provide a fair measure of the pay progress of the groups concerned, so that current pay progression is not wholly in line with the profiles of Table 52 which reflect the effects of past history. As with other features of the experience it would probably be decided to await the results of further investigations before making any change in the salary scale.

Conclusion

22.44 We shall make the first actuarial investigation of Scheme X on the actuarial basis employed for the initial calculations. This course is followed in the interests of simplicity and does not represent a considered judgement of the basis. A final point on the basis is that it was not necessary in the initial calculations to specify rates of dividend yield and dividend growth, but on the present occasion we will assume a rate of dividend growth of 4 per cent. Since the assumed overall yield is 9 per cent. this implies a rate of dividend yield on future purchases of ordinary shares of

$$\delta_{9\%} - \delta_{4\%}$$

i.e. 4.696 per cent. p.a. The assumption of price increases at 6 per cent. p.a. underlies the basis.

THE ACTUARIAL INVESTIGATION:
BENEFIT AND CONTRIBUTION VALUES

THE ACTUARIAL INVESTIGATION: BENEFIT AND CONTRIBUTION VALUES

The volume of calculation

23.1 The regular actuarial investigation of a pension scheme serves the following purposes among others.

(i) It is the occasion on which the actuary assesses both the discontinuance and the long term financial position of the scheme, and reviews the contribution rates.

(ii) It is the opportunity for the actuary to look in depth at the financial working of the scheme and thus review and extend his understanding of it.

(iii) The calculations made for the investigation are likely to be referred to again by the actuary, updated as appropriate, as the basis of any costings he may be called on to make during the period before the next valuation.

For all these reasons the actuarial investigation is normally a major piece of work with extensive calculations. We will illustrate the type of work involved by performing the calculations for the first actuarial investigation of Scheme X.

23.2 In this chapter we outline the calculation of the present capital value of the expected future benefit payments and contribution receipts. The processes are essentially the same as those of Chapters 14 to 16 in connection with contribution rates, and although the calculations outlined in the present chapter are extensive the reader who has understood the earlier chapters should not find the present discussion difficult. The main new points of detail that have to be dealt with are as follows.

(i) The members will have accumulated G.M.P. rights during their years of contributory membership of the scheme, so that in the calculations connected with G.M.P.s it will be necessary to deal with these accrued rights as well as with the rights expected to arise from future service.

(ii)   It will be necessary to deal in the calculation of the liabilities with persons who are in receipt of pension and with other persons who have left with entitlement to preserved pensions. These two groups have no counterpart in the original contribution calculations.

23.3   Although the consequences of contracting-out, and in particular the calculations in connection with G.M.P.s, have to be properly allowed for, their full complexity would distract the reader from more fundamental matters. We shall therefore in this book leave the material of Chapter 15 to represent the main numerical treatment of G.M.P.s and other aspects of contracting-out. The G.M.P. adjustments in the present calculations are shown in the various tables but are not commented on in the main part of the present chapter. However, a discussion of the G.M.P. adjustments appears in paragraph 23.16 onwards for those readers who wish to be reminded of the points in more detail. Adjustments to the main valuation calculations for contracting-out requirements other than aspects of the G.M.P. will be ignored, on the grounds that these were found in Chapter 15 to be unimportant.

Contributing members

23.4   We deal first with the liabilities in respect of contributing members of Scheme X at the investigation date. Table 34 contained a summary of the data in respect of these members. We show in Table 53 the calculation of the liabilities and contribution values for the members in Group D at the investigation date (initial and subsequent entrants combined) before adjustment for G.M.P.s. It will be seen that these calculations are similar to those of Table 14.

23.5   The results of the similar calculations over the whole of the membership at the investigation date are summarised in successive Tables as follows.

Group	Values	Table
The survivors at the investigation date of the initial entrants	Past service	54
	Future service	55

The survivors at the investigation date of entrants after the Commencement Date	Past and future service separately	56
All active members at investigation date	One year's membership	57

Current pensioners

23.6 There are at the investigation date a number of persons in receipt of pension, and we now turn to the valuation calculations in respect of these persons. As noted in paragraph 21.36, they fall into the following groups.

(i) Five persons who retired on grounds of age at age 65 (data shown in Table 37).

(ii) Twelve persons who retired in normal health before attainment of normal pension age (data shown in Table 40).

(iii) Nine persons who retired on grounds of ill- health and who survived until the investigation date (data in Table 42).

(iv) Nine widows in receipt of pension at the investigation date, of whom eight are in receipt of pension following the death during employment of contributing members and one on the death of an ill-health pensioner (data in paragraphs 21.48 and 21.49).

23.7 The annuities are based on a(55) mortality for males and females, rated up five years for ill-health pensioners. The amounts of pensions in the data as at the investigation date include the 5 per cent. increase granted on that date. The annuities are based on a rate of interest of 9 per cent. and a continuous rate of increase of 3 per cent. p.a. Strictly there should be allowance for the fact that the next pension increase will not take place until one year after the investigation date. We shall not, however, make special allowance for this point; it is thought preferable to use the method conventionally used in which the annuities are continuous. In practice a small overall adjustment might be made in respect of such points. We now deal with the valuation of the liabilities for each of these groups.

Retirements at age 65

23.8 It will be recalled that the five persons who retired at age 65 did so immediately upon the setting up of Scheme X so that their pension does not include any G.M.P. element. The valuation of the benefits is straightforward; it is shown in Table 58. We will use a proportion married of 90 per cent., on the assumption that reliable up-to-date information on the marital status of each individual is not available. There is an outstanding guarantee period of two years at the investigation date so that the pensions payable to the retired employees are valued by an annuity throughout life, with payment guaranteed for a minimum of two years. The contingent reversionary pension to the widow is one-half of the pension which would have been payable to the member had he not given up pension in exchange for lump sum at retirement. The prospective amounts involved as at the valuation date are shown at the foot of Table 37. These amounts are valued by a reversionary annuity allowing for 3 per cent. annual increases both before and after the widow's pension becomes payable.

Early retirements in normal health

23.9 We turn to group (ii) of paragraph 23.6, namely persons who retired in normal health before attainment of normal pension age during the first three years of operation of Scheme X. The valuation calculations are shown in Table 59. It will be seen from column (6) that we have not allowed for the precise unexpired period of the five year guarantee for each individual but have used a four year unexpired period as a convenient and reasonable approximation. The G.M.P. adjustment is explained in paragraph 23.23.

Ill-health retirements

23.10 The valuation of the ill-health pensions in course of payment at the valuation date is similar in principle to the valuation of the pensions payable to persons in normal health who retired before age 65. The calculations are shown in Table 60 and the G.M.P. adjustments are explained in paragraph 23.23.

Pensions payable to widows

23.11 The pensions payable to widows are valued by annuities throughout life. As noted in paragraph 23.23, the non-G.M.P.

element is valued with allowance for 3 per cent. p.a. increases (i.e. at a rate of interest of 5.825 per cent.) and the G.M.P. element by a flat annuity (i.e. at 9 per cent.). The circumstances in which a widow's pension is payable from the State scheme are governed by complex rules and it cannot be automatically assumed that each widow in receipt of a pension from a contracted-out occupational scheme will also be in receipt of an element of earnings-related pension from the State. If she is not in receipt of such a pension then it follows that she is not being provided with cost of living increases on the G.M.P. element of her occupational pension, so that it may be appropriate for increases on this element to be provided from the resources of the occupational scheme. We will assume in the present case that all widows are in receipt of pension from the State scheme so that increases in the occupational pension are made only on that element in excess of the widow's G.M.P. The calculations are shown in Table 61.

Preserved pensions of early leavers

23.12 Under Spec. 9(ii) the G.M.P. and non-G.M.P. parts of the preserved pension of an early leaver are treated as separate entitlements; there is no 'franking'. The calculations in this connection therefore involve the separate valuation of the G.M.P. and non-G.M.P. elements of preserved pensions. The calculations are shown in Table 62. The function in column (5) is that required to value the excess over G.M.P. of the member's preserved pension and it is of the form

$$(1.05)^{65-x} \frac{D_{65}}{D_x} \ \ddot{a}_{\overline{65} \ \overline{5|}}$$

where the 'D' functions are at a rate of interest of 9 per cent. and the annuity is at a rate of interest of 5.825 per cent. to allow for 3 per cent. p.a. increases after payment.

23.13 The function in column (6) values the corresponding widow's pension. The opening amount of the widow's pension on death before or after the member's preserved pension has started to be paid is equal to one-half of the amount of the member's pension (whether prospective or in payment) at the date of death. Since the member's pension rights increase at the rate of 5 per cent. p.a. during the period of preservation and at 3 per cent. p.a. after payment has started the function in column (6) is not a straightforward reversionary annuity to the wife. It is calculated by the method illustrated in Table 11(a).

23.14   It may occur to the reader that the process of placing a present capital value on preserved pension rights for the purpose of the actuarial investigation is in principle the same as the process of placing a capital value on preserved pension rights for the purpose of arriving at a transfer value which might be paid from a scheme. This is indeed the case (subject to any consequences of the 1985 Act provisions mentioned in paragraph 19.2) so that, for instance, the factors in column (5) of Table 62 are the same for a given age as those calculated on the first formula of paragraph 19.27 in connection with the payment of transfer values.

23.15   As to the valuation of the widow's reversionary pension, in practice the data for a valuation would be unlikely to include reliable information as to whether an ex-member with a preserved pension was married or not. The scheme office would not be in close touch with ex-members and any information on marital status could not be relied on. In these circumstances the question of the inclusion of a proportion married in calculations of the type shown in Table 62 would be considered on its merits.

Contracting-out

23.16   As mentioned in paragraph 23.3, in describing the main valuation calculations we have not dwelt on the adjustments for contracting-out. The remainder of this chapter is concerned with these adjustments, which we will take as relating solely to matters arising in connection with the G.M.P. In practice allowance for G.M.P.s is often made by abbreviated or approximate methods. We use fuller methods here for those readers who may find a lengthier treatment of the subject helpful. For most benefits the important point is that under Spec. 9(i) of Scheme X, pension increases are not to be provided on the G.M.P. content of a pension in course of payment after the pensioner has attained State pensionable age. Benefit values have first been calculated as if the whole of each pension increased at 3 per cent. p.a. during its course of payment, so that the adjustment involves the substitution of a flat annuity for an increasing annuity in respect of the appropriate element of pension. A different point arises for early leavers. The position here is that, because of the provisions of Spec. 9(ii) of Scheme X (approximating to the anti-franking legislation), the G.M.P. and non-G.M.P. elements of the preserved benefit entitlements of an early leaver are to be treated as separate entitlements. The adjustment for G.M.P. in this case therefore arises from the division of the scale pension at the date of early leaving into the G.M.P. and non-G.M.P. elements and the separate subsequent treatment of these entitlements. Some G.M.P. points on the various membership groups and benefits are as follows.

Active members: pensions on normal age retirement

23.17 The active members at the investigation date have been accruing G.M.P. rights during their contributory membership of Scheme X and will accrue further rights during their future membership. These past and future service aspects of G.M.P. are dealt with separately in the valuation. Table 63 shows for members in Group D how the G.M.P. rights in respect of past service at the investigation date are accumulated to age 65 (even if the member has retired before attaining that age) and how the difference in value between an increasing annuity and a flat annuity commencing at that age is allowed for. The saving of £700 shown at the foot of this table appears in column (3) of Table 54. Table 63 has much the same structure as Table 19; points of detail are as follows.

Columns (2) and (3) These relate to the period before the member retires. In view of the number of Section 21 Order revaluations included in the amount of the accrued G.M.P. rights at the investigation date, the number 'n' of such future increases to be allowed for is taken as one more than the difference between the age last birthday at retirement as shown in column (1) of the Table and 33 (the age of the Group D members at the investigation date) for retirement ages up to 63. At retirement ages 64 and 65 the G.M.P. revaluation rules mentioned in paragraph 15.11 lead to the values of 'n' shown.

Column (4) This shows the extent of fixed rate revaluation during the period after retirement and up to attainment of age 65.

23.18 As to future service G.M.P.s, Tables 64 and 65 are based on data as at the investigation date but are otherwise identical to

Tables 18 and 19. The saving of £11,300 shown at the foot of Table 65 appears in column (3) of Table 55.

Active members: pensions on early retirement

23.19   The calculations in respect of members retiring with an immediate pension before age 65 in other circumstances, e.g. on grounds of ill-health or with an actuarial reduction, are similar to those of Tables 63 to 65. In ill-health cases appropriate allowance is of course made for the higher expected mortality rates of pensioners.

Active members: widows' pensions on death after retirement

23.20   As to the saving in pension increases on the G.M.P. element of the widow's reversionary pension after retirement, the position was explained in paragraph 15.46 et seq but for convenience a brief recapitulation is as follows. It will be recalled that the G.M.P. rights of an ex-member increase at the chosen rate of 8½ per cent. p.a. until the member attains age 65, the G.M.P. remaining constant in payment after that age. The widow's G.M.P. is equal to approximately one-half of that of the member (whether the member's G.M.P. is prospective or in payment). Should the widow's pension come into payment before the member attains age 65, the amount of the widow's pension will include allowance for 8½ per cent. increases on the member's G.M.P. pension from the date of his retirement up to the date of his death. Should her pension not come into payment until after the member attains age 65, the opening level of the widow's pension will reflect 8½ per cent. increases up to the date of the member's attainment of age 65 and no increases thereafter. The opening level of the widow's G.M.P. pension having thus been established, the saving in pension increases is then calculated as the difference between that opening level operated on by an annuity increasing at 3 per cent. p.a. and the same opening level operated on by an annuity which is flat in payment. Table 21 indicates the type of calculation involved for normal age retirement of the member; calculations for other types of early retirement are similar in principle.

Early leavers

23.21 The effect of the G.M.P. arrangements on an early leaver's preserved pension can be considered in two parts. In the first place it remains the case that there is a saving due to the absence of pension increases on the G.M.P. element when the ex-member attains age 65 (and which for Scheme X is the date when the pension comes into payment). In the second place, the effect of Spec. 9(ii) is that the G.M.P. element in a preserved pension enjoys increases at 8½ per cent. instead of the normal Scheme X rate during the period before it comes into payment. The effect of these influences was illustrated in Table 20 and, except for the fact that past service as well as future service G.M.P.s have to be dealt with, the calculations at the investigation date are similar.

23.22 As far as widow's G.M.P. pensions are concerned, the calculations for an ex-member who is an early leaver with a preserved pension are the same as those for an ex-member who has taken an immediate pension early. No new points are therefore involved in the calculations for widow's pensions.

Current and preserved pensions

23.23 We have dealt so far with the adjustments arising from the existence of the G.M.P. in respect of persons who were active members of Scheme X at the investigation date. It is also, however, necessary to make the appropriate adjustments for the various classes of person set out in paragraph 23.6 and for ex-members with preserved pensions. It will be appreciated that the calculations for these groups are similar to those set out above except that they do not involve the decrement rates of the service table, because the persons concerned have already passed out of the service table as various types of exit. Brief comments are as follows.

Table 59 column (10)

Table 60 column (10)

This function is of the form

$$1.085^{64-x} \frac{D_{65}}{D_x} (\bar{a}_{65} - \bar{a}_{65})$$
$$9\% \quad 5.825\% \quad 9\%$$

In Table 60 a five year age rating is included. Any part of the five year guarantee period which will remain outstanding on attainment of age 65 is ignored. The function in column (9) of Table 62 is similar but in this case a five year guarantee is included, since payment of the pension does not start until age 65.

Table 59 column (11)

Table 60 column (11)

Table 62 column (10)

This is the rather complex type of reversionary annuity described in paragraph 23.20.

Table 61 columns (6) and (7)

Since we are dealing here with a widow's G.M.P. in payment the annuities involved in these columns are straightforward female annuities payable throughout life, one including 3 per cent. p.a. increases and the other of flat amount.

Summary

23.24 The various values calculated in this chapter are summarised in Tables 66, 67, 68 and 69.

THE ACTUARIAL INVESTIGATION: VALUATION OF ASSETS

THE ACTUARIAL INVESTIGATION: VALUATION OF ASSETS

24.1   The next stage of the actuarial investigation is the settling of the value to be placed on the investments for the purpose of the investigation. We will approach this matter by reminding the reader of the simplified example of the valuation process which appeared in paragraphs 21.8 to 21.12. In paragraph 21.8 we set out a profile of expected future cash flows in respect of

(i)   benefits,
(ii)   assets at the investigation date, and
(iii) contributions.

The reasoning of the example led us to calculate the present value at the investigation date of those three future sets of cash flow, using for this purpose the rate of interest expected to be earned on new money in the future. We are now in the process of applying this procedure to the investigation of Scheme X.

24.2   We ended Chapter 23 with a reference to Table 69. In that table we arrived at benefit liabilities which, taking past and future service together, totalled £8,624,000. The present value of future normal joint contributions was shown as £6,354,400. Without anticipating the discussion of Chapter 29 on cash flow projections, these two values are the present values of the future benefit flows and normal contribution flows set out in Table 74, i.e. they represent item (i) and (except for the employer's special contributions) item (iii) of the previous paragraph. We now need to arrive at item (ii) of the previous paragraph, i.e. we need in principle to arrive at a profile of the future cash flow from the investments held by Scheme X at the investigation date and to calculate the present value of this cash flow.

24.3   To follow out this principle precisely in any particular case would be an extremely complex process. The complication flows from the fact that the future investment proceeds usually represent the sum of widely disparate elements, as will be seen from the following contrasting examples.

(i)   A fixed-interest gilt-edged investment definitely redeemable at a fixed future date provides future income, and a future capital payment, of known fixed amounts at known future dates.

(ii) The future proceeds from a property owned by a pension scheme and leased to a tenant consist in the first place of the rents, which will be subject to review at intervals stated in the lease, less any expenses falling on the trustees. The outcome of a rent review will depend on many considerations at the time of the review including both general economic conditions and factors specific to the type and quality of the building and its location. Superimposed on these variables is the question of the tenant's continuing ability to pay the rent. The value of the property when the lease expires will depend on whether it is still at that time a marketable property, what if any expenses may be involved in updating the building and the terms and period of any new lease which may be negotiated with the existing or new tenants.

Clearly the full theoretical model of the expected future cash flows from the whole range of investments held by the typical pension scheme is unmanageably complex. Nevertheless, one possible approach is simply to value each type of investment by whatever method appears both reasonable and practicable. We now discuss this approach.

The present value of the expected future proceeds from various types of investment

Ordinary shares

24.4   It will be recalled that in Chapter 11 we discussed the rate of interest to be obtained on new investments made in the future, and we showed that if ordinary shares could be purchased at an immediate dividend yield of d, and dividends grew at rate g per annum, the holding of ordinary shares would give a yield of i where

$$\delta_i = \delta_g + d$$

Our assumptions for Scheme X are that ordinary shares are bought on an immediate dividend yield of 4.696 per cent. and that the dividend stream from a given holding grows at 4 per cent. p.a. These assumptions lead to our total rate of accumulation of 9 per cent. p.a. In the discussion of paragraph 11.7 we did not explicitly mention the eventual sale of the ordinary shares, but this does not introduce any new points; we are assuming that average market conditions in the future are represented by the chosen values of d, g and i so that the market value of a holding at any time is simply the amount to which the original investment has accumulated, at that time, at rate of accumulation i. Another way of putting this is to say that the present value at rate i of a share providing a dividend stream d increasing at rate g is 1, irrespective of the length of time for which the share is held.

24.5 We now have to consider the separate question of the ordinary shares held by a scheme at the date as at which an actuarial investigation is being made. We will assume first that the holdings of ordinary shares represent the same cross section of the whole United Kingdom equity market as is represented by the FT-Actuaries All-Share Index. In this case the rate of dividend increase to be assumed in future will be the rate g which is mentioned above and which is one of the items in the actuary's broad picture of future economic conditions. The annual rate of dividend income on the shares held at the investigation date is not, however, the subject of an assumption; it is a fact. Thus the actuarial investigation of Scheme X is being made as at 5th April 1982 and at that date the yield on the Index was 5.89 per cent. Thus if the whole market value of Scheme X at that date, namely £1,147,000, had been invested in the Index, the rate of dividend flow would have been

$$£1,147,000 \times .0589 = £67,558 \text{ p.a.}$$

24.6 From the last sentence of paragraph 24.4, a dividend stream of initial amount .04696 has a present value of 1 on our valuation basis. It follows that the holding referred to in the previous paragraph has a present value, for the purpose of our valuation, of

$$\frac{£67,558}{.04696} = £1,438,629$$

In arriving at this figure we have not had to specify the remote future dates at which various parts of the holding would have to be sold to meet outgo; the resources are available when required.

24.7 In the above discussion we have assumed that the holdings of ordinary shares show the same distribution as the FT-Actuaries All-Share Index. In some schemes the investment managers may indeed follow a policy for the whole or part of the assets of matching the distribution of the All-Share Index quite closely. In most cases, however, it will be found that the investment advisers have taken a positive view in respect of certain individual companies or sub-sectors of the Index and this has resulted in a distribution of ordinary shares substantially different from that of the Index. For instance, the investment managers may have arrived at a distribution of ordinary shares with a total dividend income in excess of that on the Index. Table 47 shows that this is the case for Scheme X, since the dividend yield is 6 per cent. compared with 5.89 per cent. on the Index. The hope is presumably that this higher level of immediate income will be accompanied by at least an average growth rate, so that the fund will in total have a better performance than if the assets were distributed according to the Index. On the other hand, another investment manager may have chosen a distribution of ordinary shares with an immediate dividend yield lower than that on the Index. In this case the expectation is probably that the degree of dividend growth on these low yielding shares will be so great that the combined effect of immediate yield and growth will outweigh the performance of the Index.

24.8 It would be impossible to frame the assumption about future dividend growth in the light of the particular ordinary share distribution of a scheme, and so it is not possible to arrive in these circumstances at a projected future flow of dividend income. The normal method by which this difficulty is overcome is to notionally convert the actual holding of ordinary shares into an Index holding of the same market value. In other words, the known market value of the actual holdings of ordinary shares is regarded as if it were a holding in the All-Share Index of the same market value, and the notional amount on the dividend is found by applying the known yield on the Index to this market value. The method of the preceding paragraphs is then applied to obtain the actuarial value of the holding. The difference between the investment performance as it emerges year by year and that which would have been expected by applying the actuarial assumptions to a holding in the All-Share Index is left to emerge as an item of actuarial profit or loss.

24.9 If we use this method in respect of the ordinary shares held by Scheme X the annual amount of the dividend flow following notional transformation of the ordinary share market value of £915,000 into the Index is therefore

$$£915,000 \times .0589 = £53,893$$

The present value of the future flow of dividends using the formula of paragraph 24.6 is

$$£53,893 \div .04696 = £1,147,636$$

Definitely redeemable fixed-interest gilt-edged securities

24.10 We turn to the valuation of redeemable fixed-interest gilt-edged securities. This is technically a straightforward application of compound interest methods. The income and redemption proceeds of these securities are known amounts, the risk of default being taken as nil. If there are optional redemption dates it should be assumed in the calculation that the security will be redeemed on the first optional date at which the ratio of the annual dividend to the redemption price exceeds the valuation rate of interest. The reasoning here is that since the valuation rate of interest is the expected long term rate, the government would replace the stock at the date mentioned by a new issue on cheaper terms. In practice there may be no optional date at which the position stated above will arise. In this case it is assumed that the security will be redeemed on the final option date.

24.11 The value is not affected by the possibility of sale before redemption, since this is assumed to take place on the basis of the valuation rate of interest. It is not usually thought necessary to allow precisely for the actual incidence of the dividend income during the year. If income of j per annum is expected for n years with redemption at value C after n years it is usually sufficiently accurate to take the present value as

$$j\, a_{\overline{n}|} + Cv^n$$

24.12 Table 47 shows that the nominal amount of Treasury 13¾% 2000-03 held by Scheme X is £122,000 so that the annual amount of interest is £16,775. The approximate present value as at

5th April 1982 at 9 per cent. interest, assuming redemption in the year 2000, is

$$£16,775\ a_{\overline{18|}} + £122,000\,v^{18}$$

which gives a value of some £173,000. This technical calculation is not the end of the matter; we shall consider the general position later in this chapter.

Index-linked gilt-edged securities

24.13 In order to place a discounted present value on the expected future proceeds from index-linked gilt-edged securities it is obviously necessary to make an assumption about the future rate of increase in the prices index. If the security is part-way through its term, rather than newly issued, it is also necessary to know or to estimate the amount of the next dividend payment, because this forms the base for the projection of future cash proceeds from the investment. This amount will not normally be immediately obvious, because it includes the effect of price increases since the stock was issued.

24.14 In order to value the holding by Scheme X of 2½% index-linked Treasury stock 2011 it is therefore necessary to know that both principal and interest are related to the change in General Index of Retail Prices in the United Kingdom subject to a lag of 8 months, the Base month being May 1981. In other words, the amount of a particular payment is equal to the nominal amount increased in the ratio which the Prices Index 8 months before the month of payment bears to the Index for May 1981, which was 294.1.

24.15 The Prices Index for the month 8 months before the investigation date, i.e. August 1981, was 299.3 and we will therefore take the indexation gain already existing at the investigation date as a factor of

$$229.3 \div 294.1 = 1.018$$

We will assume that the outstanding term from the investigation date, 5th April 1982, to redemption in the year 2011 is 29 years. The nominal value is £30,000 and the nominal amount of annual interest is 2½ per cent. of this figure, i.e. £750. Our approximate valuation will in principle be similar to that of the fixed-interest security in paragraph 24.12, but since we are allowing for future price indexation of 6 per cent. per annum and discounting at a rate of interest of 9 per cent., the compound interest functions will be at a rate of interest equal to

$$\frac{1.090}{1.060} - 1, \text{ giving 2.83 per cent.}$$

The value is therefore

$$1.018 \, (\text{£750}) \, a_{\overline{29|}} + 1.018 v^{29} \, (\text{£30,000}) = \text{£28,559}$$

Other assets

24.16 In practice a pension scheme is likely to have a wider range of assets than those dealt with above, including for example properties, property units and overseas investments. Many larger schemes have a substantial proportion of their assets in properties, and despite the difficulties indicated in item (ii) of paragraph 24.3 it is sometimes necessary in such a case to embark on a projection and valuation of expected future proceeds. In general however, a more common approach to the problem of valuing the wider range of assets is by transformation of the market value into a notional holding in the All-Share Index.

24.17 We will deal with the property units and overseas investments of Scheme X by the method of notional transformation into the All-Share Index. The market value is £60,000 so that the calculated value is

$$\text{£60,000} \times \frac{.0589}{.04696}$$

or about £75,000.

Cash

24.18 The cash is probably awaiting long term investments and there would be grounds for taking it into the valuation at a figure assuming such investment. Since investment conditions may change rapidly, however, we will take the cash into the valuation at its face amount.

Summary

24.19 The results of these calculations so far are summarised in the following table in which, for the purposes of subsequent discussion, we also show market value and the ratios of calculated values to market values.

	Market value	Calculated value	Ratio CV to MV
	£000	£000	
Ordinary shares	915	1,148	1.25
Fixed-interest securities	123	173	1.41
Index-linked securities	29	29	1.00
Other investments	60	75	1.25
Cash	20	20	1.00
	1,147	1,445	1.26

Marketability

24.20   We have outlined the valuation of various types of asset on the long term assumptions employed for the actuarial investigation. The fact that the assets are marketable and in particular have a definite market value (apart from such points as the uncertainties of property valuations) at the date as at which the actuarial investigation is made has not entered into our discussion except for the purpose of the notional translation of one asset into another. Although it is hoped that the reader will have followed the reasoning by which the approach to the actuarial investigation taken in this book leads to the assets being taken at a calculated value, it must be accepted that the end result, namely that the actuary takes the assets into his valuation balance sheet at a particular investigation date at a value different from their market value, sometimes causes difficulty. The point is made that the market value is the price at which the market is prepared to trade the expectations of future cash proceeds flowing from the investments; the actuary, in using a different value, is perceived as putting his judgement above that of the market.

24.21   A particular criticism flows from a situation which is commonly found and which is shown in the final column of the table in paragraph 24.19, namely that the ratio which calculated value bears to market value at the investigation date differs markedly from one type of asset to another. Thus the fixed-interest security is taken at a value 41 per cent. greater than its market value while the ordinary shares are shown at a value 25 per cent. greater than their market value. The following two aspects of this situation merit further consideration.

(i)   It appears that in the actuary's judgement the investment of
       £1 in fixed-interest gilt-edged securities is of more long term
       value to the scheme, in market conditions at the investigation
       date, than the investment of £1 of equities. To what extent
       should this influence the actuary's view on investment
       policy?

(ii)   If the investment manager of Scheme X had been aware of
       the actuarial basis for the investigation he might have chosen
       to switch the whole fund into long-dated fixed-interest
       gilt-edged securities shortly before the valuation date, even
       though this would involve dealing expenses and he might
       think the move to be against the best long term interests of
       the scheme, simply to achieve a more favourable valuation
       result. This would have led to a writing up of the market
       value of the whole fund by 41 per cent. for the purpose of the
       actuarial valuation. The investment manager might have
       reverted to a normal investment distribution after the
       valuation date.

24.22   Both these points need careful consideration. The question
raised is essentially whether it is undesirable to employ a method
which places, on each £1 of market value of an asset, an assessed
value which differs according to the nature of the asset. As to point
(i), some practitioners would reply that their actuarial basis,
representing an average long term position, will sometimes show a
favourable assessed value for one type of asset and sometimes for
another, depending on the vagaries of market conditions. It would
be unwise to redirect the whole investment strategy at frequent
intervals as a consequence of this, and the strategy should
therefore continue to be framed with moderation and reasonable
stability. As to point (ii), an actuarial valuation basis is settled and
the valuation perfomed some time after the valuation date,
because of the lapse of time involved in the preparation of the
accounts and membership data, and many practitioners would
therefore not rate the danger of an artificially motivated
investment switch very highly.

24.23   Nevertheless, many practitioners allow much weight to the
difficulties posed by the use of different levels of write-up of
market values. There is another aspect of point (i) which also has
much influence. This is that although the actuary makes his

valuations on specific assumptions, he usually has in mind that pay increases may exceed those he has allowed for, and in these circumstances he will hope for investment performance in excess of that taken credit for in advance, to offset the additional liabilities. This reasoning may well make him reluctant to take credit in advance for the whole of a favourable gilt yield, which is what we have done in arriving at the 41 per cent. write-up in paragraph 24.19

24.24   One method which is often employed to circumvent these difficulties is the valuation of a model portfolio of investments rather than of the actual investments. This is an extension of the method of substituting notional investment in the All-Share Index for actual investment, which has already been referred to. For instance we might for the purpose of the valuation make a notional transformation of the whole fund of Scheme X at the investigation date into the All-Share Index. This would lead to the asset value of £1,438,629 mentioned in paragraph 24.6

24.25   This approach has the advantage that there is no risk of the valuation processes standing between the investment managers and the investment policy best for the scheme, which is the risk envisaged in item (ii) of paragraph 24.21. Investment policy may be thought of in practical terms as the obtaining of the highest possible market value consistent with reasonable risk, and the use of this method would mean that the higher the market value, the more favourable the valuation result. The method can be criticised on the grounds that the notional spread of investments may depart so far from the actual investments held that the process becomes unrealistic. The position is, of course, that divergences in investment performance reflecting the difference between the actual asset distribution and a model portfolio will emerge as items of actuarial profit or loss at successive actuarial valuations. The model portfolio will probably have been chosen in the light of the actual asset distribution of pension schemes in general, so that the divergences that emerge in practice may prove a useful indicator as to the wisdom of the investment policy followed by the trustees of the scheme in question. We will follow the method of paragraph 24.24 for Scheme X and will take the assets into the valuation at a figure of £1,439,000.

Market values

24.26 The reader will have noted that, although it has sometimes been convenient in our discussion to express actuarial values of assets in terms of a percentage increase in market values, this does not mean that market values have been elevated to a central position in the actuarial valuation. If, for instance, the immediate dividend yield in the market on the All- Share Index was on a particular date 5 per cent. and ordinary shares were valued by division of the annual amount of dividends by .04696 as in paragraph 24.6, this would lead to an asset value equal to approximately 1.065 times the market value. If the market value rose over a short period by 10 per cent. without any corresponding increase in dividends, the immediate dividend yield would fall to 4.55 per cent. A valuation of the dividend amount at this level, by division by .04696, would lead to an assessed value equal to about 0.97 times the market value. There would in other words be an essentially unchanged actuarial valuation of the assets even though market values had changed substantially. This stability is seen by practitioners who use the method of valuation employed in this book as an advantage of this approach.

24.27 Nevertheless, as mentioned in paragraph 21.12, some practitioners see advantage in the use of a method of actuarial valuation of a pension scheme which takes the assets into account at their market value. In some versions of this method the market value on the investigation date is used, while in other cases a value which represents market values averaged over some period is employed, to give a measure of stability. Practitioners who use these methods retain the concept of valuing assets, benefit flows and contribution flows on consistent bases, but under such methods the valuation rate of interest no longer represents the yield expected to be earned on new investments made in the future but is a blend of that yield and the yield underlying the market values taken into account. Some of the methods using averaged market values are intended to smooth out fluctuations to such an extent that the end result is similar to the discounting method used in this book. The various methods incorporating market values are not discussed further here.

Special cases

24.28   We have been concerned in this discussion with the normal case of a pension scheme in full force and open to new entrants; the funds are expected to grow for an indefinite period. In practice not all pension schemes are in this position. In particular a pension scheme which has been closed to new entrants for many years and has an increasing number of pensioners and a diminishing number of employee members reaches a point where the funds begin to decline. In this case market values are of much importance, because assets will have to be sold as part of the investment policy, and market values from time to time determine the amount of the proceeds which will then become available. These special cases need to be considered individually and we do not deal further with them here.

Conclusion

24.29   In practice the actuary is not likely to follow any formula blindly in his valuation of the assets; in this as in every other aspect of the work, the final decisions will be a matter of judgement. As stated in paragraph 24.25, we will take the assets into the actuarial valuation of Scheme X at the value of £1,439,000, calculated by notional transformation of the whole fund into the All-Share Index.

CHAPTER 25

THE ACTUARIAL INVESTIGATION: ANALYSIS OF SURPLUS

THE ACTUARIAL INVESTIGATION: ANALYSIS OF SURPLUS

The preliminary valuation balance sheet

25.1 On the basis of the calculations in previous chapters it is possible to draw up a preliminary statement of the present capital values of the assets and liabilities of Scheme X at the investigation date. There is no implication that this will be the result reported to the client, since the actuary has not at this stage applied his professional judgement to the situation revealed by his calculations. This statement is set out in Table 69 and, because this will be found useful later in the discussion, the capital values are shown in two columns. The first column shows the comparison of

(i)   the liabilities for pensions in payment, the preserved pensions of ex-members and the pension rights of employee members in respect of pensionable service completed up to the investigation date, with

(ii) the value of the funds in hand and of the future payments of the employer's special contribution in respect of the initial past liability.

It will be recollected from paragraph 16.47 that the employer decided to pay an additional contribution of 12 per cent. of total payroll for the first 10 years in respect of the initial liability on the setting up of Scheme X, this to be subject to review at each actuarial investigation. Seven years' payments remain outstanding at the investigation date.

25.2 The final column of figures in Table 69 refers to the future service position. In this part of the statement the present value of the benefits that are expected to arise in respect of the future periods of pensionable service of employee members of Scheme X at the investigation date is compared with the present value of the normal contributions (i.e. contributions at the rate of 5 per cent. by the members and 8 per cent. by the employer) expected to be paid during the same periods.

25.3　If the actuarial assumptions used for the initial calculations had accurately represented the unfolding experience during the first three years, both the past service and the future service positions as revealed in Table 69 would have shown approximate financial equilibrium. The future service position does indeed show broadly this state of affairs, and this is not unduly surprising since the benefit and contribution values concerned are arrived at simply by the operation of various actuarial factors upon the pensionable salaries in force at the valuation date. Since, as will be recalled from Chapter 16, the theoretical contribution rate does not vary very greatly with age, there are virtually no factors in this comparison which could produce an unexpected result. It was noted in paragraph 16.5 that the contribution rate to cover future service liabilities was 12.9 per cent. and much the same figure is produced by the present calculations.

25.4　The past service position, however, shows a very large excess of resources over liabilities, and this is an unexpected result. The questions which naturally arise are

(i)　　whether the figures are in fact correct, and

(ii)　　if they are correct, what were the various circumstances in the three years concerned which have led to the position as revealed?

It is in order that such questions shall be properly answered that the actuary embarks on the next stage of his investigation, namely the analysis of surplus (using that word to include a shortfall) revealed by the preliminary valuation. We shall use the word profit in this chapter in a comparative sense to indicate deviations, positive or negative, from the figure expected on the actuarial basis used. We first make some general observations on the analysis of surplus and then illustrate the process with reference both to a simplified example and to Scheme X.

Purposes of the analysis

25.5　To enlarge on the previous paragraph, the analysis of surplus serves two purposes. In the first place it is intended to be an independent check on the results of the valuation, which will have involved long and complex computation. Every precaution will have been taken to ensure that the valuation calculations are correct, but the actuary will not be ready to proceed to the next stage until the surplus or deficiency revealed has been accounted for to the desired degree of accuracy.

25.6 Secondly, the analysis measures the relative financial importance of the various ways in which the experience has departed from the actuarial assumptions made. It also serves to draw attention to those financial features of the intervaluation period which are likely to recur and those which are not.

The analysis as a check

25.7 The analysis is an essential check, but for the following reasons it is not a complete check.

(i) The analysis does not check the data. If, for example, a member who died in service since the previous valuation is shown in error in the data as a surviving member at the valuation date, both the valuation and the analysis will be based on the incorrect data and will be consistent but wrong. The analysis is therefore not a substitute for the checks mentioned in Chapter 21.

(ii) As explained later in this chapter, the actuary will not expect to account for the observed surplus with complete accuracy. The question is always whether the unexplained discrepancy is within acceptable limits or not.

(iii) In practice it is common to estimate some items of profit by using figures from the valuation itself, in order to save work. The analysis is not then a completely independent check.

The analysis: old basis or new?

25.8 If the basis used in a valuation differs from that used on the previous occasion it is necessary to decide whether to calculate the expected amounts in the analysis on the old basis or the new. It was mentioned in paragraph 22.2 that the full theoretical procedure for the settling of a valuation basis involves an analysis on the old basis. It might seem from this that it would be desirable for the analysis to be done normally in this way, since it would then both provide a check and serve the purpose of paragraph 22.2. It is, however, usually found best to make the analysis on the new basis. The main reasons for this are as follows.

25.9 Consider first the analysis as a check. If the analysis is made on the old basis, this will serve to reconcile the result of a present valuation made on the old basis with the result of the previous valuation. There is no check on the result of the present valuation on the new basis. If the analysis is made on the new basis it is necessary to rework the previous valuation on the new basis as accurately as the circumstances require. The analysis then serves to reconcile the result of the present valuation on the new basis with that of the previous valuation on the new basis. Since the result of the present valuation on the new basis is the most important matter it is preferable to use a method which gives a direct check on this result, i.e. an analysis on the new basis.

25.10 Consider now the analysis as a guide to sources of profit. Although the actuary has chosen the rates for the new basis in the light of recent experience, these rates will not usually reproduce this experience exactly. When the actuary is considering the question of any special adjustments to the calculated values he will find it useful to note the financial importance of the departures of the experience during the inter-valuation period from that expected on the new basis. An analysis on the new basis is needed for this purpose.

25.11 This is particularly the case if the actuary wishes to set up a special reserve in the valuation in respect of temporary features of the experience. A knowledge of the financial effect, if any, of these features over the previous few years measured against the yardstick of the new basis is clearly of great help to the actuary in his consideration of the reserve to be set up.

25.12 Some actuaries find it a useful part of an investigation to make a rough estimate of the probable financial position of the scheme at the next investigation date. This is an aid to the deeper understanding of the financial position of the scheme, and it may also be helpful in connection with any short term advice the actuary is asked to give. This projection is made by estimating the expected growth of the fund and the various items of profit and loss up to the next valuation date. An analysis of surplus calculated on the new basis is obviously almost indispensable for this purpose, since the individual items in such an analysis will provide a basis for the actuary's rough estimates of the financial effect of whatever he expects the experience to be in the immediate future.

Complexity of full theoretical treatment.

25.13 Items of profit and loss arise because the experience of the scheme differs from that anticipated in the valuation basis. Although this is a simple concept, a full theoretical treatment of the analysis in a typical scheme is unmanageably complicated because of the large number of ways in which the experience can differ from that expected, and the interaction of these differences. Superimposed on the fundamental complexities are those arising from the contracting-out arrangements, since the G.M.P. requirement introduces what is in a sense a second set of rules operating in parallel with the main rules.

A simplified example

25.14 We will illustrate the basic features of the analysis by the use of a simplified example involving a pension scheme with the following data.

(i)   The reserve required at the beginning of a particular year is equal to 1/10th of pensionable salary for each year of pensionable service. The reserve required at the beginning of the next year is obtained by the same formula applied to the then data.

(ii) If a member leaves during the year the value of the benefit is equal to three-quarters of an amount calculated as in (i) as at the date of exit.

(iii) Interest is assumed at 9 per cent. p.a. and pay increases continuously at 8 per cent. p.a.

(iv) There are 100 members each with initial salary £1,000 p.a. and pensionable service of 11 years.

(v)   Five members are expected to leave during the year.

We will assume that events occur half way through the period concerned.

25.15 The calculation of the contribution rate theoretically required during the year, say k per cent. of pay, proceeds as follows. The first amount is calculated from the initial data and the subsequent amounts are those expected on the stated assumptions.

Total reserves at time 0

$$100 \times £1,000 \times \frac{11}{10} \qquad\qquad = £110,000$$

Total reserves at time 1

$$95 \times £1,000 \times 1.08 \times \frac{12}{10} \qquad\qquad = £123,120$$

Payments in respect of leavers at time $\frac{1}{2}$

$$0.75 \times 5 \times £1,000 \times 1.08^{\frac{1}{2}} \times \frac{11.5}{10} \qquad = £4,482$$

Contributions in first half of year

$$0.5 \times \frac{k}{100} \times 100 \times £1,000 \times 1.08^{\frac{1}{4}} \qquad = £509.7k$$

Contributions in second half of year

$$0.5 \times \frac{k}{100} \times 95 \times £1,000 \times 1.08^{\frac{3}{4}} \qquad = £503.2k$$

The equation of present values at time 0 is evidently as follows, using 9 per cent. interest.

$$110,000 = 123,120v + 4,482v^{\frac{1}{2}} - 509.7kv^{\frac{1}{4}} - 503.2kv^{\frac{3}{4}}$$

$$\therefore k = 7.467 \text{ per cent.}$$

The expected amounts of the contributions on this basis are £3,806 and £3,757 in the first and second halves of the year respectively.

25.16 We will suppose that the fund in hand at the beginning of the year is a deposit of £105,000 earning 9 per cent. p.a. A valuation balance sheet at the beginning of the year shows the following position.

	£
Reserves	110,000
Assets	105,000
Surplus	(−) 5,000

25.17 Suppose first that the experience is exactly as expected. The calculation of the value of the fund at the end of the year proceeds as follows.

		Value at end of year
		£
Initial Fund: £105,000 × 1.09	=	114,450
Contributions:		
first half of year £3,806 × $1.09^{3/4}$	=	4,060
second half of year £3,757 × $1.09^{1/4}$	=	3,839
Leavers: £4,482 × $1.09^{1/2}$	=	(−)4,679
Fund at time 1		£117,670

25.18 A valuation balance sheet drawn up at the end of the year therefore shows the following position.

	£
Reserves	123,120
Assets	117,670
Surplus	(−) £5,450

The surplus is equal to the initial surplus of (−) £5,000 increased by 9 per cent.

Analysis of surplus

25.19 The analysis of surplus in this case is of course extremely simple. The course of the fund and its liabilities has been in line with the expectation at the beginning of the year so that no unexpected items of profit or loss have arisen. This example illustrates the fact that if an actuarial surplus is left undisturbed, and the experience is in line with the expectation, the surplus grows at the assumed rate of interest.

25.20 We will now suppose that interest is in fact earned at the rate of 10 per cent. p.a., that pay increases continuously at the rate of 11 per cent. p.a. and that 9 members leave in the middle of the year. Various figures corresponding to the expected values shown in previous paragraphs are as follows.

Total reserves at time 1

$$91 \times \pounds 1{,}000 \times 1.11 \times \frac{12}{10} \qquad\qquad = \pounds 121{,}212$$

Payments in respect of leavers at time $\tfrac{1}{2}$

$$0.75 \times 9 \times \pounds 1{,}000 \times 1.11^{\frac{1}{2}} \times \frac{11.5}{10} \qquad = \pounds 8{,}178$$

Contributions in first half of year

$$0.5 \times .07467 \times 100 \times \pounds 1{,}000 \times 1.11^{\frac{1}{4}} \qquad = \pounds 3{,}832$$

Contributions in second half of year

$$0.5 \times .07467 \times 91 \times \pounds 1{,}000 \times 1.11^{\frac{3}{4}} \qquad = \pounds 3{,}674$$

25.21   The calculation of the value of the fund at the end of the year proceeds as follows.

		Value at end of year
		£
Initial Fund: £105,000 × 1.10	=	115,500
Contributions:		
first half of year £3,832 × 1.10$^{\frac{3}{4}}$	=	4,116
second half of year £3,674 × 1.10$^{\frac{1}{4}}$	=	3,763
Leavers: £8,178 × 1.10$^{\frac{1}{2}}$	=	(−)8,577
Fund at time 1		£114,802

25.22   A valuation balance sheet drawn up at the end of the year shows the following position.

	£
Reserves	121,212
Assets	114,802
Surplus	(−) £6,410

We now consider various methods of analysis of the surplus of (-)£6,410 revealed by this valuation.

Analysis: Method A

25.23   The most obvious method is perhaps to set down parallel statements of the constituents of the expected and actual figures of previous paragraphs, as follows.

| | Amounts as at end of year | | |
	Expected	Actual	Difference
	£	£	£
Initial fund	114,450	115,500	(+) 1,050
Contributions	7,899	7,879	(−) 20
Leavers	(−) 4,679	(−) 8,577	(−) 3,898
Reserves at year end	(−) 123,120	(−) 121,212	(+) 1,908
Surplus	(−) £5,450	(−) £6,410	(−) £960

25.24 Although the figures in the final column provide one way of allocating the arithmetical difference between the actual and expected surplus, it is not a very helpful way towards the understanding of the main influences at work. For instance, it will be seen that the item relating to reserves at the end of the year is a positive item, i.e. a surplus. The main feature which would be of interest to the actuary, however, is the extent to which the reserves of those remaining at the end of the year are greater than would have been expected because of salary increases in excess of those anticipated. As a further example, the item relating to leavers during the year is negative, i.e. it indicates a financial strain on the fund. In fact, however, the amount payable if a member leaves during the year is only three-quarters of an amount calculated on the same formula as the year-end reserve, so that the most useful way of analysing this feature is one which results in a measure of the surplus arising from the excess of the resources held over the benefits paid. The analysis shown above is therefore not very illuminating, and we now turn to a more useful method.

Analysis: Method B

25.25 This method involves a redistribution of the items set out in Method A. We may illustrate the process by considering the payments to leavers. If we write

$$L(n)(i)(j)$$

to indicate the accumulation to the end of the year of the amounts payable in the middle of the year for n leavers on the basis of a rate of interest of i per cent. and a rate of pay increase of j per cent.

then the amount for leavers in the final column of the table in paragraph 25.23 is equal to

$$-L(9)(10)(11) + L(5)(9)(8)$$

This can obviously be expressed as

$$-[L(9)(10)(11) - L(9)(9)(11)]$$
$$-[L(9)(9)(11) \quad - L(9)(9)(8) \;]$$
$$-[L(9)(9)(8) \quad - L(5)(9)(8) \;]$$

In other words we may divide the total difference into

(i)   the difference that arises because the actual payments are accumulated to the end of year at interest of 10 per cent. p.a. instead of 9 per cent. p.a.,

(ii) the difference that arises because the amounts of the payments for the actual number of leavers are calculated allowing for pay increases during the first half of the year of 11 per cent. and not 8 per cent., and

(iii) the difference that arises if we calculate the payment per head, and accumulate it to the end of the year, on the valuation basis, but take account of the fact that there were 9 leavers instead of the expected number of five.

25.26   The numerical values of these constituents are evidently as follows.

(i) $-9 \times 0.75 \times £1,000 \times \dfrac{11.5}{10}$

$\times 1.11^{1/2} (1.10^{1/2} - 1.09^{1/2})$ $\qquad = (-) \quad £39$

(ii) $-9 \times 0.75 \times £1,000 \times \dfrac{11.5}{10}$

$(1.11^{1/2} - 1.08^{1/2}) \, 1.09^{1/2}$ $\qquad = (-) \quad £116$

(iii) $-(9\text{-}5) \times 0.75 \times £1,000 \times \dfrac{11.5}{10}$

$\times 1.08^{1/2} \times 1.09^{1/2}$ $\qquad = \underline{(-) \; £3,743}$

$$(-) \; £3,898$$

The three constituents can be thought of as

(i)   investment profit,
(ii) salary profit and
(iii) statistical experience profit

Contributions

25.27 The corresponding elements in respect of contributions follows from the figures already calculated, as follows. Contributions in the first and second half of the year are dealt with separately.

Investment profit

$$£3,832(1.10^{3/4} - 1.09^{3/4}) + £3,674(1.10^{1/4} - 1.09^{1/4}) \quad = \quad £37$$

Salary profit

$$(0.5)100 \times £74.67(1.11^{1/4} - 1.08^{1/4})1.09^{3/4}$$
$$+ (0.5)91 \times £74.67(1.11^{3/4} - 1.08^{3/4})1.09^{1/4} \quad = \quad £104$$

Statistical experience profit

$$- (0.5)(95\text{-}91) £74.67(1.08^{3/4})(1.09^{1/4}) \quad = \quad \underline{(-)\,£162}$$
$$\underline{(-)\quad £21}$$

The difference between the total amount of $(-)£21$ and the figure of $(-)£20$ in paragraph 25.23 is due to differences in intermediate roundings of amounts. We shall arbitrarily change the figure of £104 above to £105 to avoid this distraction.

Enders

25.28 The corresponding items in respect of the enders are as follows.

Investment profit

Nil, since interest does not enter into the calculation of the enders' reserves.

Salary profit

We are dealing here with the actual number of enders, so that the salary profit is

$$-91 \times £1,000 \times (1.11 - 1.08) \times \frac{12}{10} \quad = (-)\,£3,276$$

Statistical experience profit

This is concerned with the difference between actual and expected numbers, reserves being calculated on the valuation basis. The figure is

$$(95\text{-}91)\,£1,000\,(1.08)\frac{12}{10} \qquad = (+)\,£5,184$$

25.29 The various figures from the table in paragraph 22.23, as further analysed in subsequent paragraphs, may be summarised as follows.

	Investments	Profit source Salaries	Statistical
	£	£	£
Initial Fund	(+) 1,050	–	–
Contributions	(+) 37	(+) 105	(−) 162
Leavers' benefits	(−) 39	(−) 116	(−) 3,743
Enders' reserves	–	(−) 3,276	(+) 5,184
Total	(+) £1,048	(−) £3,287	(+) £1,279

This leads to the following analysis.

	£
Accumulated surplus brought forward	(−) 5,450
Investment profit	(+) 1,048
Salary profit	(−) 3,287
Statistical experience profit	(+) 1,279
Surplus	(−) £6,410

25.30 The item referred to as 'statistical experience profit' needs further consideration. It represents the release of reserves (calculated on the valuation basis) for leavers in excess of the expected number. This may be seen by calculating the release directly as follows, the compound interest functions being at 9 per cent.

Prospective reserve at time ½ for one member (on valuation assumptions), is equal to value at time ½ of prospective reserve at time 1 less value of future contributions.

£

$$£1,000\,(1.08)\frac{12}{10}\,v^{½} - 0.5\,(£1,000)(.07467)1.08^{¾}v^{¼} = \quad 1,202.6$$

Benefit

$$£1,000\,(0.75)\,(1.08)^{½}\,\frac{11.5}{10} \qquad\qquad = \quad \underline{896.3}$$

Profit for one leaving member in excess of expected number	=	306.3
		× 4
Total profit at time ½	=	1,225.2
Accumulation to end of year	=	× 1.09^½
		£1,279

The release is not exactly one-quarter of the reserves because although the benefit is defined as three-quarters of an amount calculated as if the mid-year reserve was $\frac{n}{10}$ ths of salary, the contribution rate does not in fact provide exactly this amount in the middle of the year for a member who is expected, on the valuation basis, to remain until the end of the year.

Specification of the method

25.31 The rules of the procedure which we have developed may be summarised as follows.

(i) The surplus at the beginning of the period is accumulated to the end of the period at the expected rate of interest.

(ii) The investment profit is assessed as the difference between actual and expected rates of accumulation operating on the initial fund and the actual contribution income and benefit outgo.

(iii) Salary profit items are based on the actual numbers of members and are accumulated at the valuation rate of interest to the end of the period.

(iv) The release of reserves arising from differences between actual and expected numbers of exits is calculated on the valuation basis and is similarly accumulated to the end of the year. The further comment on this item in paragraph 25.54 should be noted.

Analysis: Method C

25.32 We are now near to a method often used in practice. There is, however, one further point of development, to allow for the form that the data in respect of the investments take in practice. The investment performance would not, of course, appear directly in the data as a rate of interest, such as the figure of 10 per cent. in the example. The financial data would instead consist of revenue accounts, investment lists showing book value and market value etc. The approach to the analysis in these circumstances is essentially that of Method B, but for convenience we shall identify it separately as Method C, which we now describe.

25.33 It will be recalled from previous chapters that under our method of valuation the value at which the assets are taken into the valuation balance sheet is an assessed figure rather than book value or market value. We will now suppose in the example that the values of the assets of £105,000 at the beginning of the year and £114,802 at the end of the year are actuarial values, i.e. they have been calculated as the discounted values of projected cash flow. They do not follow from, and are not connected with, the revenue account of the scheme for the year concerned. For the scheme in our simplified example the revenue account for the year that we have been discussing might be as follows.

	£	£
Book value of fund at beginning of year		104,000
Contributions received	7,506	
Investment income	10,000	
		17,506
		121,506
Benefits paid	8,178	
Losses less profits on sales of investments	2,000	
		10,178
Book value of fund at end of year		£111,328

The opening and closing book values and the income and capital items of investment revenue are shown for realism; they are arbitrary and, as will be seen, play no part in our calculations.

25.34 As to pay information, we would have data relating to the numbers and salaries of the members at the beginning and end of the year; in our example this would show that those members who were in the scheme throughout the year had enjoyed pay increases of 11 per cent. during the year so that our earlier example of the analysis was realistic in assuming that a figure of percentage pay increase would be available.

25.35 The valuation balance sheet at the end of the year as shown in paragraph 25.22 is unchanged. The practical application of Method C, which will be seen to involve some approximations, proceeds as follows.

Accumulation of initial surplus

25.36 The initial valuation balance sheet of paragraph 25.16 and the accumulation of the surplus to the end of the year are unchanged, giving the figure of $(-)£5,450$ as before.

Investment profit

25.37 We expect on the valuation basis to earn 9 per cent. on the initial fund and on any new money coming into the scheme during the year. The amount of new money received (i.e. money not generated by the investments themselves) during the year is equal to contributions less benefits, which from the revenue account in paragraph 25.33 amounts to $(-)£672$.

The expected value of assets at end of the year is therefore

		£
$£105,000(1.09) - £672(1.09)^{1/2}$	=	113,748
Value at which assets in fact taken into valuation balance sheet at end of year	=	114,802
	(+)	£1,054

Salary profit

25.38 Salaries are observed to have increased by 11 per cent. during the year compared with an expectation of 8 per cent. Since $111 \div 108 = 1.02778$ we will use an excess salary figure of 2.8 per cent. The excess amount of the enders' reserves is

$$\frac{.028}{1.028}$$

of those reserves. The excess amount of cash flows assumed to occur in the middle of the year, i.e. contributions and benefits, is taken as

$$\frac{.014}{1.014}$$

of those amounts. The approximations involved will be obvious to the reader; the arithmetic is as follows.

	£	£

Enders' reserves:

$$£121,212 \times \frac{.028}{1.028} = \qquad (-) \quad 3,301$$

Contributions:

$$£7,506 \times \frac{.014}{1.014} = \quad (+) \; 104$$

Leavers' benefits:

$$£8,178 \times \frac{.014}{1.014} = \quad (-) \; \underline{113}$$

$$(-) \quad 9$$
$$\times 1.09^{½}$$

$$\underline{(-) \qquad 9}$$
$$(-) \; £3,310$$

Statistical experience profit

25.39 One way of procedure is as follows.

Average reserve per head at:
    beginning of year £110,000 ÷ 100   =   £1,100
    end of year (net of salary profit item)

$$£121,212 \times \frac{1.08}{1.11} \div 91 \qquad = \quad £1,296$$

∴ middle of year, say average of above figures   =   £1,198

Reserves for excess number of leavers

$$£1,198 \times 4 = £4,792$$

Estimated profit say one-quarter of the reserves (this fraction being arrived at by general judgement and not calculation), say £1,200 at the mid-point of the year, accumulating at 9 per cent. p.a. to £1,253 at the end of the year.

Summary

25.40 The constituents of Method C are compared with the accurate figures of Method B in the following statement.

	Method B	Method C
	£	£
Accumulated surplus brought forward	(−) 5,450	(−) 5,450
Investment profit	(+) 1,048	(+) 1,054
Salary profit	(−) 3,287	(−) 3,310
Statistical experience profit	(+) 1,279	(+) 1,253
Total	(−) £6,410	(−) £6,453

The analysis total of £6,453 would be regarded as acceptably close to the actual shortfall of £6,410.

Scheme X: analysis of surplus

Method of analysis

25.41 We will use Method C for the analysis of the surplus shown by the first actuarial investigation of Scheme X. We will confine our investigation to the past service position; this is often simpler than an investigation of past and future values together. The future service position is in little need of analysis, for the reason mentioned in paragraph 25.3. The past service position at the Commencement Date was that the liabilities arising from the pensionable service credits for the initial members were to be met by a special contribution payable for approximately ten years, as mentioned in paragraph 16.47. Using figures derived from paragraph 16.26 the opening position in respect of past service rights was as follows.

	£000
Past service liabilities at Commencement Date	1,597.8
Value of a contribution of 12 per cent. of payroll payable for 10 years	
$0.12 \times £1,363,000 \times \bar{a}_{\overline{10}|}$ 1% (9.52)	1,557.1
Initial shortfall	(−)40.7

25.42 The opening position was therefore a shortfall of £40,700. This sum accumulated for three years at the valuation rate of interest of 9 per cent. p.a. would have amounted at the investigation date to £52,700. The past service position set out in Table 69 shows a surplus of £807,000 so that we have to account for profits during the three years of about £860,000.

25.43 The emergence of so large a past service surplus is surprising and it will be helpful before embarking on detailed work to consider broadly the sources of surplus which may have given rise to an amount of this magnitude. Some comments are as follows; the reader is reminded that the word 'profit' is taken to include loss.

Investment profit

The assessed value of the fund at the investigation date is £1,439,000. Since a comparatively small percentage difference of this amount from that expected would give rise to a large sum in money terms, investment performance clearly needs to be investigated.

Salary profit

It appears from Table 48 that over the whole membership salaries were much in line with the expectation over the three years. It is unlikely that salary profit will have contributed very substantially to the surplus, although the salary experience fluctuated somewhat over the age groups.

Initial liability

The initial liability was £1,597,800, a large amount. There are two respects in which substantial profits may have flowed from this. In the first place Tables 28 to 30 show that there have been large numbers of withdrawals from the initial entrants. There may therefore have been a substantial release of liabilities; this point is dealt with as part of the statistical experience. In the second place, the initial liability is being met by a special contribution fixed initially at 12 per cent. of total payroll payable for about 10 years. This special contribution enters into the position at the investigation date in two respects, firstly the accumulated amount of the contribution already paid and secondly the present capital value of the seven years' future payments outstanding at the investigation date. If the total payroll during the three years, and particularly at the investigation date, differs from that expected in the initial calculations, this may have led to substantial profit.

Pension increases

It will be recalled that total pensions have been increased at the rate of 5 per cent. each year whereas what was expected in the initial calculations was that only the excess of the pension over G.M.P. would be increased, at only 3 per cent. p.a. The difference will have placed liabilities on the scheme.

Statistical experience

It will be seen from Table 50 that withdrawals, deaths in service and ill-health retirements all showed actual numbers greatly different from those expected. Although deviations from the expected statistical experience are generally of less importance than deviations in the economic area, it may be that in this case the deviations are so great that significant profits may have arisen.

Contributions

Since we are analysing the past service position of the active members, we are concerned with the cost of the accrual of benefit rights during three specific years, and not the contribution rate relating to the expected cost of accrual of benefit rights spread over the whole of expected future membership. We shall need to consider any discrepancy between the joint normal contribution rate payable (i.e. 13 per cent. of pensionable pay) and the contribution rate theoretically required to fund the benefits during the specific three years with which we are concerned.

Practical approach

25.44 The reader is provided in the various tables with virtually all the material he would need for a highly detailed analysis. Some readers may wish to pursue this, but we shall set out an approximate analysis at the level which would often be regarded in practice as sufficient to account for the valuation result and to disclose the main sources of profit.

Investment profit

25.45 We are dealing with the performance of the actual investments in hand from time to time, and we therefore start with a fund in hand of zero. To apply the method of paragraph 25.37 we need to know the amounts of contributions less benefits in each year and these are obtained from Table 46. The calculation proceeds as follows.

Year	Amount of contributions less benefits	9% p.a. accumulating factor to investigation date	(2) × (3)
(1)	(2)	(3)	(4)
	£000		£000
1	254	1.240	315
2	345	1.138	393
3	361	1.044	377
Expected value of assets			1,085
Actuarial value of assets			1,439
Investment profit			(+)354

There is therefore an item of surplus of £354,000 to be taken into account in the analysis as investment profit.

25.46 It is a matter for decision how far this item should be further analysed. The assessed value of the fund has been derived from the application of a factor to the market value of the assets, and as it is assumed that the accounts will have been audited and the market value of the assets established and checked there is not likely to be any error in this respect. It is of interest to note that the market value of the assets as shown in Table 47 is £1,147,000, which is not vastly greater than the expected figure of £1,085,000 shown above. The bulk of the profit therefore comes from the difference between market value and assessed value.

25.47 The basis for the adjustment of market value was explained in the previous chapter. The point is that the All-Share Index yield of 5.89 per cent. at the investigation date coupled with our assumption of 4 per cent. p.a. dividend growth produces a long term rate of return substantially greater than the valuation rate of 9 per cent. p.a., so that the notional dividend flow produced by unit market value has a present capital value greater than unity on the valuation basis. Another way of putting this is to say that the high level of the investment performance over the first three years is due not so much to the level of market values as to the fact that each £1 of market value is producing a greater dividend flow than expected. We will not examine investment performance further, although analysis is sometimes carried out in some depth.

Salary profits

25.48 We turn to the investigation of the financial effect of the divergence of actual increases in pensionable pay from those expected. We will apply the figure of actual to expected salaries of 99 per cent. shown in Table 48 to the whole of the active members' past service liabilities at the investigation date, ignoring the variations with age shown in column (6) of Table 48. In the artificial circumstances of the Scheme X data, entrants after the investigation date have the same pay progress as initial entrants, but in practice the fact that liabilities relate partly to new entrants for whom a salary experience is seldom calculated is an additional complication.

25.49 The method of paragraph 25.38 is applied as follows.

£000

Liabilities for enders:

$$\frac{0.01}{0.99} \times 1{,}896.4 \text{ (Table 69)} \qquad = (+) \ 19$$

Contributions:

$$\frac{0.005}{0.995} \times 1{,}377.5 \text{ (Table 46)} \times 1.09^{\frac{1}{2}} \qquad = (-) \ 7$$

Benefits:

$$\frac{0.005}{0.995} \times 800 \text{ (see below)} \times 1.09^{\frac{1}{2}} \qquad = (+) \ \underline{4}$$

$$(+) \ \underline{16}$$

The figure of £800,000 in the last item is an approximation to the capital value, at the middle of the period, of the benefit payments during the period and the pension liabilities at the end of the period. Contributions are considered further immediately below and in paragraphs 25.65 and 25.66.

Special contribution profit

25.50 Turning to the special company contributions payable in respect of the initial liability it was noted in paragraph 25.41 that in the initial calculations it was assumed that these contributions would be based from time to time on a payroll of £1,363,000 increasing at the rate of 8 per cent. p.a. The compound interest function $\bar{a}_{\overline{10|}}$ was in fact used as if the amount of £1,363,000 was an annual rate at the Commencement Date. Had the assumptions implicit in the calculation of the value of £1,557,100 in paragraph 25.41 been borne out in practice, the total capital value at the investigation date of special contributions paid and to be paid would have been calculated as follows.

Paid in year 1	: $1.08^{1/2} \times 1.09^{2\frac{1}{2}}$	=	1.289
Paid in year 2	: $1.08^{1\frac{1}{2}} \times 1.09^{1\frac{1}{2}}$	=	1.277
Paid in year 3	: $1.08^{2\frac{1}{2}} \times 1.09^{1/2}$	=	1.266
Payable for 7 years	: $1.08^3 \times \bar{a}_{\overline{7}\rvert}$ (6.762)	=	8.518
			12.350

$$0.12 \times £1,363,000 \times 12.350 = £2,020,000$$

25.51 The actual payments operated on in a similar way produce the following results.

			£000
Paid in year 1	: $£188,412 \times 1.09^{2\frac{1}{2}}$	=	234
Paid in year 2	: $£224,400 \times 1.09^{1\frac{1}{2}}$	=	255
Paid in year 3	: $£248,370 \times 1.09^{1/2}$	=	259
Payable for 7 years :			
$.012 \times £2,021,700$ (Table 34) $\times \bar{a}_{\overline{7}\rvert}^{1\%}(6.762)$		=	1,640
			2,388

25.52 The special contributions therefore represent at the investigation date an asset which has a value assessed on the valuation rate of interest of £2,388,000, which is to be compared with the expected value of £2,020,000. We have already taken into account in paragraph 25.49 the contribution loss arising from the fact that salary increases were somewhat less than expected, but we will not make the small adjustment theoretically required on that account to the profit of £368,000 now revealed; we will take this figure into the analysis.

Increases in pensions

25.53 We have to compare the increases given on pensions in payment, namely 5 per cent. p.a. on the gross pension, with those expected, namely 3 per cent. p.a. on the pension less, after attainment of State pension age, the G.M.P. content. Since this G.M.P. content in pensions in payment at the valuation date is small we will ignore this aspect and regard actual to expected pension increases as

$$\frac{1.05}{1.03} = 1.019 \text{ p.a.}$$

compounded according to the number of such increases that have in fact been enjoyed. We will assume without close investigation that current pensions forming the liability of £346,800 at the investigation date have enjoyed on the average 2 years' increases so that the excess rate is twice 1.9 per cent. or say 3.8 per cent. This gives a profit of

$$(-) \; \frac{0.038}{1.038} \; \times \; £346,800 \; = \; (-) £13,000$$

or say (−) £14,000 to include some small allowance for the excess payments already made at the valuation date. We will regard this as also covering the small cost of the excess increases on preserved pension rights.

Statistical experience

25.54 We turn to the various aspects of the statistical experience. In the artificially simple circumstances of our earlier example the analysis in this area involved a comparison of the actual and expected numbers of exits, the difference in numbers being operated on by the profit per head as outlined in item (iv) of paragraph 25.31. In the more complicated circumstances of Scheme X we need in theory to deal entirely separately with the expected profit and with the actual profit, allowing for the fact that the difference between the actual and expected experience for any particular decrement is not simply a matter of total numbers but is also influenced by any differences between the expected and actual profiles in such matters as age, duration and salary of the persons concerned. In fact we shall not go into great detail in respect of these decrements, but the reader should note that it is sometimes necessary to do so.

Reserves at exit

25.55 We shall need to assess, for the various groups that we shall investigate, the amounts of reserves held immediately before the members concerned became exits. The large volume of work involved in making a full valuation for each individual at the date of exit would not be justified; we need some simple method that will sufficiently serve the purpose. It is not difficult or unduly onerous to calculate the product of salary and pensionable service for a leaver at the date of exit, so that if we can arrive at a factor to apply to this product to give an approximation to the full past service reserve at the date concerned, this will provide a convenient method.

25.56   We can use the figures of the table in paragraph 16.22 for this purpose. These represent the cost of a year's accrual of benefit rights, which is what we require for present purposes, except that as noted in that paragraph they were based on pay in the previous year instead of the current year. We need to allow for this and to exclude the cost of cover for death in service capital sums, which we shall deal with separately in the analysis. The figures indicate that a rate of about 13.5 per cent. might be appropriate.

25.57   We estimated in paragraph 16.17 that the release of liability arising from the absence of pension increases on the G.M.P. represented a reduction of about 1.0 in the percentage contribution rate then being considered. When we are calculating reserves for the purpose of the analysis, we shall be faced with the complication that some of the past years of pensionable service with which we are concerned are not contracted-out years, so that no adjustment for G.M.P. arises, while years of contributory membership are contracted-out. We shall avoid these complications by using an overall factor assessed on approximate lines. For simplicity we shall use a factor of 0.125 for all our calculations. This represents 12.5 per cent. of salary in the previous year and is therefore not comparable with a contribution rate applicable to current salary from time to time.

Withdrawals

25.58   It will be seen from Table 50 that the actual number of withdrawals was 234 compared with an expected number of 52. Table 51 shows that the actual withdrawals were made up of 210 leavers with a refund of contributions and appropriate payments to the State scheme in respect of G.M.P.s, 13 leavers with preserved pension and 11 persons transferring to other pension schemes with payment of a transfer value. For simplicity we will take the whole of the expected number of withdrawals into our approximate calculations for withdrawals with a return of contributions, so that when we consider leavers with preserved pensions or payment of a transfer value it will be assumed that no exits were expected.

Withdrawals with refunds

25.59 We are therefore concerned with 210 withdrawals of which 52 were expected. We shall not look into any difference between the age, salary and pensionable service profiles of these groups but will simply estimate the profit at exit for the 210 persons concerned and then assume that one-quarter of this profit (approximately representing 52 cases out of 210) was expected. The calculation of the product, for the 210 cases, of pensionable duration at exit and pensionable salary in the year before exit is a straightforward matter. It results in a figure of £1,470,000. We will therefore take the reserves at exit as 12.5 per cent. of this amount, i.e. £184,000. The consolidated revenue account of Table 46 shows that total payments in respect of early leavers with a refund amounted to about £80,000 so that the release of reserves was about £104,000. As noted above we will assume that about one-quarter of this was expected, so that the balance of £78,000 goes into the analysis as an item of profit in the middle of the period, giving an amount of £85,000 at the end of the period after adding interest at the valuation rate for one year (as an approximation to the mean period involved, bearing in mind the incidence of the payments).

Withdrawals with preserved pension

25.60 A similar calculation of estimated reserves at exit for the 13 members who withdrew with preserved pensions gives estimated reserves at exit of £49,000, or about £53,000 at the investigation date after allowing for interest. The liabilities for preserved pensions and associated benefits at the valuation date are shown in Table 69 as £29,300 so that a profit item of £24,000 is taken into the analysis.

Withdrawals with transfer payments

25.61 A similar calculation for the 11 members who withdrew with payment of a transfer value indicates reserves at exit of about £100,000. The accounts in Table 46 show total transfer payments of £62,000 so that the profits at exit were about £38,000, giving a profit of £43,000 after the addition of interest to be taken to the analysis.

Death in service: capital sums

25.62 We have implicitly assumed in the above discussion that the cost of capital sums on death in service would be covered by a contribution of about 1 per cent. of pensionable salaries. This is obtained from the total of column (9) of Table 16, bearing in mind the total salaries in force. The total amount of such a contribution during the three years is about £55,000 whereas the total lump sums paid on death in service amounted to £128,000 (see Table 43). The relationship of these two figures reflects the heavy mortality experience in service shown in Table 50. This item therefore gives rise to an amount of profit of $(-)$ £73,000 in the middle of the period or $(-)$ £83,000 at the end of the period after allowing for interest.

Death in service: widows' pensions

25.63 We now have to compare the reserves set up for widows' pensions with the reserves released in respect of the deceased members. A calculation of reserves at the date of death on the lines of those made previously indicates total reserves of about £126,000. Table 68 shows reserves for widows' pensions in payment at the investigation date of £70,500 and we also have to allow for the payments of such pensions made before the investigation date. We will assume that the liability in the middle of the period for widows' pensions was £75,000, which is £51,000 less than the reserves held for the members at the date of death. Table 50 shows that about one-half of the cases were expected so that there is an item of profit of one- half of £51,000, i.e. £26,000, at the middle of the period or £30,000 at the end of the period after allowing for interest.

Ill-health pensions

25.64 It will be recalled from Table 50 that the ill-health retirement experience was exceptionally heavy and the possible amount of the financial strain is such as to justify a similar type of calculation to those above. Reserves at exit are estimated at £113,000, and one ill-health pensioner died before the valuation date. The liability for ill-health pensions at the valuation date is shown in Table 66 as about £96,000; transferring this liability to the middle of the period and adjusting for payments made in the meantime the liability immediately after ill-health retirement was perhaps £122,000. This shows a surprisingly small financial strain. This is partly due to the fact that the two largest cases, in Groups Q and S, occurred at advanced ages, so that no great acceleration of payment was involved. Another factor is the reduction in extra cost consequent upon the assumption of heavy ill-health pensioners' mortality. We will assume a strain of £10,000 at the investigation date.

Contributions

25.65 Normal joint contributions have been paid during the three year period at the rate of 13 per cent. of total pensionable salaries from time to time. We have already assumed in the analysis that a contribution of 1 per cent. was allocated to the cost of the capital sum benefits on death in service so that a 12.0 per cent. contribution remains. We need to consider how this rate of contribution compares with the cost of setting up the appropriate benefit rights on the valuation basis for the three years.

25.66 We are thus concerned in principle with the cost of a year's accrual of benefit rights. These rights are all part of contracted-out employment, so that the cost is diminished by the saving from the absence of pension increases on the G.M.P. mentioned in paragraph 16.17. In that paragraph we arrived at a contribution rate of 12.1 per cent. including the cost of capital sums on death in service so that our estimate is that the cost of setting up the accruing pension rights is 11.1 per cent. of pensionable salaries during the year concerned. We thus have a margin in the contribution rate for the purpose of the present analysis equal to 0.9 per cent. of pensionable salaries. It will be seen from the consolidated revenue account in Table 46 that the amount of a 1 per cent. contribution during the three year period is about £55,000 so that the amount of the margin with interest, giving a figure of £56,000, is taken into the analysis.

Summary

25.67 The various items referred to in the preceding discussion may be summarised as follows.

Source of profit	(+)	(−)
	£000	£000
Initial surplus brought forward		53
Investment performance	354	
Salary experience	16	
Pension increases		14
Withdrawals with refund	85	
Withdrawals with preserved pension	24	
Withdrawals with transfer payment	43	
Death in service: capital sums		83
Death in service: widows' pensions	30	
Ill-health retirements		10
Normal contributions	56	
Special contributions	368	
Total	976	160

25.68 It will be seen that the items combine to give an expected surplus of £816,000 compared with the actual surplus of £807,000. There are many items which we have not taken into the analysis, principally because they are assumed to have small financial significance. One example of this is mortality after retirement; the number of pensioners is small and any deviation from the expected experience would probably be of little consequence. Given the incomplete nature of the analysis, and the generally approximate approach, we will regard the above results as providing an adequate check on the valuation result and a satisfactory indication of the main sources of profit during the three years.

CHAPTER 26

THE ACTUARIAL INVESTIGATION: DISCONTINUANCE SOLVENCY

THE ACTUARIAL INVESTIGATION: DISCONTINUANCE SOLVENCY

26.1 The main calculations for the actuarial investigation of a pension scheme are usually made on the assumption that the scheme will continue in full force indefinitely. This is of course the normal expectation of those concerned with a scheme in the absence of special circumstances. However, before the actuary can consider what advice to tender to his client the finances of the scheme need to be investigated from a different viewpoint. This is concerned with the position if the scheme were discontinued. Two main aspects normally arise, as follows.

(i) *Discontinuance solvency* The issue here is whether, if the scheme had been discontinued on the valuation date, the funds in hand would have been sufficient to secure current and preserved pensions and the accrued rights of contributory members.

(ii) *Solvency certificate A* This arises only for schemes used for contracting out. The position was outlined in paragraphs 4.41 to 4.43.

Discontinuance solvency

26.2 The subject of discontinuance solvency was introduced in paragraph 21.2 but for convenience the main points are now repeated. The issue first came to prominence in the United Kingdom at a time of very low market values of investments, at the end of 1974. Trustees and others became concerned with the question of whether, if the difficulties in which many employers found themselves at that time resulted in a forced discontinuance of a pension scheme, the assets then in the hands of the trustees would be sufficient to provide for the continuance of pensions in payment, the securing of the preserved rights of ex-members and the provision of the accrued pension rights of each employee member. The natural interpretation of the latter term for this purpose is the preserved pension to which the member would have become entitled as an early leaver. With each of these benefits would be associated the appropriate death benefits.

26.3 It has subsequently become increasingly common for the trustees of schemes to keep the members informed from time to time on this matter. Many trustee bodies attach to each year's accounts and balance sheet of the scheme a statement by the actuary dealing both with the long term solvency and contribution rates of the continuing scheme and with solvency on discontinuance, normally based on the most recent full actuarial investigation. An example of such a statement appeared in paragraph 21.3. It is not clear at the time of writing how the disclosure requirements of the Social Security Act 1985 mentioned in paragraph 17.21 will affect such statements.

26.4 As indicated above, in looking at discontinuance solvency the actuary will normally regard the 'accrued rights' of employee members as being the preserved benefits which would have been provided under the normal rules of the scheme if all the members had become individual early leavers at the investigation date. Members who, because they did not satisfy the preservation requirements of the scheme, would have been entitled as individual early leavers to a refund of contributions, could not under Inland Revenue rules take a refund on the discontinuance of the whole scheme, and are therefore included for this purpose with the other members as entitled to preserved pensions.

Undefined rights

26.5 We will therefore regard the liabilities in the investigation of discontinuance solvency as representing the benefits already in payment, the preserved rights of ex-members and the preserved pensions of the employee members treated as if they were all early leavers at the investigation date. Even this, however, is not a precise specification of benefits. The reader will recall from previous chapters that in private sector schemes in the United Kingdom it is often the case that increases on pensions in course of payment are not promised, or are promised at only a modest level, but the trustees use their best endeavours to provide a satisfactory level of increase from time to time and schemes are often funded with such a level in mind. There is therefore a question to be settled as to whether the assessment of discontinuance liabilities should take into account only the rate of pension increase, if any, provided for in the rules or a rate more in line with what has in fact been provided in a recent period or is being funded for as far as the on-going position is concerned. This issue has to be treated on its merits. There may be similar uncertainties about the rate of increase in the preserved pensions of early leavers before they come into payment, although increases on any G.M.P. element will certainly have to be allowed for as must the increases on part of the non-G.M.P. element introduced under the Social Security Act 1985.

Realisation or continuation of assets

26.6 In some cases of discontinuance it would not be feasible for the trustees or their successors to carry on the scheme as a closed investment trust for the benefit of the current and prospective beneficiaries. In this case any test of solvency on discontinuance must imply that the assets would be converted into cash and the market value at the valuation date used to buy immediate and deferred annuities in the market. In other cases discontinuance might be interpreted in the sense that the trustees would continue the scheme as a closed investment trust. In this case the calculations of discontinuance solvency are not necessarily concerned with market values of investments and market annuity rates at a given date but are more akin to the calculations in previous chapters.

Comparability of solvency levels

26.7 If we follow the first alternative referred to in the previous paragraph we will compare the market value of the assets (usually taken as mid-market values for this purpose) with the cost of buying immediate and deferred annuities corresponding to the benefits in payment and the prospective rights of other members of the scheme concerned. This calculation does not therefore rest on actuarial projections of various sorts but is concerned instead with the market value of the assets and the terms on which immediate and deferred annuities may be purchased in the market. The reader will therefore see that this is in concept a method of assessing solvency which is consistent between one scheme and another, since it involves no matters left to the individual judgement of the actuary. There has been much discussion in the United Kingdom in recent years about methods of comparing solvency of pension schemes which are not dependent on individual judgement, and this method clearly has attractions from this point of view.

Volume of calculation

26.8 In fact, however, it is unusual for discontinuance solvency levels to be calculated with the degree of precision which would enable the results to be used for the purpose mentioned in the previous paragraph. Some reasons for the widespread use of more approximate methods are as follows.

(i)   Trustees normally aim to give scheme members no more than broad information about discontinuance solvency levels.

(ii)   The actuary does not normally use discontinuance calculations as the basis of the numerical advice that he tenders; this is generally based on his calculations assuming a continuing scheme.

(iii)   The comparison of market values of assets with the commercial and State scheme premium cost of buying out the benefits will vary from day to day, because of the volatility of market values and the changing terms offered by life offices, and it is therefore not worthwhile to calculate the precise ratio on a particular date.

(iv)   Although immediate annuity rates in the market are published regularly, the bulk terms for the discontinuance of a pension scheme of a reasonable size would probably be a matter for negotiation. Furthermore, market rates for the large volume of deferred annuity contracts which would normally be involved cannot usually be estimated with any degree of accuracy, since such rates are not published regularly.

(v)   If a scheme is insolvent on a discontinuance test the members will probably be more anxious to have an indication of the time that will be taken for such solvency to be achieved than with the precise degree of insolvency. The actuary will probably be able to estimate the timescale on approximate lines.

(vi) In normal circumstances a scheme which is reasonably well funded on a continuing basis will often show a comparatively high ratio (of much more than 100 per cent.) when assets are compared with discontinuance liabilities. This is because the latter incorporate the future increases which would be provided on the preserved benefits of early leavers, and as far as the non-G.M.P. element is concerned these increases will normally be less than the expected future increases in pay which are brought into the past service liabilities in the valuation of the continuing scheme. A precise calculation of a high level of discontinuance solvency would serve no purpose, and indeed its publication might be misleading in that the members might suppose that it indicated the presence of a large disposable surplus.

Against these arguments for the broad approach should be set the fact that the actuary may need to use some or all of the same calculations in connection with his contracting-out solvency certificate if this is called for. This may necessitate more accurate calculations, but it is still likely that a broad method will be used in the first instance to arrive at a first indication of the position.

Discontinuance solvency: Scheme X

26.9 Practitioners differ in their approach to the various questions raised so far in this chapter. We will illustrate some of the points involved by reference to Scheme X. We will suppose that the actuarial statements appended to the accounts for year 1 and year 2 have merely stated that the rates of contribution are in accordance with actuarial advice and are such as, on the assumptions used, are likely to lead to solvency in the long term. Year 3 is assumed to be the first year in which a statement is to be made about the level of discontinuance solvency.

Method assuming realisation of assets

26.10 In looking at discontinuance solvency for Scheme X we will assume that the market value of the assets in hand at the investigation date is to be compared with the total cost of buying immediate or deferred annuity policies as the case may be (with appropriate death benefits) to match

(i) the pensions in payment,

(ii) the rights of persons who were entitled to preserved pensions as at the investigation date, having left Scheme X before that date, and

(iii) the preserved pension rights which would have been provided for the active members had they all left with entitlement to such rights at the investigation date.

We will take into account only the rate of increase on pensions in course of payment set out in the specification in Chapter 13, i.e. 3 per cent. p.a. We will make crude calculations to arrive at a first approximation to the position, which will enable us to judge whether more accurate calculations are needed.

Pensions in payment

26.11 It will be recalled from Table 69 that the value of pensions in payment at the valuation date, including the associated death benefits, was £346,800. The total pensions in payment as shown in Table 66 amounted to £28,746 p.a. so that the crude average annuity value was 12.1. This value represents the resultant of a wide range of immediate and contingent annuities on a rate of interest of 9 per cent. with allowance for 3 per cent. p.a. increases, i.e. an effective rate of about 5.8. (It will be recalled that, since none of the pensions payable to males have G.M.P. element payable to a pensioner aged over 65, the only pension element in payment on which 3 per cent. p.a. increases are not currently being granted from Scheme X is the small G.M.P. content of the widows' pensions in payment, and this is ignored for present purposes.)

26.12 The investigation date is taken as 5th April 1982. At this date it was possible to buy immediate annuities in the market on extraordinarily favourable terms, the interest basis being as high as 15 or 16 per cent. Allowing for the assumed rate of pension increase of 3 per cent. p.a. this implies that our first approximation to a market cost of the pensions in payment might be obtained by using an average annuity based on interest of about 12 per cent. instead of 5.8 per cent. Given the mix of liabilities in Table 66 this might imply an average factor of about 7.5 instead of 12.1. Thus by proportion a first approximation to the cost of buying out the current pensions and associated death benefits at the valuation date is £0.21 million.

Preserved pensions

26.13 It will be recalled that the liabilities shown in Table 69 for ex-members with preserved pensions have been based on a rate of interest of 9 per cent., coupled with the appropriate rates of increase of the G.M.P. and non-G.M.P. elements in deferment and in payment. As noted earlier, the terms on which life offices are prepared to sell deferred annuities in bulk upon the discontinuance of a pension scheme are much more difficult to gauge than the terms relating to immediate annuities. Since the liability is comparatively small, and given the age distribution in Table 62, we will use the value of £29,300 as shown in Table 69 as our first approximation to the cost of purchase in the market.

Active members

26.14 The past service liabilities of some £1.9m. in respect of active members as shown in Table 69 are of course calculated on the assumption that their future contributory membership of Scheme X will follow its normal course as implied by the service table, salary scale, earnings escalation assumption and other features of the actuarial basis. We now have to estimate the liabilities on the assumption that all these active members received early leavers' benefits upon the discontinuation of Scheme X at the investigation date. This involves the calculation of the accrued rights at the investigation date, divided between the G.M.P. and non-G.M.P. elements, and (since we are using a method which assumes realisation of assets) the estimation of State scheme premiums for the G.M.P. element and of the cost of purchase of appropriate deferred annuity policies in the market for the non-G.M.P. elements.

26.15 Table 34 shows the relevant data for the employee members at the investigation date. In Table 70 the initial entrants and subsequent entrants have been combined and the amount of the accrued pension rights calculated by applying the pension fraction of 1/80 to the amounts of salary times pensionable service from Table 34. The total amount of accrued G.M.P.s has also been taken from that Table.

State scheme premiums

26.16 As to the amount of the Accrued Rights Premiums payable to the State scheme in respect of the accrued G.M.P.s shown in

Table 70, it will be recalled that the investigation date is deemed to be 5th April 1982. At that time market conditions were such that the application of the market level indicator resulted in Accrued Rights Premiums equal to 68 per cent. of their standard value. Columns (5) and (6) of Table 70 shows the calculation of the approximate amount of Accrued Rights Premiums rates, the premium rates before adjustment as shown in column (5) being taken from the official premium tables.

Non-G.M.P. element

26.17 The interest basis on which life offices would sell bulk deferred annuities would probably range from a rate near to that underlying immediate annuity rates at ages near to retirement down to an assumed long term rate of interest at the younger ages. Column (7) of Table 70 shows an assumed cost of purchasing unit non-G.M.P. pension rights and associated death benefits allowing for 5 per cent. p.a. growth during the period of deferment and 3 per cent. p.a. increases in payment. The figures have been prepared purely for illustrative purposes and no research has been made into the rates which life offices might in fact have charged for such contracts on the date concerned. Column (8) of Table 70 shows the estimation of the cost of providing the non-G.M.P. element of the preserved rights and the associated death benefits by application of these rates to the amounts in column (4) of the Table.

Summary

26.18 The estimated liabilities for current pensioners, early leavers with preserved pensions and employee members are brought together and compared with the market value of the assets in the following statement.

	£ million
First approximation values of discontinuance benefits:	
pensions in payment	0.21
existing preserved pensions	0.03
employee members' rights regarded as preserved	
pensions:	
G.M.P.	0.15
non-G.M.P.	0.98
Total	1.37
Market value of assets (see Table 47)	1.15

26.19 It will be seen that the first assessment of discontinuance solvency indicates that the cost of providing the various benefits is in excess of the amount of the available assets. Although discontinuance solvency has not been reached it is clear that the funding pattern is likely to produce it soon, since the present position has been reached after a period of only three years from the Commencement Date, at which time there were no assets to set against the very large initial liabilities. An actuarial statement to be appended to the trustees' report would probably cover both the position at the investigation date and the way in which this had developed from the position at the setting up of Scheme X, since a bald statement merely showing that the scheme was not solvent on a discontinuance basis would give to the members a misleading impression of what is a quite satisfactory situation. We will not pursue further the estimation of the level of discontinuance solvency.

Solvency Certificate A

26.20 We turn to the other aspect of solvency mentioned in paragraph 26.1, namely the preparation of solvency certificate A for schemes such as Scheme X which are used for contracting out. It will be recalled that a specimen of this certificate is shown at the end of Chapter 4. We are not concerned in the preparation of the certificate for Scheme X with the overall position on discontinuance solvency but solely with the liabilities with which the solvency certificate is concerned. These were outlined in paragraph 16.49 but for convenience we list them below.

(i) G.M.P.s in course of payment and accrued rights to such G.M.P.s, on the basis that these liabilities are cleared by payment of the appropriate premiums to the State scheme.

(ii) Equivalent pension benefits. This relates to a superseded State pension scheme. The point is not now of great practical importance and we are not concerned with such benefits in Scheme X.

(iii) Current pensions other than the current G.M.P.s covered in (i) above.

(iv) Any other liabilities which have a priority equal to or greater than the above liabilities in a winding up.

(v) Expenses of administration.

As to priorities, we stated in paragraph 16.50 that we would assume that the trust deed and rules of Scheme X would be drawn up in such a way that current pensions and accrued G.M.P. rights have highest priority on discontinuance.

26.21 As in the assessment of overall discontinuance solvency the actuary will make a rough preliminary assessment of the position since this will make clear whether more accurate calculations are necessary. On general grounds the expectation would be that the position in respect of Scheme X would cause no difficulties. This is because the contribution rate payable has included a substantial element in respect of benefits other than those listed above. For instance, the element of the contribution rate relating to the year by year cost of the accrual of benefits covers the full scale pensions and not merely the G.M.P., and the element of the contribution rate intended to clear over a period the initial past service liability has no counterpart in the liabilities described above.

26.22 It will indeed be obvious from the figures in paragraph 26.18 that there is no difficulty in completing solvency certificate A as far as the position at the investigation date is concerned. The cost of securing pensions (including G.M.P.s) in course of payment and the accrued rights to G.M.P.s of the active members is only some £0.36m. and the market value of assets greatly exceeds this amount. The position is virtually certain to remain satisfactory during the next five years. The issues that arise in connection with solvency certificate A in practice are often much more complex, and the position much more finely balanced, than in the case of Scheme X. Each case has to be treated on its merits.

CHAPTER 27

THE ACTUARIAL INVESTIGATION: RESULT

THE ACTUARIAL INVESTIGATION: RESULT

The basis of professional judgement

27.1 When the work described in previous chapters has been completed the actuary will have the following information at his disposal.

(i) Present capital values as at the investigation date of the expected future contribution flows and expected future benefit flows in respect of the persons with an interest in the scheme as at that date and of the expected future proceeds from the assets held at that date. These values will have been calculated on the actuarial basis chosen, including allowance for expected future pay increases, on the assumption that the scheme continues in force. Calculations relevant to various alternative funding plans may have been made.

(ii) Some knowledge of the effect on the figures in (i) of variations in the actuarial basis. In some cases this will involve merely rough calculations, while at the other extreme full valuations on different bases may have been made. We have not dealt specifically with this aspect in our calculations for Scheme X, but the reader who has followed the arithmetic of earlier chapters will appreciate that the effect of a change in the earnings escalation or pension increase assumptions can be roughly estimated on the basis of the average ages of those involved.

(iii) An understanding of the main items of actuarial profit or loss which have led to the result revealed, starting from the result shown by the previous valuation or other major calculations.

(iv) The contribution rate or rates appropriate for entrants in the future on the various bases involved in (i) and (ii) above.

(v) Values of assets and liabilities, which may be approximate, on the assumption of discontinuance of the scheme on the investigation date.

The exercise of professional judgement

27.2   The first stage of the investigation at which considerable professional judgement is involved was that of settling the long term actuarial assumptions on which the main calculations were to be made. The immediately preceding chapters have dealt with the details of these calculations; although these are complex their execution does not in general involve the exercise of professional judgement. Now that the actuary has at his disposal the various figures referred to in the preceding paragraph we arrive at the second stage at which such judgement is involved. In this chapter we outline some of the points which may arise as the actuary decides, on the basis of the figures available to him, on his view of the current position of the scheme and the advice that he should tender to his client. There are a number of reasons why the actuary will wish to reflect on the figures as calculated, and may decide to adjust them before settling the result.

Analysis of surplus

27.3   The actuary will examine in detail the various items of actuarial profit and loss that have given rise to the result revealed by the investigation of the continuing scheme. This analysis will concentrate attention on any financially important areas in which the recent experience has deviated from the long term assumptions. The actuary will have to decide (if necessary after discussion with the employer) which of these items are likely in his view to be non-recurring. He may decide to make an adjustment to the calculated figures in respect of any special factors which are likely to feature in the experience for a further limited period.

Economic factors

27.4   A further ground for special adjustments may arise from time lags associated with economic factors. In times of varying inflation, for instance, there is some evidence that changes in the amount of the flow of dividends on ordinary shares may be expected to occur a certain period after a variation in the rate of price inflation has taken place. Thus an exceptional pay increase which appeared in a period before the investigation date of a pension scheme, and will have been included in the data and thus increased the liabilities, may have represented a response to a period of unusually high price inflation which has not yet come through as an increase in dividend flow which would raise the value of the assets. The actuary might feel it appropriate, in his assessment of the value of the assets, to take account of a likely improvement in dividend flow.

Post-investigation date events

27.5 Since the calculations are, inevitably, completed some time after the investigation date, the actuary will have a certain knowledge of events after that date available to him by the time that he comes to settle the result, quite apart from speculative matters such as that mentioned in the previous paragraph. This further knowledge will certainly relate to broad economic factors, and there may also be information about events which have happened in the narrower field of the scheme or company concerned following the investigation date. The aim of the actuary is to put forward the position of the scheme as he sees it on the most up-to-date information available, and it is therefore perfectly proper and indeed necessary for him to take into account events which have happened after the investigation date if he thinks this appropriate. In recent years in the United Kingdom substantial redundancies or other changes in the membership provide examples of such events.

Strength of basis

27.6 Another aspect which may need to be reviewed is the whole question of the strength of the valuation basis. As has been noted earlier, the basis chosen will represent one of a possible range of bases. It is likely that the position of the chosen basis within the possible range will have been discussed with the client, or at least indicated to him, at the previous investigation. It may, however, be appropriate to adopt a different stance as far as the basis is concerned on the current occasion. An example of this might be the policy as to reserving for future pension increases. It will be recalled that, at least in private sector schemes in the United Kingdom, there may be a wide range of possibilities as to the extent to which pension increases should be funded in advance. For example, if a particular intervaluation period has been profitable it may be decided to reserve for a greater degree of pension increase (if such a course is appropriate under the rules) rather than to show a large surplus.

Consultation

27.7 It is proper for the actuary to discuss such matters with all the parties who have a legitimate interest in the scheme. As far as his professional position is concerned, his principal will normally be the trustees of the scheme, but the employer may have a close interest in its finances, particularly if the structure of the scheme is such that the employer meets the balance of the cost. The final responsibility for the basis of course remains with the actuary.

Scheme X

27.8 The application of professional judgement to the calculated figures involves a close knowledge of the surrounding circumstances and other factors affecting a scheme. The main point to bear in mind is that the calculated figures are not an end in themselves, but provide the raw material for the exercise of professional judgement. It has not been thought useful to illustrate this stage by reference to Scheme X; we will assume that the position shown in Table 69 is the final result.

27.9 The main issue that will arise from the valuation of Scheme X is clearly the fact that the employer can reduce the special contributions which he is paying in respect of the initial liability. These contributions arise under Spec. 10(ii) of Scheme X, and although the arrangement is specified only in outline the implication is that the employer should not pay more than is necessary to meet the specified liability. In our analysis of surplus in Chapter 25 we looked at the working of Scheme X as a whole over the first three years. A (positive or negative) part of the surplus shown at the investigation date will have arisen from aspects of Scheme X other than the initial liability and the special contributions to meet it, and it might be thought that in principle we need to remove the financial effects of those aspects from the analysis of surplus in order to consider what adjustment may be made in the employer's special contributions.

27.10 While there is something in this point, it should be noted that under Spec. 10(i) of Scheme X there is considerable flexibility in the employer's normal contributions, which may vary between 1½ times and twice the total contributions of the members as recommended by the actuary from time to time. The implication is that a surplus or shortfall arising from the normal year-by-year working of Scheme X (separate from the working of the scheme in respect of the initial liability) would lead in the first instance to an adjustment of the employer's contributions rather than a change in the benefits or in the members' contribution rates. We will assume that the whole of the surplus is regarded as disposable, that it is used to reduce the employer's special contributions, and that the rate of these contributions is in fact halved with effect from the valuation date, leading to an almost exact equality of assets and liabilities in Table 69.

The investigation result: general issues

27.11 The question of the action to be taken in respect of the surplus or shortfall revealed by an actuarial valuation often needs careful consideration. Some miscellaneous examples of the points that arise are as follows.

(i) Sometimes the question arises of whether the members' contributions should be increased as part of the action to clear a shortfall. An argument against such a course is that the members whose liabilities have contributed most to the shortfall are likely to be the older members with long service, but the members who would pay most by way of increased contributions are young members with many years of expected future service. A proposal for an increase in the members' contribution rates is likely to seem inequitable to these younger members.

(ii) In recent years a widespread use of surplus has been to provide special increases on pensions in course of payment. In schemes with reasonably adequate scales of benefit at retirement, but inadequate guaranteed pension increases, this is often seen by all concerned as a reasonable use of surplus. A further justification for this course is that the employee members in a 'final pay' scheme have an automatic first call on the resources of the scheme because of the final pay promise, so that pensioners have a reasonable claim on any surplus resources that emerge after this first call has been met.

(iii) Sometimes members of a scheme have fixed amount pension entitlements in the scheme in respect of some period of past pensionable service, in addition to 'final pay' pension entitlements in respect of current service. It may be reasonable to use part of any surplus to increase these fixed entitlements, on the grounds that profits from the performance of the investments held in respect of these amounts will not, by definition, have been offset by extra liabilities consequent on pay increases greater than those anticipated. Another point that is sometimes overlooked is that if the preserved rights of early leavers are increased from surplus there is likely to be pressure for any such fixed amount rights of remaining members to be increased also. The case is not, however, straightforward, because the early leaver could argue that his rights would have been increased with pay increases had he remained, whereas the member with fixed amount entitlements cannot advance this argument.

(iv) In considering use of surplus it is often necessary to distinguish between benefit improvements which are likely to lead in due course to an increase in the contribution rates and those that are not. Thus if an employer is firmly of the opinion that he cannot contemplate any increase in contributions but he is content for surplus to be used for benefit improvements, an increase in pensions in course of payment would be an acceptable improvement since it has no implications for the benefit scales. An increase in the pension fraction for existing employee members, however, would be a different matter, even if the cost of the past and future service improvement was covered by surplus. Unless the administrative complexity of a different scale for future new entrants was accepted, the improvement might necessitate an increase in contribution rates in due course.

Many such points arise in practice, either as a result of particular provisions of the trust deed and rules or on wider grounds as illustrated above. Each case has to be considered on its merits.

Contribution rates

27.12 In the above discussion we have not dealt explicitly with contribution rates, but the regular investigation is of course the occasion for the review of contribution rates and we now consider this matter briefly. It is comparatively seldom that the contribution rates of members are altered, so that we are mainly concerned with the employer's contributions. The use of surplus for a short term reduction in, or cessation of, the employer's contributions was discussed in paragraph 8.89 et seq.

27.13 It will be recalled that we discussed various different funding plans in Chapter 8. Under Plan F the contribution rate for Scheme X would have emerged directly from the valuation result by use of the reasoning of paragraph 8.74. However, under this plan there is no separation of the contribution to cover the cost of the current accrual of benefit and the contribution to cover a past service shortfall, and we are of course making a clear distinction between these in the funding of Scheme X.

27.14 The contribution rates for Scheme X were settled in paragraph 16.47. The general situation was that the normal accrual of benefit required a joint contribution of 13 per cent., that it was thought reasonable for the members to pay 5 per cent. and the employer therefore 8 per cent., and that as the employer could afford 20 per cent. in all, 12 per cent. was available in respect of the initial liability. We are assuming that the rate of 12 per cent. will be reduced to 6 per cent. (see paragraph 27.10) but we have not yet explicitly decided whether the employer's normal contribution rate of 8 per cent. remains satisfactory. The future service position revealed in Table 69 is of a virtual equality of liabilities and contribution values, so that there is no obvious need to change the employer's normal rate. The information in the various tables will enable the reader to compare the contribution rates at the Commencement Date under the various funding plans considered in Chapter 16 with the corresponding rates at the investigation date. This approach will confirm that the employer's rate may remain unchanged, and we will assume that this is the decision.

CHAPTER 28

THE ACTUARIAL INVESTIGATION: REPORT

THE ACTUARIAL INVESTIGATION: REPORT

Introduction

28.1 The settling of the valuation result marks the end of one stage of the actuary's work and the beginning of a new and equally important stage. The trustees and others concerned have now to have conveyed to them the actuary's view of the scheme's finances, in order that they may carry out on an informed basis whatever duties are placed on them by the trust deed and rules. They will be relying on the actuary to convey to them the position as he sees it, in terms that they may reasonably be expected to understand. Typically, most readers of the actuary's letters and reports on an actuarial investigation will be persons who have limited knowledge of pensions and limited time to give to the subject, and the actuary needs to choose his words accordingly.

Preliminary reporting of results

28.2 The trust deed and rules of a scheme will almost certainly require the actuary to submit a report to the trustees on the results of his investigations. Because of this, and because the matters dealt with are usually of such importance as to merit a formal document, most investigations involve the preparation of a formal report. It is, however, quite common for the results of an investigation to be conveyed in the first instance in a less formal way, usually by means of a letter setting out the essential features of the investigation and its result. We will not dwell on this informal stage of communication, but turn to a discussion of the formal valuation report.

The style of the report

28.3 With the increasing complexity of pension matters, the actuary is usually in frequent correspondence with most of his clients. The valuation report is only one of many documents that he sends to his client. The style and form of the report will be governed by the general rules applying to all such correspondence. It should be written in language which is clear and simple, but precise, and the contents should be set out in the most logical order. The actuary will need to avoid terms which he is accustomed to giving a particular meaning but which may have a different meaning to the client. For instance, the actuary considering the two constituents of future salary increase referred to in paragraph 9.28 may for his own purposes think of the increases which are assumed to be enjoyed if overall levels of pay remained stable as the 'normal' or the 'basic' scale. The client may, however, be accustomed to think of a certain degree of escalation as 'normal', and 'basic' earnings may mean to him earnings excluding overtime, commission and such payments. It is necessary to make every effort to use terms which cannot be misinterpreted.

28.4   Within these general rules, the style of the report will depend upon the type of client to which it is addressed. Clearly the style and content of a report on the small pension scheme of an employer whose officials are unfamiliar with the concepts and problems involved will differ greatly from those of a report on the scheme of a large organisation with actuaries on its staff and its own pension department.

The inclusion of recommendations

28.5   The contents of the report will depend on the detailed wording of those parts of the trust deed and rules under which the report is prepared and submitted. The contents will also depend on the precise part that the report plays in the dialogue between the actuary and his client. Practice in this connection varies widely. On the one hand an actuary and his client may use the report as the document on which discussions flowing from the result of the investigation are based. In this case the actuary will probably complete the report fairly soon after the valuation result is settled and he will confine its contents to factual material and to matters upon which he has made up his mind and is unlikely to be moved. On the other hand the actuary may report the result of the valuation to his client by means of the preliminary letter or other document short of a formal report as mentioned in paragraph 28.2, and will wait until all the consequent discussions and negotiations are completed before issuing his formal report. In this case the report may include not only the material mentioned above but also a full description of the recommendations made and the action taken.

28.6 Both these approaches are met with in practice. The second has the advantage that the valuation report when finally issued includes a full description of the action taken and is therefore of great value as a reference document. Despite this many actuaries employ the first approach, preferring to use the valuation report as the formal document to which all parties concerned can refer as the discussions proceed. It may be that the rules of the scheme formally lay specific duties upon the actuary when the valuation result is known. In this case the second approach is probably preferable, with the report incorporating the recommendations or other observations that the actuary is required to make.

Main purpose of the report

28.7 Whichever of the courses discussed above is followed, the main intentions are to convey advice to the client in an unambiguous way and to provide the necessary degree of background information to enable the client to understand the broad basis of the advice given. There are two further aspects which are likely to be of increasing importance in the future. The first relates to statutory requirements for the disclosure of information and the second to professional guidance.

Statutory requirements

28.8 The general subject of disclosure of information to pension scheme members formed a major part of a report of the Occupational Pensions Board dated October 1982 entitled 'Greater Security for the Rights and Expectations of Members of Occupational Pension Schemes'. The O.P.B. attached much importance to disclosure, on the grounds that the existence of an informed membership with access to basic information would in itself be a powerful factor tending towards an improvement in the level of security of pension rights.

28.9 As noted in paragraph 17.21, various requirements on disclosure of information appeared in the Social Security Act 1985. At the time of writing the associated regulations are awaited and it is not clear what effect they will have on the matter under discussion.

Professional Guidance

28.10   The O.P.B. Report and subsequent discussions led to the issue by the Institute and Faculty in April 1984 of Guidance Note GN9 entitled 'Retirement Benefit Schemes – Actuarial Reports'. This Guidance Note is comparatively brief and for convenience it is reproduced at the end of this chapter. The Note is clearly set out and it is thought that the significance of most of the points will be clear to the reader of this book. Some points of interest are as follows.

Funding objectives

28.11   It will be recalled from previous chapters that there is a variety of possible approaches to funding levels. If the particular approach involved relies for its stability on a continuing flow of new entrants or on some other particular set of circumstances this should be mentioned in the report. It may also be helpful to the client to distinguish between the past service and future service positions.

Valuation assumptions and method

28.12   The actuary should seek to convey to his reader the nature of the calculations that he has made. The notion of estimating expected future cash flows into and out of the scheme may not cause difficulties to his readers, but the further step involved in discounting these expected cash flows to present capital values involves a concept which is likely to be difficult and unfamiliar to some readers. If the assets have been taken at a calculated value this may well be another unfamiliar concept. The actuary should therefore aim to make clear the broad nature of the processes that he has carried out.

28.13   There should be a statement of the main economic assumptions made in valuing the benefits, contributions and assets. As to the statistical assumptions, although such matters as the decrement rates involved in the service table may appear to be highly technical it is desirable to give a brief description of these and in particular to draw attention to ways in which the basis differs from that used on the previous occasion and the reason for any changes.

Contribution rate

28.14 The form of the valuation result will depend, amongst other things, on the way in which the employer's contribution rate is defined. If this rate is intended to be sufficient to cover the balance of cost, after allowing for the assets in hand and any contributions payable by the members, the result statement will be framed accordingly. If the employer's and employees' contribution rates are both laid down in the trust deed and rules, the result will be to show a surplus or shortfall and the trust deed and rules will lay down the action then to be taken.

Current funding levels

28.15 This is the subject that we have discussed under the title of discontinuance solvency. In reporting on the level of such solvency the actuary will bear in mind the points made in Chapter 26 about the degree of precision to be aimed at. A further point whose significance may need to be emphasised in a scheme which has not attained discontinuance solvency concerns the existence of prior charges upon a discontinuance. If for instance pensions in course of payment have a first call on the available resources, the employee members should be enabled to judge roughly the degree of cover provided, for their accrued rights, by the residual assets. This is a point which may well not occur to the lay trustee or employee member unless his attention is drawn to it.

Conclusion

28.16 In the formal report the actuary has to reconcile the need to deal precisely with technical material with the need to communicate with his readers in a way that is accessible to them. Most of his readers will not be full-time pension specialists, and his report will have to make its claim on its readers' time on its merits. It cannot be overstressed that the need to communicate clearly is of the first importance.

GN9

INSTITUTE OF ACTUARIES
STAPLE INN HALL,
HIGH HOLBORN,
LONDON, WCIV 7QJ
Telephone: 01-242 0106
Telegraphic Address: Actinst London WC1

FACULTY OF ACTUARIES
23 ST. ANDREW SQUARE,
EDINBURGH,
EH2 1AQ
Telephone: 031-556 6791

April, 1984.

GUIDANCE NOTE GN9

RETIREMENT BENEFIT SCHEMES - ACTUARIAL REPORTS

Introduction

1.1   When a retirement benefit scheme is to be set up, and at
        intervals thereafter, it is usual for an actuarial report to
        .be prepared.   Normally such an actuarial report would be
        prepared for the employer or the trustees.

1.2   These guidelines relate to the preparation of such reports
        for schemes where the benefits are defined and the ultimate
        costs are initially unknown, but the guidelines should also
        be followed, so far as possible, for other types of scheme.

1.3   The guidelines apply whether the actuary is acting as an
        individual, as a partner, as a director in a corporate body
        or in the course of his employment.

1.4   The actuary who signs the report should ensure that, as soon
        as possible after completion, it reaches the person for whom
        it was prepared without interference or amendment.

1.5   The requirement of 1.4 need not inhibit the quoting of a
        contribution rate to an intermediary on a provisional basis
        prior to the setting up of a scheme, but in that event the
        actuary should send a report in accordance with that
        requirement as soon as sufficient information is available.

1.6   The guidelines have been prepared with United Kingdom
        requirements and conditions in mind.   Where a member is
        practising outside the United Kingdom and the Council of the
        Institute or the Faculty (as the case may be) has agreed,
        the guidelines may be replaced by guidance given by an
        actuarial body of the country in which the actuary
        practises.

Purpose of the Guidelines

2.1   The purpose of the guidelines is to ensure that reports
        contain sufficient information to enable the expected future
        course of a scheme's contribution rate and funding level to
        be appreciated.   It is not intended to restrict the
        actuary's freedom of judgment in choosing the method of
        valuation and the underlying assumptions.

2.2   The actuary needs to bear in mind that his advice may be
        made available to third parties who can reasonably be
        expected to rely on it.

The Report

Items for inclusion

3.1   The items in the following list are normally to be regarded
        as essential components of any report.   Other information
        may often be desirable and suitable explanations of some
        features or trends may be very important, for example, the
        effect on the funding level of an improvement in benefits
        with retroactive effect.

Basic Information

3.1.1   An opening statement showing to whom the report is
        addressed, the purpose for which the valuation is
        made and the dates as at which the current
        valuation and, if applicable, the immediately
        preceding valuation were conducted.

3.1.2   A statement of benefits which have been valued
        (for example, by a summary of the terms of the
        scheme or by reference to appropriate documents).
        If there has been any recent practice of granting
        benefits beyond those prescribed in the rules, it
        should be made clear whether or not such practice
        has been assumed to continue.

3.1.3   A brief summary of the data on which the
        investigation is based including a description of
        the assets.   If the actuary has any reservations
        as to the reliability of the data, such
        explanation or qualification as is appropriate
        should be given.

Inter-valuation Period

3.1.4   A statement of the rates of contribution payable during the inter-valuation period; and a commentary on any material developments during such period and on any significant variations in experience from the assumptions made at the previous valuation.

Funding Objectives

3.1.5   An explanation of the funding objectives and of the method being employed to achieve those objectives. The implications in terms of stability of contribution rates and of future funding levels should also be explained.

Valuation Assumptions and Method

3.1.6   A statement of the assumptions made in valuing both the liabilities and the assets and of the method employed in deriving the contribution rate in 3.1.8 below. Attention should be directed particularly to those assumptions to which the contribution is sensitive.

3.1.7   Comments on the compatibility of the basis of valuing the assets with that of valuing the liabilities. The actuary should also comment if it is considered that the investment policy is inappropriate to the form and incidence of the liabilities.

Contribution Rate

3.1.8   The contribution rate recommended to achieve the funding objectives. If such objectives imply a changing contribution rate (as a percentage of the relevant earnings), an indication as to the extent and timing of such change should be given.

Current Funding Levels

3.1.9   A statement as to whether or not, in the actuary's opinion, the assets would have been sufficient at the valuation date to cover liabilities (including any dependants' contingent benefits) arising in respect of pensions in payment, preserved benefits, and accrued benefits (which will normally be related to pensionable service to, and pensionable earnings at, the date of valuation, but may in some cases depend also on members' own

contributions).   If there is any shortfall in the
coverage an indication of the degree of shortfall
should be given having regard to the priorities
attaching to various categories ` of benefits on
winding-up.

3.1.10   A statement as to the on-going funding position if
this is not otherwise conveyed by the comments on
the funding objectives and the contribution rate.

CHAPTER 29

PROJECTIONS OF CASH FLOW

PROJECTIONS OF CASH FLOW

Introduction

29.1   As the spread of computers led to the general accessibility of vast computing power, there was speculation that more use would be made in the actuarial investigation of a pension scheme of cash flow projections, i.e. the explicit calculation of the amounts of contribution income and benefit outgo expected in each future year, on the actuarial assumptions used, in respect of the persons with an interest in the scheme at the investigation date. Such a method had previously been out of the question in most cases because of the heavy volume of calculation involved.

29.2   In fact projection of cash flow has not so far become a part of normal technique. The manual methods of calculation illustrated in previous chapters involve the use of commutation columns directed to the calculation of present capital values, the traditional means by which actuaries reduce large volumes of calculation to manageable proportions. Such methods continue to be widely used in pension scheme work. Furthermore, the computer based method described in Chapter 10 which has been used for the large scale calculations in this book involves the calculation of amounts of pension at the time that they start to be paid but not the subsequent tracking of outgo year by year. The main reasons why cash flow projections have not gained ground as a working method are now discussed.

Economy of calculation

29.3   The first reason follows from the principle that calculations should be no more extensive than is required to provide the basis of advice. The fundamental process of the actuarial investigation involves in principle the projection of cash flow and the linking of one future period with another by the investment of surplus income or the realisation of investments to pay benefits. This linkage is conveniently allowed for by the process of discounting to present capital values, which also has the advantages that complicated transactions extending over a long future period are thereby summarised in a few figures and that least weight is given to events in the remote future where uncertainty is greatest. The explicit calculation of expected future year by year cash flow would feature in this process only if this turned out to be the best method of arriving at present capital values. Experience has not so far shown this to be the case.

Options

29.4 A second reason why explicit cash flow projection has not become common follows from the presence in most pension schemes of options available to members involving alternatives of equivalent actuarial value. Examples of these are the ability to take part of the retirement benefit as a cash sum instead of a pension, the ability to retire early with a reduced immediate pension and the facility often found to give up personal pension in exchange for a reversionary pension to a dependant. These options do not affect the financial balance of the scheme, since they are actuarially equivalent in value, but they have a substantial effect on cash flow. In particular the exercise of the option to convert pension into a lump sum on retirement clearly has a large effect on cash flow in the year of retirement. Assumptions about the extent to which such options will be exercised from time to time in the future are inevitably rather speculative, so that projections of cash flow cannot be made with great hope of precision when such options are available.

New entrants

29.5 A further point to be noted is that cash flow projections are based on the persons with an interest in the scheme at the investigation date. In the main investigation, persons who may enter after the date concerned are not dealt with in detail, since there are no data in respect of them and the normal contributions payable for them are assumed to be sufficient to support their benefits. This is obviously a valid approach for the main calculations in the investigation, but the future year by year cash flow is greatly affected by the incidence of new entrants and the detailed calculation of expected future cash flows without allowance for new entrants usually has limited relevance.

Range of bases

29.6 A fourth point arises from the concept, mentioned earlier in this book, that the actuarial basis chosen for any calculation is merely one of a range of possible bases. It is known that the experience will in fact differ from that embodied in the actuarial basis but the aim is usually to choose the basis so that deviations from it will broadly be financially self-compensating; in special circumstances a strong or weak basis may be chosen deliberately. This concept is difficult to carry over into the calculation of year by year cash flows. It would of course be possible to set out a range of possible amounts of cash flow year by year but the wide divergences between amounts projected for remote future years on difference bases tends to emphasise the speculative nature of the figures.

Usefulness of cash flow projection

29.7 The various criticisms and drawbacks of cash flow projection as noted above are material, but they would have to be overcome if cash flow projections were recognised as a necessary part of the basis of advice. We indicated in paragraph 29.3 why this is not so for the main actuarial investigation, but it is also necessary to consider the position in respect of investment policy. It might be thought that the projection of cash flow would play a useful role in the selection of different types of investment and of the term of redeemable investments within various markets.

29.8 Here again, however, the method has not so far been found to be of great use in practice. A very large part of the investment policy of pension schemes in the United Kingdom is directed towards equity type investments and while some such investments, such as property and index-linked gilts, have a term which is definable with greater or lesser precision, ordinary shares do not have any such term. Thus even though cash flow projections may show that in the absence of new entrants a certain requirement for capital proceeds from investments will arise in some remote future year it is not possible to use this information in the choice of investments.

29.9   At the time of writing it is not clear whether the paper by A.J. Wise on the matching of assets and liabilities, mentioned in paragraph 20.14, will lead to practical methods involving the projection of benefit and contribution cash flows and their matching by assets in the field of pension schemes.

The calculation of expected cash flows

29.10   Despite their limited general use, it is sometimes necessary to make projections of expected cash flows. The need may arise, for instance, in a scheme which is closed to new entrants, in which the future course of income and outgo will become gradually more relevant for investment policy. We now outline the methods involved and illustrate them with examples taken from the data for Scheme X.

29.11   As an example of the complications involved we consider in principle the calculation of the cash flow arising in some future year in respect of widows' pensions which start to be paid on the deaths of persons who had become early leavers from a pension scheme. It is obvious that the following persons at a particular investigation date may lead to this benefit flow at some future date.

(i)   Existing widows at the investigation date whose pensions began to be paid upon the deaths of persons who had been at some previous time early leavers from the scheme concerned.

(ii)   Persons who are now in receipt of pension from the scheme, having at some previous time been early leavers with preserved pension, and upon whose death a widow's pension will become payable.

(iii)   Persons who are at the investigation date entitled to preserved pensions from the scheme by virtue of having been early leavers at some previous date, who will in due course start to receive their pensions, and upon whose subsequent death a widow's pension will start to be paid.

(iv)   Persons who are at the investigation date entitled to preserved pensions from the scheme by virtue of having been early leavers at some previous date and who before their pension starts to be paid will die, with payment of a widow's pension starting at their death.

(v)   Persons who are at present employee members but who will subsequently become early leavers and in respect of whom the sequence of events in (iii) will then take place.

(vi) Persons who are at present employee members but who will subsequently become early leavers and in respect of whom the sequence of events in (iv) will then take place.

29.12   It will be obvious that the calculations involve a very wide range of summations. In schemes that are used for contracting-out there is added to this basic complexity the necessity to deal with the G.M.P. It will be recalled that in Scheme X we are assuming that the G.M.P. element of an early leaver's preserved rights will be accumulated at 8½ per cent. p.a. during the period until the early leaver attains State pensionable age, which in this particular case coincides with the date on which his preserved pension comes into payment, and that after that date no pension increases will be provided from Scheme X on this element of his rights. The non-G.M.P. element on the other hand is assumed to enjoy 5 per cent. p.a. increases during the period of preservation and 3 per cent. p.a. increases thereafter. All these points have to be dealt with in the projection of the cash flow arising from the particular benefit under consideration, and the calculations are very complex.

An example of cash flow calculation

29.13   To illustrate calculation methods we will consider the cash flow expected to occur in Scheme X in the year starting 20 years after the investigation date in respect of pensions payable to those of the initial entrants who were members at the investigation date and who are expected to retire on grounds of age. We will ignore the option to give up pension for a cash sum on retirement and we will also ignore the fact that part of the pension will be G.M.P. and will not enjoy increases in payment.

29.14   It will be recalled that retirement on grounds of age can take place at age 60 or later, so that the persons involved in our calculations will be those aged 40 or over amongst the initial entrants summarised in Table 34. The calculations are set out in Table 71. Column (1) of this table shows the ages of the persons concerned. Columns (2) and (3) show further relevant data taken from Table 34. Column (4) shows the various assumed average ages at which retirement on grounds of age may take place and column (5) shows the period of membership between the investigation date and the date at which these various ages are attained. Column (6) shows the product of salary and future service, and the sum in column (7) shows the value of salary times pensionable service at retirement, based on the salary in the data at the investigation date. In column (8) the pension fraction is applied to give a figure of the initial amount of pension but based on salary levels at the investigation date.

29.15 We now have to allow for the probability that retirement will indeed take place at the various ages set out in column (4) and for the fact that the salaries on which the pension would be based would be the 'final three-year average' salary at the date of retirement and not the salary in the investigation data. Columns (9) to (12) show the relevant calculations and the figures in column (12) are therefore the expected opening annual amount of pension on retirement assuming that no pension is commuted.

29.16 It remains to estimate from the figures in column (12) the pension outgo which will persist until the 20th year from the investigation date. This involves the appropriate allowance for the survival of the members concerned and allowance for the fact that pensions in payment are to receive increases at the rate of 3 per cent. p.a. Columns (14) to (18) will be largely self-explanatory. A point which may need explanation is the use of the figure 1.000 in certain entries in column (14). This is a convenient, though not strictly accurate, way of allowing for the five year guarantee of the member's pension. It will be recalled that an annuity involving a five year guarantee was used in the main calculations, to approximate to the value of the actual benefit on death after retirement. The method of column (14) is a quite close approximation to the method used in the valuation and this has the virtue that discounting of the cash flow calculated can be used as an effective check against the present values calculated in the main valuation. Table 71 leads to the total figure in column (18) of £576,700 which is the estimated age pension outgo, in the 20th year from the investigation date, arising in respect of persons concerned, subject to the qualifications set out above.

Scheme X: summary cash flow projections

29.17 For the reasons explained earlier the reader should not attach too much weight to figures such as that in the previous paragraph. However, the cash flow profile in respect of the main benefits of Scheme X in respect of the employees who were members at the investigation date may be of interest. Figures for the initial entrants who were members at the investigation date are shown in Table 72 and figures for entrants during the first three years in Table 73. In all cases commutation and the consequences of the G.M.P. content of pensions have been ignored.

29.18 Some readers may find it helpful to see the total projected flows of benefits and normal joint contributions in respect of the 411 employee members of Scheme X at the investigation date. These are summarised in Table 74. The figures do allow for the absence of pension increases on the G.M.P. element of a pension in payment after the pensioner attains State pensionable age but we do not illustrate the calculations involved since they are extremely lengthy and complex. The figures do not include any allowance for surrender of pension for a capital sum on retirement. It will be recalled from Table 69 that the liabilities for active members at the investigation date amount to £1,896,400 for past service benefits and £6,351,500 for future service benefits, a total of £8,247,900 and that the present value of future normal joint contributions is £6,354,400. These figures represent the cash flows summarised in Table 74 discounted to present values at the rate of 9 per cent. p.a. These figures cannot be precisely reproduced from those of Table 74 because of the grouping in five-year bands but any reader who wishes to check this relationship roughly will readily be able to do so by applying the appropriate compound interest discounting factors at 9 per cent. p.a.

CHAPTER 30

TAKEOVERS AND MERGERS

TAKEOVERS AND MERGERS

Introduction

30.1 Takeovers and mergers of companies are a very common occurrence in the United Kingdom and they often give rise to complex problems in the area of pensions. Suppose that Company C is sold by Group A to Group B, with the employees continuing to do the same work; their employment with Company C continues uninterrupted and superficially little has changed. Even in this apparently simple case there are substantial pension issues to be dealt with. The employees cannot remain in Pension Scheme A and the question of how to deal with the pension rights they have accrued in that scheme, and whether a change to the contribution and benefit scales of Scheme B for future service will cause difficulties compared with their previous expectations, have to be faced.

30.2 A potentially more complex type of case is that in which a part of the activities of Company C (represented perhaps by a single factory) is sold by Group A to Group B, the remaining operations of Company C staying with Group A. The employees concerned experience a termination of employment, since they enter the service of Group B while Company C stays with Group A. Because there is a termination of employment the pension preservation law outlined in Chapter 3 and other statutory requirements (e.g. those on a termination of contracted-out employment) have to be reckoned with. The case is thus materially different from the first case mentioned above. Another difference between the two cases may well be that the trust deed and rules of Scheme A cover the fairly straightforward first case in which Company C ceases to be a company participating in the trust deed of Scheme A but may not provide adequately for the more complex circumstances of the second case.

30.3 The situations met with in practice are extraordinarily diverse, and the pension difficulties are often compounded by the fact that the main negotiations between the principals have been conducted in secrecy, are to be concluded in haste and contain provisions on pensions which have been entered into without a complete understanding of their implications. In practice each case has to be dealt with on its merits, but we now discuss some of the issues that commonly arise when some or all of the employees of Company C move from Group A to Group B. We refer to the vendor and purchaser as Groups of companies, but this is merely a convenient way of denoting ultimate ownership. Many vendors and purchasers are companies and not Groups of companies, and the distinction is of no consequence for the present discussion.

30.4 In this discussion we shall be pointing out potential difficulties rather than describing solutions, because the latter depend greatly on the circumstances of each case, and in particular on the provisions of the trust deed and rules of Scheme A and on the general attitudes of the vendor and the purchaser. It is impossible to generalise on the latter point; some takeovers or mergers are conducted with goodwill on both sides while in others this is far from the case.

Constructive dismissal

30.5 Although the matter is beyond the scope of this book, it should be noted that the concept of 'constructive dismissal', which is included in employment law, may have a bearing on the pension aspects of takeovers and mergers. In the wider context of employment law and practice a tribunal may rule that an employee who resigns because of conduct by his or her employer has been 'constructively dismissed'. For a tribunal to rule in this way the employer's action has to be such that it can be regarded as a substantial breach of the employment contract indicating that he or she intends no longer to be bound by the contract; an example of this might be where the employer arbitrarily demotes an employee to a lower rank or poorer paid position. The contract is what has been agreed between the parties, whether orally or in writing or a combination of both, together with what must necessarily be implied to make the contract workable. In the narrower pension context with which we are now concerned it is quite common when a transfer of employees takes place for the receiving employer to undertake that the pension rights provided for the transferring employees shall be overall no less favourable, for service up to the transfer date and for service after the transfer, than those applying in their previous scheme. This practice has developed in order to avoid the possibility of claims of constructive dismissal by the employees concerned. The matter needs to be borne in mind, but it is by no means a settled point. Many employers, for instance, while accepting the need to make appropriate arrangements for the past service pension rights of a group of employees being taken on, would feel that in respect of future service the employees should be subject to the normal provisions of their new employer's pension scheme, irrespective of how these compared with their previous pension arrangements. We do not refer to this aspect again in the following discussion but consider only the wider issues.

The parties and their interests

30.6 Among the parties that will or may be involved in the pension aspects of a transfer of employees are the following.

(a) The transferring employees.
(b) The trustees of Scheme A.
(c) The trustees of Scheme B.
(d) Group A as vendors of the undertaking concerned.
(e) Group B as purchasers of the undertaking concerned.
(f) The Inland Revenue authorities.
(g) The Occupational Pensions Board.

Some of the points which will arise for these various parties are as follows. We will assume that the pension schemes involved are final pay schemes. A numerical example drawn from Scheme X follows later in this chapter.

The transferring employees

30.7 The transferring employees will be concerned with the impact of the change on their pension arrangements in respect of both past and future service. We will consider the past service position first. As members of Scheme A the employees will have accrued entitlement to a pension based on final pay. They will no doubt look for some arrangement which effectively ensures that this final pay promise continues to be honoured in respect of their service with Group A. Had they been individual voluntary early leavers from Scheme A they would have been entitled only to early leavers' rights, and the reader will be aware from previous chapters of the way in which these rights typically fall short of the rights of continuing members. The employees may well be unwilling to accept that the pension rights which they have accrued up to the date of transfer should be prejudiced by an action of their employer, decided on for his own reasons and outside their control.

30.8 They will probably therefore be seeking credits of pensionable service in Scheme B, since these will then give rise to final pay type benefits in that scheme. The precise terms of conversion of Scheme A service into Scheme B service would of course depend on the details of the schemes. Thus if Scheme A and Scheme B had pension fractions of 1/70th and 1/60th respectively but were otherwise identical, a credit of 6/7ths of a year of pensionable service in Scheme B for each year of past membership of Scheme A might seem reasonable to the transferring employees.

30.9 Sometimes the takeover of Company C by Group B may be the only alternative to closure of the company by Group A, with consequent redundancies amongst the employees. This suggests that the general policy of Group A and the trustees of Scheme A in respect of employees involved in bulk transfers out should influence their general policy as to redundancies. This principle is not, however, always followed in practice; pension benefits on redundancy and pension benefits on bulk transfers out often tend to be regarded as separate subjects.

30.10 As to future service, it is unlikely that the pension scheme of Group B will be identical to that of Group A. Transferring employees invited to join Scheme B for future service will therefore have to consider the contribution and benefit arrangements of that scheme. The extent if any to which Group B will be prepared to make any special arrangements in Scheme B for the future membership of the transferring employees will depend on circumstances. If the issue is seen to be a major one, Group B may agree to such special arrangements although this increases the administrative work in Scheme B. In extreme cases Group B will set up a pension scheme virtually identical to Scheme A for the transferring members.

30.11 The transferring employees may be given the option of not joining Scheme B for their future service with Group B, in which case they would of course be required to become members of the State earnings-related pension scheme.

The trustees of Scheme A

30.12 Turning to the second of the interested parties listed in paragraph 30.6, the trustees of Scheme A must, in this as in other matters, operate strictly in accordance with the terms of their trust deed and rules. If the circumstances of a transfer are covered by the trust deed and rules the trustees must therefore ensure that the appropriate provisions are carried out. This may however place them in difficulty. As was indicated in paragraph 30.2, the trust deed and rules of pension schemes do not always provide appropriately for the various complexities of takeovers and mergers that arise in practice. Thus it might be that in the circumstances of a particular transfer involving terminations of employment, the only benefit available to the transferring employees is the normal benefit provided to voluntary early leavers from the scheme. This might, for instance, be so in the case described in paragraph 30.2 if the trust deed and rules of Scheme A simply provided for benefits to early leavers without distinguishing between voluntary and involuntary cases. Transfer values to Scheme B would represent the value of early leavers' rights in Scheme A and would not in principle be sufficient to buy in Scheme B any rights better than those provided to early leavers from Scheme A.

30.13 As indicated above this is not likely to be thought a satisfactory benefit. In these circumstances the trustees of Scheme A will have to consider their obligation to the transferring members. Although the trustees are prevented from achieving what they would regard as appropriate terms for the transferring members as far as their own trust deed and rules are concerned they may well wish to ensure that the employers are aware of any difficulties that may arise in respect of the transfer of pension rights.

30.14 There will often be circumstances when the action to be taken in respect of a particular transfer is not laid down precisely in the trust deed and rules but the trustees are required to come to certain decisions on the advice of the actuary. We will illustrate some of the issues that arise in such a case in the example taken from Scheme X later in this chapter.

Subsequent application of transferred assets

30.15   Another aspect of the stance of the trustees of Scheme A is that they will probably wish to ensure as far as possible that any amount passing as a transfer payment will be used for the benefit of the transferring employees and not for the generality of the members of Scheme B. While this is a desirable principle it is not normally possible to follow it through with complete precision in practice. For instance, if Scheme A is well funded but Scheme B inadequately funded the transfer of members from Scheme A to Scheme B with an appropriate share of the funds will be likely to raise the level of solvency of Scheme B taken as a whole. Even if undertakings have been given in respect of the terms for the transferring members it will almost certainly be the case that if Scheme B is wound up shortly afterwards a part of the benefit of the enhanced level of solvency will go to the advantage of members of Scheme B who are not transferred members.

Remaining members

30.16   The trustees of Scheme A should not of course agree to terms for the transferring members or transfer payments in respect of them which would be to the disadvantage of the remaining members of Scheme A. This suggests that the amount to be transferred in respect of the members moving from Scheme A to Scheme B, assuming that all the rights are dealt with by transfer payment, should not be more than the 'fair share' of the assets of Scheme A in respect of the transferring members.

Surplus

30.17   The idea of a 'fair share' of the assets is not wholly straightforward. For instance, if there is a surplus when the funds of Scheme A are compared with its past service liabilities, and a share of the fund for the transferring members is calculated as

$$\text{Total funds} \times \frac{\text{transferring past service liabilities}}{\text{total past service liabilities}}$$

this will include a share of surplus, i.e. it will be an amount exceeding that required to set up benefit rights in Scheme B equivalent to the past service rights of the ransferring employees in Scheme A assuming the same actuarial basis in the two schemes. The trustees of Scheme A might not desire to transfer more than was needed to procure equivalent benefits in Scheme B (although this is an issue that the Scheme A trustees would have to consider on its merits, since they have a duty to the leaving as well as the remaining members), in which case it would be desirable from their point of view that if the terms of Scheme A governing the transaction provided for a share of the fund to be calculated, the terms should also provide for any surplus to be disregarded in such a calculation. If this limitation could not be incorporated in the arrangements it would be necessary for Group A to be aware of the position, since any excess of the amount transferred between pension schemes over the cost of setting up equivalent benefits might appropriately be allowed for in the main transaction between the groups. Indeed, if the normal contributions of Group A were based on a "balance of cost" provision (see paragraph 8.86) the Group would have a direct interest in any past service surplus, since if this were retained in the fund the first call on it at the next actuarial valuation would be in reduction of the Group's contributions.

Shortfall

30.18 If there is an overall shortfall in Scheme A instead of the surplus mentioned in the previous paragraph, different difficulties arise. Thus a 'share of fund' calculated by the method of the previous paragraph and transferred out of Scheme X shortly after its Commencement Date would represent only a very small amount, whereas an individual early leaver would have been granted a preserved pension in respect of the whole of his past service.

Interim arrangements

30.19 The Inland Revenue authorities will allow an interim period during which the transferred employees may remain as members of Scheme A even though they have moved to the employment of Group B. This provision is often used, since its purpose is to allow time for the various calculations and administrative arrangements involved in the transfer to be made in good order.

30.20   Participation in Scheme A during this interim period raises points for decision. For instance, the transferred employees have moved to the employment of Group B and it is the management of Group B who determine the salary levels of these employees during the interim period. The trustees of Scheme A are therefore in the position of running a scheme which contains members whose salary progression is no longer within the control of Group A. There are clearly potential difficulties in the assessment of the share of the fund appropriate to the transferring members, because if a share calculation is made as at the end of the interim period and the transferring employees have received exceptional pay increases in the meantime their liabilities in Scheme A calculated on the basis of pay at the date of calculation, and hence their calculated share of the assets, might be larger than is appropriate.

30.21   In many respects it is more straightforward if the split of funds is made as at the beginning of the interim period. In this case the trustees of Scheme A simply have stewardship of the appropriate share of their funds during the interim period, on behalf of the trustees of Scheme B. Contributions are added and benefit costs deducted from this section of the Scheme A funds during the iterim period, and an agreed addition made for investment earnings, until it is possible to make the payment.

30.22 Sometimes   substantial   redundancies   amongst   the employees concerned follow a takeover or merger. The alternative courses mentioned in the two preceding paragraphs may well have different implications as to which scheme is most affected by any pension profits or costs arising from such redundancies during the interim period. The trustees of Scheme A may well take an interest in this point since the financial significance for their scheme may be material. This concludes our disussion of the position of the trustees of Scheme A.

The trustees of Scheme B

30.23   As far as the trustees of Scheme B are concerned, they are to receive a bulk entry of new members. If these transferring employees are leaving their accrued rights as the responsibility of

Scheme A, in the form of preserved pensions in that scheme, then the Scheme B trustees are simply admitting new entrants in the normal way and few problems are likely to arise. If on the other hand the transferring employees are invited to transfer their accrued rights in Scheme A to Scheme B, with the passing of transfer payments between the two sets of trustees, the trustees of Scheme B obviously have a duty to ensure that such a transaction is not to the disadvantage of the existing members of Scheme B. Thus they will need to be involved in the discussion of the terms of transfer and will need to take advice from their actuary.

30.24 In general the trustees will wish the pension element of the transfer to cause as little difficulty as possible within Scheme B. This implies that the transferring members should not enjoy any special contribution or benefit arrangements unless this is absolutely necessary. There have been examples in the United Kingdom of companies which have been very active in the takeover and merger field and have gone to great lengths to accommodate particular facets of the pension arrangements of groups of persons transferring into the employment of the company, with the result that the pension arrangements of the company have acquired large numbers of special features with a consequent increase in the administrative burden and the general burdens on the trustees. The personnel officials of Group B may wish to be as accommodating as possible in respect of any pension difficulties, so as to ease the almost inevitable personnel problems involved in the whole transaction, so that this is an area where the views of Group B and those of the trustees of Scheme B may not wholly coincide.

Group A as vendors of Company C

30.25 Group A's main concern is likely to be the obtaining of the best possible price for Company C, and the various issues under this heading are not our concern. Since Group A will stand, to a greater or lesser extent, behind the finances of Scheme A, many of the issues that concern the trustees of Scheme A as noted above may also concern Group A.

Group B as purchasers of Company C

30.26 The first point which requires care as far as Group B is concerned may well arise early in the negotiations, since Group A will no doubt seek far-reaching promises as to the maintenance of the pension rights and expectations of the transferring employees and Group B will have to consider carefully how to respond to this. There is a long history of cases in which the purchasers have given undertakings on pensions without appreciating the full implications at the time, and these undertakings have sometimes proved very costly to honour. Sometimes this is because the funding level of Scheme A was not properly understood by Group B. Thus the main point for Group B is that it should be well advised on pension matters from the start of the negotiations. We comment again in paragraphs 30.40 and 30.41 on the position of the receiving company.

The Inland Revenue authorities

30.27 Although the arrangement for an interim period of participation of the transferred employees in their original scheme is common, it requires the agreement of the Inland Revenue authorities who are therefore consulted in most cases of takeovers and mergers. A further point is that if bulk transfer values are paid as part of the transaction the Revenue authorities will be interested in the arrangements and should be asked to approve them as far as Scheme B is concerned.

The Occupational Pensions Board

30.28 The O.P.B. are concerned with the proper observation of the preservation requirements outlined in Chapter 3 and the contracting-out arrangements outlined in Chapter 4. As noted earlier, a takeover or merger may or may not involve a termination of employment as far as the transferring employees are concerned. If there is such a termination then the statutory requirements in respect of preservation and contracting-out have to be satisfied and the O.P.B. may need to be approached in this connection. The main points involved are ones of administration and practice and we do not deal with them further here.

A bulk transfer from Scheme X

30.29 As an example we will suppose that all the employees aged 43 who are members of Scheme X at the investigation date are involved in an activity which Company X proposes to dispose of to another employer. For simplicity we will assume that the new employer runs a pension scheme with the same members' contribution scale and benefit scales, and costed on the same actuarial basis, as Scheme X. We will assume that all the employees involved will transfer to the new pension scheme, assuming satisfactory terms are offered, rather than elect for normal early leavers' rights in Scheme X, and we will consider the amount to be transferred from Scheme X in the light of the factors discussed earlier in this chapter. Transfer of employees and transfer of the appropriate amount will for simplicity be assumed to occur simultaneously. Table 76 provides a summary of various capital values as at the investigation date, for all the persons with an interest in Scheme X at that date and for the employees aged 43.

30.30 It will be recalled that the actuarial investigation of Scheme X revealed a substantial surplus, and that we assumed that the special contributions of Company X which are payable for a further seven years from the investigation date are reduced from 12 per cent. to 6 per cent. of total payroll, thus creating an approximate equality of assets and liabilities in Scheme X immediately after the investigation date.

Market values and assessed values

30.31 It will be seen from Table 47 that the market value of the assets of Scheme X at the investigation date was £1,147,000, but Table 69 shows that they were taken into the valuation at an assessed value of £1,439,000. The market value was therefore approximately 80 per cent. of the assessed value. In the present discussion we shall be working from the figures in Table 76, and it must be borne in mind that the present capital values shown have been calculated by a method and on a basis consistent with the assessed value of investments referred to above. Some of the figures of the transfer amount emerging in the subsequent discussion will therefore need to be multiplied by 0.80 in order to arrive at the cash, or market value of assets, to be transferred. It is found in practice that the need for this adjustment, and its amount, is often a point of contention and negotiation between the various parties involved.

Methods of calculation

30.32 We now disuss various methods of calculating the transfer amount. We will first consider the amount which the trustees of the receiving scheme might reasonably hope to receive. It will be recalled that the receiving scheme is assumed to have the same contribution and benefit scales as Scheme X and to be financed on the same actuarial assumptions.

30.33 In these circumstances the trustees of the receiving scheme are being asked to set up a credit of one year of pensionable service for each such year counting in Scheme X. This involves an initial past service liability of £127,700 as shown in Table 76(3). Applying the market value factor it follows that if the receiving trustees approach the matter in this way they would hope to receive assets with a market value of £102,200.

30.34 We assume above that the receiving trustees would be concerned only with the initial past service liability. It may be, however, that they would also take into account the expected future benefits and contributions in respect of the transferring employees. We will assume that the normal joint contributions payable in the receiving scheme are at the rate of 13 per cent. as in Scheme X and that there is no feature in the receiving scheme corresponding to the company's special contributions of 6 per cent. to Scheme X. In this case the relevant figures for the transferring members from Table 76 are as follows.

	£
Past service liabilities	127,700
Future service liabilities	275,100
Gross liabilities	402,800
Future joint contributions	284,700
Net liabilities	£118,100

This method leads to net liabilities of £118,100 giving a required market value to be transferred of £94,500. It is perhaps unlikely in practice that the receiving trustees would be willing to accept less than an amount calculated by the past service method. We will therefore assume that the receiving trustees would be looking for an amount of £102,200.

Discontinuance liabilities

30.35 We now consider some different ways in which the trustees of Scheme X might arrive at the amount to be transferred. In order not to limit the discussion we will assume that the trust deed and rules of Scheme X gives the trustees wide discretion as to the amount to be paid in the particular circumstances involved. One extreme position is that this should be simply the amount equivalent to the benefits to which the members would have been entitled as voluntary early leavers, i.e. £62,700 as shown in Table 76(10). The reasoning is that these are the benefits that the members would receive on discontinuance, and until Scheme X is more fully funded no greater amount is justified. Such an approach might also possibly be adopted if the trustees of Scheme X were aware that firm undertakings had been given to the transferring employees by the purchasing company in respect of their past pension rights and that there was no risk of Company X being asked to meet any of the cost. In this case the trustees of Scheme X by paying out only a comparatively small amount would be acting to the advantage of the remaining members without placing any penalty on the transferring employees.

Share of fund: ratio of past service liabilities

30.36 We next consider a method by which the share of the fund to be transferred is calculated as a proportion equal to the ratio of the past service liabilities for the members concerned to all past service liabilities. The figures appear in the first three rows of Table 76 and the application of the appropriate ratio to the total market value is as follows.

$$(\frac{127.7}{1,896.4 + 29.3 + 346.8}) \times £1,147,000 = £64,500$$

It will be seen that the amount of £64,500 may be regarded as a fair share of the available assets in hand taking into account current and past service liabilities allowing for expected future pay increases.

Share of fund: ratio of total liabilities

30.37 An extension of this approach is represented by the inclusion in the liability calculations of future service as well as past service. The inclusion of future service raises the question of whether only the normal joint contributions or the total contributions should be included in the calculations and the following statement contains figures on each method.

	Transferring members	Total
	£000	£000
Current and preserved	–	376.1
Actives: past	127.7	1,896.4
future	275.1	6,351.5
	402.8	8,624.0
Normal contributions	284.7	6,354.4
	118.1	2,269.6
Special contributions	40.6	820.3
	77.5	1,449.3

It will be seen that the transfer amounts obtained under the two methods are as follows.

$$\frac{77.5}{1,449.3} \times £1,147,000 = £61,300$$

$$\frac{118.1}{2,269.6} \times £1,147,000 = £59,700$$

30.38 In this particular example the figures flowing from the inclusion of future service do not differ very greatly from the figure based on past service alone as shown in paragraph 30.36. This is not, however, always the case. If the theoretical contribution rate varies markedly with age the net addition to past service liabilities consequent upon the inclusion of future service liabilities and contributions may be substantially positive or substantially negative. This is accentuated when the future contributions include a special element as in this example.

30.39 The above discussion does not exhaust the possible methods of calculation but we will not pursue the subject further. It will be seen that whatever method of calculation is used the amount is much below the amount which the trustees of the receiving scheme will regard as necessary to set up the appropriate past service credits. This is inevitable given the position shown in Table 69 in relation to past service, namely that the value of the funds in hand is very much less than the value of the current and past service liabilities, with the balance being met by future special payments from the employer. It is unlikely that the trustees would think it appropriate to include in a cash transfer from the funds a value relating to contributions which they have not yet received, so that the position represents a genuine difficulty in the proposed transaction.

The position of the receiving company

30.40 What should be the stance of the receiving company in the face of these uncertainties? One response to this question is that it is very important that the receiving company should be aware of the funding position of Scheme X and of its implications at an early stage of the negotiations. For instance it is possible that the result of the actuarial investigation of Scheme X might have been presented to the receiving company in the following terms instead of in the form of Table 69.

	£000
Current and preserved pensions	376.1
Liabilities in respect of active members	8,247.9
Total liabilities	8,624.0
Future contributions	7,994.9
Net liabilities	629.1
Funds in hand	1,439.0
Surplus	809.9

The receiving company might have supposed from this statement that there was an adequacy of funds.

30.41 In practice a more realistic response to the question posed at the beginning of the previous paragraph is that the purchaser should

(i)   establish the pension liabilities he is being asked to accept, or feels it necessary to accept,

(ii)   establish what assets will be available from the transferring scheme, and

(iii) form a view on how, if at all, the relationship between (i) and (ii) affects the purchase price he is prepared to pay.

Further reading

30.42 A paper presented to the Institute of Actuaries Students' Society by R.J. Chapman and R.J. Jagelman in December 1979 entitled 'Pension Aspects of Takeovers and Mergers' deals with the subject of this chapter in much more detail. Practical aspects of the subject are discussed at length in a paper submitted to the Institute of Actuaries by A.S. Garner, P.N. Thornton and A.J. Wise in November 1985 entitled 'Pension Aspects of Takeovers: A Review of Practice'. Both these papers are recommended to readers who wish to study the subject further.

CHAPTER 31

CONTRACTING-OUT REVIEWED

CONTRACTING-OUT REVIEWED

Introduction

31.1 We noted in paragraph 4.2 that contracting-out proved very popular in 1978; about 90 per cent. of the active members of occupational pension schemes were in the event contracted-out. Nevertheless, opinions and circumstances change, and even a course of action which was overwhelmingly popular needs to be reviewed from time to time. An opportunity for doing this arose in connection with the first five-yearly review of contracting-out carried out by the Government Actuary. His reports to the Secretary of State were published in March 1982 as Cmnd 8516 entitled 'Occupational Pension Schemes: Review of Certain Contracting-Out Terms'. Readers who wish to pursue the matter in detail will find in this document a very clear explanation and discussion of the financial issues involved.

31.2 Changes in the terms of the State scheme contribution abatement, and in the terms of buy-back of the G.M.P. into the State scheme, flowed from this report. Although as noted in paragraph 4.47 the financial issues represent only one element in the situation, these changes needed to be considered by employers, trustees and members of occupational schemes. The following questions amongst others arose.

(i) Has contracting-out proved to be a sensible course as far as the comparison of the State scheme contribution abatements with the benefits to be provided is concerned?

(ii) Does the revised State scheme contribution abatement for the second five years of contracting-out represent an important change in the terms of the deal?

(iii) Is the change in buy-back terms an important factor in the situation?

We were not able to consider the detailed finances of contracting-out in Chapter 4, but now that the reader has studied the technical material in earlier chapters it is possible to look at the actuarial aspects of contracting-out and this chapter contains a discussion centred on these three major points.

The financial issue involved

31.3 It will be understood from earlier chapters that when contracting-out was introduced, an employer who did not wish to change the total earnings-related retirement benefits being provided to his employees had in principle the following alternatives.

(i)   To arrange for his employees to participate in the State earnings-related scheme and to cut down the benefits of his own scheme appropriately so that the total benefits remain as before.

(ii)   To arrange for his employees to be contracted-out of the new State earnings-related scheme, with the consequence that the joint contributions to the State scheme of employees and employer would be reduced by the contracting-out abatement and the benefits of the occupational scheme would incorporate the G.M.P. (and would have to satisfy the other contracting-out requirements, although this may by ignored for present purposes).

The immediate financial issue was therefore essentially whether the 7 per cent. contribution abatement was sufficient to provide the G.M.P. benefits.

The financial basis of contracting-out

31.4 It will be recalled that the G.M.P. entitlements of a contracted-out member are revalued in line with national average earnings while the person remains a member of the occupational scheme and are a flat amount in payment after the person has attained State pensionable age. The main economic assumptions which the Government Actuary had to make in assessing the contribution abatement were therefore concerned with the absolute rate of interest in the period after attainment of State pensionable age (since this determines the capital cost of providing the flat G.M.P. amount on attainment of that age) and the excess of the interest rate over the rate of increase in national average earnings while the G.M.P. entitlements are accruing.

31.5 The Government Actuary's original assumptions in this connection were as follows.

Rate of interest   9 per cent. p.a.
Rate of revaluation of G.M.P.   Approx. 8 per cent. p.a.

The 8 per cent. rate of revaluation is described as approximate because the Government Actuary has stated that in fact he used a net rate of 1 per cent. p.a. during the revaluation period so that the assumed percentage rate of revaluation was

$$100 \left[\frac{1.09}{1.01} - 1 \right] = 7.9$$

We shall take the rate as 8 per cent. for the purposes of the present discussion. An addition of 7 per cent. was made to the calculated figures to allow for the expenses of the occupational pension scheme and this led to a State scheme contribution abatement of about 6½ per cent. Following various representations and discussions about the risks involved in contracting-out an abatement of 7 per cent. was finally decided on by the Government and this was the rate used during the first five years of contracting-out. The Government Actuary stated that an assumption of 9 per cent. p.a. interest and 8½ per cent. p.a. revaluation of earnings, together with the expense loading, approximately reproduced the contribution abatement of 7 per cent.

31.6 The standard tables for State scheme premiums (see paragraph 4.39) are calculated on bases consistent with those leading to the contribution abatement of 7 per cent., so that for present purposes the main economic assumptions may be regarded as a rate of interest of 9 per cent. and a rate of earnings revaluation of 8½ per cent. p.a. The State scheme premiums incorporated a loading for expenses at the rate of 2 per cent.

31.7 The reader should refer at this stage to the first part of Table 75 which represents an approximate method of arriving at the 7 per cent. contribution abatement. Notes on this table are as follows.

Column (2) shows the standard accrued rights premiums for the central age of the age group in column (1). These represent in principle the cost of unit accrual of G.M.P. at the age concerned, allowing for expected future revaluation. They are in principle of the form $\dfrac{\text{'M'}}{\text{D}}$ mentioned in Chapter 9, with appropriate prefixes and suffixes.

Columns (3), (4) and (5) represent a calculation made in the middle year of the first five years of contracting-out.

Column (3) shows the assumed distribution of relevant earnings in the contracted-out workforce which the Government Actuary employed in his initial calculation of the contracting-out abatement. The proportions do not add up to exactly unity because age groups below age 25 are excluded on the grounds that a Contributions Equivalent Premium would normally be paid for early leavers in this category, and this takes them outside the scope of the calculations for longer term members.

The accrual rates in column (4) follow from the age at April 1978. For instance, the central age in the male age group 25-29 is 27 and a man aged 27 in April 1980 would have been 25 in April 1978 and is assumed to have a G.M.P. accrual rate of 1/160ths or 0.62 per cent.

The percentage rate at the foot of column (5) is first divided by 0.9346 to give a valid average rate; it is necessary to do this because the figures in column (3) total 0.9346 and not unity. These percentage rates are then multiplied by 1.05 because in his calculations the Government Actuary included a loading for expenses of 7 per cent. in the abatement figure but only 2 per cent. in the Accrued Rights Premium factors.

It will be seen that this method leads to an approximate figure for the abatement of 7.11 per cent., compared with the actual figure of 7 per cent.

31.8   On the basis of this preliminary discussion we now consider the first question raised in paragraph 31.2, namely whether contracting-out was a financially sensible course during the first few years after 1978. In the normal case of a scheme with both male and female members the comparison of the age and sex distribution of the membership with the distribution used in the Government Actuary's calculation of the contribution abatement would be relevant, but we will assume here that this comparison would not show divergences between these two distributions large enough to be of great significance. We will therefore concentrate on the economic issues.

31.9 An occupational scheme used for contracting-out may be thought of as having had the use of the 7 per cent. abatements in State scheme contributions and will have accumulated a notional fund, forming part of its general assets, by the investment of these abatements. The corresponding liabilities which the scheme has taken on are represented by G.M.P. entitlements; some of these will already have come into payment but the majority will represent promises of future payments. The question whether contracting-out had been profitable so far therefore hinges mainly on the comparison of

(i) the notional fund together with expected future investment earnings with
(ii) the capital needed to provide the promised benefits when they come into payment.

31.10 The question cannot be answered with certainty, because the future yield on the notional fund is not known and neither is the rate at which the promised G.M.P. benefits will increase in future under the effect of further Section 21 Orders until they come into payment. One way of approaching the question is to look at the position if the typical financial experience of schemes during, say, the first four years of contracting-out continued indefinitely, and then to consider what the effect of changes in this financial experience might be. The question is then whether the rates of investment yield and G.M.P. revaluation during the opening years of contracting-out led to profit or loss when compared with the Government Actuary's assumptions.

31.11 This is best considered in two parts, as follows.

(i) During the period before the member attains State pensionable age is the rate of accumulation of investments likely to be more or less favourable than a ½ per cent. excess over earnings increases?
(ii) Is the capital needed at the time that a member attains State pensionable age, to fund the G.M.P. as it then comes into payment, likely to be more or less than that required on a 9 per cent. interest basis?

In presenting the matter in this way the probability of death before attainment of State pensionable age is ignored, in the interests of simplicity.

31.12 The Section 21 Order for the tax year 1982/83 laid down the following rates of revaluation of G.M.P.

Year G.M.P. earned	Revaluation
	%
1978/79	78.3
1979/80	57.3
1980/81	31.5
1981/82	10.1

The multiplier for four annual increases was thus 1.783, which is equivalent over four years to an average annual rate of dynamisation of 15.6 per cent. compound.

31.13 What was the investment return on the State scheme contribution abatements to set against this growth in the G.M.P.? As noted in paragraph 11.7, an approximate measure of the investment yield on an ordinary share which divorces the figure from fluctuations in market values is the sum of the initial yield on purchase and the rate of growth in the flow of dividends from year to year. The flow of dividends on the shares representing the F.T.-Actuaries All-Share Index increased between March 1978 and March 1982 at an annual rate of 13 per cent. This period included a phase of exceptional dividend growth and also a phase of comparative lack of growth. The initial yield on the index exceeded 5 per cent. (our central assumption for this element as noted in paragraph 11.19) for much of this period, as it has over many periods in the past, so that on this measure the long term yield obtained was in excess of 5 + 13, i.e. 18 per cent. p.a. The return on the All-Share Index over this period taking into account actual market values at the beginning and end of the period, as well as dividend flows, was 16.6 per cent. p.a.

31.14 Occupational schemes are not invested wholly in equity shares, but allowing for the typical distribution of assets of pension schemes it is likely that over the contracting-out period to April 1982 the average scheme would have earned a return on the investment of State scheme contribution abatements somewhat greater than the rate of increase in the G.M.P. entitlements. The effective margin of ½ per cent. in the Government Actuary's assumptions was probably exceeded to a small extent.

31.15 The question 'Were the first four years of contracting-out profitable?' may therefore be put in the form 'Does the rate of growth in G.M.P.s of 15.6 per cent. p.a. and an investment yield somewhat more than this represent a profitable experience in the long term?'. This brings us to the second aspect of profitability, namely the question of the capital which the occupational scheme must accumulate at State pensionable age to provide the G.M.P. benefits thereafter. The comparative costs of providing a level pension (with a half rate reversionary pension to the widow in the case of male members) on mortality assumptions which approximately reproduce the State scheme premium rates at State pensionable age and at various rates of interest are shown in the following table.

| Rate of interest | Capital required at age 65 (males) 60 (females) to provide a level pension of £1 per annum throughout life, with a reversionary pension of 50p per annum to a widow | |
	Males	Females
%	£	£
7	9.5	11.0
9	8.3	9.4
11	7.3	8.2
13	6.6	7.2
15	6.0	6.5
17	5.5	5.9

31.16 On the basis of an investment yield of 16 per cent., representing the extraordinary high investment returns during the opening four years of contracting-out, the amount estimated from the table is £5.75 for males as compared with the amount of £8.3 on the 9 per cent. interest basis underlying the State scheme contribution abatement, and £6.2 for females compared with £9.4. In these investment conditions the G.M.P. can therefore be provided at retirement for a sum of less than 70 per cent. of the amount at retirement allowed for in the contracting-out abatement terms.

31.17   In respect of the capital required at State pensionable age, the experience of schemes was therefore highly favourable. The figures quoted earlier indicate that investment yields somewhat exceeded the rate of G.M.P. indexing. Thus in respect of both the relevant factors the financial experience in the opening years of contracting-out was favourable.

The persistency of the favourable early experience

31.18   It is necessary to form a view on the risk that the satisfactory position at the end of the first four years of contracting-out will disappear by reason of unfavourable future experience. This depends on the answers to the two questions of paragraph 31.11 as far as future years are concerned. It is thought that most actuaries would take an optimistic view as to question (i), on the basis of the reasoning in Chapter 11. On the second question, a fall in investment yields would in general be an unfavourable feature, but at the time of writing it seems unlikely that a fall would proceed so far as to bring average long term yields below the assumption. Thus it is likely that actuaries will continue to be able to advise that, as far as the comparison of contribution abatement and G.M.P. liabilities is concerned, contracting-out is a financially sensible course.

Revised contribution abatement

31.19   We turn to the second question of paragraph 31.2, namely whether the change in the State scheme contribution abatement for the second five years, which is a reduction in the joint rate from 7 per cent. to 6.25 per cent. of relevant earnings, represents an important change in the terms of the deal between State scheme and occupational scheme. The Government Actuary has stated that on unchanged assumptions as to investment yields and rates of G.M.P. increase the abatement in State scheme contributions for employees and employers taken together in the second five years of contracting-out would be expected to be less than that in the first five years by about three-quarters of one per cent., for two main reasons.

31.20   The first flows from the nature of the G.M.P. It will be recalled that the G.M.P. accrual rate falls as age at April 1978 diminishes. The average age at April 1978 of the persons who constitute the workforce from time to time will diminish with the passage of the years, so that the average rate of accrual of G.M.P., and hence the abatement in State scheme contributions which represent the assessed cost of this accrual, will also fall. The second factor stated by the Government Actuary is that as the original rates of contribution abatement were necessarily calculated well in advance of April 1978 the distribution of the contracted-out workforce by age and sex was then a matter of speculation, but in considering the terms for April 1983 the Government Actuary had available to him data as to the distribution by age and sex of the original contracted-out workforce in 1978 and he used these proportions for the calculations he has now made.

31.21 It is possible to make calculations on approximate lines in this connection, and these are shown in the second part of Table 75. Notes on the various columns are as follows.

Columns (2), (3), (7) and (8) represent a calculation made in the middle year of the second five years of contracting-out but based on the distribution of relevant earnings assumed in the Government Actuary's calculations for 1978. If we use the actual figure of 7.00 per cent. for the first five years this calculation indicates why the abatement would fall by about ½ per cent. because of the lower average rate of G.M.P. accrual, even if the assumption on the distribution of relevant earnings remained unchanged.

Columns (2), (6), (7) and (9) represent a calculation made as at the central year of the second five year period. A comparison of columns (8) and (9) reveals the ¼ per cent. difference which arises because of the change in the weighting by distribution of relevant earnings. Column (9) reproduces the contribution abatement which in fact holds during the second five years.

31.22 These calculations thus help to explain why a reduction of about three-quarters of one per cent. in the State scheme contribution abatement for contracting-out was to be expected as a consequence of the two factors mentioned by the Government Actuary. The change in the contribution abatement is a genuine worsening of the terms to the extent of the ¼ per cent. reduction arising from the use of the revised earnings distribution, since this represents the elimination of a fortuitous profit margin. The answer to the second question posed in paragraph 31.2 is therefore that the element in the revision which is not a natural consequence of the fall in the average rate of G.M.P. accrual is comparatively small, and does not amount to a very significant change in the terms of the deal.

The Government Actuary's analysis

31.23 We should make it clear that the calculations of Table 75 are intended to throw light on the various points and are not meant to represent the Government Actuary's own reasoning. In particular he presents his basis as one involving 9 per cent. interest and 8 per cent. earnings increase together with a contingency margin, which is technically different from the basis used here.

31.24 It appears from published documents that the Government Actuary's own analysis of the joint rate of State scheme contribution abatement is as follows.

	First five years	Second five years
	per cent.	per cent.
Abatement on 9 per cent. interest and 8 per cent. earnings increases and allowing for 7 per cent. expenses	6.56	5.88
Adjustment to allow for interest on C.E.P.s	–	0.09
	6.56	5.79
Margin for contingencies	0.44	0.46
	7.00	6.25

31.25 The adjustment to allow for interest on C.E.P.s needs explanation. We explained in paragraph 4.30 that the G.M.P. entitlements of early leavers in their first five years of membership may be bought back into the State scheme by payment of a C.E.P. equal to the total amount of the contribution abatements enjoyed while they were contracted-out. No interest is added to the abatements in this calculation, and as the absence of interest may be regarded as an advantage to the occupational scheme vis-à-vis the State scheme, the adjustment has been included to provide an amount in token of such interest. There is of course no relationship between the actual amounts of the adjustment and of the lost interest in individual cases.

Change in buy-back terms

31.26   The third question referred to in paragraph 31.2 relates to a change in the M.L.I. element of the buy-back terms, the effect of which is to increase the amounts of State scheme premium payable in various market conditions. The position was outlined in paragraph 4.39. The situation is that the standard tables of premiums payable when a G.M.P. liability is bought back into the State scheme are calculated on actuarial assumptions consistent with those underlying the contracting-out abatement in State scheme contributions. The premiums payable are based on the standard tables adjusted by the Market Level Indicator or M.L.I.

31.27   Different standard tables and M.L.I. are used according to whether the G.M.P. being transferred to the State scheme represents the future pension of an employee on the one hand or a pension already in payment on the other. We shall consider the former case only. In this case the M.L.I. procedure produces a percentage of the standard premium which may be described as

$$\frac{260}{\text{Yield on F.T. Actuaries All-Share Index}} + 35 \left\{ \begin{array}{l} \text{Market price of 13 per} \\ \text{cent. 25 year Gilt-Edged} \\ \text{Stock} \div \text{price if market} \\ \text{rate of interest was 9 per} \\ \text{cent.} \end{array} \right.$$

This complex formula is framed on the assumption that long-term normality in the investment market is represented by a rate of interest of 9 per cent. and an immediate dividend yield on the equity index of 4 per cent., conditions which give an M.L.I. of

$$\frac{260}{4} + 35 = 100 \text{ per cent.}$$

31.28   As to departures from long term normality, the second term of the formula ensures that the buy-back premiums vary to some extent in line with gilt-edged prices. The first term of the formula, covering equities, is not so straightforward. An equity is bought in the hope that its dividends, and consequently its market price, will increase with the passage of time. It would not be fair to use an M.L.I. which led to a higher State scheme premium simply because market values of equities had increased, since such an increase would be expected to occur as part of the total yield on equity investment even in the stable long term conditions of normality. Nor is it intended that the M.L.I. should open an escape route for occupational schemes simply because their equity investments had performed badly and the market values were therefore low.

31.29 It is for these reasons that the first part of the formula is framed in terms of an index yield rather than a market price index. The intention is to protect funds which have to buy back when prices are low because interest rates and equity yields are high. A consequence of this is that the Government Actuary had to settle on an immediate dividend yield – namely 4 per cent. – to represent normality, and dividend yields were markedly higher than this during the opening years of contracting-out. During the first half of the 1970s the M.L.I. formula taken as a whole would have given a result sometimes above and sometimes below 100 per cent. During the first four years of contracting-out, however, the M.L.I. was consistently below 100 per cent., varying between about 60 and 80 per cent., because interest rates and the dividend yield on equities were high. The Government Actuary concluded that the M.L.I. system gave too much reduction when yields are high and should be amended. The change is being phased in over a period of five years and represents a gradual stiffening of the terms of buying back. In these circumstances the question arose of whether it would be to the advantage of employers and trustees to buy back G.M.P.s into the State scheme before the terms changed, or during the period of gradual change, with a view to crystallising the profits from the favourable financial experience during the early years of contracting-out.

31.30 The matter is too detailed to be considered extensively here, but an important point to note is that the issue is not simply a narrow financial one; other issues have to be weighed against any financial advantage that may be perceived. This is because the facility is available only if an occupational scheme ceases to be used for contracting-out. The Government's stance is that occupational pension schemes should not be permitted to give up their contracted-out status temporarily in order to buy G.M.P.s back into the State scheme, and thus obtain a financial advantage at the expense of the National Insurance Fund, if the intention is then to resume contracting-out. The Occupational Pensions Board has power to cancel a new contracting-out certificate where it is clear that the arrangements have been exploited in this way.

31.31 The question of whether to buy back is therefore a matter of weighing any possible financial advantage against the wider implications of a major change of policy from contracting-out to participation. The issues that were taken into consideration in the discussions leading up to the original decision to contract-out would all have to be taken into account if participation and buy back is to be considered.

31.32 In particular the following points would arise; they represent a formidable list of difficulties.

(i) The accrued rights of members in the occupational scheme for pensionable service since April 1978 would have to be reduced in token of the fact that additional benefits were to be provided from the State scheme in respect of that period.

(ii) It would have to be decided whether these reductions should correspond precisely to the G.M.P. amounts returned to the State scheme or should be based on some broader approach. If the former course is chosen, the scale of reduction would vary from member to member; if the latter, the total pension from occupational scheme and State scheme together would represent a departure from the original 'target' pension scale.

(iii) An appropriate scale of reduction of pension rights in the occupational scheme for future service, to allow for the increased benefits from the State scheme with its various accrual rates, would have to be devised.

(iv) The increase in contributions of members to the State scheme would be payable out of after-tax income whereas the effect of any reduction in their contributions to the occupational scheme would be diminished by the effect of tax relief; some adjustment in pay might therefore be asked for.

(v) It would have to be acknowledged to members and any trades unions concerned that the proposed change in policy was not unconnected with the crystallisation of profit. The expected size of the profit, and the question of who was to share in it, would inevitably be an issue in the discussions which might be difficult to resolve.

31.33 It is thought that the number of schemes in which these difficulties were considered to be outweighed by the potential financial advantage of buying back was very small, if indeed there were any such schemes.

CHAPTER 32

INSURED SCHEMES

INSURED SCHEMES

Introduction

32.1 In this book we have been mainly concerned with the following aspects of occupational pension schemes.

(i) The legislative framework.
(ii) Design of contribution and benefit scales.
(iii) Financial structure including funding levels and valuation.

In many chapters it was not necessary to specify whether the scheme was invested in stock exchange securities, properties, overseas securities and other investments, or alternatively invested in some way through a life office. For instance, items (i) and (ii) above, and most matters relating to the relationship of the trustees to the members, apply whatever the vehicle of investment. In the later chapters dealing with the actuarial investigation of a scheme it has, however, been assumed that the scheme has identifiable assets. This category is taken as including the case of a 'segregated fund' managed by a company associated with a life office, since typically such a fund consists of identifiable assets; the company managing the investments acts as investment manager of the fund and there is no pooling of investments with those of other pension schemes.

Pooled investments

32.2 This chapter contains a brief discussion of schemes whose assets are not held in the form of a group of specific identifiable investments but are pooled in some way with the investments of other schemes. We mention first the 'managed fund' arrangement and we then consider some points on insured schemes as typified by deposit administration and deferred annuity arrangements. Insured schemes play a major role in the field of pensions in the United Kingdom, and there are many thousands of such schemes, many with comparatively small memberships which could not be easily dealt with by a directly invested arrangement. In the discussion of insured schemes we are not concerned with the calculation of premium rates and other matters relating to the life office involved, since these matters are dealt with elsewhere in the course of reading for the examinations of the Institute of Actuaries and Faculty of Actuaries. We are concerned rather with those aspects of insured schemes on which an employer or trustees may seek the advice of an actuary independent of the life office concerned. The reader should note that in the types of scheme discussed in this chapter the policy document taken out by the scheme trustees with the life office or managed fund company is crucial, since this is the legal document defining the arrangements.

Managed funds

32.3 Under the typical managed fund arrangement the trustees of a scheme above a certain minimum size are enabled to employ the contributions of the scheme in purchase of investment units in the fund of a company set up for the sole purpose of investing the contribution of such schemes. This fund (the 'managed fund') enjoys all the taxation privileges of approval. The company running the managed fund is normally associated with a life office, and the company or the life office carry out the administration of each of the participating pension schemes to an extent agreed with the trustees of that scheme, and charge the trustees a fee for this work. Some charges are not explicit, being taken directly out of the funds, so that a fee for investment services, for instance, is not always appropriate.

32.3A The assets and profits of the managed fund belong indirectly to the various bodies of trustees concerned by way of their ownership of units, and the trustees of each scheme are informed from time to time of the market value of the assets underlying each unit. In most cases the income of the underlying investments is reinvested in the units and so increases their value; in a few cases income emerges separately. A variety of units is available in the typical managed fund. Some are specialised, such as U.K. equity units, property units and overseas securities units. Other units provide a mix of assets. The proportion of a scheme's income to be invested in each type of unit is normally settled by the trustees in discussions with the managing company, but practice varies and some managing companies press strongly for the choice to be left to them. Should the trustees of a scheme withdraw from the fund their rights are governed by the policy document. Usually they are entitled to the value of their units based on current market values of underlying assets less the costs of realisation, but the managing company may have the right to pay out over a period rather than in a single cash sum.

32.4 No insurance risk is borne by the managed fund. Pension benefits may be paid by the trustees deducting each instalment of pension from the contributions received by them, only the balance being used in the purchase of units, or by purchase of an annuity from the associated, or another, life office. The participating schemes are therefore essentially separate schemes in everything except investment. Each bears its own risk in respect of the various rates of decrement and other rates referred to in previous chapters (apart from any insurance of death in service benefits, and apart from pensioners' mortality if pensions are set up by purchase of annuities) except that the investment risks and profits are shared with the other participating schemes. As to the long-term working of the scheme, the reader should note the point made in paragraph 8.16 concerning the liquidity position if investment income is automatically re-invested and hence used to increase the value of the units.

32.5 The chapters of this book dealing with the actuarial investigation apply to schemes invested in a managed fund just as to directly invested schemes. The assets are represented by units in the managed fund whose market value at or near the investigation date will be known so that there is no difficulty in the notional translation of the assets into a model portfolio for the purpose of the valuation, on the lines of paragraph 24.24.

32.6 No points of particular difficulty arise in an employer's consideration of this method of finance. He will assess the value of the skill which the life office will bring to the management of the investments and of the administrative services offered against the charges, both explicit and drawn from investment income, which will be made for these services. In large schemes there are often holdings in a number of different managed funds, either as a matter of deliberate policy or as a result of the absorption over the years of smaller schemes with managed fund investments. We do not consider managed funds further.

Insured schemes

32.7   Some common situations in which independent advice is sought in connection with insured schemes are as follows.

(i)   A pension scheme is being introduced for the first time and the employer, having decided on the scheme of benefits, wishes to be informed of the general issues involved in the choice between the various possible methods of financing the scheme.

(ii)   A large company or group of companies whose pension arrangements have not been rationalised requires a survey of its schemes to be carried out and recommendations made. In such cases the existing schemes often include both insured and non-insured schemes.

(iii)   An employer wishes to compare proposed schemes put forward by different life offices with each other or with a proposed directly invested scheme.

(iv)   An employer or trustees wish to have independent advice on the amount of the premiums which should be paid from time to time to an insured scheme in which the pace of funding is flexible.

(v)   A change from an insured scheme to another such scheme or to a directly invested scheme is being considered and advice is required on the termination and other provisions of the insured scheme.

As mentioned in paragraph 32.2, the two main types of insured scheme which will be involved are as follows.

Deposit administration

32.8   This type of arrangement involves the accumulation of premiums in the appropriate fund of the life office as a deposit credited with a rate of interest. Many life offices lay down a formula defining in terms of some published index or indices the rate of accumulation which it will provide on money paid to it by the trustees of pension schemes. It might for example be provided that money paid in at a given date would be accumulated up to the date of retirement of the member concerned at a rate of compound interest related to the market yield on a particular gilt-edged security on the date that the money was paid in. The yield is usually defined in practice in terms of some more complex index involving a combination of fixed interest and ordinary share indices, or in terms of the published gross interest yield on the funds of the life office concerned. The arrangement may also involve the allocation to the trustees of their share of any capital appreciation or depreciation on the assets underlying the accumulation index. The formula by which this share is to be calculated will be laid down.

32.9 When a benefit is paid the amount (or, in the case of a pension, the capital amount required to purchase the pension) is drawn from the accumulation account. When a pension becomes payable it may be possible to withdraw the necessary capital to purchase the pension in the best market rather than from the life office concerned, although a financial penalty may be involved. There is likely to be a financial penalty if it is desired to withdraw cash other than under the normal working of the pension scheme concerned, since this represents an unplanned payment as far as the life office is concerned. The policy will provide for any penalties involved.

32.10 Deposit administration schemes are designed to ensure that the policyholder receives directly a substantial part of all the proceeds of the investment of his premiums, and to this extent they are 'with profit' in character. The arrangement involves no risk cover before retirement unless the terms of accumulation involve significant guarantees. There may be separate insurance of death benefits.

Funding plans and control periods

32.11 As to the rate of contribution required for a pension scheme financed by this method, it is of course necessary for the life office actuary to make calculations using essentially the methods described earlier in this book. The rate of interest employed will be the effective long term rate which the actuary judges will be obtained by the trustees on the premiums paid to the life office regarded as investments, or possibly a rate which is pitched at a conservative level. The rates of pay escalation and other features of the actuarial basis of his calculations will be settled bearing in mind the interest assumption.

32.12 In some life offices it is customary to make the projections underlying these calculations over the whole expected future working lifetime of the employees concerned. In many other life offices the projections are limited to a 'control period' such as 20 years. In the latter case the funding aim for an employee aged 35 is obviously to provide the resources necessary to fund appropriate deferred benefits at age 55. Some offices use a method under which these deferred benefits are benefits calculated as if the member concerned would be an early leaver at age 55. This normally produces a somewhat lower contribution rate than does projection over the whole of the expected future working lifetime, since there is substituted, for pay increases between age 55 and normal pension age, the appropriate level of increase in preserved benefits. Some offices aim for a higher funding level at the end of the control period.

32.13 Some insurance companies provide as part of their quotations contributions assessed to meet costs arising over a much shorter period, such as five years. This produces a low contribution rate but it is normally found that the quotation makes clear that the contribution rate so calculated is at a level lower than is likely to be sustained in the long run, and a more stable long term contribution rate is often quoted in addition. The use of control periods was mentioned briefly in paragraph 8.78. A discussion of the practical effects of differing control periods, and of differing target funding levels at the end of the period, is beyond the scope of this book. Any reader wishing to pursue the subject will find an enlightening analysis in Part 3 of the paper entitled 'A Financial Framework for Pension Funds' presented by D.J.D. McLeish to the Faculty of Actuaries in February 1983.

Deferred annuity schemes

32.14 We turn to the type of scheme under which the contributions, net of expenses and life assurance costs, are used to buy deferred annuities. The contributions if any of each employee will normally be used to secure deferred annuities for the individual concerned. Under most deferred annuity schemes the contributions of the employer have traditionally been used to purchase the full expected pension rights of the members concerned in order of their seniority. This method has the advantage of concentrating resources on the more stable part of the working population. However, now that preservation has to be reckoned with and contracting-out may also be involved, the early leaver even at a young age has to have the appropriate preserved benefits and allowance for this necessitates some modification of the method of allocating resources to the most senior employees. The general plan under which the employer's contribution is not allocated as an amount of contribution to each individual, but is used instead to purchase benefits in some rationally determined way, is normally referred to as 'controlled funding'.

Blurred distinction

32.15 Although the obligation of the life office to the trustees is, in principle, represented by amounts of deferred annuity under this system compared with an accumulated sum under deposit administration, the distinction between deposit administration and deferred annuity financing is often blurred. For instance, a deferred annuity contract in which no allowance is made for the possibility of death or withdrawal before the member reaches retirement age may differ little from a deposit administration accumulation based on compound interest with bonus additions. The issues that arise in settling contribution rates are likely to be much the same under the two types of arrangement.

General issues on insured schemes

32.16 We consider below some of the points with which the independent actuary normally deals on insured schemes, but first it will be useful to mention the type of employer who normally seeks this advice. It will be clear from earlier chapters of this book that the setting up and running of a directly invested occupational scheme involves a considerable volume of work for the employer and the trustees. Even though they can call on experts in the various fields, a substantial amount of their own time is bound to be involved. While this will be justified in many cases there are large numbers of employers who operate on too small a scale for the necessary resources to be made available, or who prefer not to become too closely involved in pension matters. The great social role of insured pension schemes is to provide, for the employees involved in such cases, pension schemes designed reasonably closely to their particular needs which it would not have been possible to provide in any other way.

32.17 Statistics showing the distribution of occupational schemes by number of members according to the type of investment medium confirm that the overwhelming majority of small schemes are financed by means of insurance contracts. In recent years it has become less common for precise statistics in this connection to be drawn up, because the development of pension scheme financing has led to some blurring of the distinction between insured and directly invested schemes. Thus as mentioned earlier the pension scheme of a large concern may well have a substantial part of its assets invested in the managed funds associated with various life offices, either because such investments are thought desirable in their own right or as a consequence of the absorption of smaller schemes. It remains the case that employers who seek independent advice on insured schemes are likely to be persons who are not familiar with the details of pension schemes or their methods of finance; the actuary consulted on such a matter will therefore need to take particular care that the points he makes are understood by his client, and in general the issues covered will not be highly technical.

Insured scheme quotations: a case history

32.18   We will illustrate some of the issues that arise by means of an example based on an actual case. An employer of small size obtained quotations from seven life offices for a new scheme, to provide conventional benefits. We will consider the points that arose under the following headings.
(i)   Benefit design.
(ii)   Cost of benefits.
(iii)   Expenses.
(iv)   With-profit contracts and guarantees.
(v)   Flexibility.
(vi)   Discontinuance.

The reader should study this case history for general background rather than as a matter of detail and should bear in mind that as a life office's pension business usually involves a large number of small schemes, it is inevitable that scheme design will have to fit in with the life office's standard products and procedures as well as the desires of the client.

Benefit design

32.19   The scheme specification sent to the life offices was, in outline, as follows.

(i)   Employees to participate in State earnings-related scheme.

(ii) Member's pension on retirement at age 65 (males) and 60 (females) to be a specified fraction of final year's pay for each year of pensionable service.

(iii) Ill-health pension to be scale pension at date of ill-health retirement.

(iv) Specified levels of capital sum death benefit and of widows' pensions on death in service and death after retirement.

(v)   No funding for pension increases.

(vi) Members' pensions to be commutable within Inland Revenue limits.

(vii) Pensionable service to be period of membership of scheme, but the employer wished to know the extra cost involved if the initial entrants were permitted to count their period of employment before the setting up of the scheme as pensionable service.

32.20 A necessary first step in the analysis of quotations is to examine whether the benefits specified in these quotations are in fact those asked for, since the quotation submitted by each life office will necessarily reflect to some extent its particular products, procedures and internal machinery. In the case in question, three life offices quoted for pensions based on average annual pay during the best consecutive three years out of the ten years preceding retirement and the other four defined pay as pay in the final year or something closely equivalent. On the assumptions about future inflation which are commonly used in present day conditions the difference between a three-year average and a final year assumption is quite significant as far as contribution rates are concerned (since it represents roundly one year of pay escalation). It is therefore necessary to look closely at the benefits that are in fact being offered.

32.21 A somewhat similar point arose in the case under consideration in connection with ill-health pensions. The desired scale was the accrued scale pension at the date of retirement. None of the life offices concerned quoted precisely for this; some did not mention ill-health retirement benefits, others provided for a pension actuarially reduced for early payment and one provided for a pension based on the full prospective pensionable service which would have been completed at normal pension age.

32.22 These matters may need to be probed with the life offices concerned not simply because of any effect on estimated costs but to establish whether or not they reveal a genuine difficulty which the life office might have in providing to the trustees benefits matching those which the trustees desire to provide to the members under the trust deed and rules of the scheme.

Cost of benefits

32.23 The employer will find from the various quotations that even if (as is assumed) they are based on the same membership data, the amounts of contribution suggested for the opening years of the scheme will differ from one quotation to another. The reader will know from previous chapters that such differences inevitably arise from the variety of actuarial bases and funding plans which will underly the calculations made in the different life offices. The employer may, however, not be familiar with this concept; in his own business experience it is likely that specific goods or services have a specific price, and it may therefore be necessary to explain that the amounts of contributions set out in the various quotations are no more than estimates flowing from various assumptions.

32.24 The total contribution rates (as a percentage of total pensionable pay) recommended in the quotations, and the interest and pay escalation assumptions on which they were based, were as follows.

Quotation	Contribution rate for normal benefits	past service costs	Assumptions Interest	Pay escalation
	%	%	% p.a.	% p.a.
A	7.2	1.5	9.5	8.5
B	5.1	1.3	9.0	8.5
C	8.0	1.6	9.0	9.0
D	7.1 or 5.3. (note 1)		(note 2)	7.0
E	8.9	1.5	8.0	6.5
F	6.2 or 5.7 (note 3)		7.5	7.0
G	6.0	1.5	9.0	8.5

Note 1:

This life office did not separate the costs of the normal accrual of benefit and the past service provision. In its quotation Pensionable Service was defined as contributory membership of the scheme, and it was therefore assumed that past service costs has not been dealt with. The alternative contribution rates arose because the rate of 5.3 per cent. was described as a short term rate (based on a maximum projection period of 20 years) whereas the contribution of 7.1 per cent. was described as a more stable long term rate. The life office concerned strongly recommended the payment of contributions at the higher rate.

Note 2:

The investment yield assumption was not specified as a rate of interest but rather as a continuation of bonuses at a specified level.

Note 3:

The general circumstances of these alternative contribution rates are the same as in note 1 but it appeared from the detailed quotation that past service costs were included in this case.

32.25 It will be seen that the relationships between various figures in the above table are difficult to understand, bearing in mind the interest and escalation assumptions on which they are based. It was necessary in practice to analyse the funding plans, and this was possible since they were quite fully set out in the various quotations. Most of the quotations involved a 20 year projection although quotation A and the lower contribution of quotation F were stated to relate to only a five year projection. Even after this analysis, however, the quotations did not appear readily comparable. This is partly because the interest and escalation assumptions related to the period while contributions were being paid and resources accumulated. The costs depend not only on this period but also on the cost of purchasing annuities at normal retirement date and it was necessary to look into this matter in order to establish whether the various quotations appeared to be broadly consistent. This point was not in fact satisfactorily resolved.

32.26 Another aspect of cost is the frequency of payment of contributions assumed in the quotations. In some cases in our example the contribution was stated to be the amount payable annually in advance and the loading to be added to this amount for monthly or other payments was set out. In other cases the quotation stated that the contribution was assumed to be payable monthly.

32.27 As noted at the end of paragraph 32.23, it was necessary to make clear to the employer that these diverse quotations represented no more than estimates on various bases and funding assumptions. The point of most importance to the employer is the return which he may expect to receive on the premiums which the trustees of the scheme pay to the life office regarded as investments. The various quotations conveyed no information about this, since they did not show the premium rates or current bonus rates for the annuity contracts involved. It may be useful to use the regularly published tables of purchase price of immediate annuities in order to assess the competitive position of various life offices, but even these positions can change quite rapidly in the market and may not be relevant to the pension scheme contracts of the life office concerned. Thus the most important aspect of cost is to ensure that the employer understands the nature of what is being offered and the uncertainties about future performance, while providing him with such information as is available about the level of charges and the life office's performance record in the past.

32.28 There will be cases where the financial issues are sufficiently important for it to be necessary for the actuary to seek details of premium rates and bonus rates from the life office concerned and hence to calculate the effective investment yield represented by these rates. While such figures are illuminating it is necessary to bear in mind that they may not represent a long term yield, because under a controlled funding method where premiums paid are allocated to the benefits of older members the effective term of the bulk of the contracts may be much shorter than might have been supposed.

32.29 Another indirect aspect of benefit costs arises in connection with the amount of cover which will be provided without medical examination. Commonly when a pension scheme is being set up the employees at the time will be given the option of joining the scheme but will not be forced to do so. Thus the proportion of existing employees who will elect for membership of a scheme cannot be known in advance. In these circumstances life offices are in some difficulty in deciding on the extent to which they will provide cover for death in service benefits, which may be very substantial, since they do not know whether there will be special risks in connection with those of the existing employees who choose to enter the scheme. Consequently life office pension scheme quotations often lay down the proportion of initial entrants who must join the scheme in order for life assurance cover up to certain specified limits to be provided to all initial entrants without medical examination. Most of the quotations involved in our case history dealt with this matter, and typically the required degree of take-up if substantial life assurance cover without medical examination was to be provided varied from 75 per cent. to 95 per cent.

Expenses

32.30 The allowance for expenses may or may not be apparent from the quotations submitted. In our case history two of the life offices concerned set out explicitly the formulae that would determine the deduction from premiums for expenses, but the other quotations were silent on this matter. A point to note in this connection is that in framing the expense allowance the life office actuaries will make an assumption about the average size of the pension scheme which will be concerned. An employer who is contemplating a scheme with an expected number of members markedly larger or smaller than average will therefore need to look for any premium rebates or loadings involved. For a larger scheme a rebate might apply not only because the normal expense loading would relate to a smaller scheme but also because a large scheme might be able to accept a lesser administrative service from the life office. Most of the quotations in our case history mentioned these matters in reasonable detail.

32.31 Another aspect of expenses is the cost of the administrative work that remains with the employer. It was noted earlier that one advantage of an insured scheme which is particularly relevant to the small employer is that the insurance company takes much of the administrative burden involved in the running of the scheme (including payment of pensions) from the employer and the trustees, who may for instance hardly be aware that the Superannuation Funds Office and the Occupational Pensions Board are involved, and will almost certainly not be greatly concerned with the calculation of benefit.

32.32 This does not, however, mean that no administrative burden falls on the employer. The work of charging and collecting contributions, ensuring that tax relief is obtained on them and the Inland Revenue notified of changes, the keeping and updating of basic records for onward transmission to the insurance company and the answering of day-to-day queries from members must in the nature of things be done largely by the employer. An employer not familiar with pension schemes may find it difficult to judge the volume of administrative work which will be left with him and the actuary may be able to help by referring him to some other client who is involved with a comparable scheme. The employer may find it possible to arrange that the administrative work involved in the scheme will be carried out as a secondary job by someone already in his organisation, and in this case it may be that the real cost to him of running the scheme may not be much in excess of the actual amounts of contribution payable to the insurance company.

With-profit contracts and guarantees

32.33 The employer will be familiar with the general concept of non-profit and with-profit policies from his knowledge of life assurance. In the context of pension schemes, however, the range of application of bonus credits is wider than in conventional life assurance policies; bonuses are likely to be distributed in one or more of the following ways.

(i)   As a deduction from premiums.
(ii)   As additions, at regular intervals, to the purchased annuities.
(iii) As special additions when annuities come into payment. These additions may represent market conditions at the time, but they are more likely to be an allowance for capital growth of the insurance company's assets during the period that the contract has been in force.

The employer will probably have decided as a matter of policy on the level of benefit to be provided from the proposed scheme, so that he may well prefer a premium rebate to any other method of bonus declaration. It would be necessary to ensure that the employer was aware that a certain level of bonus would have been taken credit for in advance in the contribution rate calculation, and there would only be the possibility of excess resources to the extent that the actual bonus level from time to time exceeded that assumed.

32.34 As to any guarantees, in a with-profit scheme a deterioration in the experience may be reflected in the rates of normal or special bonuses rather than the premiums rates, so that the significance of any guarantee is diminished. The level of guarantees in non-profit schemes (which schemes are in any event rare) is likely to be of minor importance, since the guarantee is likely to be pitched at a level well below any reasonable expectation of the future experience.

Flexibility

32.35 An employer's pension scheme is part of his general conditions of service and pay structure. Subject to the protection of members' interests he will wish to be able to alter the scheme, wind it up, merge it, vary the pace at which he contributes to it or make other changes from time to time with the minimum of inconvenience or financial loss. A life office underwriting an insured scheme has to consider the interests of other policyholders and of any shareholders, and has its own administrative procedures. The existence of a life office as a party to the pension arrangements thus makes the situation more complex than in a directly invested scheme, and this may militate against the degree of flexibility that the employer needs.

32.36 In our case history a particular study of the quotations was made to establish any circumstances where unexpected events (short of discontinuance which is touched on separately below) might lead to extra expense. Some quotations explicitly mentioned that a deduction would be made from any cash required early, e.g. from payment of a transfer value. Others explicitly stated that there would be no penalty in these circumstances.

32.37 Another aspect of flexibility is the facility to use cash for purchase of benefits from a life office other than that involved in the main contract. Some of the life offices concerned in our case history provided an 'open market' option without penalty while others did not. Such an option effectively shortens the average expected term of the investment with the life office and this may influence the terms offered.

Discontinuance

32.38 The uncertainties of industrial and commercial life have been referred to earlier in this book. They are particularly relevant for smaller employers since these may be less able to meet economic difficulties or may be more likely to be absorbed by larger groups. Thus the questions of what will happen under an insurance contract if a pension scheme is discontinued, or if the trustees wish to discontinue their contract with the life office, are of considerable importance.

32.39 As far as discontinuance of the scheme is concerned, the trust deed and rules will lay down the actions which the trustees must take and the benefits which are available to the various prospective beneficiaries, including those currently in receipt of pension, ex-members with entitlement to a preserved pension and contributing members. The trust deed and rules will not lay down the terms of the contract between the trustees and the life office since this is governed by the policy document.

32.40 As to the latter document, the initial quotations from life offices would not normally be accompanied by examples of the full legal documentation. It may not therefore be immediately clear what rights the trustees would have in respect of their policy in the event of discontinuance of the scheme or on discontinuance of the policy while the scheme continues. It is essential for such matters to be clarified.

32.41 The policy will almost certainly provide, upon the cessation of premium payments to the life office, for the benefits to be made paid up. The pensions of retired members will be provided for, subject to adequacy of the available resources (which would normally be taken for granted since the annuities would have been purchased at retirement), but the preserved pensions available to the individual members will depend on the amount of deferred annuities purchased at the time.

32.42 A different set of circumstances in which termination of a policy may arise is that in which the trustees wish to transfer the assets of the scheme from deferred annuities to a managed fund associated with the life office concerned. This for instance may well happen when a scheme grows beyond a certain size and the trustees believe that an increase in investment return which might flow from conversion of the assets from deferred annuities to units in a managed fund might offset any penalty involved in the discontinuance of the original policy. The trustees and the employer will need an actuarial investigation to be made to assess the alternatives available on such a winding up, which would normally be

(i)   retention by the life office of the funds concerned with provision of paid up deferred annuities,

(ii) a transfer to a managed fund, or

(iii) payment of a surrender value as cash to the trustees.

Life offices normally offer better terms if cash is to be transferred to their associated managed fund than if it is to be paid as a surrender value to the trustees, and the latter will need to take advice in weighing the possible advantage of having cash freely available for investment against any possible financial penalty, compared with the transfer to the managed fund.

TABLES

The actuarial basis underlying the tables is as follows.

Interest	9 per cent. p.a.
Pay increases	Promotional scale of Table 2 plus 8 per cent. p.a. escalation
Pension increases	3 per cent. p.a.
Service table and salary scale	Table 2
Immediate dividend yield (see para 22.44)	4.696 per cent.
Dividend growth	4 per cent. p.a.
Pensioners' mortality	
normal health	a(55)
ill-health retirements	a(55) + 5
wives and widows	a(55)
Proportion married	90 per cent.
Age difference between husbands and wives	3 years

Table 1 *Initial membership data for Scheme X*

Group	Age	Number of members	Annual Salary of each member	Past service of each member	Total annual salary ÷ 1,000	Total (salary × duration) ÷ 1,000
			£	years	£'000	
A	20	30	2,400	–	72	–
B	25	20	2,800	3	56	168
C	25	35	3,000	4	105	420
D	30	30	3,000	5	90	450
E	35	20	3,200	6	64	384
F	35	15	3,400	6	51	306
G	35	5	6,800	4	34	136
H	40	20	3,400	10	68	680
I	40	10	3,600	19	36	684
J	45	20	3,400	24	68	1,632
K	45	30	3,600	23	108	2,484
L	45	5	6,000	21	30	630
M	50	30	4,000	23	120	2,760
N	50	35	5,000	26	175	4,550
O	55	5	10,000	31	50	1,550
P	55	10	6,000	28	60	1,680
Q	60	10	6,000	37	60	2,220
R	60	5	6,200	30	31	930
S	60	5	10,000	39	50	1,950
T	65	5	7,000	33	35	1,155
Total		345			1,363	24,769

Table 2   *Scheme X: service table and salary scale before escalation*

Age x	l_x	w_x	d_x	i_x	r_x	s_x	Age x
18	100 000	10 000	80			1.00	18
19	89 920	8 992	72			1.10	19
20	80 856	8 085	65			1.21	20
21	72 706	6 907	58			1.33	21
22	65 741	5 917	59			1.46	22
23	59 765	5 080	54			1.59	23
24	54 631	4 371	49			1.73	24
25	50 211	3 766	50			1.87	25
26	46 395	3 248	46			2.02	26
27	43 101	2 802	47			2.16	27
28	40 252	2 415	44			2.29	28
29	37 793	2 079	45			2.42	29
30	35 669	1 784	46			2.55	30
31	33 839	1 557	47	3		2.67	31
32	32 232	1 354	49	3		2.78	32
33	30 826	1 171	49	3		2.88	33
34	29 603	1 007	50	6		2.98	34
35	28 540	856	51	6		3.08	35
36	27 627	746	52	6		3.18	36
37	26 823	644	54	8		3.28	37
38	26 117	548	55	8		3.38	38
39	25 506	459	56	8		3.48	39
40	24 983	375	57	10		3.58	40
41	24 541	295	61	10		3.68	41
42	24 175	218	65	12		3.78	42
43	23 880	143	69	12		3.88	43
44	23 656	71	76	14		3.98	44
45	23 495		82	14		4.08	45
46	23 399		92	16		4.18	46
47	23 291		100	19		4.28	47
48	23 172		108	21		4.38	48
49	23 043		120	23		4.47	49
50	22 900		130	28		4.56	50
51	22 742		143	32		4.65	51
52	22 567		156	39		4.73	52
53	22 372		170	44		4.81	53
54	22 158		184	53		4.88	54

continued

Table 2 (continued) *Scheme X: service table and salary scale before escalation*

Age x	l_x	w_x	d_x	i_x	r_x	s_x	Age x
55	21 921		200	61		4.95	55
56	21 660		217	71		5.01	56
57	21 372		236	83		5.07	57
58	21 053		254	99		5.13	58
59	20 700		276	118		5.19	59
60	20 306		297	146	4 061	5.24	60
61	15 802		253	153	2 370	5.29	61
62	13 026		228	178	1 303	5.33	62
63	11 317		216	217	1 132	5.37	63
64	9 752		203	265	975	5.40	64
65	8 309				8 309		65

Table 3   *Scheme X: salary scale with escalation*

Age x	s_x no escalation	$(1.08)^x$	s_x with escalation $(2) \times (3)$	$z_{x+\frac{1}{2}}$
(1)	(2)	(3)	(4)	(5)
18	1.00	3.996	4.00	
19	1.10	4.316	4.75	
20	1.21	4.661	5.64	
21	1.33	5.034	6.70	5.25
22	1.46	5.437	7.94	6.23
23	1.59	5.871	9.33	7.37
24	1.73	6.341	11.0	8.71
25	1.87	6.848	12.8	10.2
26	2.02	7.396	14.9	12.0
27	2.16	7.988	17.3	13.9
28	2.29	8.627	19.8	16.2
29	2.42	9.317	22.5	18.6
30	2.55	10.063	25.7	21.3
31	2.67	10.868	29.0	24.2
32	2.78	11.737	32.6	27.4
33	2.88	12.676	36.5	30.9
34	2.98	13.690	40.8	34.7
35	3.08	14.785	45.5	38.8
36	3.18	15.968	50.8	43.3
37	3.28	17.246	56.6	48.3
38	3.38	18.625	63.0	53.9
39	3.48	20.115	70.0	60.0
40	3.58	21.725	77.8	66.7
41	3.68	23.462	86.3	74.1
42	3.78	25.339	95.8	82.3
43	3.88	27.367	106	91.3
44	3.98	29.556	118	101
45	4.08	31.920	130	112
46	4.18	34.474	144	124
47	4.28	37.232	159	137
48	4.38	40.211	176	152
49	4.47	43.427	194	168
50	4.56	46.902	214	185
51	4.65	50.654	236	205
52	4.73	54.706	259	225
53	4.81	59.083	284	248
54	4.88	63.809	311	272

continued

Table 3 (continued)   *Scheme X: salary scale with escalation*

Age x	s_x no escalation	$(1.08)^x$	s_x with escalation $(2) \times (3)$	$z_{x+\frac{1}{2}}$
(1)	(2)	(3)	(4)	(5)
55	4.95	68.914	341	298
56	5.01	74.427	373	327
57	5.07	80.381	408	358
58	5.13	86.812	445	391
59	5.19	93.757	487	428
60	5.24	101.257	531	467
61	5.29	109.358	579	510
62	5.33	118.106	630	556
63	5.37	127.555	685	606
64	5.40	137.759	744	659
65				686

Table 4 Scheme X: salary scale and contribution functions

Age x (1)	s_x (2)	l_x (3)	v^x @ 9% (4)	D_x (3) × (4) (5)	$\bar{D}_x$ (6)	$s_x\bar{D}_x$ (7)	$s\bar{N}_x$ (8)
55	341	21 921	.00874	191.59	182.65	62 284	490 537
56	373	21 660	.00802	173.71	165.51	61 735	428 253
57	408	21 372	.00736	157.30	149.71	61 082	366 518
58	445	21 053	.00675	142.11	135.12	60 128	305 436
59	487	20 700	.00619	128.13	121.73	59 283	245 308
60	531	20 306	.00568	115.34	98.83	52 479	186 025
61	579	15 802	.00521	82.33	72.29	41 856	133 546
62	630	13 026	.00478	62.26	55.97	35 261	91 690
63	685	11 317	.00439	49.68	44.44	30 441	56 429
64	744	9 752	.00402	39.20	34.93	25 988	25 988
65		8 309	.00369	30.66			

$$ {}^s\bar{a}_{55} = \frac{{}^s\bar{N}_{55}}{{}^sD_{55}} = \frac{490{,}537}{59{,}584} = 8.23 $$

Table 5 *Scheme X: age retirement functions*

Age x (1)	r_x (2)	$\dfrac{v^{x+\frac12}}{v^{65}}$ @ $x=65$ @ 9% (3)	C_x^r (2)×(3) (4)	$\dfrac{\bar a_{\overline{x+\frac12\,5}|}}{\bar a_{\overline{65\,5}|}}$ @ $x=65$ (5)	C_x^{ra} (4)×(5) (6)	$\dfrac{z_{x+\frac12}}{z_{65}}$ @ $x=65$ (7)	$zC_x^{ra} \div 10$ (6)×(7)÷10 (8)	$zM_x^{ra} \div 10$ Σ(8) (9)	$z\bar M_x^{ra} \div 10$ (9)−½(8) (10)	$z\bar R_x^{ra} \div 10$ Σ(10) (11)
55								45 112	45 112	366 971
56								45 112	45 112	321 859
57								45 112	45 112	276 747
58								45 112	45 112	231 635
59								45 112	45 112	186 523
60	4 061	.00544	22.1	10.477	232	467	10 834	45 112	39 695	141 411
61	2 370	.00499	11.8	10.221	121	510	6 171	34 278	31 193	101 716
62	1 303	.00458	6.0	9.963	60	556	3 336	28 107	26 439	70 523
63	1 132	.00420	4.8	9.702	47	606	2 848	24 771	23 347	44 084
64	975	.00385	3.8	9.440	36	659	2 372	21 923	20 737	20 737
65	8 309	.00369	30.7	9.309	285	686	19 551	19 551		

$$\frac{zM_{55}^{ra}}{sD_{55}} = \frac{451,120}{59,584} = 7.57$$

$$\frac{z\bar R_{55}^{ra}}{sD_{55}} = \frac{3,669,710}{59,584} = 61.6$$

Table 6   Scheme X: ill-health retirement functions

Age x (1)	i_x (2)	$v^{x+\frac{1}{2}}$ @ 9% (3)	C_x^i (2)×(3) (4)	$\bar{a}_{\overline{x+\frac{1}{2}\,5|}}$ (5)	C_x^{ia} (4)×(5) (6)	$z_{x+\frac{1}{2}}$ (7)	$^zC_x^{ia}$ (6)×(7) (8)	$^zM_x^{ia}$ Σ (8) (9)	$^z\bar{M}_x^{ia}$ (9)−½(8) (10)	$^z\bar{R}_x^{ia}$ Σ (10) (11)
55	61	.00837	0.51	10.477	5.3	298	1 579	31 672	30 883	192 030
56	71	.00768	0.55	10.221	5.6	327	1 831	30 093	29 177	161 147
57	83	.00705	0.59	9.963	5.9	358	2 112	28 262	27 206	131 970
58	99	.00646	0.64	9.702	6.2	391	2 424	26 150	24 938	104 764
59	118	.00593	0.70	9.440	6.6	428	2 825	23 726	22 313	79 826
60	146	.00544	0.79	9.178	7.3	467	3 409	20 901	19 197	57 513
61	153	.00499	0.76	8.916	6.8	510	3 468	17 492	15 758	38 316
62	178	.00458	0.82	8.654	7.1	556	3 948	14 024	12 050	22 558
63	217	.00420	0.91	8.395	7.6	606	4 606	10 076	7 773	10 508
64	265	.00385	1.02	8.138	8.3	659	5 470	5 470	2 735	2 735

$$\frac{^zM_{55}^{ia}}{^sD_{55}} = \frac{31,672}{59,584} = 0.53$$

$$\frac{^z\bar{R}_{55}^{ia}}{^sD_{55}} = \frac{192,030}{59,584} = 3.2$$

Table 7 *Scheme X: preserved pension functions*

Age x (1)	w_x (2)	$v^{x+1/2}$ @ 9% (3)	C_x^w (2) × (3) (4)	$z_{x+1/2}$ (5)	$^zC_x^w$ (4) × (5) (6)	$\bar{a}\,x\overline{\lvert 65\ 5\rvert}$ (7)	$^zC_x^{w/a}$ (6) × (7) (8)	$^zM_x^{w/a}$ Σ (8) (9)	$^z\bar{M}_x^{w/a}$ (9) − ½(8) (10)	$^z\bar{R}_x^{w/a}$ Σ (10) (11)
35	856	.04692	40.2	38.8	1 560	2.487	3 880	23 795	21 855	88 797
36	746	.04304	32.1	43.3	1 390	2.586	3 595	19 915	18 117	66 942
37	644	.03949	25.4	48.3	1 227	2.690	3 301	16 320	14 669	48 825
38	548	.03623	19.9	53.9	1 073	2.798	3 002	13 019	11 518	34 156
39	459	.03324	15.3	60.0	918	2.910	2 671	10 017	8 681	22 638
40	375	.03050	11.4	66.7	760	3.028	2 301	7 346	6 195	13 957
41	295	.02798	8.3	74.1	615	3.151	1 938	5 045	4 076	7 762
42	218	.02567	5.6	82.3	461	3.279	1 512	3 107	2 351	3 686
43	143	.02354	3.4	91.3	310	3.414	1 058	1 595	1 066	1 335
44	71	.02160	1.5	101	151	3.555	537	537	269	269

$$\frac{^zM_{35}^{w/a}}{^sD_{35}} = \frac{23{,}795}{57{,}038} = 0.42$$

$$\frac{^z\bar{R}_{35}^{w/a}}{^sD_{35}} = \frac{88{,}797}{57{,}038} = 1.56$$

Table 8   Scheme X: death after age retirement widow's pension functions

Age x	C_x	$\bar{a}_{x+\frac12\mid x-3+\frac12}\,(x=65)$ $\bar{a}_{65\mid 62}\,(x=65)$	$C_x^{r(wa)}$ $(2)\times(3)\times0.9$	$z_{x+\frac12}\,(x=65)$ $z_{65}\,(x=65)$	$^zC_x^{r(wa)}\div10$ $(4)\times(5)\div10$	$^zM_x^{r(wa)}\div10$ $\Sigma(6)$	$^z\bar{M}_x^{r(wa)}\div10$ $(7)-\frac12(6)$	$^z\bar{R}_x^{r(wa)}\div10$ $\Sigma(8)$
(1)	(2)	(3)	(4)	(5)	(6)	(7)	(8)	(9)
55						12 987	12 987	107 664
56						12 987	12 987	94 677
57						12 987	12 987	81 690
58						12 987	12 987	68 703
59						12 987	12 987	55 716
60	22.1	2.991	59.5	467	2 779	12 987	11 597	42 729
61	11.8	3.048	32.4	510	1 652	10 208	9 382	31 132
62	6.0	3.100	16.7	556	929	8 556	8 091	21 750
63	4.8	3.148	13.6	606	824	7 627	7 215	13 659
64	3.8	3.191	10.9	659	718	6 803	6 444	6 444
65	30.7	3.210	88.7	686	6 085	6 085		

$$\frac{^zM_{55}^{r(wa)}}{^sD_{55}}=\frac{129{,}870}{59{,}584}=2.18$$

$$\frac{^z\bar{R}_{55}^{r(wa)}}{^sD_{55}}=\frac{1{,}076{,}640}{59{,}584}=18.1$$

Table 9 Scheme X: death after ill-health retirement widow's pension functions

Age x (1)	C_x (2)	$\bar{a}_{x+\frac{1}{2}\|x-3+\frac{1}{2}}$ (3)	$C_x^{r(wa)}$ $(2)\times(3)\times 0.9$ (4)	$z_{x+\frac{1}{2}}$ (5)	$^zC_x^{r(wa)}$ $(4)\times(5)$ (6)	$^zM_x^{r(wa)}$ Σ (6) (7)	$^z\bar{M}_x^{r(wa)}$ $(7)-\frac{1}{2}(6)$ (8)	$^z\bar{R}_x^{r(wa)}$ Σ (8) (9)
55	0.51	3.668	1.68	298	501	12 977	12 727	82 889
56	0.55	3.754	1.86	327	608	12 476	12 172	70 162
57	0.59	3.837	2.04	358	730	11 868	11 503	57 990
58	0.64	3.915	2.26	391	884	11 138	10 696	46 487
59	0.70	3.989	2.51	428	1 074	10 254	9 717	35 791
60	0.79	4.058	2.89	467	1 350	9 180	8 505	26 074
61	0.76	4.121	2.82	510	1 438	7 830	7 111	17 569
62	0.82	4.177	3.08	556	1 712	6 392	5 536	10 458
63	0.91	4.227	3.46	606	2 097	4 680	3 631	4 922
64	1.02	4.268	3.92	659	2 583	2 583	1 291	1 291

$$\frac{^zM_{55}^{r(wa)}}{^sD_{55}} = \frac{12,977}{59,584} = 0.22$$

$$\frac{^z\bar{R}_{55}^{r(wa)}}{^sD_{55}} = \frac{82,889}{59,584} = 1.39$$

Table 10   Scheme X: death in service widow's pension functions

Age x (1)	C_x^d (2)	$\bar{a}_{x-3+\frac{1}{2}}$ (3)	$C_x^{d(wa)}$ $(2) \times (3) \times 0.9$ (4)	$z_{x+\frac{1}{2}}$ (5)	$^zC_x^{d(wa)} \div 10$ $(4) \times (5) \div 10$ (6)	$^zM_x^{d(wa)} \div 10$ Σ (6) (7)	$^z\bar{M}_x^{d(wa)} \div 10$ $(7)-\frac{1}{2}(6)$ (8)	$^z\bar{R}_x^{d(wa)} \div 10$ Σ (8) (9)
55	1.67	13.288	19.97	298	595	6 686	6 389	32 628
56	1.67	13.095	19.68	327	644	6 091	5 769	26 239
57	1.66	12.895	19.27	358	690	5 447	5 102	20 470
58	1.64	12.687	18.73	391	732	4 757	4 391	15 368
59	1.64	12.472	18.41	428	788	4 025	3 631	10 977
60	1.62	12.250	17.86	467	834	3 237	2 820	7 346
61	1.26	12.020	13.63	510	695	2 403	2 055	4 526
62	1.04	11.783	11.03	556	613	1 708	1 401	2 471
63	0.91	11.539	9.45	606	573	1 095	809	1 070
64	0.78	11.289	7.92	659	522	522	261	261

$$\frac{^zM_{55}^{d(wa)}}{^sD_{55}} = \frac{66,860}{59,584} = 1.12$$

$$\frac{^z\bar{R}_{55}^{d(wa)}}{^sD_{55}} = \frac{326,280}{59,584} = 5.5$$

Table 11(a)   Scheme X: annuity for widow's pension on death after withdrawal

Age x (1)	d_x a(55)m (2)	$l_{x-3+\frac{1}{2}}/l_{41}$ a(55) f (3)	$v^{x+\frac{1}{2}}$ @ 9% (4)	$1.05^{x+\frac{1}{2}-44}$ (5)	$\bar{a}_{x+\frac{1}{2}-3}$ @ 5.825% (6)	(2) × (3) × (4) × (5) × (6) (7)
44	3 065	.999	.02160	1.025	14.979	1 016
45	3 342	.997	.01982	1.076	14.855	1 056
46	3 636	.995	.01818	1.130	14.725	1 095
47	3 965	.993	.01668	1.186	14.590	1 136
48	4 308	.990	.01530	1.246	14.449	1 174
49	4 712	.987	.01404	1.308	14.302	1 221
50	5 130	.985	.01288	1.373	14.149	1 264
51	5 596	.981	.01182	1.442	13.990	1 310
52	6 109	.978	.01084	1.514	13.825	1 356
53	6 667	.975	.00995	1.590	13.652	1 404
54	7 250	.971	.00913	1.669	13.474	1 446
55	7 891	.967	.00837	1.753	13.288	1 488
56	8 587	.962	.00768	1.840	13.095	1 528
57	9 350	.957	.00705	1.932	12.895	1 572
58	10 178	.953	.00646	2.029	12.687	1 612
59	11 079	.947	.00593	2.130	12.472	1 653
60	12 056	.941	.00544	2.237	12.250	1 691
61	13 108	.935	.00499	2.349	12.020	1 726
62	14 241	.929	.00458	2.466	11.783	1 760

continued

Table 11(a) (continued) Scheme X: annuity for widow's pension on death after withdrawal

Age x (1)	d_x a(55)m (2)	$l_{x-3+\frac{1}{2}}/l_{41}$ a(55) f (3)	$v^{x+\frac{1}{2}}$ @ 9% (4)	$1.05^{x+\frac{1}{2}-44}$ (5)	$\bar{a}_{x+\frac{1}{2}-3}$ @ 5.825% (6)	(2) × (3) × (4) × (5) × (6) (7)
63	15 450	.920	.00420	2.589	11.539	1 784
64	16 745	.911	.00385	2.719	11.289	1 803
						30 095

Widow's pension on death before age 65: $30{,}095 \div D_{44}$ (a(55)m 9%) (21,670) $= 1.389$

Widow's pension on death after age 65:

$$\frac{l_{65}}{l_{44}}_{\text{m}} \times \frac{l_{62}}{l_{41}}_{\text{f}} \times v^{21} \times (1.05)^{21} \times \bar{a}_{65|62}$$

a(55)   a(55)   9%   5.825%

$= .820 \times .907 \times 0.1637 \times 2.7860 \times 3.210 = \underline{1.090}$

$\underline{2.479}$

Table 11(b) *Scheme X: functions for widow's pension on death after withdrawal*

Age x (1)	$^zC_x^w$ (2)	$\bar{a}'_{x+\frac{1}{2}|y+\frac{1}{2}}$ (3)	$^zC_x^{w(wa)}$ (2) × (3) × 0.9 (4)	$^zM_x^{w(wa)}$ Σ (4) (5)	$^z\bar{M}_x^{w(wa)}$ (5) − ½(4) (6)	$^z\bar{R}_x^{w(wa)}$ Σ (6) (7)
35	1 560	1.991	2 795	16 450	15 053	60 001
36	1 390	2.045	2 558	13 655	12 376	44 948
37	1 227	2.101	2 320	11 097	9 937	32 572
38	1 073	2.158	2 084	8 777	7 735	22 635
39	918	2.215	1 830	6 693	5 778	14 900
40	760	2.273	1 555	4 863	4 085	9 122
41	615	2.332	1 291	3 308	2 663	5 037
42	461	2.391	992	2 017	1 521	2 374
43	310	2.450	684	1 025	683	853
44	151	2.509	341	341	170	170

$$\frac{^zM_{35}^{w(wa)}}{^sD_{35}} = \frac{16,450}{57,038} = 0.29$$

$$\frac{^z\bar{R}_{35}^{w(wa)}}{^sD_{35}} = \frac{60,001}{57,038} = 1.05$$

Table 12 *Scheme X: death in service capital sum benefit functions*

Age x (1)	d_x (2)	$v^{x+\frac{1}{2}}$ @ 9% (3)	C_x^d (2) × (3) (4)	s_x (5)	$^sC_x^d$ (4) × (5) (6)	$^sM_x^d$ Σ (6) (7)
55	200	.00837	1.67	341	569	6 836
56	217	.00768	1.67	373	619	6 267
57	236	.00705	1.66	408	677	5 648
58	254	.00646	1.64	445	734	4 971
59	276	.00593	1.64	487	794	4 237
60	297	.00544	1.62	531	855	3 443
61	253	.00499	1.26	579	730	2 588
62	228	.00458	1.04	630	655	1 858
63	216	.00420	0.91	685	623	1 203
64	203	.00385	0.78	744	580	580

$$^s\bar{A}_{55}^d = \frac{^sM_{55}^d}{^sD_{55}} = \frac{6{,}836}{59{,}584} = 0.11$$

Table 13 *Scheme X: Valuation factors*

| Age | Member's pension | | | | Widow's pension on death after retirement | | | | Widow's pension on death in service | |
| | Age | | Ill-health | | Age | | Ill-health | | | |
(1)	M/D (2)	R/D (3)	M/D (4)	R/D (5)	M/D (6)	R/D (7)	M/D (8)	R/D (9)	M/D (10)	R/D (11)
20	6.53	281.8	0.62	23.4	1.88	81.5	0.23	8.87	1.98	62.7
23	6.86	275.5	0.65	22.6	1.98	79.7	0.24	8.61	2.05	59.7
25	7.02	267.9	0.67	21.8	2.02	77.5	0.24	8.33	2.07	56.9
28	7.23	253.9	0.68	20.3	2.08	73.5	0.25	7.82	2.09	52.2
30	7.41	245.5	0.70	19.5	2.13	71.1	0.25	7.51	2.11	49.2
33	7.68	231.4	0.73	18.0	2.21	67.0	0.26	6.99	2.13	44.6
35	7.87	221.6	0.74	17.0	2.27	64.2	0.27	6.63	2.14	41.4
38	8.04	202.1	0.75	15.1	2.32	58.6	0.27	5.94	2.11	35.8
40	8.07	186.7	0.74	13.6	2.33	54.1	0.27	5.41	2.07	31.7
43	7.99	160.9	0.72	11.3	2.30	46.7	0.27	4.55	1.95	25.4
45	7.86	142.5	0.69	9.7	2.26	41.4	0.26	3.95	1.85	21.2
48	7.61	115.3	0.65	7.5	2.19	33.5	0.25	3.07	1.65	15.4
50	7.52	98.7	0.62	6.1	2.17	28.8	0.24	2.54	1.51	12.1
53	7.47	75.8	0.57	4.3	2.15	22.2	0.23	1.82	1.29	7.8
55	7.57	61.6	0.53	3.2	2.18	18.1	0.22	1.39	1.12	5.5
58	7.76	39.9	0.45	1.8	2.24	11.8	0.19	0.80	0.82	2.7
60	8.01	25.1	0.37	1.0	2.31	7.6	0.16	0.46	0.58	1.3
63	7.90	14.1	0.32	0.3	2.43	4.4	0.15	0.16	0.35	0.3
65	8.59	–	–	–	2.67	–	–	–	–	–

continued

Table 13 (continued) Scheme X: Valuation factors

Age	Capital sum on death in service (12)	Member's preserved pension on withdrawal M/D (13)	Member's preserved pension on withdrawal R/D (14)	Widow's pension on death after withdrawal M/D (15)	Widow's pension on death after withdrawal R/D (16)	Contribution factor (17)
20	0.19	1.76	15.88	1.38	11.76	39.42
23	0.19	1.48	11.70	1.13	8.51	38.08
25	0.20	1.27	9.19	0.96	6.60	36.77
28	0.20	0.98	6.03	0.71	4.25	34.54
30	0.20	0.80	4.38	0.57	3.05	33.25
33	0.21	0.56	2.47	0.39	1.69	31.21
35	0.21	0.42	1.56	0.29	1.05	29.86
38	0.20	0.23	0.61	0.16	0.40	27.29
40	0.20	0.13	0.25	0.09	0.16	25.28
43	0.19	0.03	0.02	0.02	0.02	21.89
45	0.18					19.44
48	0.16					15.73
50	0.15					13.44
53	0.13					10.22
55	0.11					8.23
58	0.09					5.25
60	0.06					3.30
63	0.04					1.80

Table 14 *Scheme X: calculations for initial membership: Group D*

Money amounts in £ 000

(1)	Age	30
(2)	Total salaries	90
(3)	Total (salary × duration ÷ 2)	225
	Members' age pensions	
(4)	$^zM_{30}^{ra}/^sD_{30}$	7.41
(5)	$^z\bar{R}_{30}^{ra}/^sD_{30}$	245.5
(6)	(2) × (4) × 1/80	8.3
(7)	(3) × (4) × 1/80	20.8
(8)	(2) × (5) × 1/80	276.2
	Members' ill-health pensions	
(9)	$^zM_{30}^{ia}/^sD_{30}$	0.70
(10)	$^z\bar{R}_{30}^{ra}/^sD_{30}$	19.5
(11)	(2) × (9) × 1/80	0.8
(12)	(3) × (9) × 1/80	2.0
(13)	(2) × (10) × 1/80	21.9
	Widows' pensions on death after age retirement	
(14)	$^zM_{30}^{r(wa)}/^sD_{30}$	2.13
(15)	$^z\bar{R}_{30}^{r(wa)}/^sD_{30}$	71.1
(16)	(2) × (14) × 1/160	1.2
(17)	(3) × (14) × 1/160	3.0
(18)	(2) × (15) × 1/160	40.0
	Widow's pensions on death after ill-health retirement	
(19)	$^zM_{30}^{i(wa)}/^sD_{30}$	0.25
(20)	$^z\bar{R}_{30}^{i(wa)}/^sD_{30}$	7.51
(21)	(2) × (19) × 1/160	0.1
(22)	(3) × (19) × 1/160	0.4
(23)	(2) × (20) × 1/160	4.2
	Widows' pensions on death in service	
(24)	$^zM_{30}^{d(wa)}/^sD_{30}$	2.11
(25)	$^z\bar{R}_{30}^{d(wa)}/^sD_{30}$	49.2
(26)	(2) × (24) × 1/160	1.2
(27)	(3) × (24) × 1/160	3.0
(28)	(2) × (25) × 1/160	27.7
	Members' preserved pensions on withdrawal	
(29)	$^zM_{30}^{w|a}/^sD_{30}$	0.80
(30)	$^z\bar{R}_{30}^{w|a}/^sD_{30}$	4.38
(31)	(2) × (29) × 1/80	0.9
(32)	(3) × (29) × 1/80	2.3
(33)	(2) × (30) × 1/80	4.9

continued

Table 14 (continued)   *Scheme X: calculations for initial membership:*
Group D

Money amounts in £ 000

Widows' pensions on member's death after withdrawal
with preserved pension

(34)	$^{z}M_{30}^{w(wa)}/{}^{s}D_{30}$	0.57
(35)	$^{z}\bar{R}_{30}^{w(wa)}/{}^{s}D_{30}$	3.05
(36)	$(2) \times (34) \times 1/160$	0.3
(37)	$(3) \times (34) \times 1/160$	0.8
(38)	$(2) \times (35) \times 1/160$	1.7

Lump sum on death in service

(39)	$^{s}M_{30}^{d}/{}^{s}D_{30}$	0.20
(40)	q_{30}	0.0013
(41)	$(2) \times (39) \times 2$	36.0
(42)	$(2) \times (40) \times s_{30}/s_{29} \times 2$	0.3

Contributions

(43)	$^{s}\bar{a}_{30}$	33.25
(44)	$.01 \times (2) \times (43)$	29.9

Table 15 *Scheme X: capital values for pre-Scheme service*

£ 000

Age (1)	Members' age pensions (2)	Members' ill-health pensions (3)	Widows' pensions on death:			Early leavers		Total (9)
			after age retirement (4)	after ill-health retirement (5)	in service (6)	members' pensions (7)	widows' pensions (8)	
25	25.9	2.5	3.7	0.4	3.8	4.7	1.8	42.8
30	20.8	2.0	3.0	0.4	3.0	2.3	0.8	32.3
35	40.7	3.8	5.9	0.7	5.5	2.1	0.7	59.4
40	68.9	6.3	9.9	1.2	8.8	1.1	0.4	96.6
45	233.4	20.6	33.6	3.9	27.4			318.9
50	343.9	28.3	49.5	5.5	34.6			461.8
55	152.3	10.7	21.9	2.2	11.3			198.4
60	255.5	11.9	36.8	2.6	9.2			316.0
65	62.0	–	9.6	–	–			71.6
	1 203.4	86.1	173.9	16.9	103.6	10.2	3.7	1 597.8

£ 000

Table 16   *Scheme X: capital values for one year's membership*

Age (1)	Members' age pensions (2)	Members' ill-health pensions (3)	Widows' pensions on death: after age retirement (4)	after ill-health retirement (5)	in service (6)	Early leavers members' pensions (7)	Early leavers widows' pensions (8)	Capital sums on death in service (9)	Total (10)
20	5.9	0.6	0.9	0.1	0.9	1.6	0.6	0.1	10.7
25	14.2	1.3	2.0	0.2	2.1	2.6	1.0	0.4	23.8
30	8.3	0.8	1.2	0.1	1.2	0.9	0.3	0.3	13.1
35	14.7	1.4	2.1	0.3	2.0	0.8	0.3	0.6	22.2
40	10.5	1.0	1.5	0.2	1.3	0.2	0.1	0.5	15.3
45	20.3	1.8	2.9	0.3	2.4			1.6	29.3
50	27.8	2.3	4.0	0.4	2.8			3.7	41.0
55	10.4	0.7	1.5	0.1	0.8			2.2	15.7
60	14.1	0.7	2.0	0.1	0.5			4.5	21.9
	126.2	10.6	18.1	1.8	14.0	6.1	2.3	13.9	193.0

Table 17 *Scheme X: capital values for expected future membership*

£ 000

Age (1)	Members' age pensions (2)	Members' ill-health pensions (3)	Widows' pensions on death: after age retirement (4)	after ill-health retirement (5)	in service (6)	Early leavers members' pensions (7)	widows' pensions (8)	Capital sums on death in service (9)	Total (10)	Value of 1 per cent. contribution (11)
20	255.1	21.2	36.9	4.0	28.4	14.3	5.3	27.3	392.5	28.5
25	540.7	44.0	78.2	8.4	57.4	18.5	6.6	63.7	817.5	59.3
30	276.2	21.9	40.0	4.2	27.7	4.9	1.7	36.0	412.6	29.9
35	413.5	31.7	59.9	6.2	38.6	2.9	1.0	61.6	615.4	44.5
40	243.1	17.8	35.2	3.5	20.7	0.3	0.1	41.8	362.5	26.3
45	367.5	25.1	53.4	5.1	27.4			74.8	553.3	40.1
50	364.6	22.6	53.1	4.7	22.3			89.2	556.5	39.7
55	84.4	4.4	12.4	1.0	3.8			25.2	131.2	9.0
60	44.3	1.8	6.7	0.4	1.2			17.3	71.7	4.6
	2 589.4	190.5	375.8	37.5	227.5	40.9	14.7	436.9	3 913.2	281.9

Table 18 *Scheme X: calculation of G.M.P. amounts: Group D*

Tax year beginning 6th April (1)	Age at beginning of year (2)	Salary during year (3)	Lower earnings limit during year (4)	Relevant earnings during year (5)	G.M.P. earned during year (6)	Total revalued G.M.P. at end of year (7)
		£	£	£	£	£
1978	29	3,000	910	–	–	–
1979	30	3,427	983	2,444	17	17
1980	31	3,867	1,061	2,806	20	39
1981	32	4,347	1,146	3,201	23	65
1982	33				26	96
1983	34				29	132
1984	35				33	176
1985	36				37	227
1986	37				42	287
1987	38				47	357
1988	39				53	438
1989	40				59	532
1990	41				66	640
1991	42				73	764
1992	43				82	907
1993	44				91	1,071
1994	45				101	1,258
1995	46				113	1,471

continued

Table 18 (continued) Scheme X: calculation of G.M.P. amounts: Group D

Tax year beginning 6th April (1)	Age at beginning of year (2)	Salary during year (3) £	Lower earnings limit during year (4) £	Relevant earnings during year (5) £	G.M.P. earned during year (6) £	Total revalued G.M.P. at end of year (7) £
1996	47				125	1,714
1997	48				139	1,991
1998	49				154	2,304
1999	50				170	2,659
2000	51				188	3,060
2001	52				208	3,512
2002	53				229	4,021
2003	54				251	4,594
2004	55				276	5,238
2005	56	49,733	7,269	42,464	303	5,959
2006	57	54,400	7,851	45,984	328	6,764
2007	58	59,333	8,479	49,663	355	7,660
2008	59	64,933	9,157	53,634	383	8,656
2009	60	70,800	9,890	57,927	414	9,762
2010	61	77,200	10,681	62,560	447	10,990
2011	62	84,000	11,535	67,562	483	12,351
2012	63	91,333	12,458	72,968	521	13,861
2013	64	99,200	13,455	78,808		

Table 19 *Scheme X: G.M.P. calculations: Group D age retirements*

Age x (1)	G.M.P. at retirement (2)	Fixed rate revaluation (3)	G.M.P. at age 65 (2) × (3) (4)	C_x (5)	$\dfrac{D_{65}}{D_{x+\frac{1}{2}}}$ x < 65 (6)	(4) × (5) × (6) ÷ 1,000 (7)
	£		£			£000
60	8 656 × 1.08 + 414 × 0.5 = 9 555	1.085^3	12 204	22.1	0.627	169.1
61	9 762 × 1.08 + 447 × 0.5 = 10 766	1.085^2	12 674	11.8	0.694	103.8
62	10 990 × 1.08 + 483 × 0.5 = 12 111	1.085	13 140	6.0	0.769	60.6
63	12 351 × 1.08 + 521 × 0.5 = 13 600	1.000	13 600	4.8	0.853	55.7
64	13 861	1.000	13 861	3.8	0.949	50.0
65	13 861	1.000	13 861	30.7	1.000	425.5
						864.7

$$£\,000$$

$$30 \times 864.7/D_{30}\ (2688.40) \qquad\quad = \ 9.649$$

$$9.649 \times \bar{a}\,\overline{_{65\,\overline{5}|}}\ 5.825\%\ (9.309) = 89.8$$

$$9.649 \times \bar{a}\,\overline{_{65\,\overline{5}|}}\ 9\%\ (7.679) \quad\ = 74.1$$

Table 20 Scheme X: withdrawal benefits and G.M.P.

Group D

Age (1)	C_x^w (2)	$\dfrac{D_{65}}{D_{x+\frac{1}{2}}}$ a(55) 9% (3)	(2) × (3) (4)	$z_{x+\frac{1}{2}}$ (5)	$3{,}000 \div$ s_{29} (22.5) × (5) (6)	$x + \frac{1}{2} - 30$ (7)	(6) × (7) ÷ 80 = preserved pension (8)	G.M.P. element in (8) (9)	(8) − (9) = non-G.M.P. element in (8) (10)
					£ pa		£ pa	£ pa	£ pa
30	128.8	.0409	5.263	21.3	2 840	0.5	18	9	9
31	103.1	.0446	4.597	24.2	3 227	1.5	61	28	33
32	82.3	.0487	4.005	27.4	3 653	2.5	114	54	60
33	65.3	.0531	3.469	30.9	4 120	3.5	180	83	97
34	51.5	.0580	2.989	34.7	4 627	4.5	260	118	142
35	40.2	.0633	2.546	38.8	5 173	5.5	356	159	197
36	32.1	.0691	2.219	43.3	5 773	6.5	469	209	260
37	25.4	.0755	1.919	48.3	6 440	7.5	604	266	338
38	19.9	.0824	1.640	53.9	7 187	8.5	764	333	431
39	15.3	.0901	1.378	60.0	8 000	9.5	950	412	538
40	11.4	.0984	1.122	66.7	8 893	10.5	1 167	503	664
41	8.3	.1076	.893	74.1	9 880	11.5	1 420	608	812
42	5.6	.1175	.658	82.3	10 973	12.5	1 715	728	987
43	3.4	.1284	.437	91.3	12 173	13.5	2 054	866	1 188
44	1.5	.1405	.211	101	13 467	14.5	2 441	1 025	1 416

continued

Table 20 (continued) Scheme X: withdrawal benefits and G.M.P. Group D

Age	$(1.05)^{65-x-\frac{1}{2}}$ (11)	$(9) \times (11)$ (12)	$(10) \times (11)$ (13)	$(4) \times (12)$ (14)	$(4) \times (13)$ (15)	$(1.085)^{63-x}$ (16)	$(9) \times (16)$ (17)	$(4) \times (17)$ (18)
		£ pa	£ pa					
30	5.383	48	48	253	253	14.763	133	700
31	5.127	144	169	662	777	13.607	381	1 751
32	4.883	264	293	1 057	1 173	12.541	677	2 711
33	4.650	386	451	1 339	1 565	11.558	959	3 327
34	4.429	523	629	1 563	1 880	10.653	1 257	3 757
35	4.218	671	831	1 708	2 116	9.818	1 561	3 974
36	4.017	840	1 044	1 864	2 317	9.049	1 891	4 196
37	3.826	1 018	1 293	1 954	2 481	8.340	2 218	4 256
38	3.643	1 213	1 570	1 989	2 575	7.687	2 560	4 198
39	3.470	1 430	1 867	1 971	2 573	7.085	2 919	4 022
40	3.305	1 662	2 195	1 865	2 463	6.530	3 285	3 686
41	3.147	1 913	2 555	1 708	2 282	6.018	3 659	3 267
42	2.998	2 183	2 959	1 436	1 947	5.547	4 038	2 657
43	2.855	2 472	3 392	1 080	1 482	5.112	4 427	1 935
44	2.719	2 787	3 850	588	812	4.712	4 830	1 019
				21 037	26 696			45 456
× number of members				30	30			30
× $\bar{a}_{\overline{65}\,\overline{5}|}$				9.309	9.309 (5.825%)			7.679 (9%)
÷ D_{30}				2 688.4	2 688.4			2 688.4
				£2,185	£2,773			£3,895

Table 21 Scheme X: G.M.P. calculations: widows' pensions on death after age retirement   Group D

Tax year of retirement beginning 6th April (1)	Age x at retirement (2)	C_x (3)	Tax year of death or attainment of age 65 (4)	Age at death or attainment of age 65 $= x + t$ (5)	Amount equal to twice widow's G.M.P. (6)	Probability of event in (4) given retirement at age in (2) (7)
2009	60½	22.1	09/10	60¾	8 656	.0071
			10/11	61½	9 555	.0154
			11/12	62½	10 367	.0167
			12/13	63½	11 248	.0181
			13/14	64½	12 204	.0196
			13/14	65	12 204	.9232
2010	61½	11.8	10/11	61¾	9 762	.0078
			11/12	62½	10 766	.0169
			12/13	63½	11 681	.0184
			13/14	64½	12 674	.0199
			13/14	65	12 674	.9370
2011	62½	6.0	11/12	62¾	10 990	.0086
			12/13	63½	12 111	.0187
			13/14	64½	13 140	.0202
			13/14	65	13 140	.9525

continued

Table 21 (continued)   Scheme X: G.M.P. calculations: widows' pensions on death after age retirement   Group D

Tax year of retirement beginning 6th April (1)	Age x at retirement (2)	C_x^r (3)	Tax year of death or attainment of age 65 (4)	Age at death or attainment of age 65 $= x + t$ (5)	Amount equal to twice widow's G.M.P. (6)	Probability of event in (4) given retirement at age in (2) (7)
2012	63½	4.8	12/13	63¾	12 351	.0095
			13/14	64½	13 600	.0206
			13/14	65	13 600	.9699
2013	64½	3.8	13/14	64¾	13 861	.0105
			13/14	65	13 861	.9895
2013	65	30.7	13/14	65	13 861	

continued

Table 21 (continued) Scheme X: G.M.P. calculations: widows' pensions on death after age retirement Group D

$\dfrac{D_{x+t-3}}{D_{x-3}}$ $a(55)f$ 9% (8)	(3) × (6) × (7) × (8) (9)	$\bar{a}_{x+t-3}$ $a(55)f$ 5.825% $\bar{a}_{65\vert 62} @ x+t = 65$ (10)	$\bar{a}_{x+t-3}$ $a(55)f$ 9% $\bar{a}_{65\vert 62} @ x+t = 65$ (11)	(9) × (10) ÷ 100 (12)	(9) × (11) ÷ 100 (13)
.9767	1 327	12.190	9.394	162	125
.9111	2 963	12.020	9.297	356	275
.8296	3 174	11.783	9.162	374	291
.7548	3 396	11.539	9.021	392	306
.6863	3 628	11.289	8.873	409	322
.6535	162 718	3.210	2.114	5 223	3 440
.9767	878	11.959	9.264	105	81
.9106	1 955	11.783	9.162	230	179
.8285	2 101	11.539	9.021	242	190
.7532	2 242	11.289	8.873	253	199
.7173	100 516	3.210	2.114	3 227	2 125
.9764	554	11.720	9.127	65	51
.9099	1 236	11.539	9.021	143	111
.8272	1 317	11.289	8.873	149	117
.7877	59 152	3.210	2.114	1 899	1 250
.9764	550	11.474	8.984	63	49
.9091	1 223	11.289	8.873	138	109
.8658	54 818	3.210	2.114	1 760	1 159

continued

Table 21 (continued)   Scheme X: G.M.P. calculations: widows' pensions on death after age retirement   Group D

$\dfrac{D_{x+t-3}}{D_{x-3}}$ $a(55)f\,9\%$ (8)	$(3)\times(6)\times(7)$ $\times(8)$ (9)	$\bar{a}_{x+t-3}$ $a(55)f\,5.825\%$ $\bar{a}_{65\,62}\,(a\ x+t=65)$ (10)	$\bar{a}_{x+t-3}$ $a(55)f\,9\%$ $\bar{a}_{65\,62}\,(a\ x+t=65)$ (11)	$(9)\times(10)\div100$ (12)	$(9)\times(11)\div100$ (13)
.9763	540	11.221	8.835	61	48
.9523	49 633	3.210	2.114	1 593	1 049
1.0000	425 553	3.210	2.114	13 660	8 996

	30 504	20 472
× number of members	30	30
× for widow's GMP	0.5	0.5
× proportion married	0.9	0.9
÷ 1% of D_{30}	26.884	26.884
	£15.318	£10,280

Table 22 Scheme X: G.M.P. calculations for widows' pensions on death in service

Age x (1)	C_x^d (2)	Amount equal to twice widow's G.M.P. (3)	$\bar{a}_{x-3+\frac{1}{2}}$ $a(55)f$ 5.825% (4)	$\bar{a}_{x-3+\frac{1}{2}}$ $a(55)f$ 9% (5)	(2) × (3) × (4) ÷ 100 (6)	(2) × (3) × (5) × 100 ÷ 100 (7)
30	3.35	–	–	–	–	–
31	3.14	17	16.159	11.195	9	6
32	2.94	39	16.093	11.170	18	13
33	2.75	65	16.023	11.155	29	20
34	2.57	96	15.950	11.130	39	27
35	2.41	132	15.872	11.103	50	35
36	2.26	176	15.791	11.075	63	44
37	2.12	227	15.706	11.045	76	53
38	1.99	287	15.616	11.012	89	63
39	1.87	357	15.522	10.977	104	73
40	1.75	438	15.423	10.939	118	84
41	1.72	532	15.320	10.899	140	100
42	1.68	640	15.211	10.856	164	117
43	1.63	764	15.098	10.810	188	135
44	1.64	907	14.979	10.761	223	160
45	1.63	1 071	14.855	10.709	259	187
46	1.66	1 258	14.725	10.655	307	223
47	1.67	1 471	14.590	10.595	358	260
48	1.67	1 714	14.449	10.533	414	301

continued

Table 22 (continued)   Scheme X: G.M.P. calculations for widows' pensions on death in service

Age x (1)	C_x^d (2)	Amount equal to twice widow's G.M.P. (3)	$\bar{a}_{x-3+\frac{1}{2}}$ $a(55)f$ 5.825% (4)	$\bar{a}_{x-3+\frac{1}{2}}$ $a(55)f$ 9% (5)	$(2) \times (3) \times (4)$ ÷ 100 (6)	$(2) \times (3) \times (5)$ ÷ 100 (7)
49	1.68	1 991	14.302	10.467	478	350
50	1.68	2 304	14.149	10.396	548	402
51	1.69	2 659	13.990	10.321	629	464
52	1.69	3 060	13.825	10.243	715	530
53	1.69	3 512	13.652	10.159	810	603
54	1.68	4 021	13.474	10.071	910	680
55	1.67	4 594	13.288	9.978	1 019	766
56	1.67	5 238	13.095	9.879	1 145	864
57	1.66	5 959	12.895	9.775	1 276	967
58	1.64	6 764	12.687	9.665	1 407	1 072
59	1.64	7 660	12.472	9.548	1 567	1 199
60	1.62	8 656	12.250	9.425	1 718	1 322
61	1.26	9 762	12.020	9.297	1 478	1 144
62	1.04	10 990	11.783	9.162	1 347	1 047
63	.91	12 351	11.539	9.021	1 297	1 014
64	.78	13 861	11.289	8.873	1 221	959
					20 213	15 284

Table 23 *Scheme X: figures for revision of capital values in Table 17 to allow for G.M.P.s*

Age x (1)	Members' age pensions			Members' ill-health pensions		
	G.M.P. with p.i. (2)	G.M.P. no p.i. (3)	(2) – (3) (4)	G.M.P. with p.i. (5)	G.M.P. no p.i. (6)	(5) – (6) (7)
20	42.2	34.8	7.4	2.8	2.3	0.5
25	127.5	105.1	22.4	8.2	6.9	1.3
30	89.8	74.1	15.7	5.6	4.7	0.9
35	151.8	125.1	26.7	9.3	7.8	1.5
40	120.2	99.3	20.9	7.1	6.0	1.1
45	231.0	190.5	40.5	13.1	11.1	2.0
50	249.7	206.0	43.7	13.2	11.2	2.0
55	49.1	40.6	8.5	2.3	2.0	0.3
60	26.3	21.7	4.6	1.1	0.9	0.2
	1087.6	897.2	190.4	62.7	52.9	9.8

continued

Table 23 (continued)   Scheme X: figures for revision of capital values in Table 17 to allow for G.M.P.s

Widows' pensions on death after age retirement			Widows' pensions on death after ill-health retirement			Widows' pensions on death in service		
G.M.P. with p.i. (8)	G.M.P. no p.i. (9)	(8) – (9) (10)	G.M.P. with p.i. (11)	G.M.P. no p.i. (12)	(11) – (12) (13)	G.M.P. with p.i. (14)	G.M.P. no p.i. (15)	(14) – (15) (16)
7.2	4.8	2.4	1.0	0.7	0.3	5.8	4.3	1.5
21.6	14.5	7.1	2.9	2.1	0.8	16.2	12.2	4.0
15.3	10.3	5.0	2.0	1.4	0.6	10.2	7.7	2.5
25.8	17.3	8.5	3.2	2.3	0.9	16.0	12.2	3.8
20.4	13.7	6.7	2.4	1.7	0.7	11.5	8.7	2.8
39.2	26.3	12.9	4.4	3.1	1.3	19.3	14.8	4.5
42.4	28.4	14.0	4.4	3.0	1.4	16.9	13.0	3.9
8.3	5.6	2.7	0.7	0.5	0.2	2.4	1.8	0.6
4.5	3.0	1.5	0.3	0.2	0.1	0.7	0.5	0.2
184.7	123.9	60.8	21.3	15.0	6.3	99.0	75.2	23.8

continued

Table 23 (continued)   *Scheme X: figures for revision of capital values in Table 17 to allow for G.M.P.s*

| Members' preserved pensions on withdrawal | | | Widows' pensions on death after withdrawal | | |
Non-GMP element (17)	GMP element (18)	(17) + (18) (19)	Non-GMP element (20)	GMP element (21)	(20) + (21) (22)
10.1	9.1	19.2	3.7	2.5	6.2
11.5	13.5	25.0	4.1	3.7	7.8
2.8	3.9	6.7	1.0	1.1	2.1
1.3	2.5	3.8	0.4	0.6	1.0
0.2	0.3	0.5	0.1	0.1	0.2
25.9	29.3	55.2	9.3	8.0	17.3

Table 24   Scheme X: capital values for expected future membership allowing for G.M.P.s

£ 000

Age x (1)	Members' age pensions (2)	Members' ill-health pensions (3)	Widows' pensions on death: after age retirement (4)	after ill-health retirement (5)	in service (6)	Early leavers Members' pensions (7)	Widows' pensions (8)	Capital sums on death in service (9)	Total (10)	Value of 1 per cent. contribution (11)
20	247.7	20.7	34.5	3.7	26.9	19.2	6.2	27.3	386.2	28.5
25	518.3	42.7	71.1	7.6	53.4	25.0	7.8	63.7	789.6	59.3
30	260.5	21.0	35.0	3.6	25.2	6.7	2.1	36.0	390.1	29.9
35	386.8	30.2	51.4	5.3	34.8	3.8	1.0	61.6	574.9	44.5
40	222.2	16.7	28.5	2.8	17.9	0.5	0.2	41.8	330.6	26.3
45	327.0	23.1	40.5	3.8	22.9			74.8	492.1	40.1
50	320.9	20.6	39.1	3.3	18.4			89.2	491.5	39.7
55	75.9	4.1	9.7	0.8	3.2			25.2	118.9	9.0
60	39.7	1.6	5.2	0.3	1.0			17.3	65.1	4.6
	2 399.0	180.7	315.0	31.2	203.7	55.2	17.3	436.9	3 639.0	281.9

Table 25 Scheme X: factors for the conversion of a transfer value received into a pensionable service credit. No allowance for G.M.P.

Age x (1)	$^zM_x^{ra}/^sD_x$ (2)	$^zM_x^{r(wa)}/^sD_x$ (3)	$^zM_x^{d(wa)}/^sD_x$ (4)	$(2)+0.50((3)+(4))$ (5)	$^j\bar{A}_x^w$ (6)	$(5)/80(1-(6))$ (7)
25	7.69	2.26	2.07	9.85	0.40	0.21
35	8.61	2.54	2.14	10.95	0.13	0.16
45	8.55	2.52	1.85	10.73	–	0.13
55	8.10	2.40	1.12	9.86	–	0.12

Table 26 Scheme X: Transfer values payable: widows' pensions

Age	Revaluation factors:		d_x	$v^{x+\frac12-55}$	Widow's annuity age $x+\frac12-3$		$(2)\times(4)\times$	$(3)\times(4)\times$
x	non-GMP	GMP	l_{65} $\begin{array}{c}x<65\\x=65\end{array}$ $a(55)m$	v^{10} $\begin{array}{c}x<65\\x=65\end{array}$	$\bar{a}_{65:62}$ @ $x=65$		$(5)\times(6)$ $\div1000$	$(5)\times(7)$ $\div1000$
					5.825%	9%		
(1)	(2)	(3)	(4)	(5)	(6)	(7)	(8)	(9)
55	1.025	1.000	7 891	.958	13.288	9.978	103	75
56	1.076	1.042	8 587	.879	13.095	9.879	106	78
57	1.130	1.130	9 350	.806	12.895	9.775	110	83
58	1.186	1.226	10 178	.740	12.687	9.665	113	89
59	1.246	1.330	11 079	.679	12.472	9.548	117	96
60	1.308	1.444	12 056	.623	12.250	9.425	120	102
61	1.373	1.566	13 108	.571	12.020	9.297	124	109
62	1.442	1.700	14 241	.524	11.783	9.162	127	116
63	1.514	1.844	15 450	.481	11.539	9.021	130	124
64	1.590	2.001	16 745	.441	11.289	8.873	133	131
65	1.629	2.084	788 316	.422	3.210	2.114	1 740	1 466
							2 923	2 469

Non-GMP pension: $2.923 \times 0.5 \div (l_{55} \div 1000)(907) = 1.61$
GMP pension: $2.469 \times 0.5 \div (l_{55} \div 1000)(907) = 1.36$

Table 27 *Examples of investment proceeds*

	Time (1)	Fixed interest gilt-edged security (2)	Ordinary share (3)	(4)	Index-linked gilt-edged security (5)	(6)
Income	1	9	5.09	5.09	3.09	3.09
	2	9	5.28	5.28	3.26	3.26
	3	9	5.47	5.47	3.45	3.45
	4	9	5.67	5.67	3.65	3.65
	5	9	5.88	5.88	3.86	3.86
	6	9	6.10	6.10	4.09	4.09
	7	9	6.32	6.32	4.32	4.32
	8	9	6.56	6.65	4.57	4.63
	9	9	6.80	7.08	4.84	5.04
	10	9	7.05	7.54	5.12	5.48
	11	9	7.31	8.04	5.41	5.95
	12	9	7.58	8.56	5.72	6.47
	13	9	7.86	9.12	6.06	7.03
	14	9	8.14	9.72	6.41	7.64
	15	9	8.44	10.36	6.78	8.31
Capital	15	100	171.96	213.78	232.20	288.63
Accumulation (a)		364	364	—	364	—
Accumulation (b)		416	—	453	—	453

Table 28   Scheme X: initial entrants: experience in year no. 1

| Group | Salary per head in year £ | Number at start of year | Number who during the year: | | | | | | | Number at end of year |
| | | | withdrew with: | | | died in service | retired with immediate: | | | |
			return of contri- butions	preserved pension	transfer payment		ill- health pension	reduced scale pension	scale pension	
A	2,800	30	6							24
B	3,200	20	5							15
C	3,400	35	6							29
D	3,600	30	5							25
E	3,600	20	4							16
F	3,700	15	2							13
G	7,500	5	1							4
H	3,800	20		2						18
I	4,000	10		1	1					8
J	3,800	20				1				19
K	4,000	30					1			29
L	6,600	5								5
M	4,400	30					2			28
N	5,500	35			1					34
O	11,000	5			1	1				3
P	6,600	10						1		9

continued

Table 28 (continued)   Scheme X: initial entrants: experience in year no. 1

| | | | Number who during the year: | | | | | | | |
| | | | withdrew with: | | | | retired with immediate: | | | |
Group	Salary per head in year	Number at start of year	return of contri- butions	preserved pension	transfer payment	died in service	ill- health pension	reduced scale pension	scale pension	Number at end of year
	£									
Q	6,600	10				1			2	7
R	6,800	5							2	3
S	11,000	5								5
T	–	5							5	nil
Total		345	29	3	3	3	3	1	9	294

Table 29 *Scheme X: initial entrants: experience in year no. 2*

| | | | Number who during the year: | | | | | | | |
| | | | withdrew with: | | | retired with immediate: | | | |
Group	Salary per head in year	Number at start of year	return of contri-butions	preserved pension	transfer payment	died in service	ill-health pension	reduced scale pension	scale pension	Number at end of year
	£									
A	3,200	24	5							19
B	3,600	15	4							11
C	3,800	29	6							23
D	3,800	25	4							21
E	4,000	16	3							13
F	4,100	13	1							12
G	8,300	4	1	1						1
H	4,200	18		1	2					15
I	4,400	8		1						7
J	4,200	19		1		1	1			16
K	4,400	29			1					28
L	7,300	5								5
M	4,800	28								28
N	6,100	34			1					34
O	12,100	3								2
P	7,300	9							2	7

continued

Table 29 (continued)   *Scheme X: initial entrants: experience in year no. 2*

| | | | Number who during the year: | | | | | | | |
| | | | withdrew with: | | | died in service | retired with immediate: | | | |
Group	Salary per head in year	Number at start of year	return of contributions	preserved pension	transfer payment		ill-health pension	reduced scale pension	scale pension	Number at end of year
	£									
Q	7,300	7					1			6
R	7,500	3								3
S	12,200	5				1				4
T	–	nil							nil	nil
Total		294	24	4	4	3	2	2	–	255

Table 30   Scheme X: initial entrants: experience in year no. 3

Group	Salary per head in year £	Number at start of year	withdrew with: return of contributions	preserved pension	transfer payment	died in service	retired with immediate: ill-health pension	reduced scale pension	scale pension	Number at end of year
A	3,700	19	4							15
B	4,100	11	3							8
C	4,300	23	4	1	1					17
D	4,300	21	3	2						16
E	4,500	13	2				1			10
F	4,600	12	1							11
G	9,100	1								1
H	4,700	15		1						14
I	4,900	7								7
J	4,600	16			1		1			14
K	4,900	28			1	2				25
L	8,000	5								5
M	5,200	28		2						26
N	6,700	34			1		2			31
O	13,300	2								2
P	8,000	7						2		5

continued

Table 30 (continued) *Scheme X: initial entrants: experience in year no. 3*

Group	Salary per head in year	Number at start of year	Number who during the year:							Number at end of year
			withdrew with:			died in service	retired with immediate:			
			return of contributions	preserved pension	transfer payment		ill-health pension	reduced scale pension	scale pension	
	£									
Q	8,100	6				1			1	5
R	8,200	3							2	nil
S	13,400	4					1			3
T	–	nil							nil	nil
Total		255	17	6	4	3	5	2	3	215

Table 31 Scheme X: new entrants in first three years

Group	Entrants in year 1			Entrants in year 2			
	No. of entrants	No. of leavers in: year 2	year 3	No. of entrants	No. of leavers in year 3	No. of entrants in year 3	Number remaining at time 3
A	28	12	8	28	12	28	52
B	24	12	8	24	12	24	40
C	20	12	8	20	12	20	28
D	16	8	4	16	8	16	28
E	12	4	4	12	4	12	24
F	8	4	4	8	4	8	12
G	4			4		4	12
Total	112	52	36	112	52	112	196

Table 32 *Scheme X: Progression of individual salaries*

Group	1976/77 Salary	1977/78 Salary	1978/79 Salary	1979/80 Salary	1979/80 RE	1980/81 Salary	1980/81 RE	1981/82 Salary	1981/82 RE
	£	£	£	£	£	£	£	£	£
A	1,900	2,100	2,400	2,800	1,786	3,200	2,004	3,700	2,296
B	2,200	2,400	2,800	3,200	2,186	3,600	2,404	4,100	2,696
C	2,400	2,600	3,000	3,400	2,386	3,800	2,604	4,300	2,896
D	2,400	2,600	3,000	3,400	2,386	3,800	2,604	4,300	2,896
E	2,600	2,800	3,200	3,600	2,586	4,000	2,804	4,500	3,096
F	2,700	3,000	3,400	3,700	2,686	4,100	2,904	4,600	3,196
G	5,400	6,000	6,800	7,500	6,006	8,300	7,104	9,100	7,696
H	2,700	3,000	3,400	3,800	2,786	4,200	3,004	4,700	3,296
I	2,900	3,100	3,600	4,000	2,986	4,400	3,204	4,900	3,496
J	2,700	3,000	3,400	3,800	2,786	4,200	3,004	4,600	3,196
K	2,900	3,100	3,600	4,000	2,986	4,400	3,204	4,900	3,496
L	4,800	5,200	6,000	6,600	5,586	7,300	6,104	8,000	6,596
M	3,200	3,500	4,000	4,400	3,386	4,800	3,604	5,200	3,796
N	4,000	4,400	5,000	5,500	4,486	6,100	4,904	6,700	5,296
O	8,000	8,700	10,000	11,000	6,006	12,100	7,384	13,300	8,996
P	4,800	5,200	6,000	6,600	5,586	7,300	6,104	8,000	6,596
Q	4,800	5,200	6,000	6,600	5,586	7,300	6,104	8,100	6,696
R	5,000	5,400	6,200	6,800	5,786	7,500	6,304	8,200	6,796
S	8,000	8,700	10,000	11,000	6,006	12,200	7,384	13,400	8,996
T	5,600	6,100	7,000	—	—	—	—	—	—

Table 33   *Scheme X: employee members in Group D at investigation date*

	Pensionable service per head at investigation date	Salary* times pensionable service per head	Number of Members	Total Salary	Total of salary times pensionable service
	years	£		£ p.a.	£
Initial entrants	5.5	23,650	16	68,800	378,400
Subsequent entrants in:					
Year 1	2.5	10,750	4	17,200	43,000
Year 2	1.5	6,450	8	34,400	51,600
Year 3	.5	2,150	16	68,800	34,400
			44	£189,200	£507,400

*Salary used is salary in year preceding investigation date, i.e. £4,300 per head.

continued

Table 33 (continued) *Scheme X: employee members in Group D at investigation date*

Accrued GMP	Relevant earnings per head (see Table 32) in:			RE (year 3) + 1.194 RE (year 2) + 1.429 RE (year 1)	Accrued GMP per head p.a. = 1/140th of revalued RE	Number of Members	Total accrued GMP
	Year 1	Year 2	Year 3				
	£	£	£	£	£		£
Initial entrants	2,386	2,604	2,896	9,415	67.25	16	1,076.0
Subsequent entrants in:							
Year 1	1,193	2,604	2,896	7,710	55.07	4	220.3
Year 2	–	1,302	2,896	4,451	31.79	8	254.3
Year 3	–	–	1,448	1,448	10.34	16	165.4
							£1,716.0

Table 34   Scheme X: employee members at investigation date

	Initial entrants				Subsequent entrants			
Age	Number	Total Salary	Total (Salary times pensionable service) ÷ 1,000	Total Accrued GMP	Number	Total Salary	Total (Salary times pensionable service) ÷ 1,000	Total Accrued GMP
		£ 000		£ 000		£ 000		£ 000
23	15	55.5	166.5	0.6	52	192.4	214.6	0.8
28	25	105.9	513.1	1.4	68	284.4	258.6	1.1
33	16	68.8	378.4	1.1	28	120.4	129.0	0.6
38	22	104.7	619.1	2.0	48	272.4	335.8	2.2
43	21	100.1	955.1	2.3				
48	44	226.9	3,282.3	6.9				
53	57	342.9	5,283.6	11.0				
58	7	66.6	1,172.1	2.0				
63	8	80.7	1,775.3	2.4				
Total	215	1,152.1	14,145.5	29.7	196	869.6	938.0	4.7

Table 35 *Scheme X: Calculation of preserved benefits for early leaver from Group H in year no. 3*

Salary in:

	£
half year before Commencement Date	1,700
year no. 1	3,800
year no. 2	4,200
half-year no. 3	2,350
Average salary over three years	$12,050 \div 3 = £4,017$

Pensionable service at exit   7.5 years

Initial amount of preserved pension

$$\frac{7.5}{80} \times £4,017 \qquad\qquad = \quad £377 \text{ p.a.}$$

Relevant earnings in:

	£
year no. 1	2,786
year no. 2	3,004
half-year no. 3	1,648

Revalued relevant earnings at date of exit
$£1,648 + 1.194(£3,004) + 1.429(£2,786) \qquad = £9,216$

GMP at date of exit
$£9,216 \div 100 \qquad\qquad = \quad £92 \text{ p.a.}$

Amount of preserved benefits at investigation date
(including 5 per cent. increase on that date.)

Non-GMP

$(£377 - £92) \times 1.05 \qquad\qquad = \quad £299$

GMP

Number of complete tax years between date
of leaving and investigation date = zero.

Therefore no $8\frac{1}{2}$ per cent. increases on GMP.

Amount at investigation date   =   £92

Table 36 *Scheme X: preserved pension rights as at valuation date of early leavers during first three years*

Group (1)	Year of leaving (2)	Scale pension at date of leaving (3)	GMP at date of leaving (4)	Prospective pension at valuation date:	
				Excess over GMP (5)	GMP (6)
		£ p.a.	£ p.a.	£ p.a.	£ p.a.
C	3	203	50	161	50
D	3	226	57	177	57
D	3	226	57	177	57
G	2	313	90	246	98
H	1	221	14	240	16
H	1	221	14	240	16
H	2	293	48	270	52
H	3	377	92	299	92
I	1	423	15	472	18
I	2	520	52	516	56
J	2	607	60	603	65
M	3	805	138	700	138
M	3	805	138	700	138

Table 37 *Scheme X: retirements at age 65*

Five retirements in Group T at Commencement Date
Average annual salary per head over final three years

$(£5,600 + £6,100 + £7,000) \div 3$ = £6,233

Initial annual pension per head $\dfrac{16.5}{80} \times £6,233$ = £1,286 p.a.

Commutation
£1,000 p.a. of pension per head given up for lump sum of £9,310
Total lump sum payments £9,310 × 5 = £46,550 in year 1

Pension payments
Year 1 : (£1,286 − £1,000) × 5 = £1,430
Year 2 : £1,430 × 1.05 = £1,500
Year 3 : £1,500 × 1.05 = £1,575

Data at investigation date
Five pensioners aged 68 with total pension £1,575 × 1.05 = £1,654 p.a.
Outstanding guarantee period of pension at valuation date 2 years
Total contingent reversionary pensions to widows
$£1,286 \times 5 \times (1.05)^3 \times 0.5$ = £3,722 p.a.

Table 38 Scheme X: early retirements during first three years

Group (1)	Year of retirement (2)	Average annual salary over final three years (3)	Pensionable service at retirement (4)	Scale pension at retirement (3) × (4)/80 (5)	Age at retirement (6)	Actuarial reduction factor for early retirement (7)	Initial amount of pension payable before commutation (8)
		£ p.a.	years	£ p.a.		per cent.	£ p.a.
Q	1	5,633	19.0	1,338	60.5		1,338
Q	1	5,633	19.0	1,338	60.5		1,338
Q	3	6,983	21.0	1,833	62.5		1,833
R	1	5,833	15.5	1,130	60.5		1,130
R	1	5,833	15.5	1,130	60.5		1,130
R	3	7,167	17.5	1,568	62.5		1,568
R	3	7,167	17.5	1,568	62.5		1,568
P	1	5,633	14.5	1,021	55.5	18	837
P	2	6,283	15.5	1,217	56.5	16	1,022
P	2	6,283	15.5	1,217	56.5	16	1,022
P	3	6,967	16.5	1,437	57.5	14	1,236
P	3	6,967	16.5	1,437	57.5	14	1,236

Table 39 Scheme X: early retirements during first three years

Group (1)	Year of retirement (2)	Scale or reduced pension (3)	Pension commuted (4)	Year 1		Year 2		Year 3	
				Pens. (5)	L.S. (6)	Pens. (7)	L.S. (8)	Pens. (9)	L.S. (10)
		£ p.a.	£	£ p.a.	£	£ p.a.	£	£ p.a.	£
Q	1	1,338	200	569	2,094	1,195		1,255	
Q	1	1,338	200	569	2,094	1,195		1,255	
Q	3	1,833	300					767	2,988
R	1	1,130	200	465	2,094	977		1,025	
R	1	1,130	200	465	2,094	977		1,025	
R	3	1,568	300					634	2,988
R	3	1,568	300					634	2,988
P*	1	837	200	319	2,338	669		702	
P*	2	1,022	300			361	3,438	759	
P*	2	1,022	300			361	3,438	759	
P*	3	1,236	300					468	3,366
P*	3	1,236	300					468	3,366
				£2,387	£10,714	£5,735	£6,876	£9,751	£15,696

* – actuarially reduced pension

Table 40   *Scheme X: early retirements during first three years*

	Member's pension at investigation date:		Member's accrued GMP at investigation date
Group	actual	notional for widow's pension	
(1)	(2)	(3)	(4)
	£ p.a.	£ p.a.	£ p.a.
Q	1,317	1,549	41
Q	1,317	1,549	41
Q	1,610	1,925	233
R	1,077	1,308	43
R	1,077	1,308	43
R	1,331	1,646	240
R	1,331	1,646	240
P	737	969	41
P	796	1,127	132
P	796	1,127	132
P	983	1,298	232
P	983	1,298	232

Table 41 Scheme X: ill-health retirements during first three years

Group (1)	Year of retirement (2)	Scale pension (3) £ p.a.	Pension commuted (4) £ p.a.	Year 1		Year 2		Year 3	
				Pens. (5) £ p.a.	L.S. (6) £	Pens. (7) £ p.a.	L.S. (8) £	Pens. (9) £ p.a.	L.S. (10) £
E	3	262	–					131	
J	2	607	200			203	2,710	427	
J	3	725	200					263	2,674
K	1	507	200	153	2,746	322		169	
M	1	565	200	183	2,558	383		402	
M	1	565	200	183	2,558	383		402	
N	3	1,127	300					413	3,711
N	3	1,127	300					413	3,711
Q	2	1,571	300			635	3,066	1,335	
S	3	3,199	500					1,349	4,980
				£519	£7,862	£1,926	£5,776	£5,304	£15,076

Table 42

Scheme X: ill-health pensioners who retired during the first three years and survived to the investigation date

Group	Member's pension at investigation date:		Member's accrued GMP at investigation date
	actual	notional for widow's pension	
(1)	(2)	(3)	(4)
	£ p.a.	£ p.a.	£ p.a.
E	275	275	72
J	449	669	66
J	551	761	115
M	423	654	25
M	423	654	25
N	868	1,183	186
N	868	1,183	186
Q	1,401	1,732	132
S	2,834	3,359	274

Table 43 *Scheme X: lump sum payments and widows' pensions on death in service during first three years*

| Member's group (1) | Year of death (2) | Rate of widow's pension: | | Year 1 | | Year 2 | | Year 3 | |
		scale (3)	GMP (4)	Widow's pension (5)	L.S. (6)	Widow's pension (7)	L.S. (8)	Widow's pension (9)	L.S. (10)
		£ p.a.	£ p.a.	£ p.a.	£	£ p.a.	£	£ p.a.	£
G	2	157	25			79	16,600	164	
J	1	unmarried			7,600				
J	2	304	17			152	8,400	318	
K	3	369	42					185	9,800
K	3	369	42					185	9,800
O	1	940		470	22,000	987		1,036	
Q	1	669		335	13,200	702		738	
R	3	784	83					392	16,400
S	2	1,376	38			688	24,400	1,443	
				£805	£42,800	£2,608	£49,400	£4,461	£36,000

Table 44 *Scheme X: initial entrants: withdrawals with return of contributions in year no. 1*

Group (1)	Number of withdrawals with return of contributions (2)	Annual salary per head in year no. 1 (3)	Relevant earnings per head in year no. 1 (4)	2½ per cent. of (3) (5)	3½ per cent. of (4) (6)
		£	£	£	£
A	6	2,800	1,786	70.00	62.51
B	5	3,200	2,186	80.00	76.51
C	6	3,400	2,386	85.00	83.51
D	5	3,400	2,386	85.00	83.51
E	4	3,600	2,586	90.00	90.51
F	2	3,700	2,686	92.50	94.01
G	1	7,500	6,006	187.50	210.21
				£2,487.50	£2,436.49

Note: Totals of columns (5) and (6) involve multiplication by column (2)

Table 45   Scheme X: transfer value payments during first three years

Group (1)	Year of withdrawal (2)	Preserved Pension		Transfer value factor		Amount of transfer values paid in:		
		non-GMP (3)	GMP (4)	non-GMP (5)	GMP (6)	Year 1 (7)	Year 2 (8)	Year 3 (9)
		£	£			£	£	£
C	3	153	50	2.85	6.39			756
H	2	245	48	4.61	6.90		1,461	
H	2	245	48	4.61	6.90		1,461	
I	1	408	15	4.46	6.85	1,922		
J	3	610	115	5.69	7.13			4,291
K	2	550	65	5.49	7.09		3,480	
K	3	615	123	5.69	7.13			4,376
N	1	768	28	6.31	7.26	5,049		
N	3	941	186	6.77	7.35			7,738
O	1	1,842	38	7.53	7.49	14,155		
O	2	2,088	136	7.81	7.54		17,333	
						£21,126	£23,735	£17,161

Table 46 Scheme X: revenue accounts for the first three years and consolidated figures

		Year 1	Year 2	Year 3	Total
		£	£	£	£
Income					
Fund at beginning of year		–	263,279	641,014	–
Members' contributions		78,505	93,500	103,487	275,492
Employer's contributions: normal		125,608	149,600	165,580	440,788
special		188,412	224,400	248,370	661,182
Investment income		9,000	33,000	61,000	103,000
		£401,525	£763,779	£1,219,451	£1,480,462
Expenditure					
Age retirements:	pensions	1,430	1,500	1,575	4,505
	lump sums	46,550	–	–	46,550
Early retirements:	pensions	2,387	5,735	9,751	17,873
	lump sums	10,714	6,876	15,696	33,286
Ill-health retirements:	pensions	519	1,926	5,304	7,749
	lump sums	7,862	5,776	15,076	28,714
Lump sums on death in service and after retirement		42,800	49,400	37,014	129,214
Widows' pensions		805	2,608	4,546	7,959

continued

Table 46 (continued) *Scheme X: revenue accounts for the first three years and consolidated figures*

	Year 1	Year 2	Year 3	Total
	£	£	£	£
Payments in respect of early leavers:				
Return of contributions including interest and tax less Certified Amounts	1,617	10,354	21,472	33,443
Contributions Equivalent Premiums	2,436	14,855	29,337	46,628
Transfer payments	21,126	23,735	17,161	62,022
Fund at end of year	263,279	641,014	1,062,519	1,062,519
	£401,525	£763,779	£1,219,451	£1,480,462

Table 47 *Scheme X: investments at investigation date*

	Book Value	Market Value	Notes
	£000	£000	
UK ordinary shares	836	915	Current divident yield 6.0%
Fixed-interest gilt-edged securities:			
Treasury 13¾% 2000-03	118	123	Nominal value £122,000
Index-linked gilt-edged securities:			
Treasury 2½% index-linked 2011	29	29	Nominal value £30,000
Property units	30	32	Current yield 4.0%
Overseas ordinary shares	30	28	Current dividend yield 3.0%
Cash	20	20	
	1,063	1,147	

Table 48 *Scheme X: salary experience of employees who were members throughout first three years*

Age at date of investigation $= x$ (1)	Total salaries in year ended on Commencement Date (2) £ 000	s_{x-1}/s_{x-4} (from Table 3) (3)	Total salaries in year ended on investigation date: expected $(2) \times (3)$ (4) £ 000	actual (5) £ 000	$(5) \div (4)$ per cent. (6)
23	36.0	1.672	60.2	55.5	92
28	73.4	1.573	115.5	105.9	92
33	48.0	1.449	69.6	68.8	99
38	76.2	1.387	105.7	104.7	99
43	72.8	1.369	99.7	100.1	100
48	167.6	1.347	225.8	226.9	100
53	259.0	1.335	345.8	342.9	99
58	50.0	1.312	65.6	66.6	102
63	60.0	1.294	77.6	80.7	104
	843.0		1,165.5	1,152.1	99

Table 49   *Scheme X: specimen calculations for experience in first three years. Group D*

Age at beginning of year of exposure (1)	Initial entrants (2)	Number of years of exposure arising from:			Total (6)
		New entrants in:			
		Year no. 1 (3)	Year no. 2 (4)	Year no. 3 (5)	
30	30	0.5 (16)			38
31	25	16	0.5 (16)		49
32	21	8	16	0.5 (16)	53

	Probability of event shown in year:		
	withdrawal (7)	death in service (8)	ill-health retirement (9)
	0.050	0.0013	
	0.046	0.0014	.0001
	0.042	0.0015	.0001

continued

Table 49 (continued)   *Scheme X: specimen calculations for experience in first three years. Group D*

| | Expected number of: | | | Actual number of: | | |
	withdrawals (6) × (7) (10)	deaths in service (6) × (8) (11)	ill-health retirements (6) × (9) (12)	withdrawals (13)	deaths in service (14)	ill-health retirements (15)
	1.9	0.05		5	—	—
	2.3	0.07		12	—	—
	2.2	0.08	0.01	17	—	—
	6.4	0.20	0.01	34	—	—

Table 50   *Scheme X: experience in first three years*

Age at beginning of year of exposure (1)	Expected number of:			Actual number of:		
	withdrawals (2)	deaths in service (3)	ill-health retirements (4)	withdrawals (5)	deaths in service (6)	ill-health retirements (7)
20 – 24	17.6	0.2		47		
25 – 29	21.3	0.3		94		
30 – 34	6.4	0.2		34		
35 – 39	5.3	0.4	0.1	40	1	1
40 – 44	1.0	0.2		9		
45 – 49		0.6	0.1	4	4	3
50 – 54		1.2	0.3	4		4
55 – 59		0.4	0.1	2	1	
60 – 64		0.8	0.5		3	2
	51.6	4.3	1.1	234	9	10

Table 51 *Scheme X: numbers of withdrawals in first three years*

Age at beginning of Scheme year of exit	Number of withdrawals with:			
	return of contributions	preserved pension	payment of transfer value	Total
20 – 24	47			47
25 – 29	92	1	1	94
30 – 34	32	2		34
35 – 39	39	1		40
40 – 44		6	3	9
45 – 49		1	3	4
50 – 54		2	2	4
55 – 59			2	2
Total	210	13	11	234

Table 52   *Scheme X: salary profiles*

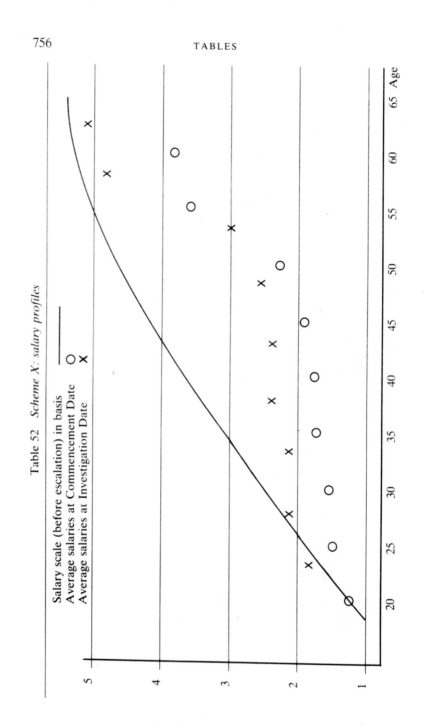

Salary scale (before escalation) in basis —————
Average salaries at Commencement Date ◯
Average salaries at Investigation Date ✕

Table 53 *Scheme X: calculations at investigation date: Group D*

Money amounts in £ 000

(1)	Age	33
(2)	Total salaries	189.2
(3)	Total (salary × pensionable service)	507.4
	Members' age pensions	
(4)	$^zM_{33}^{ra}/^sD_{33}$	7.68
(5)	$^z\bar{R}_{33}^{ra}/^sD_{33}$	231.4
(6)	(2) × (4) × 1/80	18.2
(7)	(3) × (4) × 1/80	48.7
(8)	(2) × (5) × 1/80	547.3
	Members' ill-health pensions	
(9)	$^zM_{33}^{ia}/^sD_{33}$	0.73
(10)	$^z\bar{R}_{33}^{ia}/^sD_{33}$	18.0
(11)	(2) × (9) × 1/80	1.7
(12)	(3) × (9) × 1/80	4.6
(13)	(2) × (10) × 1/80	42.6
	Widows' pensions on death after age retirement	
(14)	$^zM_{33}^{r(wa)}/^sD_{33}$	2.21
(15)	$^z\bar{R}_{33}^{r(wa)}/^sD_{33}$	67.0
(16)	(2) × (14) × 1/160	2.6
(17)	(3) × (14) × 1/160	7.0
(18)	(2) × (15) × 1/160	79.2
	Widows' pensions on death after ill-health retirement	
(19)	$^zM_{33}^{i(wa)}/^sD_{33}$	0.26
(20)	$^z\bar{R}_{33}^{i(wa)}/^sD_{33}$	6.99
(21)	(2) × (19) × 1/160	0.3
(22)	(3) × (19) × 1/160	0.8
(23)	(2) × (20) × 1/160	8.3
	Widows' pensions on death in service	
(24)	$^zM_{33}^{d(wa)}/^sD_{33}$	2.13
(25)	$^z\bar{R}_{33}^{d(wa)}/^sD_{33}$	44.6
(26)	(2) × (24) × 1/160	2.5
(27)	(3) × (24) × 1/160	6.8
(28)	(2) × (25) × 1/160	52.7

continued

Table 53 (continued)   *Scheme X: calculations at investigation date: Group D*

Money amounts in £ 000

	Members' preserved pensions on withdrawal	
(29)	$^zM_{33}^{w|a}/{}^sD_{33}$	0.56
(30)	$^z\bar{R}_{33}^{w|a}/{}^sD_{33}$	2.47
(31)	$(2) \times (29) \times 1/80$	1.3
(32)	$(3) \times (29) \times 1/80$	3.6
(33)	$(2) \times (30) \times 1/80$	5.8
	Widows' pensions on member's death after withdrawal with preserved pension	
(34)	$^zM_{33}^{w(wa)}/{}^sD_{33}$	0.39
(35)	$^z\bar{R}_{33}^{w(wa)}/{}^sD_{33}$	1.69
(36)	$(2) \times (34) \times 1/160$	0.5
(37)	$(3) \times (34) \times 1/160$	1.2
(38)	$(2) \times (35) \times 1/160$	2.0
	Lump sum on death in service	
(39)	$^sM_{33}^{d}/{}^sD_{33}$	0.21
(40)	q_{33}	0.0016
(41)	$(2) \times (39) \times 2$	79.5
(42)	$(2) \times (40) \times s_{33}/s_{30} \times 2$	0.7
	Contributions	
(43)	$^s\bar{a}_{33}$	31.21
(44)	$.01 \times (2) \times (43)$	59.0

Table 54 Scheme X: past service values for members at investigation date: initial entrants
£000

Age x (1)	Members' age pensions			Members' ill-health pensions		
	Before G.M.P. adjustment (2)	G.M.P. adjustment (3)	(2) – (3) (4)	Before G.M.P. adjustment (5)	G.M.P. adjustment (6)	(5) – (6) (7)
23	14.3	0.2	14.1	1.4		1.4
28	46.4	0.7	45.7	4.4		4.4
33	36.3	0.7	35.6	3.4	0.1	3.3
38	62.2	1.7	60.5	5.8	0.1	5.7
43	95.4	2.2	93.2	8.6	0.2	8.4
48	312.4	7.1	305.3	26.6	0.4	26.2
53	493.6	12.3	481.3	37.7	0.7	37.0
58	113.7	2.5	111.2	6.6	0.1	6.5
63	175.4	3.3	172.1	7.2	0.1	7.1
	1 349.7	30.7	1 319.0	101.7	1.7	100.0

continued

Table 54 (continued)   Scheme X: past service values for members at investigation date: initial entrants
£000

Widows' pensions on death after age retirement			Widows' pensions on death after ill-health retirement			Widows' pensions on death in service		
Before G.M.P. adjustment (8)	G.M.P. adjustment (9)	(8) – (9) (10)	Before G.M.P adjustment (11)	G.M.P. adjustment (12)	(11) – (12) (13)	Before G.M.P. adjustment (14)	G.M.P. adjustment (15)	(14) – (15) (16)
2.1	0.1	2.0	0.2		0.2	2.1		2.1
6.7	0.2	6.5	0.8		0.8	6.7	0.2	6.5
5.2	0.2	5.0	0.6		0.6	5.0	0.2	4.8
9.0	0.6	8.4	1.1	0.1	1.0	8.2	0.4	7.8
13.7	0.7	13.0	1.6	0.1	1.5	11.6	0.5	11.1
45.0	2.4	42.6	5.1	0.3	4.8	33.8	1.2	32.6
71.1	4.2	66.9	7.5	0.5	7.0	42.5	1.6	40.9
16.4	0.9	15.5	1.4	0.1	1.3	6.0	0.2	5.8
27.0	1.0	26.0	1.7	0.1	1.6	3.9	0.1	3.8
196.2	10.3	185.9	20.0	1.2	18.8	119.8	4.4	115.4

continued

Table 54 (continued) Scheme X: past service values for members at investigation date: initial entrants
£000

	Members' preserved pensions on withdrawal			Widows' pensions on death after withdrawal			Total past service values		
	Before G.M.P. adjustment (17)	G.M.P. adjustment (18)	(17) + (18) (19)	Before G.M.P. adjustment (20)	G.M.P. adjustment (21)	(20) + (21) (22)	Before G.M.P. adjustment (23)	G.M.P. adjustment (24)	After G.M.P. adjustment (25)
	3.1	1.0	4.1	1.2	0.2	1.4	24.4	(+) 0.9	25.3
	6.3	1.5	7.8	2.3	0.3	2.6	73.6	(+) 0.7	74.3
	2.6	0.6	3.2	0.9	0.1	1.0	54.0	(−) 0.5	53.5
	1.8	0.4	2.2	0.6		0.6	88.7	(−) 2.5	86.2
	0.3	0.1	0.4	0.1		0.1	131.3	(−) 3.6	127.7
							422.9	(−) 11.4	411.5
							652.4	(−) 19.3	633.1
							144.1	(−) 3.8	140.3
							215.2	(−) 4.6	210.6
	14.1	3.6	17.7	5.1	0.6	5.7	1,806.6	(−) 44.1	1,762.5

Table 55 *Scheme X: future service values for members at investigation date: initial entrants*
£000

Age x (1)	Members' age pensions			Members' ill-health pensions		
	Before G.M.P. adjustment (2)	G.M.P. adjustment (3)	(2) – (3) (4)	Before G.M.P. adjustment (5)	G.M.P. adjustment (6)	(5) – (6) (7)
23	191.2	7.2	184.0	15.7	0.4	15.3
28	336.2	16.2	320.0	27.0	0.9	26.1
33	199.0	11.3	187.7	15.5	0.6	14.9
38	264.5	17.8	246.7	19.7	0.9	18.8
43	201.3	16.9	184.4	14.2	0.9	13.3
48	326.9	35.6	291.3	21.2	1.7	19.5
53	324.8	37.2	287.6	18.4	1.7	16.7
58	33.2	3.6	29.6	1.5	0.1	1.4
63	14.2	1.0	13.2	0.3		0.3
	1 891.3	146.8	1 744.5	133.5	7.2	126.3

continued

Table 55 (continued) Scheme X: future service values for members at investigation date: initial entrants
£000

Widows' pensions on death after age retirement			Widows' pensions on death after ill-health retirement			Widows' pensions on death in service		
Before G.M.P. adjustment (8)	G.M.P. adjustment (9)	(8) – (9) (10)	Before G.M.P. adjustment (11)	G.M.P. adjustment (12)	(11) – (12) (13)	Before G.M.P. adjustment (14)	G.M.P. adjustment (15)	(14) – (15) (16)
27.6	2.6	25.0	3.0	0.3	2.7	20.7	1.3	19.4
48.6	5.8	42.8	5.2	0.7	4.5	34.5	2.6	31.9
28.8	4.0	24.8	3.0	0.5	2.5	19.2	1.7	17.5
38.3	6.4	31.9	3.9	0.7	3.2	23.4	2.5	20.9
29.2	6.1	23.1	2.8	0.6	2.2	15.9	2.0	13.9
47.6	12.8	34.8	4.4	1.3	3.1	21.9	3.6	18.3
47.5	13.5	34.0	3.9	1.2	2.7	16.7	2.8	13.9
4.9	1.3	3.6	0.3	0.1	0.2	1.1	0.2	0.9
2.2	0.5	1.7	0.1		0.1	0.2		0.2
274.7	53.0	221.7	26.6	5.4	21.2	153.6	16.7	136.9

continued

Table 55 (continued)   Scheme X: future service values for members at investigation date: initial entrants
£000

	Members' preserved pensions on withdrawal			Widows' pensions on death after withdrawal			Capital sums on death in service	Total values			Value of 1 per cent. contribution
	Before G.M.P. adjustment (17)	G.M.P. adjustment (18)	(17) + (18) (19)	Before G.M.P. adjustment (20)	G.M.P. adjustment (21)	(20) + (21) (22)	(23)	Before G.M.P. adjustment (24)	G.M.P. adjustment (25)	After G.M.P. adjustment (26)	(28)
	8.1	2.5	10.6	3.0	0.6	3.6	21.7	291.0	8.7	282.3	21.1
	8.0	2.4	10.4	2.8	0.6	3.4	42.3	504.6	23.2	481.4	36.6
	2.1	0.7	2.8	0.7	0.2	0.9	28.2	296.5	17.2	279.3	21.5
	0.8	0.2	1.0	0.3		0.3	42.9	393.8	28.1	365.7	28.6
							38.2	301.6	26.5	275.1	21.9
							74.3	496.3	55.0	441.3	35.7
							89.4	500.7	56.4	444.3	35.0
							11.4	52.4	5.3	47.1	3.5
							6.2	23.2	1.5	21.7	1.5
	19.0	5.8	24.8	6.8	1.4	8.2	354.6	2 860.1	221.9	2 638.2	205.4

Table 56 *Scheme X: values for members at investigation date: new entrants*
£000

	Members' age pensions			Members' ill-health pensions		
Age x (1)	Before G.M.P. adjustment (2)	G.M.P. adjustment (3)	(2) – (3) (4)	Before G.M.P. adjustment (5)	G.M.P. adjustment (6)	(5) – (6) (7)
Past service values						
23	18.4	0.2	18.2	1.7		1.7
28	23.4	0.5	22.9	2.2	0.1	2.1
33	12.4	0.4	12.0	1.2		1.2
38	33.7	1.9	31.8	3.1	0.1	3.0
	87.9	3.0	84.9	8.2	0.2	8.0
Future service values						
23	662.7	24.9	637.8	54.3	1.4	52.9
28	902.7	43.5	859.2	72.4	2.4	70.0
33	348.3	19.5	328.8	27.1	1.1	26.0
38	688.1	45.2	642.9	51.3	2.4	48.9
	2 601.8	133.1	2 468.7	205.1	7.3	197.8

continued

Table 56 (continued) Scheme X: values for members at investigation date: new entrants
£000

	Widows' pensions on death after age retirement			Widows' pensions on death after ill-health retirement			Widows' pensions on death in service		
	Before G.M.P. adjustment (8)	G.M.P. adjustment (9)	(8) – (9) (10)	Before G.M.P. adjustment (11)	G.M.P. adjustment (12)	(11) – (12) (13)	Before G.M.P. adjustment (14)	G.M.P. adjustment (15)	(14) – (15) (16)
	2.7	0.1	2.6	0.3		0.3	2.7	0.1	2.6
	3.4	0.2	3.2	0.4		0.4	3.4	0.2	3.2
	1.8	0.1	1.7	0.2		0.2	1.7	0.1	1.6
	4.9	0.6	4.3	0.6	0.1	0.5	4.4	0.4	4.0
	12.8	1.0	11.8	1.5	0.1	1.4	12.2	0.8	11.4
	95.8	9.0	86.8	10.4	1.1	9.3	71.7	4.5	67.2
	130.6	15.6	115.0	13.9	1.8	12.1	92.8	7.1	85.7
	50.4	7.0	43.4	5.3	0.8	4.5	33.5	2.9	30.6
	99.7	16.3	83.4	10.1	1.8	8.3	60.9	6.4	54.5
	376.5	47.9	328.6	39.7	5.5	34.2	258.9	20.9	238.0

continued

Table 56 (continued)   Scheme X: values for members at investigation date: new entrants
£000

	Members' preserved pensions on withdrawal			Widows' pensions on death after withdrawal			Capital sums on death in service	Total values			
	Before G.M.P. adjustment	G.M.P. adjustment	(17) + (18)	Before G.M.P. adjustment	G.M.P. adjustment	(20) + (21)		Before G.M.P. adjustment	G.M.P. adjustment	After G.M.P. adjustment	Value of 1 per cent. contribution
	(17)	(18)	(19)	(20)	(21)	(22)	(23)	(24)	(25)	(26)	(27)
	4.0	1.3	5.3	1.5	0.3	1.8		31.3	(+) 1.2	32.5	
	3.1	1.3	4.4	1.2	0.3	1.5		37.1	(+) 0.6	37.7	
	0.9	0.3	1.2	0.3	0.1	0.4		18.5	(−) 0.2	18.3	
	1.0	0.4	1.4	0.3	0.1	0.4		48.0	(−) 2.6	45.4	
	9.0	3.3	12.3	3.3	0.8	4.1		134.9	(−) 1.0	133.9	
	28.2	8.8	37.0	10.2	2.2	12.4	75.1	1 008.4	(−) 29.9	978.5	73.3
	21.4	6.8	28.2	7.5	1.6	9.1	113.6	1 354.9	(−) 62.0	1 292.9	98.2
	3.7	1.1	4.8	1.3	0.2	1.5	49.3	518.9	(−) 30.0	488.9	37.6
	2.1	0.6	2.7	0.7	0.1	0.8	111.5	1 024.4	(−) 71.4	953.0	74.3
	55.4	17.3	72.7	19.7	4.1	23.8	349.5	3 906.6	(−)193.3	3 713.3	283.4

Table 57 Scheme X: members at investigation date: capital values for one year's membership
£000

Age x (1)	Members' age pensions			Members' ill-health pensions		
	Initial entrants (2)	New entrants (3)	All members (4)	Initial entrants (5)	New entrants (6)	All members (7)
23	4.8	16.5	21.3	0.5	1.6	2.1
28	9.6	25.7	35.3	0.9	2.4	3.3
33	6.6	11.6	18.2	0.6	1.1	1.7
38	10.5	27.4	37.9	1.0	2.5	3.5
43	10.0		10.0	0.9		0.9
48	21.6		21.6	1.8		1.8
53	32.0		32.0	2.4		2.4
58	6.5		6.5	0.4		0.4
63	8.0		8.0	0.3		0.3
	109.6	81.2	190.8	8.8	7.6	16.4

continued

Table 57 (continued) *Scheme X: members at investigation date: capital values for one year's membership* £000

	Widows' pensions on death after age retirement			Widows' pensions on death after ill-health retirement			Widows' pensions on death in service		
	Initial entrants (8)	New entrants (9)	All members (10)	Initial entrants (11)	New entrants (12)	All members (13)	Initial entrants (14)	New entrants (15)	All members (16)
	0.7	2.4	3.1	0.1	0.3	0.4	0.7	2.5	3.2
	1.4	3.7	5.1	0.2	0.4	0.6	1.4	3.7	5.1
	1.0	1.7	2.7	0.1	0.2	0.3	0.9	1.6	2.5
	1.5	3.9	5.4	0.2	0.5	0.7	1.4	3.6	5.0
	1.4		1.4	0.2		0.2	1.2		1.2
	3.1		3.1	0.4		0.4	2.3		2.3
	4.6		4.6	0.5		0.5	2.8		2.8
	0.9		0.9	0.1		0.1	0.3		0.3
	1.2		1.2	0.1		0.1	0.2		0.2
	15.8	11.7	27.5	1.9	1.4	3.3	11.2	11.4	22.6

continued

Table 57 (continued)　*Scheme X: members at investigation date: capital values for one year's membership* £000

	Members' preserved pensions on withdrawal			Widows' pensions on death after withdrawal			Capital sums on death in service			Total values		
	Initial entrants (17)	New entrants (18)	All members (19)	Initial entrants (20)	New entrants (21)	All members (22)	Initial entrants (23)	New entrants (24)	All members (25)	Initial entrants (26)	New entrants (27)	All members (28)
	1.0	3.6	4.6	0.4	1.3	1.7	0.1	0.4	0.5	8.3	28.6	36.9
	1.3	3.5	4.8	0.5	1.3	1.8	0.3	0.7	1.0	15.6	41.4	57.0
	0.5	0.8	1.3	0.2	0.3	0.5	0.2	0.4	0.6	10.1	17.7	27.8
	0.3	0.8	1.1	0.1	0.3	0.4	0.5	1.3	1.8	15.5	40.3	55.8
							0.6		0.6	14.3		14.3
							2.3		2.3	31.5		31.5
							5.7		5.7	48.0		48.0
							1.8		1.8	10.0		10.0
							3.3		3.3	13.1		13.1
	3.1	8.7	11.8	1.2	3.2	4.4	14.8	2.8	17.6	166.4	128.0	294.4

Table 58   *Scheme X: values at investigation date*

Current pensions following retirement at normal pension age (Data from Table 37)

		£
Members' pensions: £1,654 $\times \bar{a}_{68\overline{2|}}$ (8.235)	=	13,621
Widows' reversionary pensions: £3,722 $\times$ $\bar{a}_{68|65}$ (3.303) $\times$ 0.9	=	11,064
		£24,685

Table 59 Scheme X: values at investigation date

Current pensions following early retirement in normal health (Data from Table 40)

Age x (1)	Number of cases (2)	Members' pensions		G.M.P. (5)	$\bar{a}_{\overline{x\,|\,4}}$ (6)	$\bar{a}_{x\,|\,x-3}$ (7)
		actual (3)	Notional for widows' pensions (4)			
		£ p.a.	£ p.a.	£ p.a.		
58	5	4,295	5,819	769	11.054	2.836
63	7	9,060	10,931	881	9.757	3.124
	12	13,355	16,750	1,650		

continued

Table 59 (continued)   Scheme X: values at investigation date

Current pensions following early retirement in normal health (Data from Table 40)

	Values		Adjusting factor for GMP			
	Members' pensions (3) × (6) (8)	Widows' reversionary pensions 0.45 (4) × (7) (9)	Members' pensions (10)	Widows' reversionary pensions (11)	(5) × (10) (12)	0.45 (5) × (11) (13)
	£	£				
	47,477	7,426	1.282	1.177	986	407
	88,398	15,367	1.411	1.124	1,243	446
	135,875	22,793			2,229	853

Summary

	Value before GMP adjustment £	GMP adjustment £	Adjusted value £
Members' pensions	135,875	2,229	133,646
Widows' reversionary pensions	22,793	853	21,940

Table 60 Scheme X: values at investigation date

Current pensions following early retirement on grounds of ill-health (Data from Table 42)

Age x (1)	Number of cases (2)	Members' pensions		G.M.P. (5)	$\bar{a}_{\overline{x|4}}$ (6)	$\bar{a}_{x|x-3}$ (7)
		actual (3)	Notional for widows' pensions (4)			
		£ p.a.	£ p.a.	£ p.a.		
38	1	275	275	72	14.134	2.065
48	2	1,000	1,430	181	12.232	2.965
53	4	2,582	3,674	422	11.054	3.440
63	2	4,235	5,091	406	8.403	4.204
	9	8,092	10,470	1,081		

continued

Table 60 (continued) Scheme X: values at investigation date

Current pensions following early retirement on grounds of ill-health (Data from Table 42)

	Values		Adjusting factor for GMP			
	Members' pensions (3) × (6) (8)	Widows' reversionary pensions 0.45 (4) × (7) (9)	Members' pensions (10)	Widows' reversionary pensions (11)	(5) × (10) (12)	0.45 (5) × (11) (13)
	£	£				
	3,887	256	.676	1.608	49	52
	12,232	1,908	.738	1.592	134	130
	28,541	5,687	.790	1.557	333	296
	35,587	9,631	.998	1.424	405	260
	80,247	17,482			921	738

Summary	Value before GMP adjustment £	GMP adjustment £	Adjusted value £
Members' pensions	80,247	921	79,326
Widows' reversionary pensions	17,482	738	16,744

Table 61 Scheme X: values at investigation date
Widows' pensions following death in service or after retirement (Data from paras. 21.48 & 21.49)

Age of widow	Number of cases arising upon death:		Widows' pensions:		Value of annuity:		Value of pensions:	
	in service	after retirement	Excess over G.M.P.	G.M.P.	Increasing at 3% p.a.	flat	Excess over G.M.P.	G.M.P.
(1)	(2)	(3)	(4)	(5)	(6)	(7)	(8)	(9)
			£ p.a.	£ p.a.			£	£
35	1		146	25	15.661	11.029	2,287	276
45	3	1	1,169	111	14.519	10.565	16,973	1,173
55	1		1,088		12.790	9.721	13,916	
60	3		2,985	121	11.660	9.093	34,805	1,100
	8	1	5,388	257			67,981	2,549

Summary

	£
Value of excess over G.M.P.	67,981
Value of G.M.P.	2,549
Total value	£70,530

Table 62 Scheme X: values at investigation date

Preserved pensions of early leavers (Data from Table 36)

Age x (1)	Number of cases (2)	Members' preserved pensions		$\dfrac{D_{65}\,\bar{a}_{\overline{65.5}}}{D_x}$ (5)	$\bar{a}_{x\mid x-3}$ (6)
		Excess over G.M.P. (3)	G.M.P. (4)		
		£ p.a.	£ p.a.		
28	1	161	50	1.861	1.625
33	2	354	114	2.259	1.859
38	1	246	98	2.744	2.128
43	6	2,037	250	3.346	2.419
48	1	603	65	4.105	2.711
53	2	1 400	276	5.088	2.975
	13	4,801	853		

continued

Table 62 (continued)   *Scheme X: values at investigation date*

Preserved pensions of early leavers (Data from Table 36)

Value of excess over GMP		Factor for valuation of GMP		Value of GMP	
Members' pensions (3) × (5) (7)	Widows' reversionary pensions 0.45 (3) × (6) (8)	Members' pensions (9)	Widows' reversionary pensions (10)	Members' pensions (4) × (9) (11)	Widows' reversionary pensions 0.45 (4) × (10) (12)
£	£			£	£
300	118	4.752	2.943	238	66
800	296	4.904	2.972	559	152
675	236	5.054	2.992	495	132
6,816	2,217	5.236	2.994	1,309	337
2,475	736	5.449	2.959	354	87
7,123	1,874	5.733	2.863	1,582	356
18,189	5,477			4,537	1,130

Summary

	Value of Excess over GMP	Value of GMP	Total Value
	£	£	£
Members' preserved pensions	18,189	4,537	22,726
Widows' reversionary pensions	5,477	1,130	6,607

Table 63 *Scheme X: G.M.P. calculations at investigation date:*

Group D initial entrants: age retirements

Age x (1)	n (2)	G.M.P. at retirement 67.25×1.08^n (3)	Fixed rate revaluation (4)	G.M.P. at age 65 $(3) \times (4)$ (5)	C_x^r (6)	$D_{65} / D_{x + \frac{1}{2}}$ $(1.000$ @ age 65) (7)	$(5) \times (6) \times (7)$ $\div 1,000$ (8)
		£		£			£
60	28	580	1.085^3	741	22.1	0.627	10.3
61	29	627	1.085^2	738	11.8	0.694	6.0
62	30	677	1.085	734	6.0	0.769	3.4
63	31	731	1.000	731	4.8	0.853	3.0
64	31	731	1.000	731	3.8	0.949	2.6
65	31	731	1.000	731	30.7	1.000	22.4
							47.7

$16 \times 47.7 \div D_{33} \ (1794.1)$ $= 0.425$

$0.425 \times \bar{a}_{\overline{65}\,\overline{5}}\ (5.825\%)\ (9.309)$ $= 4.0$

$0.425 \times \bar{a}_{\overline{65}\,\overline{5}}\ (9\%\quad)\ (7.679)$ $= \underline{3.3}$

$\underline{0.7}$

Table 64 *Scheme X: calculation at investigation date of expected future service G.M.P. amounts: Group D*

Tax year beginning 6th April (1)	Age at beginning of year (2)	Salary during year (3)	Lower Earnings limit during year (4)	Relevant earnings during year (5)	G.M.P. earned during year (6)	Total revalued G.M.P. at end of year (7)
		£	£	£	£	£
1981	32	4,300	1,404	3,298	24	24
1982	33	4,814	1,516	3,744	27	52
1983	34	5,382	1,638	4,233	30	87
1984	35	6,002	1,769	4,791	34	128
1985	36	6,701	1,910		39	177
1986	37				43	234
1987	38				49	301
1988	39				55	380
1989	40				61	472
1990	41				69	578
1991	42				77	701
1992	43				86	843
1993	44				95	1,006
1994	45				106	1,192
1995	46				118	1,406
1996	47				131	1,650
1997	48				146	1,928
1998	49				161	2,243
1999	50					

continued

Table 64 (continued) Scheme X: calculation at investigation date of expected future service G.M.P. amounts: Group D

Tax year beginning 6th April (1)	Age at beginning of year (2)	Salary during year (3) £	Lower Earnings limit during year (4) £	Relevant earnings during year (5) £	G.M.P. earned during year (6) £	Total revalued G.M.P. at end of year (7) £
2000	51				178	2,601
2001	52				197	3,006
2002	53				217	3,464
2003	54				239	3,980
2004	55				262	4,560
2005	56				287	5,213
2006	57				315	5,945
2007	58				345	6,766
2008	59				378	7,685
2009	60	70,040	12,112	57,928	414	8,713
2010	61	76,371	13,081	63,290	452	9,861
2011	62	83,098	14,128	68,970	493	11,141
2012	63	90,353	15,258	75,095	536	12,568
2013	64	98,135	16,479	81,656		

Table 65 *Scheme X: G.M.P. calculations at investigation date: Group D initial entrants: age retirements*

Age x (1)	G.M.P. at retirement (2)	Fixed rate revaluation (3)	G.M.P. at age 65 $(2) \times (3)$ (4)	C_x (5)	$D_{65}/D_{x+\frac{1}{2}}$ (1.000 @ age 65) (6)	$(4) \times (5)$ $\times (6)$ $\div 1.000$ (7)
	£		£			£
60	$7685 \times 1.08 + 414 \times 0.5 =$ 8 507	1.085^3	10 866	22.1	0.627	150.6
61	$8713 \times 1.08 + 452 \times 0.5 =$ 9 636	1.085^2	11 344	11.8	0.694	92.9
62	$9861 \times 1.08 + 493 \times 0.5 =$ 10 896	1.085	11 822	6.0	0.769	54.5
63	$11141 \times 1.08 + 536 \times 0.5 =$ 12 300	1.000	12 300	4.8	0.853	50.4
64	12 568	1.000	12 568	3.8	0.949	45.3
65	12 568	1.000	12 568	30.7	1.000	385.8
						779.5

$16 \times 779.5 \div D_{33}$ (1794.1) $= 6.952$

$6.952 \times \bar{a}_{\overline{65\,5|}}$ (5.825%) (9.309) $= 64.7$

$6.952 \times \bar{a}_{\overline{65\,5|}}$ (9%   ) (7.679) $= 53.4$

$\overline{11.3}$

Table 66　Scheme X: values at investigation date

Current pensioners

	Number of pensioners	Amount of pension in payment	Value of current pension	Value of contingent pension to widow
		£ p.a.	£	£
Retired at normal pension age	5	1,654	13,621	11,064
Retired early in normal health	12	13,355	133,646	21,940
Retired on grounds of ill-health	9	8,092	79,326	16,744
Widows' pensions on death in service	8	5,468	68,000	–
Widow's pension on death after retirement	1	177	2,530	–
Total	35	£28,746　p.a.	£297,123	£49,748

Table 67   Scheme X: values at investigation date

Active members

	Initial entrants		Subsequent entrants	
	past service	future service	past service	future service
	£000	£000	£000	£000
Members' pensions: age	1,319.0	1,744.5	84.9	2,468.7
ill-health	100.0	126.3	8.0	197.8
Widows' pensions on death:				
after age retirement	185.9	221.7	11.8	328.6
after ill-health retirement	18.8	21.2	1.4	34.2
in service	115.4	136.9	11.4	238.0
Benefits on withdrawal:				
members' pensions	17.7	24.8	12.3	72.7
widows' pensions	5.7	8.2	4.1	23.8
Capital sums on death in service		354.6		349.5
Total benefits	1,762.5	2,638.2	133.9	3,713.3
1 per cent. contribution	–	205.4	–	283.4

Table 68 *Scheme X: values at investigation date*

	Past service		Future service
	£000	£000	£000
Current pensions (Table 66):			
members	226.6		
widows	70.5		
contingent widows	49.7	346.8	
Preserved pensions (Table 62):			
members	22.7		
contingent widows	6.6	29.3	
Active members (Table 67):			
members' pensions	1,541.9		4,634.8
contingent widows' pensions	354.5		1,012.6
death-in-service capital sums		1,896.4	704.1
Total liabilities		2,272.5	6,351.5
1 per cent. contribution			488.8

Table 69   Scheme X: values at investigation date

	Past service		Future service	
	£000	£000	£000	£000
Liabilities:				
current pensions	346.8			
preserved pensions	29.3			
active members	1,896.4		6,351.5	
Total		2,272.5		6,351.5
Assets:				
investments at assessed value	1,439.0			
contribution of 12 per cent. of				
total payroll for 7 years*	1,640.5			
13 per cent. contribution			6,354.4	
Total		3,079.5		6,354.4
Surplus		(+) 807.0		(+) 2.9

*Total payroll (from Table 34) = £2,021,700 p.a.
2,021.7 × 0.12 × $\ddot{a}_{\overline{7}|}$ (1% interest) (6.762) = 1,640.5

Table 70 Scheme X: discontinuance solvency at investigation date

Calculations for active members

Age (1)	Accrued scale pension (2)	Accrued GMP (3)	(2) − (3) (4)	Unadjusted ARP (5)	(3) × (5) × 0.68 (6)	Approximate deferred annuity cost factor (7)	(4) × (7) (8)
	£000	£000	£000		£000		£000
23	4.8	1.4	3.4	5.71	5.4	3.0	10
28	9.6	2.5	7.1	5.82	9.9	3.6	26
33	6.3	1.7	4.6	5.95	6.9	4.3	20
38	11.9	4.2	7.7	6.07	17.3	4.9	38
43	11.9	2.3	9.6	6.20	9.7	5.5	53
48	41.0	6.9	34.1	6.36	29.8	6.1	208
53	66.1	11.0	55.1	6.58	49.2	6.7	369
58	14.7	2.0	12.7	6.87	9.3	7.4	94
63	22.2	2.4	19.8	7.34	12.0	8.0	158
	188.5	34.4	154.1		149.5		976

Table 71 *Scheme X*

Projection of cash flow in respect of age pensions in year starting 20 years after investigation date for initial entrants who were members at investigation date.

| Age at investigation date x (1) | Data at investigation date | | Age at retirement y (4) | Future service = y − x (5) | (2) × (5) (6) | (3) + (6) (7) | (7) ÷ 80 (8) | r_y from service table (9) |
	Salary (2)	Salary × pensionable service (3)						
	£000	£000			£000	£000	£000	
43	100.1	955.1	60.5	17.5	1,751.7	2,706.8	33.8	4 061
			61.5	18.5	1,851.9	2,807.0	35.1	2 370
			62.5	19.5	1,951.9	2,907.0	36.3	1 303
			63.5	20.5	2,052.1	3,007.2	37.6	1 132
48	226.9	3,282.3	60.5	12.5	2,836.3	6,118.6	76.5	4 061
			61.5	13.5	3,063.1	6,345.4	79.3	2 370
			62.5	14.5	3,290.1	6,572.4	82.2	1 303
			63.5	15.5	3,516.9	6,799.2	85.0	1 132
			64.5	16.5	3,743.9	7,026.2	87.8	975
			65.0	17.0	3,857.3	7,139.6	89.2	8 309

continued

Table 71 (continued)   Scheme X

Projection of cash flow in respect of age pensions in year starting 20 years after investigation date for initial entrants who were members at investigation date.

Age at investigation date x (1)	Data at investigation date		Age at retirement y (4)	Future service = y − x (5)	(2) × (5) (6)	(3) + (6) (7)	(7) ÷ 80 (8)	r_y from service table (9)
	Salary (2)	Salary × pensionable service (3)						
	£000	£000			£000	£000	£000	
53	342.9	5,283.6	60.5	7.5	2,571.7	7,855.3	98.2	4 061
			61.5	8.5	2,914.7	8,198.3	102.5	2 370
			62.5	9.5	3,257.5	8,541.1	106.8	1 303
			63.5	10.5	3,600.5	8,884.1	111.1	1 132
			64.5	11.5	3,943.3	9,226.9	115.3	975
			65.0	12.0	4,114.8	9,398.4	117.5	8 309
58	66.6	1,172.1	60.5	2.5	166.5	1,338.6	16.7	4 061
			61.5	3.5	233.1	1,405.2	17.6	2 370
			62.5	4.5	299.7	1,471.8	18.4	1 303
			63.5	5.5	366.3	1,538.4	19.2	1 132
			64.5	6.5	432.9	1,605.0	20.1	975
			65.0	7.0	466.2	1,638.3	20.5	8 309
63	80.7	1,775.3	63.5	0.5	40.3	1,815.6	22.7	1 132
			64.5	1.5	121.1	1,896.4	23.7	975
			65.0	2.0	161.4	1,936.7	24.2	8 309

continued

Table 71 (continued)   Scheme X

Projection of cash flow in respect of age pensions in year starting 20 years after investigation date for initial entrants who were members at investigation date.

(9) ÷ l_x from service table (10)	$\dfrac{z_y}{s_{x-1}}$ (11)	(8) × (10) × (11) (12)	Age at time 20.5 w (13)	$\dfrac{l_w}{l_y}$ or 1.000 (14)	(12) × (14) (15)	$w-y$ $= n$ (16)	1.03^n (17)	(15) × (17) (18)
		£000			£000			£000
0.170	4.875	28.0	63.5	1.000	28.0	3.0	1.093	30.6
0.099	5.324	18.5	63.5	1.000	18.5	2.0	1.061	19.6
0.055	5.804	11.6	63.5	1.000	11.6	1.0	1.030	11.9
0.047	6.326	11.2	63.5	1.000	11.2	–	– (½ yr)	5.6
0.175	2.937	39.3	68.5	0.841	33.1	8.0	1.267	41.9
0.102	3.208	25.9	68.5	0.854	22.1	7.0	1.230	27.2
0.056	3.497	16.1	68.5	0.868	14.0	6.0	1.194	16.7
0.049	3.811	15.9	68.5	1.000	15.9	5.0	1.159	18.4
0.042	4.145	15.3	68.5	1.000	15.3	4.0	1.126	17.2
0.359	4.314	138.1	68.5	1.000	138.1	3.5	1.109	153.2
0.182	1.803	32.2	73.5	0.686	22.1	13.0	1.469	32.5
0.106	1.969	21.4	73.5	0.696	14.9	12.0	1.426	21.2
0.058	2.147	13.3	73.5	0.707	9.4	11.0	1.384	13.0
0.051	2.340	13.3	73.5	0.720	9.6	10.0	1.344	12.9
0.044	2.544	12.9	73.5	0.735	9.5	9.0	1.305	12.4
0.371	2.649	115.5	73.5	0.743	85.8	8.5	1.286	110.3

continued

Table 71 (continued) Scheme X

Projection of cash flow in respect of age pensions in year starting 20 years after investigation date for initial entrants who were members at investigation date.

(9) ÷ l_x from service table (10)	$\dfrac{z_y}{s_{x-1}}$ (11)	(8) × (10) × (11) (12)	Age at time 20.5 w (13)	$\dfrac{l_w}{l_y}$ or 1.000 (14)	(12) × (14) (15)	$w - y$ = n (16)	1.03^n (17)	(15) × (17) (18)
		£000			£000			£000
0.193	1.145	3.7	78.5	0.489	1.8	18.0	1.702	3.1
0.113	1.250	2.5	78.5	0.497	1.2	17.0	1.653	2.0
0.062	1.363	1.6	78.5	0.505	0.8	16.0	1.605	1.3
0.054	1.485	1.5	78.5	0.514	0.8	15.0	1.558	1.2
0.046	1.615	1.5	78.5	0.524	0.8	14.0	1.513	1.2
0.395	1.681	13.6	78.5	0.530	7.2	13.5	1.490	10.7
0.100	0.962	2.2	83.5	0.297	0.7	20.0	1.806	1.3
0.086	1.046	2.1	83.5	0.303	0.6	19.0	1.754	1.1
0.734	1.089	19.3	83.5	0.306	5.9	18.5	1.728	10.2
								576.7

Table 72 Scheme X

Projection of cash flow in respect of certain main benefits (before adjustment for GMP)
for initial entrants who were members at investigation date.

Years after investigation date	Members' pensions after age retirement	Members' pensions after ill-health retirement	Widows' pensions after member's death in service	Widows' pensions after member's death after age retirement
	£000	£000	£000	£000
1 – 5	93	9	9	1
6 – 10	344	37	41	12
11 – 15	1,222	105	101	54
16 – 20	2,392	176	172	174
21 – 25	3,286	229	257	397
26 – 30	4,293	301	370	714
31 – 35	5,595	402	518	1,084
36 – 40	8,272	565	678	1,478
41 – 45	10,373	618	753	1,957
46 – 50	9,430	477	722	2,514
51 – 55	7,102	304	646	2,972
56 – 60	4,564	153	525	3,048
61 – 65	2,297	55	369	2,525
66 – 70	827	13	208	1,566
71 – 75	192	2	85	673
76 and after	28	–	26	214

Table 73 *Scheme X*

Projection of cash flow in respect of certain main benefits *(before adjustment for GMP)* for new entrants who were members at investigation date.

Years after investigation date	Members' pensions after age retirement	Members' pensions after ill-health retirement	Widows' pensions after member's death in service	Widows' pensions after member's death after age retirement
	£000	£000	£000	£000
1 – 5	–	–	–	–
6 – 10	–	1	3	–
11 – 15	–	5	13	–
16 – 20	–	22	48	–
21 – 25	397	99	155	3
26 – 30	3,004	336	384	70
31 – 35	6,787	656	746	357
36 – 40	15,317	1,223	1,252	1,071
41 – 45	24,479	1,576	1,616	2,573
46 – 50	24,333	1,286	1,681	4,738
51 – 55	19,210	856	1,603	6,759
56 – 60	12,922	451	1,376	7,716
61 – 65	6,797	169	1,014	6,885
66 – 70	2,546	41	599	4,535
71 – 75	610	6	258	2,046
76 and after	90	–	84	679

Table 74   *Scheme X*   £ millions

*Projection of benefit and contribution flows in respect of
active members at investigation date.*

	Expected amount of cash flow in period in respect of:		
Five year periods from investigation date	benefits arising from pensionable service up to investigation date	benefits arising from expected pensionable service after valuation date	joint contributions at rate of 13 per cent. of pensionable pay
	m.	m.	m.
1	0.10	0.12	1.66
2	0.34	0.29	2.33
3	0.95	0.81	3.02
4	1.63	1.67	3.99
5	2.03	3.30	5.32
6	2.36	7.67	5.96
7	2.61	14.10	6.13
8	3.05	27.20	4.07
9	3.35	40.39	0.94
10	3.07	41.23	
11	2.43	35.47	
12	1.78	27.42	
13	1.10	17.79	
14	0.55	9.09	
15	0.20	3.39	
16 and later	0.06	0.96	

Value at investigation date of
cash flow discounted
at 9 per cent.
p.a., as shown in
Table 69

| | £1.8964 m. | £6.3515 m. | £6.3544 m. |

Table 75 *Estimated costs of G.M.P. accrual*

Sex and age group	ARP standard table	Assumed distribution of relevant earnings 1980-81	GMP accrual rate 1980-81	Cost of year's accrual of GMP 1980-81 (2) × (3) × (4)	Assumed distribution of relevant earnings 1985-86	GMP accrual rate 1985-86	Cost of year's accrual of GMP 1985-86	
							(2)×(3)×(7)	(2)×(6)×(7)
(1)	(2)	(3)	(4)	(5)	(6)	(7)	(8)	(9)
			%	%		%	%	%
Males								
25-29	5.80	.0920	.62	.33	.100	.56	.30	.32
30-34	5.93	.1038	.71	.44	.106	.62	.38	.39
35-39	6.05	.1083	.83	.54	.117	.71	.47	.50
40-44	6.18	.1109	1.00	.69	.100	.83	.57	.51
45-49	6.33	.1223	1.25	.97	.094	1.00	.77	.60
50-54	6.53	.1206	1.25	.98	.090	1.25	.98	.73
55-59	6.80	.0983	1.25	.84	.082	1.25	.84	.70
60-64	7.22	.0612	1.25	.55	.053	1.25	.55	.48

continued

Table 75 (continued) *Estimated costs of G.M.P. accrual*

Sex and age group	ARP standard table	Assumed distribution of relevant earnings 1980-81	GMP accrual rate 1980-81	Cost of year's accrual of GMP 1980-81 (2) × (3) × (4)	Assumed distribution of relevant earnings 1985-86	GMP accrual rate 1985-86	Cost of year's accrual of GMP 1985-86	
							(2)×(3)×(7)	(2)×(6)×(7)
(1)	(2)	(3)	(4)	(5)	(6)	(7)	(8)	(9)
			%	%		%	%	%
Females								
25-29	7.11	.0191	.71	.10	.030	.62	.08	.13
30-34	7.25	.0121	.83	.07	.018	.71	.06	.09
35-39	7.41	.0145	1.00	.11	.018	.83	.09	.11
40-44	7.59	.0173	1.25	.16	.017	1.00	.13	.13
45-49	7.80	.0202	1.25	.20	.018	1.25	.20	.18
50-54	8.06	.0199	1.25	.20	.018	1.25	.20	.18
55-59	8.41	.0141	1.25	.15	.016	1.25	.15	.17
		.9346		6.33	.877		5.77	5.22

$$\text{(5): } \div .9346 = 6.77 \times 1.05 = 7.11$$

$$\text{(8): } \div .9346 = 6.17 \times 1.05 = 6.48$$

$$\text{(9): } \div .877 = 5.95 \times 1.05 = 6.25$$

Estimated abatement   7.00

Actual abatement   6.25

Table 76 *Scheme X:*
various capital values in connection with a bulk transfer
calculation as at the investigation date

	Members aged 43		All persons with an interest in Scheme X	
	Amount	Source Table	Amount	Source Table
	£000		£000	
(1) Current pensions	–	–	346.8	69
(2) Preserved pensions	–	–	29.3	69
Active members:				
(3) past service liabilities on on-going basis	127.7	54	1,896.4	69
(4) future service liabilities on on-going basis	275.1	55	6,351.5	69
Future contribution on on-going basis:				
(5) members (5%)	109.5	55	2,444.0	68
(6) Company's normal (8%)	175.2	55	3,910.4	68
(7) Company's special (6%)	40.6*	34	820.3	69
Liabilities on discontinuance basis:				
(8) current pensions	–	–	210.0	Para 26.12
(9) preserved pensions	–	–	29.3	Para 26.13
(10) active members' past service	62.7	70	1,125.5	70

* Calculated by method at foot of Table 69 but based on payroll of transferring employees only.

INDEX SECTION

Notes

1. This section consists of a General Index which does not contain references to Scheme X except when they are of wider application, followed by a separate index relating to Scheme X.

2. References are to paragraph numbers except as follows.

    C : Chapter number

    A : Attachment at end of chapter shown

    T : Table number

    FR : Further reading list contained in the introduction for students.

    Spec. : The relevant specification of Scheme X in Chapter 13.

3. Some subjects may be more rapidly traced by use of the contents list at the beginning of the book, which shows the topic covered by each chapter, together with the contents list at the start of each chapter. It has been assumed that the reader will follow this method, and the index does not necessarily cover all references to a subject when to do so would merely duplicate the list at the beginning of a chapter.

4. When a topic is covered by a number of consecutive paragraphs the reference in this index is to the first paragraph concerned.

GENERAL INDEX

Access, equal, 4.48, 7.4
Accounts, 17.18, 21.17
Actuarial basis, C22, 27.6
Actuarial investigation
  Analysis of surplus, C25
  'Balance of cost' scheme, 21.7
  Certificate A, 26.20
  Data required, 21.13
  Discontinuance solvency, 21.2, C26
  Discounting at rate to be earned,
    21.11
  Formal nature of, 21.5
  Frequency of, 21.1
  G.M.P. data, 21.24
  Membership changes, 21.29
  Method of: example, 21.8
  Methods involving market value of
    investments, 24.27
  Miscellaneous consequences, 27.11
  Next time's result, 25.12
  Provision for, 7.35
  Report, C28
  Settling of basis, C22, 27.6
  Settling of result, C27
  Shortfall not necessarily to be
    avoided, 21.6
  Summarised data, 21.21
  Valuation of assets, 21.12, C24
Actuarial reduction of pension on
  early retirement, 19.34
Actuarial reserve, meaning of, 19.45
Actuarial statement for accounts,
  21.3
Actuarial valuation
  see Actuarial investigation
Additional voluntary contributions,
  7.23
Administrator, 17.6, 17.17
Age difference of husband and wife,
  6.13, 12.32
Agricultural land as investment,
  20.50
Allocation to provide dependants'
  pensions, 6.30
Analysis of surplus
  see Surplus, analysis of
Anti-franking, 4.36, 4.49, 5.40, 6.36,
  6.37, 6.38, 15.24, 15.38,
Assets
  see Investment

Asset matching, 20.13
Assumptions
  see Economic assumptions
  Statistical assumptions
Auditing of accounts, 17.14
Augmentation, discretionary, 7.9

Balance of cost, 8.86
Basis of actuarial investigation, C22
Bates Miss D.M., FR

Capital sum retirement benefits, 6.2
Capital sums on death after
  retirement, 6.21
Capital sums on death in service, 6.9
Ceiling nature of Revenue rules, 2.11
Certificate A, 4.42, A4.1, 13.7(v),
  26.1(ii), 26.20
Certificate, contracting-out, 17.9,
  A17.4
Cessation benefits equal to reserve,
  9.22
Chapman R.J., 30.42
Children's allowances, 6.19, 6.29
Communication of information,
  17.21, 26.3, 28.9
Commutation
  Exceptional circumstances, 6.7
  Terms of, 6.4
Computer methods, C10
Constructive dismissal, 30.5
Contracting-out
  Annual statement, 17.14, A17.5
  Cessation of by individual, 4.29
  Cessation of by scheme, 4.29, 4.37
  Definition, 4.8
  Detailed calculations, C15
  Financial basis of, 31.4, T75
  Financial experience of first four
    years, 31.8
  Financial issues involved, 31.3
  Financial surveillance, 4.40
  General issues involved, 4.45
  Popularity of, 4.2, 31.1
  Procedure, 17.8, A17.2, A17.3,
    A17.4
  Review of terms, C31
  Revision of contribution
    abatement, 31.19, T75

SCHEME X INDEX

SCHEME X INDEX 809